A World Geography of Forest Resources

AMERICAN GEOGRAPHICAL SOCIETY
SPECIAL PUBLICATION NO. 33

CONTRIBUTORS

ROBERT S. ADAMSON

ANDRÉ M. A. AUBRÉVILLE

RICHARD ST. BARBE BAKER

WILLIAM R. BARBOUR

WENDELL H. CAMP

M. D. CHATURVEDI

D. A. N. CROMER

LAURENCE J. CUMMINGS

SAMUEL T. DANA

FRANK E. EGLER

A. R. ENTRICAN

GUGLIELMO GIORDANO

DWIGHT HAIR

LESLIE R. HOLDRIDGE

J. T. HOLLOWAY

GEORGE M. HUNT

MIN SIM HYUN

H. R. JOSEPHSON

ALF LANGSAETER

D. Y. LIN

DAVID LOWENTHAL

H. F. MOONEY

ERHARD ROSTLUND

EINO SAARI

PAUL B. SEARS

R. SEWANDONO

J. W. B. SISAM

K. THORSTEN STREYFFERT

ROMAN W. SZECHOWYCZ

FLORENCIO TAMESIS

RAYMOND F. TAYLOR

EILEEN M. TECLAFF

GEORGE TUNSTELL

S. A. VAHID

RAPHAEL ZON

A WORLD GEOGRAPHY
OF FOREST RESOURCES

Edited for

THE AMERICAN GEOGRAPHICAL SOCIETY

by

STEPHEN HADEN-GUEST

JOHN K. WRIGHT

EILEEN M. TECLAFF

THE RONALD PRESS COMPANY · NEW YORK

Copyright, ©, 1956, by

THE RONALD PRESS COMPANY

———

All Rights Reserved

The text of this publication or any part
thereof may not be reproduced in any
manner whatsoever without permission in
writing from the publisher.

Library of Congress Catalog Card Number: 56–10177

PRINTED IN THE UNITED STATES OF AMERICA

PREFACE

The forest early assumed an equivocal role in human culture. It was prized
for the material it yielded and for some of the functions it performed, but
it was also regarded as a rival for the space needed for crops and flocks.
This two-mindedness about the forest has continued to confuse humanity
down to the present day.

This book is designed to help clear up some of the confusion. The
quotation, from Dr. Paul B. Sears' introductory chapter, sets the tone for
the entire work.

The book deals in large part with the world's forests as yielding materials that man cannot do without—materials that give him shelter and
heat, comfort and enlightenment, and a goodly amount of food. It tells
what most of these materials are and whence they come, and touches upon
the immense and varied unsolved problems of how yields may be sustained
in the face of ever mounting, ever changing demands. The book also considers forests as parts of the land and as features of the landscape. It points
out relationships of forests to rainfall and temperature, relief and soils,
and it discusses the effects upon the forests of human populations, institutions, needs, and desires. It gives an insight into the conflict between
those who want the forest lands for "crops and flocks" (or other things)
and those who would maintain and enlarge the forests to conserve water
and protect life and property against flood and erosion.

Six chapters are devoted to forests and wood products in their world-
wide aspects and 25 to the forest situation and problems of particular
regions. The book is largely a product of international collaboration.
Only 15 of its authors are Americans. The regional chapters, with two or
three exceptions, are the work of men who hold or have held positions of
responsible leadership in forest administration or forestry teaching or
research in the countries with which they deal. This lends an immediacy,
vividness, and authenticity to the text that more than compensates for any
disadvantages arising from the diversity of treatment inevitable in a symposium of this kind.

Most of the maps and graphs were prepared especially for this volume
by the American Geographical Society's cartographic staff. The photographs, carefully selected from prints submitted by certain of the authors,
as well as from other sources, illustrate diverse types of forests, tree
species, forest enterprises, and wood products. They are grouped together
by topics for convenient reference and comparison. The authors and
editors have tried to bring statistical and other data as nearly up to date as

possible. The organization and editing of such a book, however, with many authors scattered all over the world, cannot be hurried, and the volume has been in the making over a number of years. Hence, the reader is cautioned against assuming uncritically that specific statements in the present tense necessarily describe conditions exactly as they are today.

The American Geographical Society expresses its gratitude to the many persons who have participated in the making of this book, and first and foremost to Mr. S. Haden-Guest, Editorial Advisor to the Society, 1948-1954. The interest aroused by the *World Geography of Petroleum* (published by the Princeton University Press for the Society, 1950), a symposium in the editing of which he had collaborated, plus the fact that Zon and Sparhawk's *Forest Resources of the World* (2 vols.; New York, 1923) was long out of print and had had no successor, prompted Mr. Haden-Guest in 1950 to propose another world geography, on similar lines, concerning the world's forests. With the support of the Council of the Society and its then Director, Dr. G. H. T. Kimble, and with the aid of Dr. Dorothy Good, then Editor of the Society's Special Publications, Mr. Haden-Guest worked out the detailed plan for the present volume, secured authors for all but four of the papers here published, and launched the editorial work well upon its way. This work has now been brought to completion jointly by Mrs. Eileen Teclaff, of the Society's editorial staff, and Dr. John K. Wright, Research Associate and former Director of the Society, with the assistance of Drs. David Lowenthal of Vassar College, Peter Stern of the Conservation Foundation, and Richard Cowan of the New York Botanical Garden. Dr. Cowan has verified and standardized the botanical nomenclature.

The Society is deeply indebted to the authors of the volume for the time and thought that they have devoted to the writing of their several chapters and for the forbearance and good nature with which they have accepted editorial cutting and tinkering with their texts. One of the authors, Dr. Paul B. Sears, since 1952 has given the Society and the editors wise counsel in matters of policy, and several others—notably Messrs. Zon and Aubréville and Drs. Camp and Dana—have made helpful suggestions with regard to the organization of the text, the securing of papers, or both. The Society has also received substantial aid of the same nature from outside the circle of authors, among others from Mr. William N. Sparhawk, co-author with Mr. Zon of *Forest Resources of the World;* Dean Hardy L. Shirley of the New York State College of Forestry; Mr. Henry Clepper, Executive Secretary of the Society of American Foresters; and Mr. Charles A. Gillett, Managing Director of American Forest Products Industries, Inc. Valuable suggestions have also been made by Mr. Malcolm S. Black of the Union Bag and Paper Corporation; Professor H. G. Champion of Oxford University; Dean C. A. Garrett of the School of Forestry, Yale University; Dr. Tom Gill of the Charles Lathrop Pack Forestry Foundation; Professor H. S. Lutz of the School of Forestry, Yale University; Professor Aldo Pavari of the University of Florence, Italy; Dr. Nicholas

Polunin of the College of Arts and Sciences, Baghdad, Iraq; Professor C. L. Wycht of the University of Stellenbosch; and Mr. S. N. Wyckoff of the Forest Genetics Research Foundation, Berkeley, California.

Toward the editorial costs, the greater part of which have been borne by the Society, contributions from Mr. Chester H. Long of the General Electric Company, and from the Union Bag and Paper Company, are gratefully acknowledged.

The maps were prepared (for the most part under the editorial supervision of Mr. William A. Briesemeister, the Society's Senior Cartographer) by Miss M. Tegabo and Messrs. A. Tomko, N. Swanston, and S. Syska, of the Society's staff. Mrs. V. E. Baker of Hastings-on-Hudson typed many of the chapters.

CHARLES B. HITCHCOCK, Director
American Geographical Society

August, 1956

ABOUT THE AUTHORS

Robert S. Adamson, M.A., D.Sc., F.R.S.S.Af., F.R.S.A. Professor Emeritus of Botany, University of Capetown. Former President, Royal Society of Africa. Author of *The Vegetation of South Africa* (1938), *Flora of the Cape Peninsula* (1950), and numerous botanical papers.

André M. A. Aubréville, Inspecteur-Général des Eaux et Forêts de la France d'Outre-Mer. Author of *La forêt coloniale, Flore forestière de la Côte d'Ivoire,* and numerous articles on tropical forests.

Richard St. Barbe Baker, For. Dip. (Cantab.), Founder of "The Men of the Trees," forestry advisor and silviculturist. Author of numerous books, including *Green Glory* (1947) and *Famous Trees* (1953). Founder of the Forestry Association of Great Britain.

William R. Barbour, Advisor, Expanded Technical Assistance Program, Food and Agriculture Organization of the United Nations. Formerly general manager for Central America for the Plywood-Plastics Corporation and, previous to that, Chief of the Tropical Division of the U.S. Forest Service.

Wendell H. Camp, M.S., Ph.D. Head of the Department of Botany, University of Connecticut, and formerly Curator of the Department of Experimental Botany and Horticulture of the Philadelphia Academy of Sciences. Editor of the *Taxonomic Index* since 1936 and Vice-President of the section on nomenclature of the 7th International Botanical Congress.

M. D. Chaturvedi, B.Sc. (Oxon.), I.F.S. Inspector General of Forests, India; formerly Chief Conservator of Forests, United Provinces. Member of FAO Standing Committee on Forestry and Forest Products. Honorary President and Secretary-General, 4th World Forestry Conference, Dehra Dun, India.

D. A. N. Cromer, Officer-in-Charge, Forestry and Timber Bureau, Forest Resources Division, Commonwealth of Australia.

Laurence J. Cummings, Forestry Advisor, Institute of Inter-American Affairs, U.S. Foreign Operations Mission to Panama. Formerly Chief, Forestry Branch, General Headquarters, Supreme Commander Allied Powers.

Samuel T. Dana, M.F., hon. Sc.D., hon. LL.D., Dean Emeritus of the School of Natural Resources, University of Michigan. Filibert Roth University Professor of Forestry, University of Michigan, 1951-53. Until 1927, in the U.S. Forest Service and in 1923-27 Director of its Northeast Forest Experiment Station. Editor of *Journal of Forestry* 1928-30, 1942-46.

Frank E. Egler, M.S. (Minnesota), Ph.D. (Yale). Consulting Vegetationist, Aton Forest, Norfolk, Connecticut, and a Research Associate of the American Museum of Natural History with a wide understanding of the structure and ecology of plant communities and of vegetation management.

A. R. Entrican, Director of Forests, New Zealand Forest Service. An engineer in forest products, the author of many official publications, and a member of the FAO Standing Committee on Forests and Forest Products.

ix

Guglielmo Giordano, Professor, Ing. Silviculturist. Director of the Instituto Nazionale del Legno, Florence, Italy. Formerly Professor of Wood Technology, Faculty of Agriculture and Forestry, University of Florence. Chairman, Section IV, 4th World Forestry Conference, Dehra Dun, India.

Dwight Hair, Economist, U.S. Forest Service.

Leslie R. Holdridge, Head of Renewable Resources Service, Instituto Interamericano de Ciencias Agricolas, Costa Rica. Formerly Forestry Advisor for the U.S. Forest Service in Haiti, Puerto Rico, and Ecuador.

J. T. Holloway, Forest Ecologist, New Zealand Forest Service.

George M. Hunt, Director Emeritus of the Forest Products Laboratory, Madison, Wisconsin, and a national authority on all phases of wood use and research.

Min Sim Hyun, Director of the Central Forest Experiment Station, Seoul, Korea.

H. R. Josephson, M.S., Ph.D., Chief, Division of Forest Economics Research, U.S. Forest Service. With the U.S. Forest Service since 1934, except for the years 1940-42 when he was assistant professor of forest economics at the University of California, and 1942-45 when he was an air intelligence specialist in the U.S. Air Force.

Alf Langsaeter, Chief Forester of the Norwegian Forest Service and the author of numerous publications on forest economy.

D. Y. Lin, M.F. (Yale), LL.D.; President, Chung Chi College, Hongkong. Formerly Director of Forestry of China; author of the forestry sections in the *China Handbook*.

David Lowenthal, M.A. (California), Ph.D. (Wisconsin). Assistant professor and Chairman, Department of Geography, Vassar College. An editorial consultant of the American Geographical Society.

H. F. Mooney, C.I.E., O.B.E. Holds graduate degrees from Oxford (M.A.) and Dublin (Sc.D.). In Indian Forest Service 1911-47, former Conservator of Forests, Orissa. Now Forestry and Soil Conservation Advisor, British Middle East Office, Cairo.

Erhard Rostlund, Ph.D., Assistant Professor, Department of Geography, University of California, Berkeley. Born in Sweden and served in the U.S. Army before joining the University of California faculty in 1945. Author of articles on forests in *Ymer* and *Landscape*.

Eino Saari, Professor of Forest Economy, University of Finland, Helsinki. President of the 3rd World Forestry Conference (1949) and Co-President (honoris causa) of the 9th World Forestry Conference (1945). Also Vice-Chairman of the FAO European Commission on Forestry.

Paul B. Sears, Ph.D. (Chicago), hon. D.Sc. (Ohio Wesleyan), Litt.D. (Marietta College). A noted botanist, Chairman of the Yale Conservation Program and of the Committee on Natural Resources of the National Research Council.

R. Sewandono, Department of Tropical Silviculture, Instituut voor Bosbouwkunding Onderzoek, Wageningen, Netherlands. Formerly Inspector of Forests, Forest Service, Batavia. In 1949, Netherlands delegate to the Forestry and Timber Utilization Conference for Asia and the Pacific.

J. W. B. Sisam, Dean and Professor, Faculty of Forestry, University of Toronto. Prior to joining the staff of the University of Toronto in 1945, Director of the Imperial Forestry Bureau, Oxford, England. A forest engineer, the author of numerous technical publications.

K. Thorsten Streyffert, Dean of the Royal School of Forest Science, Stockholm, Sweden, with which he has been associated since 1928.

Roman W. Szechowycz, D.Sc. Eng. (Hanover), Grad. For. Eng. (Lwow). Chief Forest Officer, Gal Oya Development Board, Ceylon.

Florencio Tamesis, former Director of Forestry, Republic of the Philippines. Member of the FAO Standing Advisory Committee on Forests and Forest Products. Now General Manager, Nasipit Lumber Co.

Raymond F. Taylor, Ph.D. In the U.S. Forest Service since 1925. From 1938 to 1948, Chief, Division of Forest Management, Northeast Forest Experiment Station, and now Forester in charge of the Alaska Forest Research Center.

Eileen M. Teclaff, M.A. Research assistant, American Geographical Society.

George Tunstell, Chief of the Forest Research Division, Department of Northern Affairs and National Resources, Canada.

S. A. Vahid, specialist in forestry education. Formerly Inspector General of Forests, Pakistan, and is now Regional Forestry Officer, Near East Regional Office, FAO, Cairo.

Raphael Zon, graduate of the universities of Simbirsk, Kazan, Brussels, and Cornell. Consultant to the FAO on forestry in Slavic countries. Former Director of the Lake States Forest Experiment Station, Professor of Forestry, Honorary President, 7th International Botany Congress, 1950. Co-author of the classic work *Forest Resources of the World* (1923).

CONTENTS

GENERAL

REGIONAL

THE OUTLOOK

ILLUSTRATIONS

MAPS AND DIAGRAMS

* Based on original or other material furnished by the author without bibliographical
references.

* Based on original or other material furnished by the author without bibliographical references.

GENERAL

1. THE IMPORTANCE OF FORESTS TO MAN

Paul B. Sears

Whether or not our ancestors lived in trees, those animals which re-semble us most closely are forest dwellers, and we ourselves can climb pretty well if we have to. The earliest human sites are marked by the presence of charcoal. We have been and still are great users of wood and other forest products.

The Long Evolution of Man's Environment, First Familiar to Him as Forest

Inevitably forests are a major factor in our environment, for while their boundaries have fluctuated and are now diminished by our activities, the climates appropriate to forest at present cover about one fourth of the land area of our planet. With some notable exceptions such as the Nile Valley, the densest concentrations of human population are in regions of forest climate. Even the now forbidding and sparsely peopled tropical forest region of the Amazon sustained a considerable and advanced population at the time of its discovery by the Spaniards.

Assuming the age of the earth to be around two billion years, it is well to remember that the evidence of man's existence occupies only the last two-thousandth of that span. All other major forms of life and existing types of living communities are much older than man. He made his advent into a highly specialized kind of environment, immensely long in the making, and is himself highly specialized for that kind of environment.

Roughly, the great vegetation types can be divided into forest, grassland, scrub, and desert, in descending order of available moisture necessary for their maintenance. Because of its facilities for supplying water, food, shelter, fuel, and material for the simplest artifacts, the primitive hunter and gatherer could scarcely sever his ties with the forest. Yet, by a curious paradox, it was only by loosening those ties that he began the slow and painful upward climb toward civilization. Pastoral life in Eurasia, the growing of wheat in Asia Minor and of maize in the Central American highlands, all developed in dry and open country. Rice culture, while requiring moist climate, also required treeless swamps.

3

The Forest Not Forgotten when Man Turned to Agriculture

Early agriculture and herding did not require the clearing of forests as a preliminary operation. And where the treeless areas were dry, as in Egypt, Asia Minor, and Mexico, considerable skill in irrigation was called for, thus stimulating advance in the engineering arts, along with agriculture. However, none of these early civilizations attempted to get along without wood. Even in Egypt there was available small and inferior timber suitable for fuel and minor uses, and we know of extensive importation of high-grade lumber into Egypt as early as five thousand years ago, doubtless from Syria.

As primitive agriculture expanded, it eventually invaded forest areas. Trees were girdled with stone implements and cleared by the use of fire—a method that still persists in Latin America, northern India, the Ozarks, and elsewhere. Thus the forest early assumed an equivocal role in human culture. It was prized for the materials it yielded and for some of the functions it performed, but it was also regarded as a rival for the space needed for crops and flocks. This two-mindedness about the forest has continued to confuse humanity down to the present day, with sorry results.

Meanwhile there occurred a vast and prolonged period of postglacial desiccation, which for a millennium or more reduced the area of forest in Europe and America. This enabled the early farmers of the Neolithic to extend their operations (doubtless with the aid of fire) from Asia Minor and the Balkans northwestward toward the Baltic. There is reason to believe that similar conditions also resulted in the migration of advanced maize farmers from the Southwest into the upper Mississippi Valley. These mound builders lingered on after the climate had once again become moister, but were at length replaced by forest-dwelling cultures.

The Uses of Wood with the Development of Other Materials

The invention of metal working, first in bronze, then in iron, profoundly influenced man's relation to the forest. The operation of smelting created a technical use for fuel, hitherto needed chiefly for domestic purposes. Improved cutting tools speeded up the clearing of forests and added immeasurably to the ease of wood utilization, since better tools meant easier shaping of wood into useful articles. This in turn created a heavier draft than ever upon the forest, particularly for the construction of dwellings, public buildings, and ships. The advent of framed structures to replace laboriously built stonemasonry and perishable huts of mud and wattle or rushes and thatch marked a most significant contribution of the forest to human advancement.

It should be noted that rapid progress of the ceramic arts—glass, pottery, brick, and tile manufacture—and of such simple chemical arts as brewing and the manufacture of lye and dyestuffs all called for an expansion in the use of fuel. But it was the invention of steel, an alloy of iron and carbon, which was most devastating to the forests of Europe. For this process charcoal was the essential source of carbon. Armament and empire went hand-in-hand, and the age of Charlemagne is no more notable for its military exploits than for its wholesale destruction of forests for the manufacture of steel. An incidental, but important, by-product of such destruction has been the easier conquest and domestication of forest-dwelling tribes, thus deprived of their shelter.

Attempts to Compensate for the Strong Inroads on the Forests

There was, however, a conserving influence in the feudal military pattern. Forests were valued as hunting preserves for royalty and nobility. Thus the region of Avernus, which Virgil mentions as heavily forested, was later denuded except for the hunting preserves of the kings of Naples. Both on the Continent and in England the chief areas where forests were protected against the insatiable demand for charcoal and timber were those which, like the New Forest, were reserved for sport and recreation of the ruling class.

Meanwhile there was general ignorance of some of the less obvious functions of the forests, though Plato had linked the deforestation of the Grecian hills with the drying of the ancient springs. In 1609 Enrico Martinez stated that the washing of mud down into the Valley of Mexico and the danger of flood had been greatly increased by the destruction of forests and other plant cover on the highlands surrounding the basin. He referred to the hills as "descarnados," literally de-fleshed or stripped to the bone.

Scientific evidence as to the part played by forests in building and stabilizing the soil and regulating the flow of water is a product of fairly recent times and still incomplete. Although forested areas are obviously humid areas, their water economy becomes less efficient after clearing. It has been maintained by some authorities that the presence of forests actually increases rainfall. This was at one time the subject of considerable debate between the United States Forest Service and the Weather Bureau. It was maintained by the former that evaporation from the forest makes an important contribution to rainfall farther inland. The weight of opinion seems to be now that the chief source of precipitation comes from the ocean. The relationship of forests to moisture, while of great importance, is less obvious and direct.

Delicate Relationship of Soils to Forests

The part played by forests in soil formation offers some peculiar problems, because forests, as we have said, generally occur in relatively moist regions. Here water supply and facilities for transportation may encourage heavy concentrations of population and rapid expansion of agriculture. However, the soil formed beneath forests tends to be much shallower than that in the grasslands and to be underlaid by leached mineral subsoil. It is generally acid as well. Such soil when cleared yields heavy crops for a few years, but unless it is handled with great skill, the rich, shallow top layer is easily destroyed by oxidation and erosion. When this happens, there is a rapid loss of fertility, leading to deterioration of farm economy or to costly programs of fertilization. On more level and sandy soils such cost may be offset by the nearness of good markets, but rougher lands become the site of submarginal farms or are abandoned to second-growth forest under conditions where forest management is often difficult. Closely connected with the fact that forest soils usually offer a narrower margin for agriculture is the circumstance that on many of the poorer soils trees constitute the most profitable crop under conditions of good management. An exception occurs on certain types of glacial soil, which are rich in minerals and can be restored by skilful management.

Soils in moist, tropical forest regions present an especially difficult problem. Here the thin humus layer is rapidly destroyed by exposure, while the heavy rains tend to dissolve out nutrient minerals. Owing to the high temperature, destructive bacterial action is very rapid once the protecting forest cover is removed. Some progress has been made in transforming these soils into well-managed tropical pasture lands. However, because of the great variety of valuable products that can be obtained from tropical trees, it would seem that much more attention should be given to types of land use that depend upon the forest or upon skilful combination of tree crops with other crops, such as coffee, which can be grown in their shade.

The increasing pressure of world population in the temperate zones and the availability of extensive areas of tropical forest land make these problems especially important at this time.

Vital Relationship to Water

The value of forests in the protection of stream sources has long been recognized, whether tacitly or explicitly. The utility of the lower river basins in China and India is largely dependent upon the heavy forest cover in the vast mountain area that separates those two countries. The setting up of great public forest reserves in the United States has in view not only the future supply of timber but the protection of watersheds. This problem, however, has its complications. While it is generally agreed that forested headwaters do regulate and conserve stream flow, it has been shown that, where a large volume of flow is required for domestic uses, the presence of cleared areas, suitably protected by vegetation, may materially increase the amount of water available for runoff and immediate use.

The Complex Problem of Fire

There is a similar complication in the relation of fire to forests. While fire, along with clearing and pests, remains a great destroyer of forest and must be combatted effectively, fire can also be a useful tool for the forester. It has been demonstrated that the prudent use of fire is an important means of maintaining and improving the Southern forests of longleaf pine in the United States. Certain valuable species, such as the lodgepole pine of the Rocky Mountains, require the heat of forest fires to release their seeds from the cones.

While forest fires have always been occasioned by such natural causes as lightning or even volcanic eruptions, man causes most of the destructive fires of modern times. Much of this is due to carelessness. On the other hand, much is a direct heritage from the ancient practice of clearing the forests by fire. In many places, notably in Africa and in the southern United States, this practice has become crystallized into popular ritual, the woods are fired regularly, and the most diverse reasons are given for the practice, which is asserted to improve the grass for cattle and to control noxious insects and even human diseases. That it does "green up" the woods there can be no doubt, but the best of woods pasture is very inferior to the best-managed grass and legume pasture.

Insect and Fungus Damage

Destructive as fire is at the present time, insects and fungus pests are more so. It is possible that danger from these sources has been intensified by breaking the continuity of the great forests that once covered the eastern part of the American continent. There is, however, abundant evidence that, even under natural conditions, forests were constantly subjected to violent disturbances by many natural forces, notably high wind as well as fire and pests.

Effect of Types of Ownership

The pattern of forest ownership has changed during the course of history and still varies according to the prevailing conception of property rights. Thus the American Indian had no sense of private property in the forests, although a general group priority for hunting and other purposes was recognized. In the tropical islands of the South Pacific, the ownership of coconut palms is recognized and allocated, and during World War II military personnel who might become lost and forced to forage for food were advised to leave chits for the coconuts on certain islands, so that recompense could be made to the proper owner.

In the eastern Mediterranean area, the ownership of single olive trees may be shared, each owner claiming a certain sector, thus greatly complicating the business of improved orchard management. In Mexico the right of private exploitation of forests may be bestowed by concession, and the laws against illegal felling of large trees are strict. However, it is the custom of the natives to cut out portions of the living tree for firewood bit by bit until it falls, when it becomes the property of anyone who can salvage it.

In parts of western Europe, in addition to public forests there are extensive private holdings. These, however, are subject to strict regulations as to management, which make government, in effect, a responsible party in the enterprise. In North America, in spite of the extensive reservation of government forests, the bulk of forest land is under private ownership. Until recently this has led to ruthless exploitation—a tendency now being reversed, especially in the case of large corporate owners who see the importance of a continuing supply of timber.

Because of the long period required for the maturity of harvestable timber and the frequent pressure upon private owners to raise immediate funds, private ownership of the bulk of woodlands poses difficult and challenging economic problems. The ratio of labor costs to the value of the wood and other forest products likewise must be considered. The European peasant does not hesitate to gather faggots or bundles of twigs for fuel. On the other hand, at the present time in the United States, it is often difficult to find anyone to cut cull trees, even though given the wood for sale as fuel.

Changing Uses of Forest Products

In the days of wooden sailing ships the possession of adequate forest supplies was a major factor in naval power. Oak and cypress and, in particular, tall, straight mast timbers were essential. So were framing timbers for houses, until structural steel became available. At first it would seem that with the development of metal and other structural materials the pressure on forests would be less. The contrary is the case. Not only does wood still have many technical functions in our civilization, but the variety of uses for which it is indispensable is increasing. The great field of plastics, instead of lessening the demand for wood, has augmented it, since cellulose is a necessary ingredient in many plastics. Likewise, the insatiable demand for paper of all kinds has enlarged rather than decreased the need for wood. Thanks to technological progress, many kinds of wood which were formerly worthless for that purpose can now be used for pulp.

An interesting if minor example of the irreplaceable properties of wood is found among the Eskimos. The willow wood, which is the chief kind available to them, cannot by itself be made into bows, but when laminated with other materials lends itself well to such use. Consequently the Eskimo, before the days of firearms, traveled long distances to get supplies of this otherwise not very useful wood.

A significant phase of the use of wood in technology is afforded by the changing industrial picture due to the growing scarcity of wood. The ornate and tasteless architecture of the early post-Civil War period was closely related to the fact that at that time the white pine forests of Wisconsin and Michigan were being rapidly exploited. Under the compulsion to find markets the timber industry actually did a great deal, through the distribution of architectural plans, to promote the extravagant use of wood. The notable severity of more modern designs, while partly traceable to an improvement in public taste, can be related as well to the increasing scarcity of a once abundant building material. Communities which supported great planing and cabinet mills in the days of abundant forests lost them, sometimes without understanding why, when raw materials became scarce. These mills were replaced by factories using small-dimension materials for boxes, handles, staves, and hoops—until even the steady supply of small and inferior lumber was exhausted.

Exacting Demands for Wood on Forest Resources

So great is the continuing pressure on forest resources today that, wherever transportation is available, cutting rather generally exceeds the annual increment of merchantable timber. Reserves exist chiefly where distance or topography renders them difficult of access. Vast tropical areas of forest exist, but present their own peculiar problems. Toward the equator, the number of species in the forest community increases rapidly, so that one encounters not merely the problems of dense growth and of difficult access, but mixtures of many kinds of trees within the same small area. These trees differ so much among themselves in physical properties that profitable mass harvesting is far less simple than in more temperate regions. Because of this, the tropical forests must be harvested, if at all, for widely differing purposes.

Among the more hopeful approaches that are being made to this problem are experiments in the manufacture of tropical plywood, in which woods of very different textures, densities, and strengths can be satisfactorily combined. In any event, the harvesting of tropical timbers on a wide scale is likely to occur in the near future. Whether this will be done with more thought to a continuing supply than has been the case in temperate regions remains to be seen. A sensible world economy would certainly require it.

Lumber is, of course, but one of many forest products. The heaviest use of wood, the world over, is still for fuel. In underdeveloped countries or regions where coal is lacking, much of this tree fuel is in the form of charcoal, a far more compact source of energy than the untreated wood and one which frequently affords twice the heat value. However, much of this charcoal is prepared by primitive and wasteful methods which do not conserve the various valuable distillates produced in the charring process.

In addition to lumber, fuel, and pulp for paper and plastics, enormous amounts of wood are required for such special products as excelsior, matches, spools, tool handles, and the like. Forests are also important sources of raw materials for the chemical industry. Native rubber, resins, gums, oils, dyes, drugs, and aromatics belong in this category. While many of them can be produced in artificial plantations, the cheapness of labor and land in tropical forest areas makes the wild product a significant factor in the world market. Anyone familiar with the food habits of primitive forest dwellers knows that there are considerable possibilities for sustenance from this source, as Professor J. Russell Smith has shown.[1] It is estimated that the coconut palm alone has several hundred technical uses among native peoples, apart from the obvious one of food.

Manifold Possibilities for Wood Utilization

One of the most intriguing phases of forest utilization lies in the rare and unique qualities possessed by certain woods for particular, highly specialized purposes. The instances that could be cited are legion, including, for example: tough, straight-grained ash for medieval lances and modern tool handles; butter-like pearwood for exquisite carvings such as those of Grinling Gibbons; end grain ivory-like box for wood engraving; unsplittable lignum vitae and gum for mallets, house rollers, and bowling balls; bitter quassia, which imparts its flavor and medicinal qualities to water placed in bowls of this material; teak and cypress, so valuable for the decking of ships; dogwood for "glats" or wedges, used in splitting rails and firewood in the days when steel was scarcer than now—and so on.

Although such uses, like the uses of medicinal and food plants, were discovered before the days of modern science, it is of interest to note that the rich variety of tropical woods is now being re-explored in laboratories— as for example at Yale—in the hope of finding substitutes for the ever scarcer woods of familiar commerce, as well as of finding uses that are quite new.

Vast Implications of the Forest for Human Culture

The significance of forests to mankind goes far deeper than economic utility, whether direct, as in the case of usable forest products, or indirect, as in that of watershed protection. Forests have a powerful, though often intricate, relation to the more intangible aspects of human life.

That forests give aesthetic pleasure needs no particular emphasis. Poets and artists have made this clear enough. More is involved, however, than the simple fact that forests can delight the eye and gratify the body with their cooling shelter. At least one of Lincoln's biographers has intimated that the melancholy of that great man was partly a product of the gloom and shadow of the forest that helped condition his childhood. This may be pure guess, but there is no doubt that a prolonged stay in the tall twilight of the Engelmann spruce of the High Rockies induces a mood that

[1] J. Russell Smith. 1950. *Tree crops.* The Devin-Adair Company, New York.

is vastly relieved when one descends from them and emerges into the foothills to look out over the broad expanse of sunlit plain.

The violent deforestation of the Mexican uplands following the Spanish Conquest was accomplished by axe and fire, and consolidated by goats and other cattle brought from Europe. But there is testimony that the destruction was swifter than it might have been because of the Spanish craving for a landscape resembling that of their own treeless homeland. Forgetting alike that much of the poverty of the Spanish peninsula was due to its having been deforested and overgrazed and that much of the wealth that remained was due to tree crops such as cork, olive, and citrus fruits, the conquerors allowed themselves to repeat ancient and costly errors.

If the forest, by presence or absence, can be so deeply involved in the human emotions, it is not surprising to find it likewise involved in religious symbolism and practice. Worn, but still beautiful, is the line "the groves were God's first temples." Even though the Judaeo-Christian tradition stems from pastoral lands, its literature is rich in symbolism connected with the forest—the tree of life, the tree of the knowledge of good and evil, the wooden Cross itself.

The use of wood in altar sacrifice, the hearth as a symbol of home and worship, and ashes of wood in the ceremony of grief and repentance, are all familiar and ancient. Among the Greeks not only forests, but also individual trees, were personified as the dwelling places of god and demigod. In the Orient, crowded for living space as it is, groves surround the temples, and it is believed that it was in such groves that the living fossil, the ginkgo tree, now so much valued for its beauty in this country, was preserved from extinction.

In the Druidic worship of western Europe, as also in the robust Thor worship of the ancient Norsemen, the forest played an intrinsic part. The mistletoe was sacred in both—with a shaft of mistletoe the gentle Freya was killed by the mischievous Loki. Our use of Christmas greens and trees stems from the ancient Teutonic festivals that brightened the season of long night, during which we celebrate the birth of Christ.

Even the mood of gloom and depression that the deep shadow of the forest may induce is akin to the feeling of awe and reverence. This the primeval forest clearly inspired among the ancients—as it continues to do today—an effect not only evident in religious belief, but in the inseparable fields of poetry, music, and art.

Need of Comprehensive View of Forests for Their Appreciation and Preservation

The association of religion and superstition is usually regarded as derogatory to both. This is an unenlightened view. For the rationality of one culture is superstition in the eyes of another. Apart from the undoubted fact that many superstitions, when sympathetically examined, can be found to have their practical basis, one of the greatest of human needs is to have (or establish) some pattern of consistency in thought and belief, some pattern ample enough to embrace the many inconsistencies of daily experience. We attempt this ourselves, with science where we can, with actuarial tables where they will serve. Beyond that, we have a pathetic faith in mechanisms and a yearning to lean on the everlasting arms of government, unless we believe in something more potent.

In a simpler day the process of reconciling experience with belief was at least more picturesque. When the forests of western Europe were peopled with a magical assembly of fairies, gnomes, dragons, witches, enchanted castles, and knights, the Deity and the Great Opponent were relieved of considerable routine responsibility. Besides which, the tales were vastly entertaining—no small virtue in itself. The world's literature would be infinitely poorer without the ancient superstitions of the forest.

With the final flowering of medieval faith in western Europe into its supreme artistic expression, the cathedral, there is reason to believe that the primitive temple of trees reached its apotheosis in stone. An English traveler making his way through the primeval forests of the American Middle West early in the nineteenth century could compare them only to vast cathedrals, with the huge trunks as pillars supporting lofty green arches of foliage. His impression was more than mere coincidence. Not only the columns and arches of stone, but the delicate tracery of carving with its rich use of foliage sustain the forest theme in these superlative creations of the medieval builders, who worshipped as they built.

Granting, as we must, the increasing need of mankind both for the products of the forest and to safeguard the source of supply, we must not forget our long ambivalence of mind toward the forest as a competitor for space. Along with this goes the long emotional, artistic, and religious involvement with the forest that is graven into our racial history. It seems no accident that, powerful as the economic incentive to preserve and increase our forest resources has been, the most effective and aggressive forces in the campaign have, until recently at least, been marshalled by leaders motivated—not by need—but by their love of trees. Only with the continuing aid and increase of such leadership will the forest resources of the world be brought into the fullness of their utility to mankind.

2. THE FORESTS OF THE PAST AND PRESENT

Wendell H. Camp

The present is both a mirror of the past and a prophecy of the future. We can study forests with various objectives in mind, but to understand their present composition we must ascertain in some measure how they have come into being. Nor can we hope to foretell their future unless we have considerable comprehension of the methods—the biological mechanics—by which forests of diverse sorts have been able to persist in spite of the many geographic and often catastrophic climatic changes which have overtaken the face of the land in the more than 300 million years they are known to have existed before the advent of man. Biologically resilient as forests have been in the past, their greatest period of crisis lies ahead.

With the advent of man about a million years ago, an additional factor greatly influencing the composition and distribution of forests came into being. As a hunter, man periodically burned great areas of forest land, perhaps to drive the game to places where it might more easily be taken, or even to increase the amount of game by producing larger grazing and browsing areas; but more often through carelessness with his campfires. With the domestication of animals and the invention of agriculture well over ten thousand years ago, his influence became greatly intensified, for man is a mobile and hungry creature ever thrusting his pastures and fields into new territory. Today, with an ever expanding population, this thrust is almost entirely into forest land. Therefore it is timely for man to pause and, in an unsentimental and objective manner, consider how forests came into being, how they developed, and how forests and man fit into the general pattern of the world of which he is today a part—a world in which the future of all mankind lies.

The Climates of the Past and Present

The planet on which we live is an oblate spheroid, its equatorial region being warmer than the two polar areas. This temperature gradient, in conjunction with the earth's rotation, sets up a reasonably standard pattern of atmospheric circulation. Since the surface of the earth is neither all land nor all water, but divided into land masses surrounded by even larger areas of ocean, the physical properties of water tend to decrease seasonal contrasts near continental margins relative to those in interior regions. Any enlargement of continental areas would tend to increase the seasonal contrasts, induce steeper barometric gradients, and thus heighten the general storminess of their interiors. Conversely, any decrease in the continental areas, as by a lowering of their general masses with an encroachment of oceanic waters, would tend to bring about an amelioration of climate and a general stabilization of seasonal variations. As the geological record clearly indicates, there have been times when the parts of the continental masses exposed above oceanic waters increased for a while and then shrank, with long periods of relative quiescence between, often accompanied by extensive invasions of the sea.

The periods of increase of the exposed portions of the continents were, on the whole, correlated with periods of mountain building and the development of plateaus. The geological record also indicates that these periods of continental uplift were usually accompanied by intermittent glaciation, at least in the polar regions. Volcanic activity of greater or lesser intensity, especially near the continental margins, also was characteristic of such times. The fact that we happen to be living in one of these cycles of disturbance focuses our attention on the climatic (and consequent vegetational) features of such periods rather than on the more quiescent—and far longer—periods that have intervened between them. As Russell [1] has pointed out, man during his entire history has not known what it is to live in a "normal" climate. One may also add that, during his existence, man has not witnessed what might be termed a "normal" phytogeographic pattern.

If the surface of the earth were uniform there would be three parallel zones of higher-than-average precipitation, one in the equatorial region and the other two in the general regions of the 60° parallels of latitude. There also would be four zones of lower-than-average precipitation, two in the polar regions and two centering about 30° N and S latitude. Because of the rotation of the earth and the interaction of factors resulting from the positions of continental masses and oceans—and their unequal distribution —this theoretical pattern is greatly altered.[2] Furthermore, as Rossby [3] has noted, in the northern hemisphere the much greater percentage of land tends to disrupt the expected pattern more than it is disrupted in the southern hemisphere with its much larger areas of ocean.

There is a close correlation between effective precipitation [4] and vegetation. Hence one may draw certain inferences regarding precipitation from

---

[1] Russell (1941). For complete references see below, p. 47.

[2] Blumenstock and Thornthwaite (1941).

[3] Rossby (1941).

[4] "Effective precipitation" is essentially equivalent to the amount of water available to plants. In ascertaining it, consideration must be given not only to the actual amount of precipitation, but also to its seasonal distribution. Two otherwise similar areas with the same annual precipitation will have very different vegetation covers if one has a reasonably even distribution of rainfall, and the other marked wet and dry seasons; the one may be heavily forested and the

a generalized map of the world's vegetation types (Fig. 3). In spite of the heat, the precipitation near the equator is such that few desert areas are found there. Apart from polar wastelands, subhumid and essentially treeless regions tend to develop at the western continental margins at about latitudes 20°–30° and to trend inland in a northeastward direction in the northern hemisphere, and southeastward in the southern hemisphere. Although local conditions such as mountain ranges modify these relationships,[5] this, on the whole, is the general pattern.

The belts of heavy precipitation to be expected on a uniform-surfaced world at about 60° would also be turned northeastward on the continents of the northern hemisphere and southeastward in the southern hemisphere. In the skewing of these belts they would be depressed about 10° at the western continental margins. Their poleward trends would soon carry them into the polar subhumid areas; thus they would disappear as belts, and become more or less regional coastal areas centering at about latitude 50°. Evidences of these are to be found in the northern hemisphere in the areas of heavy precipitation in North America in the Pacific Northwest, and also in northwestern Europe. In the southern hemisphere only South America extends into sufficiently southerly latitudes for the southern superhumid area to be fully evident, as in southern Chile; but here no extended area is found, because of the southern Andes and the small total amount of land area available.

Reference to the vegetation map (p. 36) will indicate that the tropics, which we sometimes think of as characterized by heavy precipitation and an extensive development of rain forest, are by no means uniformly so. The less humid areas just north and south of the equatorial regions restrict the band of equatorial rain forest, and other factors shift it and break it into segments. Those areas, loosely referred to as "the tropics," actually are not characterized by a heavy effective precipitation and dense rain forest; the latter is a forest type of relatively limited extent. The montane rain forests

---

other may have a savanna or even grassland type of vegetation. Water loss (transpiration) is important in determining the vegetation type; therefore both the temperature and the humidity of the air, which determine its evaporative potential, must be considered. Precipitation that will support dense, broadleaf forest in cooler, and therefore more humid, regions at 40° N, will scarcely support thorn-scrub or grassland savanna in warmer, and therefore less humid, tropical regions. The slopes and drainage pattern of an area, which largely determine the rate of runoff, are also important factors. And such items as the physical structure of the soil and its seasonal fluctuations in temperature also affect the availability of reserve water, and greatly influence the types of vegetation. Numerous attempts have been made to arrive at satisfactory indices of effective precipitation by means of mathematical formulas, but, as Blumenstock and Thornthwaite (1941) have indicated, in the final analysis plants themselves are the best indicators. However, the type of vegetation cover on a particular area is not the result of a biotic summation of the *means* (averages) of these (and additional) intricately related factors, for individual factors, operating as *extremes* during even relatively short periods, may be sharply limiting in their effects.

[5] For example, the present dominant north-south trending mountain ranges near the western margin of North America produce rain shadows which turn the subhumid area in a more northerly direction than would otherwise be the case, and the dominant east-west trending mountain ranges of the central portion of the combined Afro-Eurasian land mass somewhat diminish the northeasterly trend of this subhumid area.

sometimes developing on the windward slopes of mountains in frost-free regions are superficially similar to lowland rain forests, but the two would be distinguished in any detailed analysis of forest types.

On the basis of theoretical climatology, those longer periods in the history of the world when its surface was relatively quiescent, with the exposed portions of the continents smaller than at present, and also with somewhat subdued relief, were times of "normal" climate. Vegetational zonation poleward from the equator was evident, but without the sharp gradients of today. The air may have been slightly more humid than it now is over large areas, but the total rainfall probably was somewhat less. The latter fact would tend to decrease the extent of the expected "standard" areas of superhumid climate, which were probably little better developed than they now are. Contrarily, with a more uniform air circulation, the subhumid zones entering the western margins of the continents, while in evidence, probably did not give rise to desert conditions except in the interiors of the largest of the land masses.[6]

Again on the basis of climatological considerations, it can be postulated that, during periods of world-wide continental depression and quiescence, the frost-free area of the world extended much farther poleward than at present. Theoretically the frost-free area would have reached to the neighborhood of latitudes 60° N and S; actually, judging from plant remains, it may have extended somewhat farther poleward on occasion. However, where one places the frost-free limits in relation to the 60° parallels depends to a certain extent on whether one does or does not believe in the theory of continental displacement.[7]

Lastly, on purely theoretical grounds, the polar regions of such periods would be characterized by a cool but not cold climate. Snow probably fell in winter, but along the margin of any polar sea which existed the climate is not likely to have been much more severe than it now is in southwestern

[6] The red sands and shales ("red beds"), their color caused by highly oxidized iron, have often been cited as "proof" of the widespread existence of severe desert conditions at various times in the distant past. It is here suggested that certain of these "red beds" might perhaps be considered as equally good evidence of the widespread occurrence of the so-called "tropical and subtropical climates" with reasonably abundant (but not necessarily heavy) rainfall, leading to the formation of large amounts of red lateritic soils, which contributed their burden of iron-oxide-stained silt to the deposits.

[7] The abundance at high latitudes of fossils of plants that do not seem adapted to now existing conditions in the Arctic regions has been largely responsible for keeping alive the often heated and sometimes acrimonious discussion of continental displacement ("drift") among geologists and paleogeographers. Apparently the strongest advocates of continental displacement (mostly European workers) largely disregard the climatological factors that could have led to the periodic expansion of the frost-free and temperate regions toward the poles. Conversely, those who refuse to countenance the theory (mostly American workers) are forced to expand essentially frost-free regions so far poleward, and therefore into long periods of darkness, that they may be involving themselves in serious biological troubles with the plants concerned. Probably the situation is neither all white nor all black and the truth may yet be found somewhere between, with neither the climatic zonal bands of the world being always constant, nor its continental masses or their segments always in exactly the same relative positions. A reasonable pulsing of the frost-free zone, coupled with a certain amount of continental displacement—much less than its most ardent supporters advocate—would go far toward solving some of our most perplexing paleogeographical problems.

British Columbia, northeastern Nova Scotia, northern Scotland, or southern New Zealand. The abundant plant fossils of both the Arctic and Antarctic regions offer ample testimony that these theoretical speculations are not far wrong; if theory errs, the plants indicate that it may be on the side of conservatism.

Figure 1 suggests the general configuration of the climatic pattern of the lands of a hemisphere during periods of general continental lowering. It may be taken as roughly diagrammatic of the combined land masses of North and South America (together with the present land of Antarctica), or else of the combined land masses of Europe, Asia, and Africa; in both

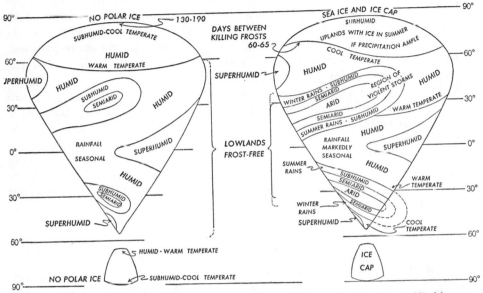

FIGS. 1 and 2. The theoretical distribution of climates at various times in the world's history, no account being taken of factors introduced by local features such as mountain ranges, etc. The land area indicated is roughly similar to the combined land masses of those present today in either the eastern or western hemisphere. FIG. 1. Conditions during a period of depression of the land masses, with a generally equable climate. FIG. 2. Conditions during a period of elevation of the land masses, with sharp climatic gradients.

cases there is more land in the northern than in the southern hemisphere. During the periods represented, the climate of the world was more generally equable than it is today. With no polar ice, the land masses nearest the poles, as just noted, enjoyed reasonably temperate conditions, with the warm-temperate zone of transition to frost-free climate at about 60°. The somewhat lower temperatures of what then were the temperate zones produced a condition sufficiently humid to limit the poleward extension of the midlatitude subhumid areas. The superhumid areas, centering at about the 50° parallels, soon dwindled in the interiors upon meeting the zone of low polar precipitation. In spite of the wide latitudinal extent of the frost-free zone, the equatorial region, on the whole, was probably but little warmer than at present. While there was a superhumid equatorial area, the general lowering of precipitation on a world-wide basis did not permit it to be very extensive. Low mountain ranges may have altered the precipitation in particular areas and brought about local or regional departures from the pattern as here outlined.

Figure 2, by contrast, indicates the corresponding general configuration during periods of continental uplift and disturbance. At such times the frost-free zone was greatly reduced in extent, the temperate regions were moved equatorward, and great areas of what we now think of as having a typical "polar climate" developed in the Arctic and Antarctic regions, accompanied by icecaps and extensive intermittent glaciation. With these changes came a marked enlargement of the subhumid areas, originating at about 30°, and a considerable increase in their aridity, especially in the continental interiors, where great wind-scoured deserts were formed. During periods of extensive continental glaciation, the lowering of the temperature along the ice fronts locally—or even regionally—reduced the extent and severity of these subhumid areas, as it did in the Great Basin area of North America during the ice maxima of the Pleistocene. Figure 2 does not represent conditions during the maxima of periods of disturbance, when the "polar climates" and continental glaciers descended to beyond the 40° parallel, as they did in certain regions several times during the Pleistocene, but a somewhat more equable condition such as we have today. The Permian appears to have been characterized by periods of much more severe climate than was the Pleistocene.

The Forests of the Past

With the aid of Figs. 1, 2, and 3, we now may roughly trace the development of the vegetation types—and especially the forest types—of the past. It should be held in mind throughout that the continents, in those periods when they were of more subdued relief, nevertheless were by no means topographically featureless. The incompletely eroded bases of former high mountain chains might have lingered on, even when the next cycle of mountain building was already beginning. The face of the land was varied, and its elevations, if not on the magnificent scale of the present Andes or Himalayas, still were sufficient to bring about modifications in the precipitation and local climatic pattern. And these elevations—the uplands of the past—have played an important role in the development of the world's vegetation, for it becomes evident, when we consider the details, that in great measure it was on such uplands that the new groups of plants underwent their primary evolution.

The Major Groups of Vascular Plants. Before we go further into the historical development of forests and forest types, it might be well to note briefly the various major groups of vascular plants. This is perhaps advisable because several groups which dominated the forests of the past are now almost extinct, having left behind only a few living remnants which no longer are arborescent. Were it not for their pasts they would be outside the scope of this discussion.

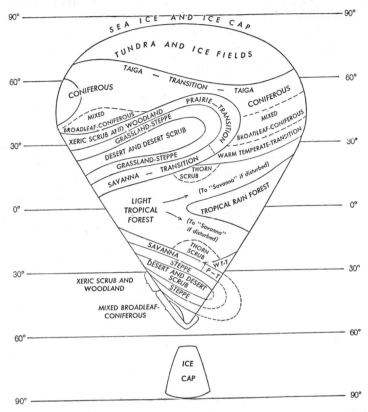

FIG. 3. The vegetation types of the present, correlated with the climates of a period of general elevation of the world's land masses (see Fig. 2). Secondary effects caused by mountain ranges and the relation of particular areas of land and ocean are not indicated.

The designations of the major groups of vascular plants may not be familiar to all. Formerly it was customary to divide the vascular plants into two groups, the *Pteridophyta* (reproducing by spores, as in the ferns, horsetails, and lycopods), and the *Spermatophyta* (reproducing by seed). Advances in our knowledge have revealed that this simple division is no longer tenable. Currently seven major groups may be recognized; these appear to have been independent as far back as we have knowledge of them in the fossil record (Fig. 4). Fortunately, each of the major groups as now defined still contains living members. Therefore each group name has been derived from the name of a living genus, although the extinct genera may have been far more numerous. Thus, the *Equisetopsida* are more or less like the modern horsetails (*Equisetum*), and the *Magnoliopsida* (the so-called "flowering plants") are more "*Magnolia*-like" than

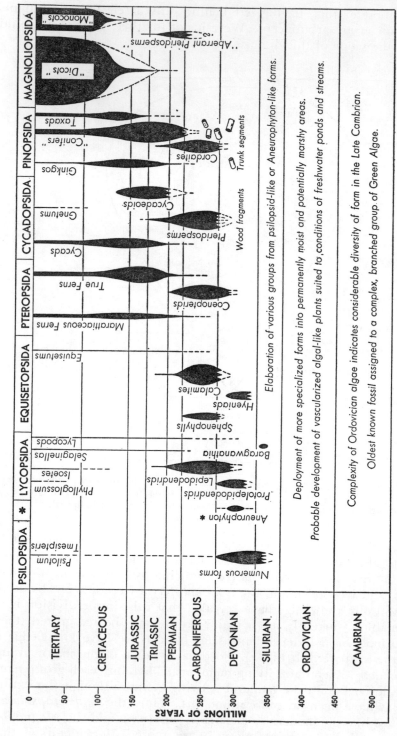

Fig. 4. The distribution through time of the phyletic lines included in the major groups of vascular plants, together with notes on the possible sequence of forms leading to them. Names of the major groups are derived from well-known living genera. * Aneurophyton, not yet satisfactorily classified.

"fern-" or "*Pteris*-like" (*Pteropsida*), and so on. In the following text, informal usage is sometimes made of the more formal group designations.

The present discussion cannot do more than briefly mention certain matters relative to the development of these groups. Figure 4 has been designed primarily to acquaint us with the names of these major groups of vascular plants, their most prominent subgroups, their known extent in geological time, and their general prominence in the world of the past as revealed by the fossil record. However, at all times we must remember that the "fossil record" to a great extent is composed of members of low-land floras which were present near estuaries or in descending basins of deposition and whose remains were thereby readily entombed in silts and muds by seasonal floods, or in the acid muck of great swamps then essentially at sea level. The variety of materials then growing on the much more extensive uplands can be conjectured only from clues in the form of logs and miscellaneous scraps which floated downstream, probably for long distances, and so were preserved in the deposits as alien waifs along with the far more abundant remains of entirely different types of the "local" lowland vegetation characteristic of the time.

Psilopsida. Of these major groups of vascular plants, only the psilopsids did not develop arborescent members, perhaps because of an inherent inability to produce either a ring of secondary wood or a soundly functional root system capable of anchoring a heavy superstructure.

Aneurophyton. The exact affinity of this material has not yet been ascertained. Reproductively it was psilopsid in character, and so usually has been classified with that group. However, it had considerable secondary growth and a good basal root system, and hence became markedly arborescent; and it differed from typical psilopsids in other characters. Some years ago this plant received much publicity under the name of *Eospermatopteris*, the supposition being that it bore seeds. Investigations with newer techniques revealed that the so-called "seeds" found associated with extensive remains of it near Gilboa, in eastern New York State, actually were spore cases—and of another and apparently unrelated plant. With the discovery of the true nature of the trees making up the "Gilboa Forest," it became evident that *Eospermatopteris* was the same plant as the earlier described *Aneurophyton*, which name it now properly bears. As our knowledge of this ancient form increases, it may be found to have played a more important ancestral role than we have so far supposed. On the basis of modern concepts, *Aneurophyton* may yet be moved from its present position in the series to one perhaps between the pteropsids and cycadopsids.

Lycopsida. The four remaining genera of this major group tell us little of the grandeur of the Carboniferous lycopsid forests. The earliest known member of the group, *Baragwanathia*, so simple that sometimes it has been classed as a psilopsid, probably was not ancestral to the entire group; if anything, it gave rise to derived forms from which our modern lycopods have descended. The lepidodendrids, a motley group, had a series of components, only a few of which seem to have come directly from the geologically preceding protolepidodendrids; all these seemingly had an indirect origin out of a common phyletic plexus, perhaps during the Silurian. The lepidodendrids, often with ample secondary growth and special systems of internal supporting tissues, were truly arborescent. Of interest, however, is the fact that both the aerial portions and root systems were dichotomously branched and similar in organization, except for such differences as we would expect between aerial and subaerial structures. Furthermore, the ultimate absorbing "rootlets" were coarse structures, seemingly little more than highly modified leaves. Hints of this old lepido-dendrid system of organization still are retained in a few modern lycopsids such as *Isoetes*. The arborescent lycopsids were not engineered to meet the competition of the structurally and physiologically more efficient groups that were to come into prominence later during the Permian period.

Equisetopsida. The hyeniads, a curious group of smallish, almost shrub-like plants, appear to be ancestral to the calamites and equisetums (the modern horsetails). The sphenophylls probably were a cognate group, at all times in their history rather weak and sprawling members of the swamp and, perhaps, moist upland communities. The arborescent calamites, abundant in the swamplands of the Carboniferous, had considerable sec-ondary growth, yet in their organization and plant habit they were remark-ably like our modern horsetails. These, in turn, may be little more than greatly reduced representatives of a collateral line developed from a basal member of the variable calamitean group no later than the Carboniferous and perhaps even in the Devonian.

Pteropsida. Although arborescent pteropsids were relatively abundant during the Carboniferous and since have been present in the several lines of this group, their arborescent nature always has been anomalous. The actual woody portion of their "trunks" never was large, the trees being primarily supported by a heavy mass of tightly intertwined roots which, originating at the bases of the leaves, grew downward, encasing the much weaker actual stem and thereby holding the plant erect. Nothing really new has happened in the basic architecture of the arborescent pteropsids since the Carboniferous. The development of numerous herbaceous and climbing pteropsids, as well as the derivation of forms suited to desert and aquatic habitats, may be merely noted.

Cycadopsida. The early history of our knowledge of this group is largely one of misunderstanding. For many years men have been astonished at the wealth of fernlike leaf impressions associated with Carboniferous strata. This easily led to the assumption, still maintained in some texts, that the Carboniferous was the "Age of Ferns." Coenopterid ferns were present, but for the most part they were both so uninteresting and so unfernlike as to be passed by. With the discovery that some of these fern-like leaves actually bore seed, a long controversy was started as to whether such forms were seed-bearing ferns, or seed plants with fernlike foliage.

Continued work on the group revealed that some never did bear seeds and also had the internal structure of true pteropsids. The bulk, however, appear to have been seed plants with fernlike leaves. More recent investigations, with improved techniques, have uncovered a large and complex series of these "seed-ferns," or pteridosperms, and have also brought to light what, at last, appears to be excellent evidence that the majority were in no way related to the ferns but are close relatives of, and in part ancestral to, the cycads. However, as we shall note later, a few of these so-called pteridosperms actually may be in the magnoliopsid line.

The cycadopsid pteridosperms were a varied lot. A number of them were arborescent, with abundant secondary growth in the roots, trunks, and branches; some may have been of considerable stature. Others were shrubby, quite a few are known to have been high-climbing and anatomically complex woody lianas, and there are hints that a number of herbaceous pteridosperms also were present. Long before they passed out of existence, the pteridosperms gave rise to both the cycads and cycadeoids. Recent investigations of their anatomical structure indicate that various of the pteridosperms were capable of withstanding periods of drought. It may have been such forms which gave rise to the characteristically more xerophytic, arborescent cycads. Another derived group, the cycadeoids, differing from the cycads in various ways, seems to have been peculiarly adapted to semidesert conditions. These thick stemmed (but always low-growing) cycadeoids also evolved a "flower," but in its structure it was a cycadopsid flower and not one which could have given rise to the magnoliopsid flower. The few remaining species of the tropical, arborescent gnetums also appear to have been derived from some ancient group of pteridosperms.

Pinopsida. As here defined, the pinopsids encompass four collective subgroups: the extinct cordaites, the ginkgos, the "conifers" (some of which do not bear cones), and the taxads. The one living species of *Ginkgo* retains a primitive leaf structure and an even more primitive type of reproductive apparatus with swimming sperm; this latter feature also is characteristic of the cordaites and of all known "conifers" until after the Permian. The taxads appear always to have stood somewhat apart from the other pinopsids, the wood structure of the group being the main clue to its basic affinity. To delve further into the intragroup relationships of the pinopsids in this place would open a controversy that is yet far from being resolved. But our uncertainty as to the exact relationships of the various pinopsid subgroups is a matter of insignificance in the face of the mystery of the origin of the group as a whole. In the upper reaches of Devonian strata, in deposits of estuarine and offshore nature, numerous trunk segments occur. Microscopical examination of these, when well preserved, reveals that they constitute a series of pinopsid forms, some already with a highly evolved wood structure. All we can say is that these numerous trunk segments prove that the pinopsids are a very ancient group, and that already in the Devonian the uplands of the world were clothed with pinopsid forests. From what we know of them, various of these ancient trees must have appeared much like modern araucarians.

Magnoliopsida. This group traditionally has been called the "angiosperms" (with covered seed), to distinguish it from the "gymnosperms" (with naked seed). A recent division of the so-called gymnosperms into *Cycadopsida* and *Pinopsida,* made necessary by their obviously different lines of descent, left the "angiosperms" standing unique without a name comparable to those of other groups. Therefore a widespread, well-known, and relatively primitive genus, *Magnolia,* has been chosen to loan its name to this major group. The dicotyledonous hardwoods as well as the monocotyledonous palms constitute such important factors in our forest economy, and are so familiar to all of us, that any discussion of their intragroup relationships in this place would be superfluous.

The often repeated concept that the magnoliopsids "came into being and underwent a great burst of evolution in the Cretaceous" is erroneous. Originally an upland group, and therefore but rarely preserved in the earlier fossil record, the magnoliopsids found no opportunity until the middle portion of the Cretaceous to migrate in sufficiently large numbers into the lowlands to become commonly and widely preserved. When the group becomes at all commonly represented, we discover that already essentially all its modern arborescent families had been evolved, and many of its modern genera also already had come into being, often with a series of species surprisingly similar to those of today. This indicates only that the magnoliopsids are not of recent origin, that they are no more "modern" than other groups of vascular plants. But the origin of the magnoliopsids is another matter.

Among the so-called pteridosperms may be found a series of forms which, even by the most conservative criteria, would be classed as aberrant for the group. In many ways these fit into our concepts of what, on purely theoretical grounds, we should expect to be forms ancestral to the magnoliopsids. But these aberrant pteridosperms were "gymnospermous" in their reproduction, whereas the magnoliopsids are typically "angiospermous"—and so the two have been kept separate by most workers. But before we thrust these seemingly insignificant aberrant pteridosperms, with their seeds borne on modified leaves, back into the cycadopsids because of the gymnospermous nature of their reproductive apparatus, let us recall that there exists a series of magnoliopsid genera, admittedly primitive in the great magnolialean-annonalean complex of tropical, arborescent forms, which, even today, open their sometimes remarkably leaflike carpels at flowering time, thus exposing the naked ovules (the future seeds) in a typically "gymnospermous" form of pollination. We now suspect, also, that some of the wood fragments of the Devonian, currently assigned in a general way to the pteridosperms, on more careful examination may yet be found to be the wood of primitive gymnospermous members of the largely angiospermous magnoliopsids. A traditional passion for large and sometimes not too precisely defined terms in our so-called "scientific language" should not be a semantic block keeping us from an understanding of the true origins and developments of our great groups of vascular plants.

THE FIRST FORESTS. Direct fossil evidence of a vascular land flora appears for the first time in Silurian strata through a scattering of psilopsid forms and the primitive lycopsid *Baragwanathia*. Primitive as these forms appear to be in the light of what came after, they seem highly advanced when we consider the differences between them and any hypothetical, vascularized alga-like form from which they might have descended. There is considerable evidence that the first steps in the evolution of a group of organisms is a slow and halting process, accompanied by many excursions into biological blind alleys and beset with numerous failures. Therefore we can but conclude, on the basis of the known forms of the Silurian, that a vascular land flora of some sort already existed in the Ordovician and gave rise to that of the Silurian. Unfortunately for us, the Silurian was a time of continental uplift and therefore one with few opportunities for the preservation of representative examples of what must have been an interesting succession of evolutionary experiments in the perfection of successful land-dwelling vascular forms. The Silurian culminated in a series of almost world-wide disturbances, accompanied by the building of great mountain ranges, which probably played much the same role that mountains always have in the development of vegetation types subsequently to become common and dominant in the lowlands. The seemingly abrupt appearance, in the lowland deposits of the Devonian, of various forms of all major groups of vascular plants except the *Magnoliopsida* (see Fig. 4), indicates that they must have been present and undergoing an active evolution on the uplands during Silurian time. And, as noted earlier, there is a possibility that certain wood fragments of the Devonian, now assigned to the cycadopsid pteridosperms, actually may be of materials in the magnoliopsid line; if this proves to be so, the magnoliopsids would then have a recorded lineage just as ancient as that of any of the vascular groups which gave rise to arborescent forms.

By Middle Devonian time the lands of the world were dominated by a series of forest types. Aneurophyton forests, mixed with gaunt-branched protolepidodendrids, were widespread in the lowlands; moist and swampy areas bore abundant psilopsids, hyeniads (the earliest known of the equisetopsids), and a variety of early coenopterid ferns. The abundant segments of waterworn trunk and other wood fragments which began to appear in the deposits indicate the presence on the uplands of extensive pinopsid forests, probably with an understory of somewhat smaller pteridospermous trees and an undergrowth of lesser sorts. Except for the dwindling and loss of a few less specialized groups, the forests of Upper Devonian time were largely a preview of what was to follow.

FORESTS OF THE CARBONIFEROUS. The Carboniferous saw the extensive development of lowland forest types, as we should expect of a period when the continents were generally at a low level. Again, however, we must presume a certain amount of upland, even with mountains of possibly considerable height, for there are far too many fragments of trunk and branch wood, with no associated leaves or other structures with which they can be related, to be accounted for in any other way. Furthermore, where else but from adjacent mountains and extensive uplands could the sediments producing the abundant sandstones and shales of the time have been derived? But it is to the lowlands, with their rich fossil record, that we turn our immediate attention.

It has usually been thought that the extensive Carboniferous lowlands were characterized by extremely heavy precipitation, and there is no doubt that swamps were widespread. What sort of "swamps" were they? The answer is to be found in the trees that inhabited them.

To live and function actively every cell must have a relatively abundant supply of oxygen and also be able to get rid of any excess of carbon dioxide produced during certain physiological reactions. Therefore, when we examine the plants of constantly wet areas, we find that those portions where the aeration is poor develop a sort of internal tissue known as aerenchyma. This specialized tissue consists of a series of ramifying ducts, channels, or connecting loose-celled structures whereby the living cells of the submerged portions can exchange air with the parts in normal atmosphere. There is little point in arguing, as some have done, that "plants were different then." Protoplasm was protoplasm, just as it is today, and there is absolutely no evidence that it had any different requirements or tolerances. The forms of the plants have, perhaps, changed somewhat (fundamentally very little), but the basic physiology seemingly has not. Therefore, we can examine the roots of these groups of Carboniferous plants and tell with considerable precision whether or not the soil in which they grew was saturated with water.[8]

Of the roots of Carboniferous plants that have been examined in any detail, only the following are known to have possessed aerenchyma: the equisetopsids in general (the sphenophylls and arborescent calamites), the marattiaceous tree fern *Psaronius,* and perhaps a few, but by no means all, of the arborescent lepidodendrids. The great bulk of the lepidodendrids and all the other arborescent forms of the time, so far as is known, were

---

[8] Repetition of life form—structural parallelism—is one of the interesting phenomena of plant life. Regardless of the diverse families from which they have been derived, the leaves of plants of the more humid temperate regions (or their segments, if compound) usually fall within a generalized pattern of tissue conformation which differs considerably from those of species of the same families in the tropical rain forest, in which there also is considerable general similarity. Likewise, desert plants derived from phyletically very different families have much in common in their gross morphology, regardless of how different their ancestors may have been in other regions. There is a generalized pattern of response to selection by the environment, indicating the common nature of vegetable protoplasm. Thus the specialized aerenchyma of plants living in poorly aerated situations—in water or in soggy soils—is not a matter of phylogeny, for it is not, and obviously never has been, limited to any group of vascular plants, but is common to all. It occurs wherever individual species of plants have ventured—and succeeded—in such environments.

devoid of it, indicating that they did not inhabit areas which were flooded and waterlogged for considerable periods. But how, then, can we explain the great deposits of coal in the Carboniferous, if they were not laid down in vast, reeking swamps? Here again the Coal Measure strata tell the story.

These abundant plant remains accumulated in slowly descending basins. Near the estuaries, which often extended well into the continental interiors, in actual depressions inland, and along streams, the equisetopsids, *Psaronius,* and a few of the many species of lepidodendrids, with their specialized root aerenchyma, were abundant. With an equable and completely frost-free climate extending at least to latitudes 60° N and S, there would be ample opportunity for rampant growth over a large portion of the land surface if soil moisture were reasonably available.

In the slowly descending basins characteristic of large areas of the land surface at various periods of the Carboniferous the soil moisture was certainly ample at all times of the year. However, this does not mean that the rainfall was necessarily excessive or the soil saturated with water, except locally. With the generally low relief of these basins would have been associated a complex pattern of saturated, poorly aerated soils, intermingled with soils that were moist but had sufficient aeration for the growth of plants without a specialized aerenchyma in their roots. So intricate was the pattern and so dense the vegetation that as the trees fell, to be preserved in the deposits, they fell in such a way as to make it seem at first glance as if they had all grown in exactly the same habitat. The same intricate pattern in the distribution of different species is easily discerned in our modern swamp forests, where we find some species capable of persisting with their roots submerged, while others, growing so close as to have their branches touching, may be seen to occupy slight rises on which the soil, although constantly moist, is much better aerated. These latter species also are likely to be found wherever the soil moisture is abundant outside the swampy zone, sometimes even on uplands.

Although moisture was reasonably constant in the lowland soils, the humidity of the air was not excessive. Careful study reveals that the great majority of the Carboniferous plants had leaves which in some manner resisted water loss through transpiration.[9] This applies to the arborescent lepidodendrids, the pteridosperms, and the cordaites—the last a group of lowland pinopsid trees then in great abundance, which sometimes formed dense stands. Even the microphyllous equisetopsid trees of the time, grow-

9 It has generally been assumed that the great deposits of coal in the Carboniferous accumulated from plants growing under conditions of very high humidity. When we examine these plants critically, it becomes evident that the majority were microphyllous or sclerophyllous—either they had small leaves which did not lose much water, or large leaves structurally built to resist water loss. Once we get over our erroneous notion that "the Carboniferous swamps were choked with a dense undergrowth of tender ferns, indicating a very heavy rainfall and constantly high humidity," and realize that the bulk of things we have been calling "ferns" actually were pteridosperms, in many instances only a few evolutionary steps away from the xerophytic cycads and cycadeoids, our former concepts of the climates over large parts of the Carboniferous world are bound to change. Even some of the ferns had leaves strongly tending to the sclerophyllous condition.

ing in their soggy environments, indicate that the atmosphere was by no means saturated with water vapor. For our purpose, however, it is perhaps not overly important what the conditions were under which these lowland forests grew, except insofar as they shed light upon the worldwide atmospheric and climatic conditions of the time and thus give clues as to what was probably happening on the even drier uplands, where the ancestors of our contemporary trees already were undergoing their primary development.

Actually, we have little first-hand evidence regarding the upland forests of the Carboniferous, apart from what is revealed by the relatively few fragments of trunk and branch wood that floated into the lowlands, there to be preserved in the deposits. While these give us valid hints, it is from the groups that migrated into the more equable lowlands during the severe climate of the Permian that we can glean a more satisfactory picture of the upland forests of the Carboniferous. Just as the wood fragments indicate, these migrants consisted mostly of a series of pinopsid forest types, with forerunners of the true "conifers" dominant among them. Often made up of giant trees (specimens with trunks up to six feet in diameter are known), these pinopsid forests probably had an understory of pteridospermous trees, shrubs, and vines (with perhaps a few herbaceous types), and there is every likelihood that ferns of diverse sorts were abundant.

The subhumid areas near the 30° parallels probably were not devoid of vegetation. The tough-leafed pteridosperms of the time were already giving rise to the cycads and cycadeoids, both admirably fitted to less humid—even xeric—conditions. Therefore, it is probable that the less severe parts of these subhumid areas supported a variety of pteridosperms suited to such conditions. And a few scattered fossils indicate that ancestral elements of certain lines, leading to those of the modern pinopsids better suited to dry areas, already were present. Cordaitean forests dominated the moist lowlands; ancestral "conifers" were beginning to take over the uplands.

If any forests grew in the cool-temperate regions and on the slopes of any higher mountains of the Carboniferous period, their nature is largely a matter of conjecture. If, however, the requirements necessary in the present are a mirror of those of the past, there is every reason to believe that abundant forests were then present in the Arctic and Antarctic regions, unless they were limited in some manner by the lack of light during the long polar winter; certainly the temperatures were no bar to the development of dense forest stands. If so large a number of pinopsids can today stand temperatures far below freezing, surely the large and variable group then extant could have included forms capable of persisting in the polar regions in the less rigorous temperate climates of the time. Their apparent abundance on upland habitats at middle latitudes during the period is an almost certain indication that the pinopsids also included a wide series of types adapted to temperate climates. And since resistance to frost in plants is physiologically closely akin to resistance to drought, there is considerable reason to believe that the poleward temperate regions of the time also supported at least a scattered assortment of pteridospermous types.

Although there is little or no evidence that the vast lowland forests of the Carboniferous contributed anything to the development of modern arborescent types, they played a most important role in relation to the use and ultimate preservation of our present-day forests. Before the widespread use of coal, wood was almost the only source of fuel. In viewing our dwindling forest resources, we may be thankful that the lowland forests of Carboniferous time, entombed in the strata of the Coal Measures, have relieved our modern forests of much of this great and potentially destructive burden.

THE GREAT CHANGE IN THE PERMIAN. The Permian opened with a climate very similar to that of the latter parts of the Carboniferous, and with the same general distribution of forest types. This pattern was soon disorganized by what may have been the greatest period of glaciation that the world has ever experienced. By comparison, it dwarfs any of the glacial cycles of the Pleistocene, which terminated the Tertiary. In the northern hemisphere evidences of Permian glaciation are known from Alaska, Massachusetts, England, France, Germany, the Ural Mountains, and India. In the southern hemisphere all of what is now Australia was covered, and extensive glacial deposits of the same age are reported from Madagascar, various parts of southern and southwestern Africa, and South America, notably Brazil, Argentina, and Bolivia. Nor is there any hint that these deposits were derived from local mountain glaciers; they were of a continental type.

The evidence of widespread glaciation during the Permian in the southern hemisphere, coupled with that of an amazing glaciation in what is now tropical India in the northern, did as much as anything to spark the far-from-settled controversy concerning the possibility of continental "drift." If, as postulated by the proponents of the theory, these glacial deposits could have been laid down in polar regions and then later transported into what ordinarily have been thought of as the temperate and tropical regions by a lateral shifting of the continental masses, there would be no need to disturb the "normal" climatic belts of the world. The possibility of at least a certain amount of continental displacement need not be ruled out. But, the story told by the forest types of the time indicates that a vast world-wide change in climates actually did take place: those groups which, since the Devonian, had been limited chiefly to frost-free regions and apparently fixed in their evolutionary potentialities were essentially wiped off the face of the earth.

Figure 2 is only a rough guide to the climatic situation during the height of the Permian glaciation. The completely frost-free zone may have dwindled to a narrow band in the equatorial regions, thus cutting down a multitude of tropical genera and species. The continental uplifts would have drained the great Carboniferous swamplands, thereby eliminating other arborescent types with which the world had been so long familiar, and interior plateau deserts with severe climates would have been extensive. It was a time of crisis for all the old forms of life—animal and plant— and many of them failed to meet the challenge.

Since there is little point in dwelling on what disappeared, let us turn to that which survived. Actually, the frost-free areas may have been rather more extensive than some students have supposed, for a few of the Carboniferous lepidodendrids, calamites, cordaites, and pteridosperms passed through the perilous times of the Permian and lingered on into the Triassic. Furthermore, the fossils tell us that the land unoccupied by glaciers was never barren of vegetation except in the worst of the arid areas and in the polar regions; there were vascular plants of one sort or another right up to the ice fronts. And the rapid development of tropical lowland forests in the Triassic also points to the presence, in the Permian, of considerable areas of at least warm-temperate climate. Figure 4 indicates, however, the remarkable change in the types of arborescent groups that took place during the Permian.

We leave this most interesting and critical period in the world's vegetational history with only one last glance. Various modern types of fern had become more evident. The cycads and cycadeoids were now common and venturing into the drier habitats then widespread. The ginkgos, the true "conifers," and perhaps even the earliest of the taxads were abundant, not only in the lowlands, but also on those uplands where the climates were not too severe. The pteridosperms, although on the wane (they were to linger on through the Triassic and into the Jurassic), still displayed a wide variety of forms. As previously noted, among these were groups which, for want of a better term, might be collectively called the "aberrant pteridosperms"—plants often with entire margined leaves and a reticulate venation. The male reproductive cells, or sperm, still were motile, and for this reason they have traditionally been classed with the pteridosperms, although recognized as distinct orders and families. Are we here getting our first glimpse of the real ancestors of the magnoliopsids? If these considerably varied "aberrant pteridosperms" actually were an independent complex of forms out of which the magnoliopsids were derived, then the Permian marks the really important point of change in the floras of the world, a closing out of the old forms and a bringing into prominence of the basic members of all the important modern arborescent groups.

The Great Pinopsid Experiment of the Triassic and Jurassic. Contemporaneously with the dwindling of the Permian ice fields and the return to a more equable climate in the Triassic, something approaching an ecological vacuum came into being, for the old forms dominant during the Carboniferous had essentially disappeared. The disturbances of the Permian had given rise to a large series of upland habitats, which were exploited by the remaining plant groups of the time. With the newly available, although still relatively small, lowland areas freed from competition by the old types, the newer types filled the many vacant ecological niches of these regions. Being in the ascendency and already the dominant upland forest type, the pinopsids began to develop an extremely divergent series of derived lowland forms.

Many of the Permian types held on into the Triassic, but in the expanding frost-free lowlands broad-leafed pinopsids began to be evident, suited to such environments. Certain modern pinopsids, such as the broad-leafed podocarps, appear to be collateral descendents from just such types. And it seems likely that a few, such as the modern *Phyllocladus*, abandoned leaves and produced broad leaflike structures by greatly flattening and expanding their lateral twigs. In the temperate lowlands further varieties of leaf forms showed themselves, some suited to humid and others to drier conditions.

In Triassic times deserts, residual from those of the Permian, or produced in the rain shadows of far-flung mountains, probably existed, and the widespread occurrence of numerous cycad and cycadeoid types suggests large subhumid areas. But the giant pinopsid trunks, abundant in the Petrified Forest of Arizona and elsewhere in Triassic formations, testify to extensive forests, and the opinion expressed by some that the Triassic world was largely dominated by true desert climates is probably erroneous. In the earlier stages of the Triassic the land masses were still elevated, and so afforded relatively few places where adequate deposits could be formed; therefore, we know little of what must have been the highly variant forest types of the time, save what can be deduced by observing the situation during the transition to the Jurassic.

A further lowering of the land masses in the Jurassic led to considerable amelioration of the climates of the world. Since it also gave opportunity for the formation of more extensive deposits, we know considerably more of the forest types of the Jurassic than we do of those of the Triassic. The cycads and cycadeoids were still abundant, indicating the persistence of subhumid areas of considerable extent. Along with the many old and now extinct groups of pinopsids, modern genera began to appear. About this time the ginkgos perfected a functional abscission layer in their leaf bases, which permitted their leaves, instead of hanging until tattered and unrecognizable, to be blown about as they fell off the trees each autumn and so to settle in depressions and become preserved. These characteristic and abundant leaf impressions permit us to ascertain that the group was widespread and common in the northern hemisphere, probably with a goodly number of species. The great bulk of the fossils has led to the conclusion that the forests of the Triassic and Jurassic were dominated by pinopsid types. But let us again remember that, although the continental masses apparently were being slowly lowered, there still were broad uplands and considerable mountainous territory, whose covering vegetation is necessarily almost unknown.

As Axelrod has pointed out, the earliest materials which can be placed among the flowering plants (magnoliopsids) with any degree of reliability have been found in Triassic strata. Materials about which there can be no argument are of increasing frequency in the Jurassic. Furthermore, by the Jurassic even these fragmentary remains indicate substantial diversity of form, with evidence that both monocotyledonous and dicotyledonous types already were in evidence. There is only one conclusion: beginning with the Triassic, and more abundantly in the Jurassic, the upland and mountainous regions, as distinguished from the more widespread areas of deposition, bore an increasingly diverse assortment of surprisingly modern magnoliopsid forest types.

By the end of the Jurassic the great experiment in diversification by the pinopsids was almost over. They had filled the numerous and often special ecological niches left vacant by the passing of the lowland forest types of the Carboniferous and Permian. They had not only achieved world-wide dominance, but had produced a diversity of kinds which they were never to display again. Of the 55 genera of pinopsids still living, 47 may be classed as relics in view of their restricted or highly disjunct present distributions, or else because their distributions today are much smaller than were those shown by their remains in Cretaceous and Tertiary deposits.[10]

THE SORTING OF THE FLORAS IN THE CRETACEOUS. Complex and varied as they were, the pinopsids between the Permian and the Cretaceous are known from such scattered localities that it is difficult to determine and compare the distributions of the various families and genera. It becomes obvious, however, that even before the Cretaceous there was a strong divergence between genera, some being predominately of the southern hemisphere and others characteristic of the northern. This separation has since been greatly intensified. Today only a few pinopsid genera have occasional species that cross the equator, and these are mostly along transequatorial mountain ranges, where they may be recently adventive.

The more critically we study our flowering plants (magnoliopsids), the more it becomes evident that the groups we are prone to think of as characteristic of the temperate regions actually have their more primitive living members in the frost-free parts of the world or have been patently derived from other groups essentially tropical in composition.[11] In view of what we know of their distribution in the Jurassic, in conjunction with the foregoing situation, we are increasingly led to the conclusion that the magnoliopsids underwent their primary evolution, not in the lowlands, but on the uplands of frost-free regions. Since there is reason to suppose that the magnoliopsids were actually present during the earlier phases of the Triassic, this primary evolution would have taken place roughly between latitudes 30° N and S, the probable limits of the frost-free conditions of the time (see Fig. 2).

Forms suited to a somewhat cooler climate might have come into being in the Jurassic, with further segregation and evolution during the Early Cretaceous of others better adapted to even more temperate conditions. In

---

[10] Li (1953) discusses the distributions and habit preferences of most of these relict pinopsid genera.

[11] Camp (1947, 1951); Axelrod (1952).

his excellent summary, based on paleontological evidence, Axelrod [12] points out that by the Mid-Cretaceous this ancestral magnoliopsid flora had become widely deployed in the frost-free regions and had also given rise to groups characteristic of the northern and southern temperate zones, which then extended into high latitudes and climatically approached the situation depicted in Fig. 1. There is a suggestion that the Paleocene—the transition from the Cretaceous to the Tertiary—saw an even wider development of a characteristically pantropic flora.

Interesting as was this deployment of the magnoliopsids during the Cretaceous—a large pantropic series, with considerably different forms in the north and south temperate regions—the forests of the time were by no means lacking in pinopsids. The latter were abundant in the cool-temperate regions, and some have remained there as characteristic forest types to this day. In the frost-free and warm-temperate parts of the southern hemisphere, broad-leafed [13] pinopsids competed successfully with the magnoliopsids, as they still do over large areas; and forms apparently better suited to cool-temperate conditions, such as then existed on what is now the Antarctic continent, were also represented. In the northern hemisphere the lowland forests of the Early Cretaceous were primarily composed of pinopsids, with a few scattered magnoliopsids, whereas by the close of the Cretaceous the arborescent magnoliopsids had increased to about 60 per cent of the total known flora, the pinopsids had dropped to about 15 per cent, and the remainder were mostly ferns, cycads, and highly evolved herbaceous materials, such as sedges and grasses. There is considerable evidence, however, that, except in equatorial regions, the uplands of the Late Cretaceous still contained abundant pinopsids.

In mapping forest cover, foresters, as a justifiably practical expedient, usually designate the stands on the basis of the dominant species present today. This practice may, however, at times give an incorrect picture of the natural forest cover, especially where the stands are known to be in ecological imbalance because of disturbance. For example, it is today usually considered expedient to map large areas in the southeastern United States as being dominated by "coniferous forest." However, as every forester in the region knows, the constant problem is to keep a stand of pine on the more productive sites from going over to a mixture with hardwoods which, to him, are "weed species." Only on exceptionally poor sites do the pines maintain their dominant position without assistance. This is clear evidence that the region basically is one of a mixed forest type. Today controlled burning is being ever more widely accepted as a legitimate silvicultural method for the control of hardwoods in the extensive southern pine forests. In a similar vein, evidence is only now accumulating that the once extensive stands of white pine in the New England states were the

---

[12] Axelrod (1952).

[13] In the southern hemisphere there are numerous "broad-leafed" (with the hyphen) pinopsid types. These are not to be confused with the traditional "broadleaf" (without the hyphen) forms of the forester, which refer only to the *Magnoliopsida*, the "angiosperms."

result of recurrent hurricanes which, periodically for a very long time, have swept the area with destructive force. Under undisturbed conditions in New England hardwood forests dominate the stands, with white pine scattered, any pure stands of it being limited to rocky outcrops and patches of extremely sterile soil. On more fertile soils in New England white pine is merely the first stage in a normal ecological succession following extensive blowdown by hurricane winds, or after clearing or fire. Here, as in the southeastern states, mixed forests of magnoliopsids and pinopsids would be the natural climatic cover.

Thus, without going into details on a world-wide basis, we may here note that mixed pinopsid-magnoliopsid forests, exhibiting an infinity of variations from region to region, but always with much the same general physiognomy, are widespread under warm- to moderate-temperate conditions if the rainfall is adequate and the areas but little disturbed. In fact, when examined objectively, the so-called "coniferous" forests of cool-temperate regions usually have admixtures of hardwood species (e.g., the yellow-birch and quaking-aspen elements of the spruce-fir forest of northeastern North America). As far as associations of species are concerned, these and similarly mixed forests, scattered across the temperate regions of both the northern and southern hemispheres, belong to what have been designated as various segments of the "Tertiary Forests"; but, as types of forest communities, they are more ancient and have their roots in the mixed pinopsid-magnoliopsid forests of the Cretaceous.

PRELUDE TO THE PRESENT (TERTIARY PERIOD). By the end of the Cretaceous all the important families of magnoliopsids containing arborescent members were present, and many of our modern genera were abundantly represented. The Tertiary marked the elaboration of species. In the Early Tertiary, the frost-free regions were somewhat more extensive than they had been in the latter part of the Cretaceous and offered ample opportunity for the basically warm-climate magnoliopsids to migrate. This probably explains the wide dispersal of so many tropical genera today, genera already in existence in the Tertiary. It also applies to the genera which today are widespread or exhibit disjunct distributions in the north temperate regions (Holarctica). Similar disjunct distributions of a series of families and genera of both magnoliopsids and pinopsids in the more temperate regions of the southern hemisphere, which seem never to have existed elsewhere, however, offer an incompletely resolved problem to paleogeographers.

By Mid-Tertiary time, the climatic pendulum was swinging back again. The frost-free zone was slowly shrinking, treeless areas began to appear in the polar regions, and the subhumid zones exhibited considerable expansion, their inner portions becoming arid.[14] This series of shifts culminated in the first of the Pleistocene glaciations.

[14] The movements of the floristic regions during the Tertiary have been summarized by Axelrod (1952).

As is well understood, a succession of ice maxima occurred during the Pleistocene, with interglacial intervals when the climate appears to have been considerably more genial than it is today. It has been calculated that the last ice maximum, covering perhaps as much as 12 million square miles of the earth's surface, locked up so much water from the world's oceans that their level was lowered about 300 feet. The fact that the melting of the ice still remaining in both hemispheres would raise the surface of the world's oceans perhaps as much as 150 feet above its present level, suggests that we may be scarcely more than half way through the present glacial regression.

There is no point here in entering the lists with those currently arguing over the actual extent of disturbance of the climatic zones during the height of the Pleistocene glaciations. The shifts certainly were not so marked as during the Permian, and the floras of the world appear to have recovered lost territory with considerable ease, except in certain areas (e.g., in Europe, where there was a considerable loss of those species and genera characteristic of the later Tertiary forests of that continent). Where there was ample room for migration, some species that appear to be closely allied to (or perhaps the same as) species in Late Tertiary strata moved southward ahead of the ice, and since then have been migrating northward again. The more genetically plastic groups apparently returned after each ice maximum, with a considerable accumulation of variability leading to the production of new species.

The Forests of the Present

We are now ready to take our theoretical representation of the climatic zones of a period of world-wide topographic and climatic disturbance (Fig. 2) and relate it to the vegetation types of the present. In Fig. 3, instead of climatic zones, generalized vegetation types appear. Here, again, it should be emphasized that local conditions, such as extensive mountain ranges, plateaus, or the relation of land and ocean masses, modify the details of the pattern. The map (Fig. 5), however, shows that the generalities hold.

Polar Regions. The north and south polar regions retain icecaps on the lands and considerable amounts of floating ice in the adjacent seas. Although vegetation occurs on summer snow-free areas (the precipitation is low and snow cover often very thin), it is stunted and presents the general aspect of *tundra*. Locally, treeless tundra may extend below 60° latitude.

Temperate Forests. The transition from the tundra to temperate conditions in the northern hemisphere is characterized by the predominance of spruce-fir forest, called *taiga*. The southern tip of South America is too temperate to have a comparable forest type.

On theoretical grounds the further transition southward from the taiga should witness a progressively greater incidence of broadleaf deciduous

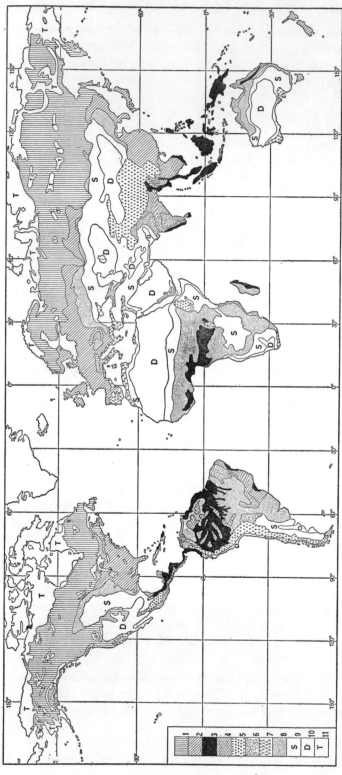

FIG. 5: The forests of the world. 1-6: MAJOR FOREST REGIONS. 1. *Coniferous forests*. Northern portion (*taiga*) mainly spruce-fir; at lower latitudes spruce and fir with other conifers and some broadleaf hardwoods. Timber, pulpwood. 2. *Mixed broadleaf-coniferous forests*. Broadleaf forests usually on better soils, coniferous types on poorer soils or in special habitats. Timber, forest products; general farming on better soils after clearing; pome and stone fruits. 3. *Tropical rain forests*. Important timbers, special tree crops, shifting agriculture. Includes unmapped areas of light forest, especially in Africa, and undifferentiated montane forest, as in Indonesia. 4. *Light tropical forest*. Timbers, important woods, special tree crops; often supports intensive tropical agriculture after clearing. 5. *Undifferentiated montane forests*. Regionally variable and complex, altitudinal tree line usually present. Timber, plateau agriculture and grazing. 6. *Thorn forest and scrub*. A few special woods and other products; seasonal grazing. 7-8: TRANSITION TYPES. 7. *Xeric scrub and woodland* ("Mediterranean scrub" forest). Local lumber, fuel, other products; specialized horticulture, winter pasture. 8. *Gallery forest and groves*. Grasslands with gallery forest along streams and scattered upland groves. Local lumber, fuel. Clearing and repeated fires produce aspect of treeless grassland. Two types may be distinguished: (*a*) *Prairie*: temperate regions above 30° N and S latitude; the great grain-raising regions of the world. (*b*) *Savanna*: tropical latitudes; partly natural but often follows disturbance of light forest; grazing, semisedentary to shifting agriculture. 9-11: AREAS WITH NO FORESTS. 9. *Steppe*. Bunch-grass, low shrubs and herbage; sometimes a few trees along main watercourses. Cattle and sheep ranching. 10. *Desert and desert scrub*. As mapped, includes some uplands with steppe and small areas of sparse forest. 11. *Tundra*. Low vegetation.

36

species; and in general this occurs. In the North American Pacific region, however, the expected superhumid area, in conjunction with the mountains and generally higher elevations, has thrown the balance in favor of the retention of predominately coniferous forests, although many broadleaf genera and species are also found, especially in the lowlands. In the eastern part of North America, in Europe, and in eastern Asia, the forests are primarily broadleaf deciduous, but coniferous elements of the north temperate forest also are abundant; this is the *Mixed Broadleaf-Coniferous Forest.*

The mixed broadleaf-coniferous forest of the southern hemisphere has much the same physiognomy as that of the northern, but with its own series of magnoliopsid and pinopsid genera. The superhumid region appears in southern Chile, greatly reduced in extent by the Andean chains; some of its characteristic species are closely related to forms living in New Zealand and other antipodean regions, or to forms known from Tertiary deposits of Antarctica.

In neither hemisphere is the transition from the temperate to the frost-free region marked by any sudden change in forest physiognomy, although the transition type is sometimes called *warm temperate forest.* This forest type often contains broadleaf evergreen species in genera (e.g., beech, magnolia, oak, persimmon) which, in the more familiar temperate forest, are characteristically deciduous; broad-leafed evergreen pinopsids, unknown in northern regions, sometimes are found associated with this forest type in the southern hemisphere. The occurrence of a fairly large number of relic genera in this transition zone may indicate that during the Early Tertiary this forest type was of much greater extent. This we should expect, for the generally warmer climate of the time would have produced a wider and even less clearly marked zone of transition between the temperate and frost-free regions.

ARID AND SEMIARID AREAS. The two central divisions of the drier areas of the world fall outside the scope of this work. The innermost, *Desert and Desert Scrub,* too dry to support anything more than a sparse vegetation, is encircled by short-grass *Steppe.* Surrounding the steppe, however, is a third segment which, vegetationally, is of interest here, for it contains arborescent material.

SUBHUMID TRANSITION AREAS. This outermost zone is transitional between grassland and forest. Near the western continental margins adjacent to or slightly within temperate regions, the rainfall occurs mostly in the winter months, the summer being hot and dry. Here a *Xeric Scrub and Woodland* is present, with trees along streams or in scattered, sparse colonies, usually accompanied by winter-green grasslands. This type of vegetation, best developed in the Mediterranean region (it is often called the "Mediterranean scrub" type) and in parts of California, also occurs in South America (Chile), southern Africa, and Australia.

As this same transitional band swings toward the continental interiors, it becomes subject to violent storms and irregular precipitation. The trees are at first limited to stream valleys, forming "gallery forests" (we shall meet this forest type again in the frost-free area). With slightly more precipitation, groves of trees and thickets of shrubs begin to appear away from streams. In the mid-continent of North America, the groves were once largely dominated by oaks, often bur oak (*Quercus macrocarpa*), and offered a welcome relief to those crossing the grasslands during the period of early settlement; stag-headed relics of some of these oak groves still stand near old homesteads, but most of them have been removed because of the danger of storm-thrown branches. In North America the shrub thickets often were dominated by thorny species of plum (*Prunus*) and hawthorn (*Crataegus*). The intervening grasslands contained relatively tall grasses and have been called *Prairie*. It is here suggested that the term "prairie" might perhaps be expanded to take in the entire vegetation complex of the region.

In its undisturbed phase the prairie is a transition grassland containing gallery forest and occasional groves of widely spaced trees, usually associated with more or less thorny shrubs. This is (or was!) as characteristic of the Asiatic, Eurasian, and South American prairies as of those of mid-continent North America. Today there is little opportunity anywhere in the world to see typical prairie. Climatically suited to the raising of excellent grain crops, for the grains are grasses, the natural prairie areas of the world are almost entirely under intensive cultivation, so great is the world's need for food. The gallery forest and scattered groves have largely fallen because of acute needs for fuel and local building material, although there is evidence that many of the groves and some of the thinner gallery forests were eliminated by prairie fires set by indigenous nomadic hunters too early to have been seen by travelers in modern times. The "treeless prairie," in large part, may be the result of clearing and fire.

Extending into the frost-free areas, the "tropical" margin of this sub-humid region becomes *Savanna* at about latitude 30°, perhaps more by definition than by any immediately visible change in vegetation. Here the precipitation strongly tends to be concentrated in the high-sun ("summer") months, although there may be a second (and usually much shorter) period of low-sun ("winter") rainfall. The savanna is characteristically a tropical grassland, often disturbed by fire, with gallery forest along the streams and with scattered groves or occasional individual trees. Palms are not infrequent, and the shrubby growths tend to be thorny. Typical *Thorn Scrub* and *Thorn Forest* usually appear adjacent to either savanna, or light tropical forest, and often develop out of these types after disturbance.

FORESTS OF FROST-FREE REGIONS. Despite the larger land areas in the northern hemisphere, more than half of the world's remaining forests are to be found in frost-free regions. In the higher mountains of the tropics, especially where contiguous to the temperate regions (e.g., in Central America), the vegetation is likely to contain genera often thought to be "characteristic" of the temperate forest, commingled with elements of more "tropical" groups. Here the rapid changes in elevation, coupled with the great number of micro-environments on rugged slopes, lead to a complex type of vegetation. At middle elevations, the forests merge into those characteristic of the adjacent tropical lowlands. In a work of this compass it would be useless to attempt any description of these frost-free montane forests. Where the precipitation is abundant—as it often is, especially on the windward sides—a *Montane Rain-Forest Complex* develops, with the dominant species often succeeding each other in relatively narrow altitudinal belts; it is "complex" because each species is present but progressively less conspicuous in a succession of adjacent zones.

DISTURBED TROPICAL AREAS AND "JUNGLE." There is a growing body of evidence that many areas of present thorn forest and related thorn scrub have developed out of both savanna and light tropical forest following disturbance, especially overgrazing. The great development of tropical savanna in many areas, however, has been accepted as a natural phenomenon by many plant geographers. As noted previously, natural savanna would be expected to occur in the climatic tension zone between tropical steppe and light forest. Nevertheless, on critical examination, it becomes evident that there is a proportional imbalance between savanna and light forest in various regions. While this is no more true of parts of Africa than of other tropical areas, it is most evident there, with far more savanna and much less light forest than we should expect on theoretical grounds. The often sharp line between relatively heavy forest and savanna, with no apparent differences in soil or precipitation, indicates that the sudden change from one vegetational type to the other is unnatural. There now is a strong tendency among recent students to conclude that wide expanses of savanna, as now defined, have been caused by fire. If so, the question is whether this is a recent happening, or whether—in some areas—it may be a legacy of the antique past. Again we may turn to Africa for evidence, evidence that has been available for a long time, but has been largely dismissed as distorted folk lore.

The *Periplus* of Hanno, the Carthaginian, the Greek translation of which still survives, is an account of a remarkable voyage of exploration along the west coast of Africa about the year 520 B.C. Hanno relates that some time after passing the mouth of the Gambia River he stopped on a coastal island, where the night was made hideous by the sound of drums, gongs, and some sort of wind instrument, and terrifying by great fires. Leaving the place in haste, Hanno sailed on, keeping Africa on his left. Day after day columns of smoke rose from the land, and by night the whole country seemed to be in flames. Whether the explorers got no farther than Nigeria, or ventured to the Cameroons, as some maintain, is of little moment here. The main point for this discussion is that Hanno recorded having seen great fires inland in Africa for days on end as he sailed along its coast.

Although Hanno failed to comprehend their nature, these fires must have been due to the annual "burning of the bush" to beat back the forest and provide land for agriculture and grazing. Thus we have evidence that for at least two and a half millennia—and how much longer we shall never know—great forest tracts in Africa have probably been regularly despoiled by fires purposely set by man, much as they are today. The result has been a great expansion of savanna at the expense of the seasonally combustible light forest; and the same thing has unquestionably happened over large areas in the Americas, in India, and in southeastern Asia.

Only within recent years have students working in tropical areas been able to divorce their thinking from ideas gleaned from previous study of the exceedingly overpopulated temperate regions and of the impoverished floras with which they are already familiar. Simplified concepts of forest ecology based on the almost diagrammatic floristic pattern of northeastern North America, or especially of northwestern Europe with its relatively few forest species, do not readily apply to the tropics, nor are the farms and pasture lands of the tropics laid out in neatly fenced plots. The number of species in a given area usually is far greater in tropical than in temperate regions; and agriculture in many parts of the tropics is fundamentally migratory, for several very definite reasons.

In the drier portions, catch crops planted during, or immediately following, the rains are the rule. Here clearing is primarily by fire, and the fires, set in the periods between rains, often get out of hand, spread over great areas, and enter the forest margin for some distance. This produces the often observed sharp line of demarcation between forest and savanna. It does not take a particularly dense human population to bring about these effects, and man has been living in the equatorial regions of both hemispheres for much longer than is sometimes supposed.

In the lowland portions of the frost-free zone that have abundant precipitation—in rain forest and light forest—there is, and for a very long time has been, a considerable population, especially near the watercourses, the "jungle roads." Here patches are cleared for the indigenous crops (and more recently for those that have been introduced) and the land is cultivated. Again, however, one familiar only with agriculture in temperate regions is prone to misinterpret the situation; the native farmer is not being indolent when he clears a plot of ground, cultivates it for a few years, and then abandons it to weeds. It is the only course open to him.

The generally high soil temperatures do not lead to humus formation, and soon the abundant rainfall so thoroughly leaches the soil of its mineral nutrients that it is necessary to abandon the plot after only a few crops. A new area is cleared, the rubbish burned where it lies (an effective method of scattering the mineral-containing ash), and a new crop planted. Unfortunately, modern plantation agriculture in the tropics far too often follows this same pattern. Under this system "fallowland" is a former cultivated area, perhaps only temporarily abandoned as no longer profitable because of the dearth of nutrient minerals in the soil and the high cost of fertilizers.

After abandonment, these cleared and briefly cultivated areas return to vegetation natural to the area, but not to the original forest type. Such tropical "weed forest" is the most rampantly growing sort of vegetation known. But remarkable as is this secondary forest, with its dense undergrowth and tangle of lianas, it is characteristic only of the disturbed areas of the region. Descriptions of these "impenetrable jungles," usually written in awed and sometimes lurid phrases by early travelers, who necessarily had to stay close to the rivers, have become the classic texts from which we have taken our concepts of tropical vegetation for much too long a time. Breaking out of this river-margin "jungle" and complex secondary growth that follows cultivation, the traveler may walk, as the writer has, day after day in the almost trackless forest of the South American equatorial region, only rarely having to swing his machete—except, if he be a botanist, to collect some choice specimen. The undisturbed tropical forest may be complex and can contain a great abundance of species, but it is far different from the "jungle" of much of our literature.

TROPICAL FORESTS. Primary tropical forest is not easy to find, although much has been so labeled by certain writers. In his excellent treatise on the world's tropical rain forests, Richards (1952) adds a most revealing footnote. In discussing what, in the original text, he characterizes as "Primary Mixed Forest ('Wet Evergreen Forest')" in Nigeria, he remarks that further work in the area "makes it seem likely that this forest has suffered disturbance in the past, and is old secondary rather than truly primary." He adds: "The same is probably true for nearly all so-called virgin or primary forest in Nigeria, and perhaps the whole of West Africa." [15] Undisturbed primary forest is usually thought to be of considerable extent in the American tropics; but it is by no means so widespread as is generally supposed.

The *Tropical Rain Forest* is perhaps our least understood vegetation type. Many forest areas in the tropics classed as "rain forest" actually are *Light Tropical Forest.* A further complication is the presence of large forest tracts on mountain slopes in the tropics which, because of the terrain and wind pattern, are well watered. These are *Tropical Montane Rain Forests;* on the middle slopes where the precipitation is usually highest, they have a composition considerably different from that of the rain forests of the lowlands. Where they are adjacent, both lowland rain forest and light forest pass into the montane rain-forest type.

The basic climatic factors behind the vegetation types of the world, as we have seen, may be ascertained in a broad way from Figs. 1 and 2. However, if we take a rather narrow zone across the equator, including those

[15] Richards (1952), 29.

areas in which rain forest would be expected to develop, we discover that it is advisable to particularize our information.

Figure 6 indicates in a diagrammatic manner the seasonal pattern of rainfall in this region. It is immediately obvious that there is only a narrow strip along the equator in which rain can be expected to fall at almost all times of the year. Here seasonal maxima may occur, but only exceptionally does any long period pass without rain. This relatively narrow equatorial band is the locale of the true rain forest, although local conditions in some places produce equivalent conditions that enlarge the occurrence of this forest type. Furthermore, some of the areas commonly mapped as rain forest actually contain considerable tracts of light forest.

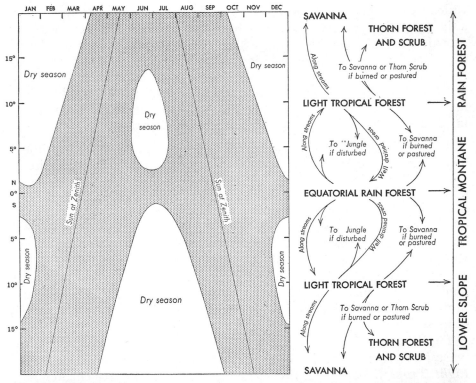

Fig. 6. Generalized pattern of wet and dry seasons in equatorial regions correlated with the main forest types. *Rain forest* extends along the better-watered stream valleys into areas otherwise primarily occupied by *light forest,* as this type similarly extends into *savanna* regions along streams. Conversely, on overdrained upland areas *light forest* often extends well into the region normally occupied by *rain forest.* Both forest types, where contiguous to mountainous areas, grade into *tropical montane rain forest.* The results of disturbance on these forest types, as by shifting agriculture, burning, or overgrazing, are indicated.

Figure 6 also shows that marked wet and dry seasons begin to be evident at only a few degrees of latitude north and south of the equator. The total annual rainfall may be very great, but, on the whole, true rain forest does not exist where the dry seasons last longer than a few weeks. However, in such areas along the main river valleys, and even along the smaller streams, the residual soil moisture is such that what might reasonably still be classed as rain forest does occur. This readily explains why observers traveling only along streams have in the past often expanded the supposed general distribution of this type of forest far beyond its actual limits. Glimpses of forest were seen in the distance, and it was supposed that it was of the same general composition as that near at hand. Actually this riparian "rain forest," intercalated with light forest, is comparable to the fingers of gallery forest that follow the streams in savanna regions.

Light forest is found in those regions near the equator where there are two yearly maxima of rain, with one of the dry seasons of about three months in length. With a shortening of the longer dry season, this forest type approaches the rain forest in character. However, on well-drained to overdrained terrain, the amount of moisture retained—the "effective precipitation"—may be low enough to produce characteristic light forest relatively close to the equator (and, in fact, in some places actually athwart it). Where the rainfall pattern is such that there is only one rainy period and a correspondingly long dry period, light forest persists until the conditions are reached where natural savanna (or in some instances thorn forest and scrub) occurs.

The light forest is obviously not a single forest "type." It may be classified on a local basis, but in broad pattern it varies from a "wet" phase to a "dry" phase through myriad nuances of vegetational association. In discussing both the rain forest and what actually is the "wetter" phase of light forest, Richards [16] indicates something of its nature. There are exceedingly complex ("mixed") types, with no species really dominant in the stands, and there are also extensive forests with single dominant species. He likens the "mixed" tropical forest to the mixed mesophytic forest of eastern North America,[17] which develops only in areas with abundantly varied micro-environments. I suggest here that the "mixed" forest of the tropics may also be a type that develops primarily in areas with a series of varied micro-environments, as yet essentially unstudied and therefore not understood. The forests near major streams, where they are subject to periodic, or occasional, inundation—areas often many miles in width—are, of course, "disturbed forests" and therefore likely to be complex, with a characteristic mixed community and a considerable amount of "jungle" undergrowth.

In the light forest, unless disturbed in some manner, the canopy is usually sufficiently close to prevent herbaceous and shrubby forms from receiving light enough to form more than a hint of junglelike undergrowth. On the whole, agriculture in the tropics is not successful in those areas characterized by typical rain forest, nor is life easy there. Hence, in his constant search for habitable places, man long ago entered the light forest, cleared the land, and set about his routine chores of cultivating it.

16 Richards (1952), chap. xi.
17 See Braun (1950).

Great areas in India, once covered with "monsoon forest" (a typical form of light forest produced by the strong periodicity of rainfall), are now given over to intensive agriculture. The more primitive pastoral agriculture of central Africa has also eliminated large stretches of light forest, but here savanna has resulted, so that it is today most difficult to distinguish between natural savanna and that which has been artificially produced by fire and overgrazing. Figure 6 gives some indication of the intercalation of the basic lowland forest types of equatorial regions, and also of what happens when they are disturbed or destroyed.

Great as are the forest resources of the tropics, we have as yet made far too little intelligent use of them. At present, the world's primary demand is for the coniferous softwoods. Numerous especially valuable timbers are today being cut from tropical forests, but the great majority of the species are ignored. Remote from the daily experience of most of us, the spoilage of the remaining areas of tropical rain forest and light forest through improper practices is not generally comprehended. Under our present economy many of the species of these forests are considered "worthless" and their normal habitats are sometimes almost wantonly destroyed. These "worthless" forms constitute at least a vast reservoir of raw cellulose; their other uses may be legion, should we study their characteristics in greater detail. Here is a great natural resource rapidly being wasted away through ignorance.

Variability and Kind

As we have seen in the foregoing outline of the origin of forest types, those times in the history of the world when the land surfaces were elevated, when mountain building was at a maximum, and when climatic disturbances were widespread marked important periods in the development of new vegetation types. In view of the changes that land surfaces and climates constantly undergo, a too rigid genetic system is a distinct disadvantage to any group of organisms. With genetic plasticity—variability—there is a greater chance of survival during any disorganization of habitat. Variability, indeed, is the basis of survival.

From the standpoint of plant systematics the species is usually considered to be the working unit. Furthermore, it is traditionally supposed to exhibit but little variation. This concept, however, is largely based on superficial morphological grounds. As we begin to study species in greater detail, examining thousands of individuals instead of only a few in each species, it becomes evident that even this so-called morphological constancy of the species has little basis in fact; we have not been scrutinizing our materials with sufficient precision. We also are learning that, with this morphological variability, there is an equally large amount of physiological variability, inherent in the genetics of the group; and, in the end, this inherited physiological variability is far more important than are differences in morphology where factors concerned with survival are involved.

Foresters have long known that, in reforestation or afforestation, it is best to use seed from sources not too far removed from the site of the new plantings. In western North America Douglas fir (*Pseudotsuga taxifolia*) grows from about latitude 55° in British Columbia to about latitude 17° in Mexico, from sea level in the Pacific Northwest to elevations of over 10,000 feet in the Rocky Mountains, and from humid to subhumid habitats. Attempts have been made to set up a series of "segregate species" from within the known morphological variability of this wide-ranging tree, but from the point of practical botanical taxonomy only the variety *glauca* is now recognized apart from the "typical" form. However, it has been found best not to move materials much more than a degree of latitude, or a climatically comparable distance in elevation, if the greatest survival and maximum growth of the planting is desired, though practical considerations usually make this impossible to achieve. As a species defined by taxonomists, Douglas fir is widespread, but each of its local biotypes has a genetic norm that fits it to a particular set of ecological conditions. Even here we can discover considerable variability, related to the precise conditions of the local micro-environments. There also is a growing body of data that day length at certain periods of the year—which, of course, is correlated with latitude—plays a very important part in the effective competition and survival of these minor biotypes.

These and similar examples might be greatly expanded. The white pine (*Pinus strobus*) is found from eastern Canada through the Appalachian Mountains, and also in the highlands of southern Mexico. When brought together at about latitude 40° N, and if protected by appropriate handling under glass, the material from Mexico grows considerably faster than does that from the central Appalachians, as in turn this grows faster than do the Canadian plants. When planted in the open at this same latitude, the more nearly local material still grows faster than does the Canadian material, but the Mexican plants die with the first hard freeze. Data of the same sort are being accumulated for hardwoods that have wide distributions, and also apply to adaptability to variant soils as well as to differences in climate—in brief, to the host of factors that influence the growth and persistence of plants.

The source of this genetic variability within species, and the mechanics of its operation within species populations, which often enables the sum of their biotypes to have considerable geographical ranges and ecological tolerances, is a subject too extensive to be developed here.[18] Nevertheless, what we can ascertain by relatively precise experimental methods with regard to what is happening among the species around us today, is indicative of what has been going on through the long span of time during which forests have covered the land.

Through such studies we come to an understanding of how it was that, in the past, groups of organisms could develop biotypic variations capable

[18] For a brief discussion see Camp and Gilly (1943).

of venturing into new habitats and new climatic regions. Thus we glean insight into the importance of the uplands and mountain ranges of the past. It was on the uplands and cooler mountain slopes of the frost-free regions that the ancestors of our modern forest trees evolved. On these same slopes, with their multitude of different micro-environments, variant forms better preadapted to conditions in temperate regions came into being, were further elaborated, could persist for long periods of time, and so be available to spread poleward during those periods when the great cyclic changes in the topography of the continental masses and their climates afforded an opportunity. Likewise, this same inherent tendency toward variation, characteristic of all life, gave rise to forms still better fitted to cooler or even to boreal climates. With a swing of the climatic pendulum in the other direction, the ancestral biotypes would necessarily have had to retreat, or, if unable to do so for some reason, become extinct, leaving behind the newly evolved forms. These derived forms are the backbone of the vegetation of our present temperate and cool-temperate forests. With further evolution, coupled with genetic isolation, these biotypic segregates could—and have—become the "boreal" and "extreme austral" species of the taxonomist.

There is a tendency of some people to think of the tropical lowlands, because of their generally equable conditions, as having had a persistent and stable series of forest communities over long periods of time.[19] This would seem to be a valid assumption on theoretical climatological grounds, and also because considerable segments of the equatorial lowlands have been in a reasonably stable geographical position, at least since the Permian. However, there is evidence that the present forest types of the lowlands have been derived in large part from more upland types, which migrated into the lowlands during the Middle and Late Tertiary. As the writer has pointed out elsewhere, the forests of the central Amazonian basin appear to be primarily composed of elements derived from the surrounding uplands, perhaps at a time no earlier than the Late Pliocene or Early Pleistocene.[20] Obviously, based as it is on the consideration of a single area, this generalization needs considerable study before it can be taken as being more widely applicable. On the whole, however, the forests of tropical lowlands do not contain what, according to generally accepted botanical criteria, are considered to be the more primitive living species of genera that have fairly broad altitudinal distributions. These are usually found on the piedmont and lower mountain slopes.

Proper utilization of our forest resources demands that trees be cut down. What comes back to take their place—or what is brought in to replace a forest area that has been despoiled by improper cutting practices—is not a thing to be decided in a casual manner. Even with selective thinning, the micro-environments have been changed, and with clear-cutting a totally new set of factors is introduced. Some few forest types regen-

19 Richards (1952), postscript.
20 Camp (1951).

erate satisfactorily; others are replaced—or might better be replaced—with different sets of materials. Whether the replacement is to be with the same biotypes, with somewhat different biotypes of the original species, or with entirely different species, depends on a considerable array of factors. These factors are within the province of scientific silviculture, but they cannot be ascertained without a great deal of painstaking research.

Biotypic variation is the fundamental mechanism leading to the evolution of the manifold kinds of organisms with which this world abounds, and an understanding of it is indispensable in any consideration of the proper utilization and regeneration of our forests, our most important replaceable natural resource.

SELECTED REFERENCES

AXELROD, D. I. 1952. "A theory of angiosperm evolution," *Evolution*, **6**:29-60.

BLUMENSTOCK, D. I., and THORNTHWAITE, C. W. 1941. Climate and the world pattern. (In *Climate and man: yearbook of agriculture*, pp. 98-127. U.S. Dept. of Agriculture, Washington.)

BRAUN, E. L. 1950. *Deciduous forests of eastern North America*. Blakiston Co., Philadelphia.

CAMP, W. H. 1947. "Distribution patterns in modern plants and the problems of ancient dispersals," *Ecol. Monogr.*, **17**:159-183.

———. 1951. "Phytophyletic patterns on lands bordering the South Atlantic Basin," *Bull. Amer. Mus. Nat. Hist.*, **99**:205-212.

——— and GILLY, C. L. 1943. "The structure and origin of species," *Brittonia*, **4**:323-385.

LI, HUI-LIN. 1953. "Present distribution and habitats of the conifers and taxads," *Evolution*, **7**:245-261.

RICHARDS, P. W. 1952. *The tropical rain forest*. Cambridge University Press, London.

ROSSBY, C. G. 1941. The scientific basis of modern meteorology. (In *Climate and man: yearbook of agriculture*, pp. 559-655. U.S. Dept. of Agriculture, Washington.)

RUSSELL, R. J. 1941. Climatic changes through the ages. (In *Climate and man: yearbook of agriculture*, pp. 67-97. U.S. Dept. of Agriculture, Washington.)

3. FOREST INFLUENCES

Samuel T. Dana

Forests are one of the most prominent geographic features of the world in which we live. They occupy nearly a third of the earth's total land area and occur wherever conditions are not too dry, too cold, or too barren to permit their growth. In addition to being one of the most conspicuous parts of the landscape, they influence the lives of human beings in many ways—mostly beneficial. They moderate local climates, reduce soil erosion, regulate stream flow, support a wide variety of industries and communities, and afford unequaled opportunities for recreation. Some of these influences can be evaluated in dollars and cents; others cannot, but are none the less important. Let us look first at some of the influences in the latter class.

Atmospheric Conditions

The climate of any given place is determined chiefly by its latitude, its elevation, and meteorological forces that operate over wide areas and at high as well as low altitudes. But within the broad limits established by these major factors, local modifications of the "microclimate" are effected by topography and forest cover. Although these effects vary greatly with different combinations of slope, aspect, kind and size of trees, density of stand, and area covered, certain generalizations as to their character are possible.

Wind Movement. The first thing that one notices on entering a forest on a windy day is the relative calm. So great is the difference that one seems to have stepped suddenly into another world. The mechanical obstruction offered by the trees deflects upward a large part of the moving mass of air, and slows down the velocity of that which enters the forest. Dense stands with heavy foliage naturally have the greatest effect. Thus, a forest of deciduous broadleaf trees has more effect on wind velocity in summer than in winter.

Observations indicate that the velocity of the wind in the interior of a forest may range from about a tenth to two thirds of that in adjacent open country, depending on the character and condition of the forest. The stronger the wind, the greater the reduction of actual velocity, but not of relative velocity. Under normal climatic conditions wind velocities within

49

a forest are typically low, seldom averaging more than a few miles per hour.

This influence on wind movement is felt not only inside the forest itself, but for a considerable distance to the leeward. Shelter belts consisting of several rows of trees are often planted to take advantages of this fact, particularly in regions where lack of natural forest cover gives the wind an unbroken sweep over long distances. Intensive studies in the plains region of the United States show that shelter belts may have a measurable influence on wind velocity to a distance of as much as fifty times the height of the trees. The greatest effect usually comes within a distance of from three to five times the height of the shelter belt, where the velocity of the wind in its lee may be 20 to 30 per cent of that in the open.

This reduction of wind movement brought about by forests and shelter belts adds to the comfort of man and beast and increases the production of crops grown to the leeward of their sheltering influence.

Temperature and Radiation. Forests exercise a moderating influence on air temperature as well as on wind movement. Here again the extent of the influence is greatest in dense stands with heavy foliage, which have the maximum effect on incoming and outgoing radiation. Protection from solar radiation, which under extreme conditions may be in the forest only 1 per cent of what it is in the open, reduces maximum temperatures throughout the year. In the forests of the United States the reduction in monthly maxima may range from about 3° F. in January to 8° F. in July.

Similarly the slowing down of outward radiation from the earth generally raises minimum temperatures throughout the year. The effect of a forest on monthly minima is less than on monthly maxima, both in summer and winter, but may amount to more than 6° F. in the United States.

Since maximum temperatures are normally lower and minimum temperatures higher in the forest, the net effect of a forest cover is to reduce materially the range in temperature at all times of the year, and also to reduce slightly the mean temperature. Evergreen trees have more influence than those with deciduous foliage. Although the actual figures may seem small, it must be remembered that the effect on absolute maximum and minimum temperatures is much greater than the effect on mean temperatures; the moderating influence of the forest is most noticeable and most welcome on extremely hot or extremely cold days.

Humidity. In general, the air in a forest is somewhat moister than that in the open, although the difference in absolute moisture content is less than would be expected in view of the large amount of water transpired by trees. Relative humidity, which varies with temperature as well as with the absolute amount of water vapor in the air, may be as much as 11 per cent higher in the forest. As in the case of temperature, the influence of the forest is much more pronounced on maximum and minimum humidities than on mean humidities.

PRECIPITATION. No subject in the field of forest influences has aroused more controversy than the effect of the forest on precipitation. Whether that effect is negligible or significant has often been argued with more heat than light. Popular belief in the efficacy of forests as "rainmakers" was formerly much more widespread than it is today. Passage of the Timber Culture Act of 1873 was undoubtedly facilitated by the hope that tree planting in the prairie region would increase the supply of water, as well as of wood. Unfortunately, so many complicating factors are involved as to make positive proof one way or the other extremely difficult.

The argument that forests increase rainfall and other forms of precipitation is based chiefly on the fact that they transpire enormous quantities of water. Trees not only use more water in the process of growth than does any other form of vegetation, but may even add more moisture to the atmosphere than is evaporated from an equal area of open water. In effect they act during the growing season as a pump, moving water from the soil to the air in almost unbelievable quantities. And whatever influence transpired water may have in increasing precipitation is strengthened by the lower temperature in and above forests, by the fact that they add to the effective height of the land, and by the friction which they offer to wind movement.

All these factors, it is asserted, tend to result in more frequent and greater precipitation—an influence that may be regional as well as local. Raphael Zon, for example, in his report to the National Waterways Commission [1] argued that "forests in broad continental valleys enrich with moisture the prevailing air currents that pass over them, and thus enable larger quantities of moisture to penetrate into the interior of the continent. The destruction of such forests . . . affects the climate, not necessarily of the locality where the forests are destroyed, but of the drier regions into which the air currents flow."

The opposing argument is that the major forces controlling precipitation operate over such wide areas—continental or even intercontinental in extent—that the presence or absence of forests can have virtually no effect. Furthermore, precipitation depends not only on the amount of moisture in the air, but on conditions favorable to its release. How forests affect these conditions, if at all, is uncertain.

Many attempts have been made to measure the influence of forests on precipitation, with widely varying results, and with even more diverse interpretations of their meaning. Although most of these studies show significantly greater precipitation in the forest than in the open, the difference may be more apparent than real. This is primarily because the greater wind velocity in the open reduces the amount of precipitation caught by rain gauges. There are also other complicating factors that make it difficult to obtain strictly comparable measurements.

[1] Zon (1927). For more complete references see p. 63.

The opinions expressed by Joseph Kittredge in his book *Forest Influences* probably represent the point of view held by most scientists today. He concludes that forests have no appreciable effect on cyclonic precipitation, but that they may increase local rainfall in temperate climates by not more than 3 per cent, and that rainfall in clearings in the forest may be about 1 per cent more than in similar situations in the open.

EVAPORATION. Forests tend to decrease the amount of water evaporated from the soil under their immediate cover and to some distance in their lee. This is due to their influence on wind movement, temperature, and humidity. One of the major objectives in the planting of windbreaks or shelter belts is to reduce evaporation and thereby increase crop production in the fields that benefit from this protection, which, as we have already seen, commonly extends over a distance many times the height of the windbreak.

Soil Conditions

TEMPERATURE. Soil temperatures are affected by a forest cover in the same way as air temperatures but to a much greater degree. Mean daily maximum temperatures at the soil surface may be reduced in summer by as much as 50° F., and absolute maxima even more. The influence of the forest varies inversely as the distance from the surface, but under some conditions may be recognizable to a depth of 30 feet.

Minimum temperatures show a similar but less pronounced increase. This influence is particularly noticeable in the winter, when soils usually freeze later and less deeply in the forest than in the open. Sometimes the soil in the forest remains unfrozen while that in adjacent open fields is frozen to a considerable depth. On the other hand, in situations where there is a heavy blanket of snow in the open and a very light blanket under a dense forest canopy, this relationship may be reversed.

These influences are due partly to the reduction of insolation and radiation by the overhead forest cover, and partly to the insulating effect of the litter and humus of the forest floor. These reduce maximum temperatures more than they increase minimum temperatures, and hence the net effect is a cooling one. In both cases the effect is beneficial. During the summer young plants are protected from high temperatures which in exposed situations in the open may be so extreme as to kill the living tissue; while during the winter reduction in the depth and period of freezing diminishes surface runoff by permitting the penetration of more water into forest soils.

COMPOSITION AND STRUCTURE. Forests have a marked influence on the composition and structure of the underlying soil. Every year they add to the forest floor large quantities of leaves, twigs, and branches, which under normal conditions are constantly decomposing to form humus. Part of this humus gradually mixes with the mineral soil beneath and also supplies it with soluble compounds carried downward by percolating water.

The amount of organic material in the forest floor varies widely with differences in climate, soil, and vegetation. Recorded data run from less than 2 tons per acre in old-growth longleaf pine in Florida to nearly 120 tons in a forest of birch, sugar maple, and spruce in New Hampshire. In general, high temperatures result in its rapid decomposition and disappearance. Ordinarily there is a gradual transition from undecomposed litter through partially decomposed duff and humus to a mixture of organic and inorganic material and eventually to mineral soil. An exception occurs in coniferous forests in the north where slow decomposition of the needles results in acid "raw humus." This raw humus does not mix well with the underlying mineral soil and in extreme cases may be peeled off like a blanket.

The usual effect of a forest cover is to improve both the chemical and the physical characteristics of the soil. Nitrogen, calcium, phosphorus, potassium, and other elements are made available in larger quantities. Even more important is the action of organic materials in making the soil more friable and crumbly. They tend to make light soils, such as sands, heavier; and heavy soils, such as clays, lighter. These effects are strengthened by the constant growth and death of the tree roots. While growing they keep pushing into and loosening up new areas of soil; when dead they add organic material to the soil and leave channels through which water may percolate more readily. Porosity of frozen soil is also increased in the forest, where it is more permeable than in the open.

MOISTURE CONTENT. Forests tend to decrease the amount of moisture in the soil by intercepting precipitation, by retaining water in the forest floor, and by transpiration. They tend to increase the amount by reducing surface runoff, by increasing the permeability of the soil, and by decreasing evaporation from it.

Much precipitation in a forest never reaches the ground because it is first intercepted by, and then evaporated from, the leaves, twigs, branches, and trunks. This loss may run as high as one tenth of an inch per shower. The amount of water that actually reaches the ground may vary from none in light showers to the great bulk of the total precipitation in heavy rains. Interception naturally increases with the density of the stand and of the foliage, and is much greater with deciduous trees in summer than in winter.

When the precipitation reaches the ground it is first absorbed by the forest floor, which has a field moisture capacity (that is, an ability to retain water against the pull of gravity) of from one to five times its own dry weight, and when saturated contains much larger quantities. Its absorptive and storage ability is much greater than that of mineral soil, the field capacity of which usually ranges from 10 to 50 per cent of its dry weight. The thicker and the more decomposed the litter and humus of the forest floor, the more water it will hold.

The amount of water that actually gets through to the mineral soil may vary from zero to 100 per cent, depending on the amount of precipitation and on the condition of the forest floor. With light showers in times of drought all of the precipitation may be retained by the forest floor; while with heavy showers and in wet periods little or none may be so retained.

On land without vegetative cover, and particularly with heavy soils, the surface layer tends to become hard and impermeable, with marked reduction in the amount of precipitation that sinks into the main body of the soil. In the forest, on the other hand, the litter slows down surface runoff and thus gives more time for the water to be absorbed by the humus, which acts as a huge sponge. More important still, the humus prevents muddying of the underlying mineral soil, which remains porous, and thus absorbs and retains much more water than does exposed soil in the open.

Enormous quantities of water are removed from the soil by transpiration. A well-stocked forest of mature trees uses more water than does any other form of vegetation. It may require from 100 to 1,400 pounds of water for every pound of dry matter produced. Transpiration is far greater in summer than in winter, and during the growing season is somewhat greater with broadleaf deciduous trees than with conifers. Its tendency is obviously to reduce the moisture content of soil in the forest as compared to that in the open. On the other hand, the reduction of evaporation in the forest, which was mentioned in the discussion of atmospheric conditions, tends to maintain the moisture content at a higher level than in the open.

The net effect of these conflicting influences varies widely with the character of the topography, the soil, the climate, and the forest. So far as any generalization is possible, it may be concluded that soils under a forest cover tend to be somewhat drier than similar exposed soils in the open on fairly level ground, and somewhat moister on steep slopes where more water is lost by surface runoff in the open than by interception and transpiration in the forest.

Erosion and Stream Flow

Of all the influences of the forest on its environment, the most obvious and the least controversial is the reduction of surface runoff of water. This prevents or substantially checks soil erosion and modifies stream flow.

ACCELERATED EROSION. Soil is constantly being moved by water and gravity from higher to lower elevations. Under normal conditions, with an undisturbed vegetative cover, this is a slow process known as "geologic" erosion. Over the centuries it has built up fertile alluvial soils in the valley bottoms. With the removal or disturbance of the vegetative cover, a striking change takes place. Larger and larger particles of soil, and even huge boulders, can now be moved, and the rate of removal is greatly increased. The beneficial process of geologic erosion is replaced by the destructive process of "accelerated" erosion. Among the harmful results are deterioration or ruin of the lands where the erosion takes place and where the coarse detritus is deposited, siltation of reservoirs, impairment of the quality of water for municipal and industrial uses, destruction of fish habitats, clogging of river channels, and increase in the volume of floods.

All kinds of vegetation serve to check erosion, but by far the most effective are well-stocked forests and well-sodded grasslands. Their influence is primarily due to their ability to reduce the amount and velocity of surface runoff.

The amount of material that water can carry at a given velocity is directly proportional to its volume. As the velocity increases, however, there is a much more than proportional increase in the cutting and carrying power of a stream. Thus, if the velocity of water is doubled, its cutting power is increased fourfold, its carrying power thirty-two-fold, and the size of the material it can carry sixty-four-fold. These facts explain the occurrence of "mud-rock" flows, the transportation by small streams of boulders weighing many tons, and up to a six-thousand-fold increase in the rate of erosion following destruction of the forest and the forest floor.

During ordinary storms much, if not all, of the precipitation is absorbed by the forest litter and humus, retained a short time, and then passed on gradually to the mineral soil beneath. The humus layer is not comparable, as has sometimes been alleged, to a blotter on a slate roof, the efficacy of which in storing water ceases as soon as it becomes saturated. Except in "raw humus," there is no sharp line between the organic surface and the inorganic subsurface material in the forest. On the contrary, there is a gradual transition from the top layer of newly fallen, undecomposed litter to partially and completely decomposed humus, to a decreasing mixture of organic with inorganic material, and finally to mineral soil. Thus there is a constant and uninterrupted downward movement of water from the temporary storage provided by the upper layers of the forest floor into the larger and more permanent soil reservoir beneath. From there the water moves slowly as a subsurface flow to springs, streams, and lakes, from which it is in time evaporated and again precipitated in the course of the hydrologic cycle.

Tree roots also help to keep the soil from being washed away in gullies and along the banks of streams, and tend to check the occurrence of landslides. Erosion by wind is virtually nonexistent in the interior of a forest, and is greatly reduced for some distance to its lee.

In many ways forests are influential in preventing the development of accelerated erosion—the greatest threat to the world's soil resources. Fortunately their influence is most effective where the danger is most acute, as on steep slopes, in clayey soils, and with heavy rainfall. Wind erosion can also be prevented or greatly reduced by properly placed windbreaks in open country, as in the Great Plains of the United States

DISTRIBUTION OF RUNOFF. For all practical purposes the total stream flow from any watershed consists of the precipitation less the sum of the losses from interception, transpiration, and evaporation. To the extent that the forest increases interception and transpiration, it tends to reduce stream flow; and to the extent that it decreases evaporation, it tends to increase stream flow. The net effect depends on the relative weight of these influences. It will obviously not be the same under all environments or at all seasons of the year.

Measurements from forested and from deforested or partially forested areas in Switzerland, Colorado, and North Carolina have shown a strong tendency toward smaller annual runoff from the forested areas. The difference was particularly marked in the spring, when melting snow and heavy rains caused the maximum seasonal runoff. The greater discharge of water from the nonforested areas also carried with it much more eroded material.

The total flow of a stream is made up of two main parts: the surface runoff and the subsurface or ground-water runoff. As we have already seen, the forest has a profound effect in reducing surface runoff and thereby increasing the amount of water available for subsurface runoff. The evidence is conclusive that in most regions surface runoff is very small or negligible from areas of undisturbed vegetation, while it may amount to half of the precipitation where the vegetation has been destroyed or seriously disturbed. However, the outstanding influence of forests in this respect is greatly weakened when the forest floor is destroyed by repeated fires, even though the trees themselves are not killed.

Reduction of surface runoff results in more uniform flow of a stream throughout the year. Maximum flow is nearly always less and minimum flow usually more from forested than from comparable nonforested areas. The tendency is to avoid sharp peaks of flow in the spring and deep troughs in the summer. The total amount of flow may be less, but its greater uniformity is highly desirable.

FLOODS. What effect these influences of the forest have on floods is a hotly debated question. Certainly forests cannot prevent an abnormally high flow of streams when heavy precipitation falls on saturated or frozen soils. If the storage basin is already full, there is nothing for any additional supply of water to do but to flow off by way of the nearest stream. On the other hand, when the soil reservoir is well below the saturation point, there may be far less surface runoff from forested areas than from those not covered by vegetation, even in severe storms.

By and large there can be no doubt that forests tend to reduce flood flow in small watersheds in hilly country. One would expect them to have a similar influence on large rivers made up of the flow of many small streams. Here, however, the situation is complicated by many factors, the combined effect of which it is difficult to evaluate. For example, the way in which precipitation is distributed over a river basin as a whole and the rate of flow of the tributary streams largely determine whether their peak discharges reach the main river simultaneously or in successive waves. Obviously the first combination will result in a much higher flood than the second, even with the same or perhaps even a smaller total runoff. Therefore, the clear-cut influence of the forest on the flow of streams from small watersheds at the headwaters of large rivers may not always be reflected in the flow of the main river. Nevertheless, the general tendency will be for the forest to decrease both maximum and total runoff, and to increase minimum runoff, throughout the river basin.

The action of the forest in reducing erosion also has an important influence on flood flow and flood damage. Small streams with steep slopes issuing from deforested or burned-over watersheds may carry several times as much solid material as water. One instance is on record in southern California where solids comprised 88 per cent of the total flow. As the stream flattens out, the larger and heavier materials are, of course, deposited; but even rivers with small gradients may carry heavy loads of sediment. This material adds significantly to the volume of the stream and increases its erosive power, particularly in time of flood. It may, in fact, be even more important than the volume of water as a source of damage.

WATERSHED MANAGEMENT. From the point of view of water supply, the ideal management of the forest, as a part of the broader field of watershed management, is that which will produce the maximum total runoff, well distributed throughout the year, with minimum erosion. Such management may not always be identical with that which will produce the largest supply of wood. Serious conflicts will, however, be the exception rather than the rule. When they do occur, the method of management to be selected must be based on relative values, among which water for domestic and industrial use, irrigation, power, navigation, and recreation may rank high.

Striking evidence of the basic importance of conserving both soil and water resources is afforded by the greatly increased attention being paid by such agencies as the Soil Conservation Service, the Tennessee Valley Authority, and the Forest Service in the United States to the promotion of more effective watershed management, in which forest planting and improved forest practices play a prominent part.

Wood, the Universal Raw Material

No less prominent than the influence of the forest on climate and runoff is its influence on industry. In fact, its tangible products affect our economic activities even more clearly and more directly than do the intangible services that it renders. They provide opportunity for the profitable employment of labor and capital in many important industries, and furnish a wide variety of indispensable consumers' goods.

Wood is sometimes known as "the universal raw material" because it is so widely distributed and can be used for so many purposes. Although for some uses it has been largely displaced by other materials, there are few articles into the composition, manufacture, or transportation of which it does not enter. While perhaps no more "indispensable" in modern civilization than many other materials, such as iron, cement, and glass, its range of use is certainly much broader than most of them.

For thousands of years, until the advent of coal, oil, and gas, wood constituted man's chief source of fuel. Even today more than half of the total consumption of wood in the world goes for this purpose. Another third in the form of lumber and structural timbers is used for the construction of buildings of all kinds. Except in urban centers and where forests are scarce or lacking, most people continue to live in wooden houses.

Lumber and dimension stock are in turn remanufactured into innumerable articles such as toothpicks, toys, sporting goods, musical instruments, handles, boats, caskets, and furniture. In the United States approximately an equal amount of lumber (about one seventh of the total cut) goes into boxes, crates, and dunnage used in the shipment of commodities. Large additional amounts of wood are used for railroad ties, poles, piling, fence posts, mine timbers, excelsior, shingles, cooperage, veneer, and plywood. Modern adhesives are greatly helping to expand the use of wood in the fields of ply and laminated construction and are making practicable the salvage of much low-grade material. Advances in engineering techniques now make possible the use of wood in members requiring high strength and long spans, where metal was formerly regarded as indispensable.

Even more spectacular advances have taken place in the chemical utilization of wood. The demand for paper and paper products seems unlimited. Each year larger and larger quantities of wood go into the manufacture of newspaper, book and magazine paper, writing paper, wrapping paper, wallpaper, building paper, pasteboard cartons, and paper board. From "dissolving pulp" come cellophane, rayon, artificial wool, and many plastics. Today one could, if one chose, be clothed wholly in textiles that originated in the forest.

A lively imagination is required to visualize the many other chemical substances that can be derived from wood. Among these are wood gas, potash, charcoal, acetone, methyl alcohol, sugar, ethyl alcohol, yeast, salicylic acid, and vanillin. Potentially the forest is the source of large quantities of motor fuel and food. During World War II, when gasoline was scarce, many automobiles in Europe were operated entirely on wood gas, which is still used to a considerable extent in trucking. Another potential substitute for gasoline is ethyl (grain) alcohol produced by the fermentation of sugar, which in turn has been produced by the hydrolysis of wood cellulose. The alcohol can also be converted into lubricating oil and synthetic rubber.

Wood sugars have already been used extensively in Europe as feed for livestock and are a possible source of food for human beings. They can also be turned into yeast of high nutritive value by inoculating them with the appropriate organisms. Edible carbohydrates and proteins are among the innumerable products obtainable from wood cellulose, which in its original state is a highly indigestible product. Lignin, the other main constituent of wood, is a comparatively unknown substance, of which little use is now made but which is likely in time to provide a wide variety of important chemical products.

Many substances other than wood and its derivatives come from trees and are ready for use with relatively little further processing. Among these are nuts, maple syrup, chewing gum, tannin, dyes, rubber, and resin. The last yields turpentine, universally used as a solvent in paints and varnishes and in the production of synthetic camphor; rosin, used by violin players and baseball pitchers and in the manufacture of soap, varnish, and paper; pine oil, used in the flotation process of separating metals from their ores and in the textile industry in the fixation of dyes; and pitch, for which chemists are just beginning to find profitable uses.

Many pages would be required merely to list the useful substances that come from trees. Wood, once regarded by some as obsolescent, is now used more widely and for more purposes than ever before. Its inherently desirable properties of high strength in relation to weight, its workability, elasticity, nonconductivity of heat and electricity, and beauty can be enhanced, and its undesirable properties of shrinking and swelling, inflammability, and susceptibility to attack by insects and fungi can be mitigated by methods developed by modern technology. Wood as wood, properly treated and handled, is one of the most useful materials known to man; while cellulose, lignin, and resin are a veritable treasure house of chemical products already in use and yet to be discovered.

The significance of forest products is emphasized further by the facts that forests are both renewable and more efficient as producers of solid substance (ligno-cellulose) than is any other crop. Here is at least one case where we can have our cake, and a rich cake at that, and eat it too. Industrially the age of the forest is ahead of us as well as behind us.

Forest and Wood-Using Industries

This situation makes it possible for man, through intelligent handling of the forest resources, to raise his standard of living by the continued and increasing production of a host of valuable, often indispensable, raw materials and finished commodities. It also provides widespread opportunities for the profitable employment of land, labor, and capital.

FOREST INDUSTRIES. Forests also constitute one of the major landscape features of the modern world. A much larger percentage of the total land area is primarily suitable for the production of forested crops than of harvested agricultural crops. This area, averaging about 30 per cent for the world as a whole and running up to 80 per cent or more in some countries and regions, supports a large number and wide variety of forest and wood-using industries. First comes the task of growing the trees—the practice of forestry. This involves the protection of the forest from fire, insects, disease, and trespass; the determination of present stands and future yields; the conduct of cultural operations, such as thinnings, to speed up the growth and improve the quality of the stand; and the final harvesting of the mature crop so as to replace it by a well-stocked new crop of desirable species, including where necessary the production and planting of nursery material.

Cultural and harvesting activities necessitate logging operations, with the transportation of the resulting products from the stump to the mill, the railroad, or the point of consumption. Housing for woods workers must be provided, and primary and secondary woods roads must be constructed. Next, for forest products not to be used in their original form as fence posts, mine props, telephone poles, piling, etc., come primary and secondary manufacturing. Saw mills, veneer mills, planing mills, box mills, pulp and paper mills, furniture factories, wood-turning factories, and a host of other plants play their part in the preparation of both rough and finished goods for use by the ultimate consumer.

All of these operations require large numbers of workers and large amounts of capital. Wherever forest supplies are abundant, the forest and wood-using industries rank high in both respects in national economies. For example, in the United States the chief manufacturing industries using wood (excluding the extractive industry of logging) account for about 10 per cent of the workers, the wages paid, and the value added by manufacture in all manufacturing industries. Capital investments are particularly heavy in the pulp and paper industry, where costly machinery is necessary.

One of the most striking features of the forest and wood-using industries is their widespread geographic distribution. Logging must obviously be conducted where the forests occur. Since logs are such a bulky commodity, it usually pays to cut transportation costs by subjecting them to at least primary manufacture near the point of origin. As a result, wood-manufacturing plants are widely scattered throughout the forest regions of the world. In the United States they comprise about a fourth of the total number of manufacturing establishments and rank next in number to those concerned with food, apparel, and printing and publishing.

FORESTS AND COMMUNITY DEVELOPMENT. Because of their large number and wide distribution, the forest and wood-using industries influence the economic and social life of a great many communities. This influence is most keenly felt in the smaller cities and towns, particularly in well-forested regions, where they often constitute the dominant interest. In such situations, the prosperity of the community rises and falls to a very considerable extent with the prosperity of the forest-based industries. These have a decidedly stabilizing influence wherever the forests are managed on a sustained-yield basis, with the average annual cut and average annual growth in balance. Ghost towns do not occur where sustained yields are obtained and where mill capacity is adjusted to the growing capacity of the forest.

One of the important aspects of any industry is its influence on other industries and on service activities. The forest and wood-using industries purchase large quantities of axes, saws, tractors, trucks, planers, lathes, digesters, paper machines, and other items of equipment; and they sell lumber, veneer, plywood, boxes, pulp, paper, and similar items to other industries for use in the manufacture and marketing of their products. Railroads in some regions depend for their very existence on the freight revenue derived first from bringing raw materials, equipment, and general supplies to communities dominated by one or more wood-using industries, and secondly from transporting the products of these industries from mill to market.

Industry in general also supports many services, such as those supplied by grocers, druggists, clothiers, doctors, lawyers, ministers, and teachers. The wood-using industries do not differ in this respect from other industries, except that in many rural districts they provide the sole or the main reason for the existence of a community. Where this is the case, they create the demand for such services; and where other industries are also present, they intensify that demand.

One further item of community concern is the relation of the forest and its dependent industries to the small landowners, and especially to the farmer. The existence of a nearby wood-using industry provides a market, which in turn should encourage thrifty management of the wood lot. The additional income thus available can have a stabilizing effect both on the farmer and on the community of which he is a part. Forestry is a key to permanence.

FORAGE AND WILDLIFE. Not all forest industries are based on the utilization of trees. In many regions forage produced in openings in the forest, and sometimes under the trees themselves, provides feed for cattle, sheep, and pigs supplementary to that which they obtain from pastures and the open range. Beef, mutton, and pork thus become in part products of the forest, the use of which for grazing may furnish an important means of support for the livestock industry. Timber production and livestock production are, however, not always compatible, and stock must be kept out of areas where grazing is injurious to the forest. Browsing and trampling are likely to be particularly harmful in hardwood forests, from which domestic livestock should ordinarily be excluded.

Many fur-bearing animals which spend at least a part of their lives in the forest provide the raw material for another important industry. Milady must have furs; and mink, otter, fisher, marten, weasel, beaver, fox, muskrat, rabbit, and many others supply them for her. Their production can well be one of the objectives of multipurpose forest management.

The taking of other forms of wildlife by sportsmen and fishermen helps to provide a market for manufacturers of arms, ammunition, and fishing gear. Users of the forest for recreational purposes step up business for makers of automobiles, cameras, clothing, insect-repellents, and gadgets of all sorts; for keepers of service stations, hotels, motels, and dude ranches; and for packers, guides and wranglers. This stimulation of economic activity may extend as far back as the iron mine, the petroleum well, and the cotton field.

Recreation, Inspiration

The most important influence of the forest as a source of recreation is not indirectly through industry, but on the recreationist himself. Its chief significance lies in the enhancement of human values rather than monetary values. The forest provides not only recreation, but "re-creation."

In the hurly-burly of modern life, with its economic pressures and nervous tensions, people need occasionally to get back to nature. Where better than in the open, and particularly in the forest, can they regain both physical and spiritual strength?

As civilization has advanced, man's relation to the forest has continually changed. To primitive man the primeval forest was generally a gloomy and forbidding place. He viewed it with mixed feelings of fear and superstition. Tree worship was common in many tribes. "The groves were God's first temples"; they were also the first temples of pagan gods.

Gradually, as tools were developed and new uses for wood were found, and as the demand for land for agriculture increased, man pushed back the forest frontier. Domination of the forest by man was a slow and difficult process which developed qualities of courage, hardihood, resourcefulness, and ruthlessness. The men who lived and worked in the forest, and whose hero was Paul Bunyan, were no weaklings.

Today throughout much of the world the early relationship is reversed. Virgin forests, except in parts of South America, Africa, and Asia, are a rarity. There is a shortage rather than a surplus of wood for industrial use. A rapidly increasing population is becoming more and more concentrated in urban centers. Even the lumberjack usually lives in town or in a comfortable camp quite unlike the crude shacks of earlier days. Forest areas of outstanding value for recreation are shrinking even as the need for recreation becomes more acute.

Different people seek re-creation of body, mind, and soul in different ways. Some like to hunt and fish with gun and rod; others prefer to use field glasses and camera. It is now the wild beast that fears man, not man the wild beast. Some like to lose themselves on camping trips in an inaccessible wilderness; others are satisfied to enjoy the beauty of the forest from the seat of an automobile. Many wish enough "roughing it" to give them the illusion that they are emulating the prowess of their forebears. Some seek health, others inspiration. All are attracted to the forest by the opportunity to find rest or strife, relaxation or stimulation, in an environment that takes them out of the stifling routine of their daily lives.

From time immemorial the forest has influenced the work of architects, painters, poets, dramatists, and preachers. It has molded the character not only of those who live and labor in it but of those who visit it only occasionally to play or to pray. In the realm of the human spirit its gifts are invaluable both figuratively and literally.

As Robert Marshall expressed it: [2] "The most important values of forest recreation are not susceptible of measurement in money terms. They are concerned with such intangible considerations as inspiration, esthetic enjoyment, and a gain in understanding. It is no more valid to rate them in terms of dollars and cents than it would be to rate the worth of a telephone pole in terms of the inspiration it gives." In face of mounting pressure for more wood for homes, furniture, magazines, rayon clothing, and other tangible goods, it is important in the management of the forest to remember that "man doth not live by bread *only.*"

Forests are an inescapable geographic fact. Not only do they dominate the landscape throughout much of the world, but they influence man's life in countless and often unsuspected ways. They temper the climate; improve the soil; reduce erosion and floods; support a wide variety of important industries; provide opportunities for the profitable employment of land, labor, and capital; stabilize communities; and offer a unique source of recreation and inspiration in close communion with nature. Their management in ways that will assure the perpetuation of these values is an urgent task, of supreme importance to the people of the globe.

SELECTED REFERENCES

FRANK, BERNARD, and NETBOY, ANTHONY. 1950. *Water, land, and people.* Alfred A. Knopf, Inc., New York.

GLESINGER, EGON. 1949. *The coming age of wood.* Simon & Schuster, Inc., New York.

KITTREDGE, JOSEPH. 1948. *Forest influences; the effects of woody vegetation on climate, water, and soil, with applications to the conservation of water and the control of floods and erosion.* McGraw-Hill Book Co., Inc., New York.

PANSHIN, A. J., *et al.* 1950. *Forest products.* McGraw-Hill Book Co., Inc., New York.

U.S. DEPT. OF AGRICULTURE. 1933. A national plan for American forestry. By ROBERT MARSHALL. *Sen. Doc. 12, 73d Cong., 1st Sess.* Government Printing Office, Washington.

ZON, RAPHAEL. 1927. Forests and water in the light of scientific investigations. (Appendix V, *Final Report of National Waterways Commission, Sen Doc. 469, 62d Cong., 2d Sess.* Government Printing Office, Washington. 1912.) Reprinted by U.S. Department of Agriculture, Forest Service, with revised bibliography.

[2] U.S. Dept. Agric. (1933).

4. PRINCIPLES AND PRACTICES OF FORESTRY

J. W. B. Sisam

Over much of the earth's land surface forests represent the climax form of vegetation and, if left undisturbed, are the dominant feature of the landscape. These natural forests are generally looked upon as one of the great resources of the world—the bounty of nature, which down through the ages has contributed much to man's comfort and enjoyment as well as to his economic progress. They have not only provided wood and other products to meet his domestic and industrial requirements, but have often had an important and usually beneficial influence on his environment, particularly in the regulation of stream flow and the maintenance of stable soil conditions.

The Development and Objectives of Forestry

A feature of fundamental importance, which distinguishes forests from some other resources, is that they are renewable. This means that the mature forest, as it is cut, may be replaced by a new crop of trees; thus a continuous yield of wood is provided from the same area of land. The application of this principle is the primary basis of forestry practice, which may be defined briefly as the growing and using of successive crops of timber.

As the practice of forestry develops, the forests often come to be looked upon less as a natural resource and more as a crop that is dependent in large measure on man's knowledge and skill. However, forestry is not concerned exclusively with growing timber as a crop; forests contribute in many other ways to the well-being of mankind, and proper forestry practices assure the maintenance and enlargement of these benefits.

Man is not a conservationist by nature: history shows that as long as the existing forest appears to be adequate to the demand, it is subject to exploitation for immediate revenue and there is little concern for its future productivity. In other words, forest conservation, involving some investment of time and money, only begins when it is apparent that current practices are endangering the resource with critical effects upon the supply of forest products and services.

Down through the centuries, as man has increased in numbers and spread over the face of the earth, he has caused and is still causing widespread destruction of the forest cover, partly of necessity to provide land for agriculture, settlement, and industrial development, partly through ignorance and greed, and partly in the belief that the forest resource is inexhaustible. This latter viewpoint is to some extent justified in the early development of countries and regions that have extensive forest wealth and relatively small populations. Here the forest is often looked upon as a hindrance to settlement and agricultural development, with the result that areas cleared may exceed requirements and include lands quite unsuitable for the purpose in mind. Man has in fact retained under intensive agriculture only a small portion of the area that was originally cleared for this purpose. It is estimated that, as a result of his activities, man has destroyed about two thirds of the world's original forest cover; the remaining forests containing merchantable timber today occupy less than one fifth of the world's land area.

In some parts of the world forest destruction has been unchecked, despite the adverse effect that this has had on the general economy and on the living standards of the people. Asia, in particular, has suffered from the effects of forest clearance and forest destruction, with widespread soil deterioration, inadequate supplies of wood to meet basic domestic needs, and low living standards for a large portion of the population.

Elsewhere, as the danger became apparent, methods of managing the forests to ensure their continued productiveness were evolved, and thus the science of forestry came into being. However, the philosophy of conservation has developed slowly, and forestry has invariably been the child of necessity: only after periods of forest destruction and land clearance has the need for husbandry and planned forest economy been realized. The transition from exploitation to management takes time and requires the solution of many problems, technical, economic, and administrative. In the beginning it may be characterized by a strong reaction against spoliation aimed at preserving the forest intact—"locking it up"—for posterity. In general, however, this is the antithesis of sound management of a renewable resource, which for its fullest development requires periodic harvesting and regeneration; an exception would be the preservation of representative samples of natural forest for scientific study and as "wilderness" areas.

Modern forestry originated in Germany and France, and much of its development during the past two centuries has taken place in northwestern Europe. Attention to forest conservation in these countries came early owing to an increasing demand for timber and firewood and the difficulty of securing wood cheaply from other countries. These conditions and the serious effects of deforestation on stream flow, particularly in montane regions, made evident an urgent need for forest management. During the nineteenth century expanding populations and the iron and coal economy of the industrial revolution created new demands for wood and gave added impetus to the development of forestry.

Slowly, and usually only as the need became urgent, other countries have followed the lead of western Europe and developed forestry practices to meet their own requirements. Such developments usually begin with restriction on the use of the forest, as in the setting aside of timber reserves, and with protection of the forest against its more serious enemies, particularly fire. These steps are followed by efforts to secure new growth after cutting, by encouraging natural reproduction and by planting: with this the practice of silviculture begins. Finally, the accessible, productive forests are managed under cutting regulations and suitable silvicultural techniques to ensure a continuous yield of timber in perpetuity. Such forests are said to be managed on a "sustained-yield" basis.

While the natural forest usually provides the starting point for a forestry program, it may not represent the optimum conditions that an area is capable of, and its perpetuation is not always looked upon as the ideal objective of forest management. The aim, rather, may be to improve the natural forest as far as possible within the limits set by the local environment, silvicultural knowledge, and economic considerations, and in view of the purpose for which the forest is to be used.

Attempts to go beyond these limits and completely change the natural forest pattern have sometimes failed. A well-known instance was the century-long attempt to convert the lowland hardwood forests of Saxony to pure Norway spruce. Despite early rapid growth, the spruce was often badly damaged by snow and frost as well as by fungal and insect attacks. By the end of the third crop of spruce, conditions had so deteriorated that hardwood species had to be reintroduced, and it was generally conceded that the plan had been unsuccessful. On the other hand, there are many examples of the successful introduction of types and species of trees different from those in the natural forest. The success of these operations depends largely on careful study of the ecological factors involved.

The aim of forestry may vary from one country to another and even between regions within the same country, depending upon local conditions. Usually the primary purpose is to grow sufficient wood to meet a country's requirements—first for domestic consumption, then for export to foreign markets. Products other than wood, usually referred to as minor forest products, may sometimes be an objective of management. These vary in importance and kind from one country to another, e.g., turpentine, resin, oils, fruits, maple syrup, bark for tanning, etc. The southeastern United States and the Landes in Gascony, France, are two regions where the production of resin and turpentine from species of pine is a major industry carried on in association with timber production.

While the production of wood and other commodities is often primary, in its broader aspects forestry is concerned with the interaction between the forest and its environment, as, for example, in the effects of the forest on the stabilization of soil, on the maintenance and restoration of soil fertility, on the regulation of stream flow, and on the provision of a suitable environment for valuable fish and wild life. The protective influences of the forest are many and far-reaching, and under certain conditions may be more important than the supplying of wood. This is particularly true in some parts of the tropics and subtropics, in crucial drainage areas, and in regions of light, sandy soil unsuitable for cultivation, where the removal of the forest cover often results in near-desert conditions. Forestry may also aim at the full development of the recreational value of an area; but even where recreation or protection are the main objectives, controlled cutting of wood can usually be carried on advantageously, if the cutting operations do not interfere with the primary purpose of management.

The term "multiple use" is widely used in referring to the management of a forest area for two or more purposes, one of which may be dominant, but not exclusive.

Bases of Forestry

Forestry may be defined as the scientific management of forests for the continuous production of goods and services. While its practice involves many problems of an economic and administrative nature, the solution of which is essential for success, its proper development must in the first place be based on a sound knowledge of the forests and of the laws that govern their development, and on an understanding of the characteristics of the individual species that make up the forests and of the interrelationship of the forests with their environment.

The forests of the world include a great many species of trees, not necessarily having any close botanical relationship, with varying adaptations to climate, soil, and topography, and more or less distinct reproductive characteristics, forms and rates of growth, sizes and ages at maturity, light requirements, and abilities to resist damage by insects and other destructive agencies. It is with an intimate knowledge of these features of the trees and tree communities that sound forestry practice must begin.

BOTANICAL RELATIONSHIPS. Trees represent many different families within the two major divisions of the spermatophytes or seed-bearing plants—the gymnosperms and the angiosperms. Trees of the gymnosperm group are more commonly known as conifers or softwoods, while those of the angiosperm group are often called broadleaf trees or hardwoods. These names do not apply universally—the wood of some gymnosperms, for example, is considerably harder than that of certain angiosperms. For most practical purposes, however, the forests of the world are classified as softwoods, temperate hardwoods, and tropical hardwoods. The dominance of the softwoods in the northern temperate forests is of special economic significance, because man has found that these woods are particularly useful. Thus the saw timber that is used throughout the world in general building and construction is 75 per cent softwood, and an even larger proportion of wood pulp comes from this class of trees.

METHODS OF REPRODUCTION. While nearly all trees reproduce from seed, some species, particularly hardwoods, also reproduce vegetatively. A new crop of trees, such as oak, chestnut, maple, and hazel, may originate as sprouts or coppice growth from the stumps of the parent trees. Other hardwoods (e.g., certain species of poplar) may produce extensive sucker growth from underground roots, while some softwoods, notably species of spruce in the northern forests, may reproduce by layering. In this case the lower branches of the parent tree form separate root systems in the moss in which they have become embedded. Vegetative propagation by one or another of these methods may play an important part in forestry practice. For example, hardwood forests have long been coppiced where wood is in constant demand for fuel: as coppice growth develops much more rapidly than do seedlings during the first few years, material of fuel-wood size can be produced by coppicing in a relatively short time.

Nearly all trees produce some seed each year after they are full grown, but large quantities of seed are usually produced only at intervals, the periodicity of seed production varying mainly with species and climatic conditions. Some species are noted for the frequency of their seed years, while others produce seed in quantity only at long intervals. Furthermore, some species may produce large quantities of very light seed, which can travel considerable distances from the parent tree, while others produce small quantities of heavy seed, which usually fall to the ground just below their points of origin.

Wind is probably the most common method of seed dispersal, and the seeds of many tree species are well adapted for this purpose, having wings, plumes, hairs, or similar attachments; other means of distribution include water, birds, and animals.

The successful establishment of a seedling depends on many factors, including the viability of the seed, the suitability of the seedbed, and the possibility of survival from such hazards as drought, frost, insects, and disease, to which the seed or seedling may be subjected. Nature makes allowance for these many adverse factors by providing large quantities of seed, of which only a very small percentage survive to become trees in the mature forest.

GROWTH CHARACTERISTICS. Living trees increase in height each year by developing new shoots from the terminal buds. The total height attained by mature trees varies widely, ranging from 20 to 30 feet for such species as hawthorn to over 300 feet for some of the eucalypts in Australia and sequoias on the west coast of North America. Within a species the rate of height growth will vary according to the inherent capacity of the individual and to local conditions of climate, soil, and topography.

Growth in diameter or girth is accomplished by cell division within a meristematic [1] layer known as the "cambium," lying just inside the inner bark. This results in the formation of a layer of wood over the whole

---

[1] Meristematic tissues are those in which new cells are being formed by cell division.

bole or trunk. Throughout the life of the tree there are alternate periods of growth and dormancy, and in general, owing to differences in the structure of the wood produced at the beginning and at the end of a growing season, the successive layers appear as a series of concentric circles when the tree is cut transversely. Where climatic conditions are such that a period of growth alternates with a period of dormancy within the year, these woody layers are known as annual rings. The yearly increase in wood volume depends primarily on diameter growth.

For the first few years after its formation the wood, then known as "sapwood," contains some living cells which store food substances and conduct water and solutions of mineral nutrients from the roots to the crown of the tree. Later the cells die, other physiological changes take place, and the wood, at this stage known as "heartwood," ceases to function except in support of the crown. Quite commonly the heartwood is darker in color, more durable, and has better timber properties than the sapwood.

The physical structure, and consequently the density and technical properties of the wood laid down by the cambium, vary considerably from one species to another. The rate of diameter growth may also have diverse influences on the strength and quality of the wood: while rapid growth increases the strength of certain hardwoods, it may produce soft, spongy, low-grade timber in some of the softwoods.

The form of the bole generally varies according to the strength required to support the crown and resist wind pressures: in a closed forest the bole approaches a cylindrical form, whereas in exposed sites it is more conical owing to the need for mechanical support. There are also considerable differences between species, especially between the two major groups of hardwoods and softwoods, in the form of the crown and bole, and in the vigor of development and persistence of side branches. Usually softwoods produce a well-defined bole with relatively small branches, while the branches of many of the hardwoods are larger and more widely spreading. Since branches produce knots, for the production of clear timber it is desirable to remove the lower dead and dying branches while they are fairly small. In general, trees growing in a closed forest have fewer and smaller branches than those growing in the open. However, the rate at which lower branches are killed by shade and subsequently drop to the ground varies with the species.

Important characteristics of the mature root system also vary from one species to another. Some species have deeply penetrating tap roots. Others have mainly shallow lateral roots, which are more likely to be sensitive to drought and ground fires and to render the trees more susceptible to wind throw.

Root modifications or adaptations that are related to the nutritional efficiency of certain species include (1) the presence of nodules containing nitrogen-fixing bacteria in the roots, particularly of alders and members of the Leguminosae, and (2) a close association between the root tips of many tree species and the mycelia of certain fungi: this association is known as "mycorrhiza."

NUTRITIONAL AND ECOLOGICAL REQUIREMENTS. For its growth and for other life processes, the tree requires food, and like other green plants it builds up its food materials from simple substances. The chemical constituents of a tree are chiefly carbon, hydrogen, and oxygen, together with some nitrogen and certain minerals such as potash, lime, iron, and phosphorus. The carbon is obtained from the small amount of carbon dioxide gas that is always present in the atmosphere and enters the plant through small openings in the leaf surface known as "stomata." Oxygen and hydrogen are obtained from the soil through the root system in the form of water carrying nitrogen (nitrates) and mineral nutrients in solution. The synthesizing of these elements to form substances that the tree requires—in particular the combination of carbon, hydrogen, and oxygen to form carbohydrates—takes place mainly in the leaves in the presence of the characteristically green matter (chlorophyll) and of sunlight, which supplies the necessary energy. Air, water, chlorophyll, and light are therefore essential to the production of the carbohydrates—in particular cellulose and lignin—which form by far the greater portion of the tree. Soil moisture is especially important, as a deficiency of water inhibits photosynthesis. Tree species differ markedly in their optimum water requirements and also in their sensitivity to departures from the optimum.

Tree species also differ greatly in the amount of light they require, or, alternatively, in the degree of shade they will tolerate. It is customary to classify species as shade-enduring or tolerant (of shade) and light-demanding or intolerant (of shade), but for most species the younger the tree and the better the soil quality on which it is growing, the greater its tolerance of shade.

The environmental factors important in tree growth—solar radiation, air temperature, humidity, precipitation, and the physical and chemical nature of the soil—are usually spoken of as the factors of site or locality, and their total effect with reference to a species as the site quality. Site quality is evaluated either directly by examination and classification of soil and other factors, or indirectly, as for example, by using ground vegetation as an indicator of soil conditions, or by relating the height of dominant trees to the age of the stand.

Since the bulk of the tree is derived from carbon dioxide and water, a relatively small demand is made on the soil in growing a crop of timber; thus land too poor for profitable cultivation may be capable of growing a crop of timber satisfactorily. Deeply penetrating roots bring up from the deeper soil strata mineral nutrients that would not otherwise be available; a relatively high proportion of these minerals may be deposited annually on the surface soil through the falling of leaves, twigs, and other debris.

The leaves, which play such an important part in the nutrition of the tree, function for only a limited time before dying. Deciduous trees lose

all their leaves at the end of the growing season, whereas evergreens lose
only a portion of the older leaves each year.

The growth and general well-being of a tree depend primarily on soil
and weather conditions. Also of vital importance to the future of each
member of the forest community is the intense competition that develops
for space and food requirements—a struggle that inevitably kills many of
the competitors and brings about significant changes in the environment
of the survivors.

LONGEVITY. Under favorable conditions a tree usually grows vigorously
until it reaches maturity, after which the growth rate gradually slows
down. Overmature trees grow little and show signs of decadence. The
normal life expectancy of trees varies widely with the species: some temperate and tropical hardwoods reach maturity in less than 100 years and
some softwoods in 100 to 200 years, but many species of both softwoods
and hardwoods require 200 to 500 years to mature. On the Pacific coast
of North America, ages of 500 to 700 years are common; the giant sequoia
in California has been known to live for over 3,000 years, an example of
extreme longevity.

RESISTANCE TO DAMAGE. Trees, like other organisms, are damaged and
destroyed by various agencies, including fire, insects, fungi, grazing animals, industrial fumes, and such climatic factors as wind, frost, and snow.
The capacity to resist such damage depends upon the vitality and the protective devices of the species. A knowledge of the relative resistance of
different tree species is of importance in forest management.

DISTRIBUTION. Apart from the chance results of geological history, the
continental distribution of tree species and the limits of tree growth, both
in altitude and latitude, depend primarily on heat; the east-west distribution, on the other hand, is more often determined by moisture conditions—
the rainfall in the interior of a continent may be too scanty to support tree
growth. Thus each species of tree has a range of natural distribution
determined primarily by climate. Obviously there is a great deal of overlapping, and many species grow under similar conditions—in fact it is
common to have a number of species sharing the same area in a mixed
stand.

Pure stands of a single species do not commonly occur in the natural
forest, though stands approaching this condition may be found where a
species is well adapted to extreme conditions of climate or soil moisture,
or where fire has brought about a situation particularly favorable to one
species. The most heterogeneous and complex forest communities are
found in tropical regions of high rainfall.

The distribution of a species within its natural range is determined
mainly by soil, topography, and competing vegetation, as well as by local
variations in climate, which also affect the long-term development of many
species: climatic races or strains develop, more or less adapted to local
variations of climate within the range as a whole. This fact accounts, in

part at least, for the wide variation in results obtained by using seed of other than local origin in establishing forests. Scots pine, for example, has developed a number of climatic races, and experience in both Europe and North America shows that efforts to introduce a "foreign" race of this species without a proper correlation of climatic conditions at seed source and planting site will almost certainly prove unsatisfactory, particularly in the susceptibility of the trees to damage by snow and sleet and the incidence of disease. This, of course, also holds true for attempts to establish any tree as an exotic outside the boundaries of its natural range. However, where the climatic conditions of two regions are similar, the introduction of tree species from the one to the other may be undertaken successfully, as, for example, in the introduction of conifers from the Pacific coast of North America into Great Britain.

An understanding of the various biological factors discussed above is of fundamental importance in the development of forestry practice, particularly in the fields of silviculture and protection. It must be emphasized, however, that practical forest management must depend also on the knowledge and application of sound business principles and on the development of suitable methods and techniques to be used in collecting, analyzing, and organizing the basic data to be obtained from the forest.

Branches of Forestry

As is implied by what has been said above, forestry has a number of subdivisions, each of which is concerned with some particular aspect or phase of the subject. Hence, an understanding of forestry itself is dependent on knowledge of its parts, the extent to which they are interdependent, and how best they may be co-ordinated.

FOREST PROTECTION

Agencies that seriously damage and may destroy forests include fire, insects, diseases, grazing animals, and adverse conditions of exposure and climate. The relative importance of these varies with local conditions.

Fire is perhaps the most spectacular. It frequently destroys not only the forest growth, but also the surface organic layer beneath, thus reducing soil fertility. Fire is most serious in the coniferous forests of temperate regions and in the dry forests of the tropics and subtropics, and is of course most difficult to control in heavily forested regions with sparse populations and poor accessibility.

Protection against fire is usually one of the first steps taken in the development of a forestry program. Appropriate legislation is passed, and organized staff and equipment and transportation facilities are provided to detect and suppress fires as they occur. Where the country is heavily and continuously wooded, strips may be cut through the forest to break the continuity of tree growth and delay or prevent the spread of fires. Clear-cut strips of this nature are known as "fireguards." Fire itself is sometimes used as a preventive measure where the annual fall of litter and the dying back of ground vegetation produce large accumulations of inflammable debris. The "early burning" of this material when moisture conditions are such as to prevent too rapid spread of fire will reduce the danger during a dry period later in the season.

Recent important advances in the field of fire protection include the use of aircraft, mainly for detection, and of meteorological data to appraise more precisely the existing degree of fire hazard, so that dangerous conditions can be quickly recognized and adequate preventive measures taken.

In some European countries forest fires are rare, and such as do occur cause negligible damage. In Norway, for example, forest properties may be insured against fire at a low premium rate. There are a number of reasons for this: (*a*) in general the forests are easily accessible and under intensive management, with annual fellings well distributed in a large number of small scattered holdings; (*b*) the forest consciousness of the people is highly developed; (*c*) the climatic conditions tend to be favorable, with well-distributed summer rains and an absence of prolonged hot, dry periods.

Despite the damage it causes, fire cannot be looked upon solely as an enemy of the forest. Under certain conditions controlled burning may prove a useful tool in securing the regeneration of valuable forest trees; it may prepare a suitable seedbed, eliminate competing vegetation, or assist in the distribution of seed. Certain conifers, for example, have serotinous [2] cones, and considerable heat is required to open them and release the seed: these species may reproduce abundantly after fire, and the resulting stand is often referred to as a "fire type." Extensive even-aged coniferous forests of the northern temperate region owe their origin to fire, as do many other commercially important forests in various parts of the world.

Insects that damage and destroy trees, and the fungi and other organisms that cause tree diseases, are present in all forests. In *endemic* proportions and in balance with their environment, they are a necessary and sometimes innocuous feature of the forest community. Even under these normal conditions, however, some insects and diseases may seriously damage commercially valuable trees. While the damage caused by fungi is usually slow in developing and of minor account in young trees, it is cumulative and may be so extensive in overmature trees as to render them valueless.

Destructive organisms may also reach *epidemic* proportions and destroy one or more tree species over wide areas. This is particularly likely to happen in overmature forests or when an organism is moved from its natural environment to new surroundings. A classical example is the chestnut blight (*Endothia parasitica*), which was brought to North America

---

[2] Late in opening. Serotinous cones are those retained on the tree for a relatively long period before opening to release the seed.

from Asia about 1900 and killed practically all of the sweet chestnut *(Castanea dentata)* in eastern America within a few years. Instances may also be cited of widespread destruction by forest insects, such as the spruce budworm *(Choristoneura fumiferana)* in the spruce and balsam-fir forests of northern and eastern Canada.

Methods used to control insects and disease include the removal of trees most susceptible to attack, the establishment of new stands containing a mixture of species rather than pure stands, and discrimination against species susceptible to an insect or disease known to be present in the locality. For example, white pine *(Pinus strobus)*, which is often badly attacked by the pine weevil *(Pissodes strobi)* and the blister rust *(Cronartium ribicola)*, should not be encouraged where these pests are commonly found, unless some effective means of control is available. Other methods of controlling forest pests include the introduction of parasites and predators, the use of chemical sprays, and the development through selection and crossbreeding of strains or hybrids that are relatively immune to attack by specific pests.

Domestic animals grazing in forest areas, particularly cattle and goats, often cause much damage by killing seedlings and compacting the soil. In the eastern Mediterranean region, where goats have been allowed to roam over the countryside, much of the forest vegetation has been completely destroyed. In many cases the only control possible is to exclude the animals; elsewhere forest grazing may be permitted under carefully controlled conditions.

Forests are normally protected against the adverse effects of weather and exposure by some adjustment in the methods of cutting and by encouraging the development of species best suited to local conditions.

SILVICULTURE

In essence, silviculture is applied forest ecology and forest genetics; it may be described as the development and use of cutting methods and cultural treatments of the forest: (1) to ensure adequate regeneration of desirable species as soon as possible after the mature stand is cut, (2) to bring about conditions favorable to the optimum yield and quality of production in keeping with the objectives of management and the condition of the forest, and (3) to maintain and where possible improve the quality or productivity of the site.

REPRODUCTION. A tree crop may be established by artificial or natural means, or by a combination of the two. In artificial reproduction, seed is sometimes sown, but more commonly young trees that have been grown in nurseries are planted on the site. In either case, the seed used is collected in the forest, preferably from trees of good form and vigor. When the crop is established by natural means, the young trees may originate vegetatively or from seed disseminated either before felling takes place or by trees left standing for the purpose at the time of logging. A new crop of young trees that becomes established in the forest before cutting takes place is known as "advance growth."

There are two principal methods of cutting the mature forest, each of which has advantages with respect to the regeneration and establishment of individual tree species:

Clear-Cutting. By this method, which results in the development of more or less even-aged stands, the forest is cut in one operation or in a succession of operations, each of which removes either a portion of the trees scattered over the whole area or all of the trees from a part of the area; these operations are continued until the original stand is completely cleared. Regeneration may be established by natural or artificial means, the former being provided for either by advance growth, or by seed lying in the surface soil at the time of cutting or made available from the crowns of felled trees or from standing trees surrounding the cutover area.

For species that require overhead protection in their youth a "shelterwood cutting" is made: the stand is opened up gradually over a period of years by making three or four successive cuts periodically over the whole area until the original stand is removed. For other species, the seed source may be the critical factor, and the stand is clear-cut except for a few mature trees, evenly distributed over the area, which are preserved to provide the seed for the next crop. This is known as "seed-tree cutting."

Quite commonly, portions of a stand are clear-cut periodically in the form of narrow strips, wedge-shaped blocks, or patches, until the stand has been completely felled. The Douglas-fir forests on the Pacific coast of North America, for example, are clear-cut in patches or blocks of a size that will permit natural regeneration by seeding-in from the surrounding uncut stand. This type of cutting is particularly applicable to species like the Douglas fir that are intolerant of shade.

The intensity of cutting and the size, form, and arrangement of clear-cut areas vary according to local conditions and requirements, particularly stand density, topography, logging methods, and the ecological characteristics of the desired species.

Selection Cutting. This method distributes cutting and regeneration continuously over the whole area, producing a single uneven-aged stand or series of such stands where trees of all ages from seedlings to mature timber occupy the area together. Scattered single trees or small groups of trees may be removed periodically throughout the whole forest, or the forest may be divided into a number of blocks, one of which is cut over in this way annually or every few years. The aim is to improve and regenerate the forest, as well as to harvest a crop: while some of the better formed mature trees may be kept in the stand for a number of years to provide seed, all dying and defective trees that are at all merchantable are removed as quickly as possible. Nonmerchantable trees may be girdled. As regeneration and early development of growing stock must take place in partial shade, this method is particularly suited to tolerant species.

AFFORESTATION. Forestry not only seeks to ensure the reproduction of existing forests, but is also concerned with the problem of establishing new forests. Afforestation may be undertaken *(a)* to reclaim forest land cleared for other purposes but best suited for the growing of forest crops, *(b)* to establish forests as an economic crop on land not previously forested, *(c)* to stabilize shifting sand and eroding soils, *(d)* to provide protection for agricultural and other crops against wind and snow damage, and *(e)* to improve seepage in drainage areas and so stabilize stream flow. Great Britain, Australia, New Zealand, and South Africa have all undertaken large-scale afforestation with the object of supplementing their natural resources. The trees used have been predominantly softwoods, particularly species of pine. One of the best-known examples of land reclamation for forestry purposes is in the Landes of Gascony, where, since the latter part of the eighteenth century, a program has been developed to fix shifting sand dunes, to drain swamps, and to afforest large areas with maritime pine *(Pinus pinaster)*, the principal source of resin and turpentine in Europe.

The use of trees in shelter belts and windbreaks to protect agricultural land is common practice in many countries, and has been practiced on a large scale in the United States and Russia. The establishment of forests to conserve water supplies has often been an important objective of forestry ever since its early beginning in Europe. In many cases, however, such forests may be used for wood production as well as for protection. In India and certain other tropical countries forests created primarily to provide small timber and fuel for the local population often help to solve the problems of flood control, erosion, and desiccation.

The success of afforestation programs depends upon many factors. Foresters must determine the suitability of species to soil and climatic conditions; they must guard against the many hazards that may arise in introducing a species or race to a new environment; they must decide whether the species grows best in a pure stand or in mixture with other species, and whether it will thrive as a pioneer under open-grown conditions or is better suited to a later stage in plant succession. The relationship of the species to its environment must be studied carefully if afforestation is to be successful.

"TENDING" OPERATIONS FOR YIELD AND QUALITY. Once the forest is established, the aim of the silviculturist will be to develop and maintain the optimum growth and quality of the stand in keeping with the objectives of management. This is accomplished mainly by cutting operations of various kinds and intensities, especially by means of thinnings carried out periodically throughout the life of the stand. These are commonly referred to as "tending" operations, as distinguished from those aimed primarily at regeneration.

Although forest trees are members of a community and, as such, contribute something toward each other's well-being—e.g., mutual protection against the elements and enrichment of their common habitat, the forest soil—there is, as noted above, a continuous and sharp competition among them for light and space, and in some cases for soil moisture and mineral nutrients. The stand density (number of stems per acre) greatly affects the intensity of this competition, and also influences the rate of growth per tree and the ultimate value of the forest to man.

Crowded conditions and keen competition are usually beneficial in the very early life of the stand: the inherently vigorous individuals become dominant, the lower branches of the trees remain small and are killed back at an early age, and the tree tends to develop a straight bole.

Later, however, too much crowding is a disadvantage. With reduced incidence of sunlight, radial development of the crowns is restricted and growth is slowed down. In fact, stagnation may take place, especially in species showing little differentiation in height growth. It is the aim of the silviculturist to make the most of early competition while this is advantageous, and to remove it when it hinders stand development—in other words, to distribute the total productive capacity of the site among the optimum number of trees to obtain the desired results. This is usually accomplished by thinning operations.

Thinnings. Cuttings made in a fully stocked to overstocked immature stand in order to increase the rate of growth of the remaining trees are known as "thinnings." In general, these are begun in the late sapling stage and are continued periodically until the stand matures: they are usually of only moderate intensity until rapid height growth is completed, the later thinnings being more severe to accelerate diameter growth. The total annual growth of an area is not materially changed by thinning, but it is confined to fewer trees whose individual increments are thereby increased. As a result, the trees reach useful sizes at earlier ages, which is particularly important when logs of large size are desired for sawing into lumber. Too heavy a thinning, however, may leave insufficient trees for full use of the productive capacity of the site.

The economic feasibility of thinning operations is largely determined by the availability of markets for small-sized material, although in some cases the improved growth of the residual trees may justify the operation.

Other Cultural Treatments. To promote more desirable species and better formed trees, and generally to improve the quality of the stand, other cultural treatments may be used, among them cleanings, liberation cuttings, and improvement cuttings.

(1) *Cleaning.* An operation in a young stand not past the sapling stage (a) to free small trees from weeds, vines, or sod-forming grasses; and (b) to provide better growing conditions by liberating crop trees from other individuals of similar age but of less desirable species or form that are overtopping or likely to overtop them.

(2) *Liberation Cutting.* The release of young trees not past the sapling stage from competition with older trees that are overtopping them.

(3) *Improvement Cutting.* A cutting made in a stand past the sapling stage to improve its composition and character by removing trees that are less desirable with respect to species, shape, or main crown canopy.[3]

Pruning. Knots in lumber are the result of branch growth; the fewer and smaller the branches, the fewer and smaller the knots and the higher the grade of lumber produced. In a young stand of proper density the lower branches are often small in diameter and die at a fairly early age. The forester may assist in the production of knot-free wood by removing the dead and dying branches from the bole of the tree with axe or knife. Care must be taken, however, not to injure the tree nor to reduce unduly the living portion of the crown. A comparison of the cost of pruning with the relative value of knot-free wood will determine the feasibility of this treatment.

SILVICULTURAL SYSTEMS. As a result of past study and experience, particularly in northwestern Europe, there has been developed a series of silvicultural systems, each incorporating the techniques that are required in the silvicultural management of a specific type of forest to maintain its distinctive form and maximum productivity.

While these systems are based primarily on the method of regeneration (whether by coppice or seeding, and with reference to the form of cutting), they are also concerned with problems affecting the protection and tending of the forest, and the harvesting of the crop and its economic utilization. Where such systems have been evolved, they will form an essential element in the plan of forest management.

FOREST MANAGEMENT. Although silviculture and management may be looked upon as two branches of forestry, the one mainly technical and the other economic, the two are interdependent and must always be co-ordinated. While silviculture may establish the ideal possibility of production within a forest, management determines the degree to which this can be realized through regulation and within the bounds of good business practice. Forest management may be defined as the application of business methods and technical forestry principles to the operation of a forest property.

Compared with other crops, a forest requires a relatively long time between its establishment and its harvesting. Revenue from an unmanaged forest may accrue only at fairly long intervals. Managed forests are organized to ensure a sustained yield of the forest crop in perpetuity. The income should include a reasonable profit on the investment, annually if possible.

Sustained yield of timber depends upon the systematic reproduction of a crop as it is harvested. It also requires that the timber be cut annually or periodically in such quantities that a continuous and fairly uniform

---

[3] These definitions are adapted from *Forest Terminology,* Society of American Foresters, Washington, D.C., 1950.

yield will be provided throughout the rotation (the period required to grow a crop from seed to maturity).

The principle of sustained-yield management may be illustrated with reference to a theoretical forest, usually termed the normal forest, in which the stands are stocked with the maximum amount of wood that the site will produce, and from which the same amount of wood product may be harvested annually forever—namely, the amount that grows annually on the whole acreage. Consider, for example, an even-aged forest that is to be harvested when fifty years of age. To have fifty-year-old timber every year, there must be a series of fifty stands of, respectively, one, two, three, and up to fifty years of age. Each year one stand becomes mature for harvesting. This stand in volume represents its own increment or growth for fifty years; also it is equal to the growth of one year on the fifty stands making up the whole forest. Accordingly, each cut is equal in amount to the current year's growth. It is assumed that each stand is reproduced as cut and that all the immature stands receive the silvicultural treatment necessary for most satisfactory growth. An alternative method, for an uneven-aged forest, is to cut over the entire area periodically, removing at each cut only the volume corresponding to the growth during the period between successive cuts. In either case, one has permanent sustained yield from a forest characterized by normal distribution of age classes, normal increment, and normal growing stock.

There is, of course, no such forest. Every forest is abnormal, having either excess or deficiency of area in the older age classes, and the opposite in younger ones, and in general a deficiency, to a greater or less extent, in volume per acre in the stands of different ages. The abnormalities in age-class distribution can be removed only by adjustments in the areas cut over in successive years, while deficiencies in volume, caused mainly by inadequate reproduction, can be made up through improvement in silvicultural practices. The normal forest is an ideal, a standard toward which forests should gradually be developed.

Such intensive management requires accurate information about tree species and sizes, total and merchantable volume, age-class distribution, growth conditions, site classes, and rotation ages, as well as about such factors as topography and drainage, which affect the efficiency of operations. Such information is obtained through enumeration or inventory surveys, supplemented and improved in recent years by aerial photographs. On the basis of this information, a management plan or working plan is evolved, which sets down the objectives of management and how they are to be attained, and allocates the kind and amount of timber to be cut each year or period of years, at least for the first part of the rotation.

LOGGING. Logging engineering is concerned essentially with the felling and removal of timber from a forest area. Even where the sole purpose is liquidation of the resource, logging techniques may be developed to a high degree of efficiency, as they have a direct and important bearing on the cost of extraction. In forests under sustained-yield management, logging methods must be developed to meet the requirements of the management plan as well as to maintain operational efficiency. Logging everywhere presents many technical problems, but particularly where the forests are difficult of access, distances are great, and the topography is rugged. In many forest regions logs are transported long distances and at relatively low cost by natural water systems, and in the northern forests winter snows often facilitate the hauling of forest products.

From the point of view of forest conservation, perhaps the most important logging objectives are (a) to prevent damage to the advance growth and the residual stand, (b) to help prepare the site for future tree crops (e.g., by soil scarification), and (c) to ensure minimum waste of wood in the trees cut.

In recent years mechanical equipment has been increasingly employed in both the felling of trees and the transportation of logs.

UTILIZATION. While it is not usual for those responsible for the growing and harvesting of timber crops to be directly concerned with their conversion and manufacture into usable products, there should be a close liaison between the two operations of forest production and wood utilization.

Wood has inherent qualities that make it particularly suitable for many purposes—good strength in relation to weight, pleasing appearance, insulation against heat and sound, ease of fastening with nails, dowels, screws, or glue, and ease of working with relatively simple tools. However, wood is by no means a homogeneous material: it differs from one species to another in structure and physical properties and hence in the use for which it is best suited.

Within environmental limitations it is desirable to grow the species that will best meet the requirements of local industry and available export markets. Furthermore, to make the fullest use of the timber crop at all stages of development and to minimize logging and manufacturing waste, it is important to co-ordinate as closely as possible forest operations and the wood-using industries and also to bring about a closer integration of the wood-using industries themselves—as, for example, the sawmill and pulp industries.

Forest Policy

In many countries forests are of vital importance to the over-all economy, not only in relation to industrial development, but also in providing benefits which may be difficult to evaluate in monetary terms. For this reason and also because of the long-term nature of the forest enterprise, most countries seek to ensure the perpetuation of their forests and to safeguard the interests of present and future generations by placing the forests under some degree of government control. In some countries the government retains ownership of a large proportion of the forested land and leases it to the wood-using industries for timber extraction: provision may be made for some degree of forest management by regulation or through agreement. Other countries have granted or sold much of their forest land to private interests, though considerable areas have sometimes been retained by the state to provide for timber reserves, recreational facilities, and the protection of drainage areas; in some cases there is considerable public control of forest management on the freehold lands. Elsewhere long-term forest management is entirely neglected, and forest policies, if any exist, may be concerned only with the method and intensity of exploitation.

Progress in the development and practice of forestry varies widely throughout the world. While forestry is well advanced in much of Europe and in certain tropical regions, only a small proportion of the accessible forests of the world is under intensive management today. In some regions man still depends on the forests for his food and shelter, and contributes little toward their development; in many countries man long ago destroyed the forests and has done little to restore them; elsewhere uncontrolled forest exploitation is still in evidence and proper protection and management lie in the future. In North America we are still in an early stage of forest conservation. In recent years, however, we have begun to see the forests as an integral part of our economic structure and to take steps against the destructive exploitation that has threatened to exhaust them.

SELECTED REFERENCES

ALLEN, S. W. 1950. *An introduction to American forestry.* 2d ed. McGraw-Hill Book Co., Inc., New York.

BOYCE, J. S. 1948. *Forest pathology.* 2d ed. McGraw-Hill Book Co., Inc., New York.

BUSGEN, M., and MUNCH, E. 1929. *Structure and life of forest trees.* (Trans. by T. THOMSON.) Chapman and Hall, London.

CHAMPION, H. G. 1954. *Forestry.* (In the Home University Library of Modern Knowledge.) Oxford University Press, London.

Empire Forestry Association. 1947. *The forest, forestry and man.* Royal Empire Society, London.

GRAHAM, S. A. 1952. *Forest entomology.* 3d ed. McGraw-Hill Book Co., Inc., New York.

HAWLEY, R. C., and STICKEL, P. W. 1948. *Forest protection.* 2d ed. John Wiley & Sons, Inc., New York.

HILEY, W. E. 1930. *The economics of forestry.* Oxford University Press, London.

————. 1954. *Woodland management.* Faber & Faber, London.

KITTREDGE, J. 1948. *Forest influences.* McGraw-Hill Book Co., Inc., New York.

PANSHIN, A. J., *et al.* 1950. *Forest products, their sources, production and utilization.* McGraw-Hill Book Company Inc., New York.

TOUMEY, J. W., and KORSTIAN, C. F. 1947. *Foundations of silviculture upon an ecological basis.* 2d ed. John Wiley & Sons, Inc., New York.

TROUP, R. S. 1952. *Silvicultural systems.* 2d ed. Oxford University Press, London.

WACKERMAN, A. E. 1949. *Harvesting timber crops.* McGraw-Hill Book Co., Inc., New York.

WILDE, S. A. 1946. *Forest soils and forest growth.* Chronica Botanica Co., Waltham, Mass.

5.   THE FOREST PRODUCTS INDUSTRIES OF THE WORLD

George M. Hunt

Man's dependence upon the products of the forest began as soon as he did and has continued ever since. The specific uses to which these products are put have changed in many respects with the passing years, and wood has been largely replaced by other materials in some uses, as in ship-building. Nevertheless, forest products still enter importantly into our daily living. Imagine, for example, what would happen to our economic life, our standard of living, and to civilization itself, without today's three major economic products of the forest: fuel, lumber, and paper. Although wood fuel is not of large importance in some countries, there are many where life would be exceedingly difficult and present activities would have to be greatly changed if wood fuel were not available. It may appear at times that we might do without lumber, and in some regions very little is used, but in those regions the living standards are low in comparison with those of Europe and North America and, furthermore, certain lumber products are still used there. Without paper from wood, however, the business of the world would halt; communications would be greatly limited; monetary systems would be disturbed; books, records, newspapers, magazines, and libraries would shrink; and our civilization would be set back hundreds of years. It is true that paper can be made from other materials, including rags, straw, grasses, bagasse, and bamboo, but not in the variety and increasing quantities required to carry on the business of the world today.

World statistics on wood consumption and on the quantities used for various purposes in different countries are not by any means complete and in many instances must be intelligent estimates rather than actual records. Detailed statistics from the U.S.S.R. and its satellites are unavailable, which presents a serious difficulty in comparing the wood industries of the world, for the production and consumption of wood in those countries make up an important percentage of the total for the world. Even from the countries that report their statistics, the data are not uniformly collected or segregated by industries and end uses, although improvement in this respect is being made.

The magnitude of the world's wood consumption is indicated by the estimate that the total wood felled throughout the world in 1953 (including the U.S.S.R.) amounted to about 1.4 billion cubic meters (Table 5–I). Possibly half of the total quantity of wood cut was used for fuel. According to the reports made to FAO, wood for industrial purposes amounted to about 56 per cent of the total in 1953, but it is pointed out that many countries do not include in their reported figures fuel wood cut for farmers' use. Thus the share of industrial wood in the total fellings may be as low as 45 or 50 per cent.

TABLE 5–I

ROUNDWOOD FELLINGS BY USE CATEGORIES AND SPECIES GROUPS, 1953

Category	Differentiated by Species		Undifferentiated		Total	Per Cent
	Conifers[a]	Nonconifers[b]	U.S.S.R.[c]	Other[d]		
	Thousand cubic meters, solid volume of roundwood					
Saw logs, veneer logs, and logs for sleepers	245,500	79,500	165,000	25,900	515,900	38
Pulpwood and pit props.	123,100	16,300	25,000	11,300	175,700	13
Other industrial wood ..	16,000	12,700	40,000	4,200	72,900	5
Total industrial wood	384,600	108,500	230,000	41,400	764,500	56
Fuel wood	49,800	338,400	170,000	42,300	600,500	44
TOTAL	434,400	446,900	400,000	83,700	1,365,000	100

[a] Food and Agriculture Organization of the United Nations [FAO], *Yearbook of Forest Products Statistics, 1954,* Table 2.
[b] *Ibid.,* Table 3.
[c] *Ibid.,* Table 1.
[d] Quantities in column 5 less sum of quantities in columns 1, 2, and 3.

Table 5–II gives the total estimated world consumption of roundwood for different purposes and shows how the relative importance of the major products varies in different parts of the world. The total estimated world fellings of wood for industrial purposes and for fuel are shown in Table 5–III.

The per capita consumption of wood for all purposes varies in different countries, and so do the proportions used for fuel and for industrial purposes, as shown in Table 5–IV. Finland and Brazil, for example, use much more wood for fuel than for industrial purposes, while in Great Britain and the Netherlands nearly all the wood is used industrially.

The forest-products industries may be classified in various ways, according to the purpose to be served. In the present discussion we shall divide them into (a) natural wood industries, in which the inherent character of the wood is not changed, although some of its properties may be improved; (b) wood-conversion industries, in which the wood is processed to change

TABLE 5-II

TOTAL UTILIZATION OF HOME-GROWN AND IMPORTED ROUNDWOOD, 1953 [a]

(In Million Cubic Meters Solid Volume of Roundwood)

Continent	Total Utiliza-tion	Commercial Disposals								Other Disposals		
		Fuel Wood	Wood for Charcoal	Pulp-wood	Saw and Veneer Logs	Mine Timbers	Poles, Piling, and Posts	Others	Total	Fuel Wood	Others	Total
World total [b]	833.1	125.3	55.3	128.5	323.7	17.4	12.1	15.0	677.3	148.2	7.6	155.8
Europe [b]	213.1	31.9	5.6	36.2	68.3	10.4	1.6	3.5	157.5	51.5	4.7	56.2
North and Central America	383.9	54.7	3.2	85.5	206.5	2.5	8.9	7.4	368.9	14.0	1.0	15.0
South America	60.8	9.6	25.7	0.3	9.5	0.5	0.1	2.3	48.0	12.5	0.3	12.8
Africa	73.6	7.6	1.6	–	3.2	0.1	0.3	–	12.8	59.7	1.1	60.8
Asia [b]	80.6	13.0	19.2	5.9	25.9	3.5	0.8	1.3	69.6	10.5	0.5	11.0
Pacific Area	20.5	8.5	–	0.6	10.3	0.2	0.4	0.5	20.5	...	...	...

[a] Extracted from FAO, *Yearbook of Forest Products Statistics, 1954*, Table 12.
[b] Not including U.S.S.R. and its satellites.
... Not available.
– None or less than 0.1.

it into other products; and (c) other forest-products industries, which extract a great variety of products, other than wood, from the forest. Each of these groups can be subdivided into primary and secondary industries and into an endless variety of other divisions, according to the nature of the processes or equipment used and the kinds of products manufactured.

TABLE 5–III

ESTIMATED FELLINGS OF INDUSTRIAL WOOD AND OF FUEL WOOD (INCLUDING WOOD FÒR CHARCOAL), AND ESTIMATED LUMBER PRODUCTION BY MAJOR WORLD REGIONS, 1953

Region	Industrial Wood [a]		Fuel Wood [a]		Lumber Production [b]	
	Million Cubic Meters	Per Cent	Million Cubic Meters	Per Cent	Million Cubic Meters	Per Cent
United States	236	31	51	8	93	38
Canada	75	10	10	2	18	7
Other America	18	2	140	23	8	3
Europe	144	19	87	15	37	15
Asia	44	6	58	10	21	9
U.S.S.R.	230	30	170	28	64	26
Africa	6	1	75	12	1	[c]
Pacific Area	12	2	9	2	4	2
TOTALS	765	100	601	100	246	100

[a] FAO, *Yearbook of Forest Products Statistics, 1954*, Table 1.
[b] *Ibid.*, Table 15.
[c] Less than 0.5 per cent.

TABLE 5–IV

ANNUAL AVERAGE PER CAPITA RATES OF CONSUMPTION OF FOREST PRODUCTS IN VARIOUS COUNTRIES DURING THE PERIOD 1949-1953 [a]
(In Cubic Meters Round Measure per Capita)

Country	Total Roundwood	Fuel Wood	Industrial Wood
Canada	3.43	1.09	2.34
Finland	3.36	2.19	1.17
Sweden	2.77	1.22 [b]	1.55
Australia	2.19	1.01	1.18
United States	2.05	0.36	1.69
U.S.S.R.	1.90	0.82 [c]	1.08
Brazil	1.82	1.74	0.80
United Kingdom	0.52	0.01	0.51
Netherlands	0.48	0.02	0.46
Italy	0.29	0.21	0.08
Malaya	0.39	0.17	0.22

[a] Selected from FAO, *Yearbook of Forest Products Statistics, 1954*, Table 44.
[b] Average, 1950-53.
[c] Average, 1952-53.

The Natural Wood Industries

FUEL. More wood is cut for fuel than for any other single purpose. It is estimated by FAO that "Farmers' own consumption accounted for about two-thirds of the fuelwood utilization." Fuel-wood production for industrial use or for sale for home use is locally important and furnishes employment for thousands of people in certain countries where other fuels are not plentiful or are relatively expensive, but, as a rule, it is the work of small producers with limited equipment.

Where labor is cheap and fuel scarce, as in many parts of Asia, wood may be carried long distances by cart or animal-back for sale in markets, and even twigs and bushes are sought after for domestic fuel. In other countries, of which Japan and India are examples, much wood is converted into charcoal, which is preferred for domestic fuel because it is smokeless, simpler to burn, and provides more easily controlled heat. Charcoal is also extensively used in Japan for truck and bus fuel. In well-timbered countries the extent to which the forests are gleaned for fuel is influenced largely by the cost of labor and by the price and availability of fuels other than wood. This is why in Canada, the United States, some of the Baltic countries, and other parts of the world enormous quantities of standing and down wood are left in the forests, which in central and southern Europe and much of Asia would be greatly prized and find a ready market for fuel.

In the production of lumber and other wood products, the sawdust, planer shavings, trimmings, edgings, and other residues for which no other profitable use is found, are often used as boiler fuel in the producing plant or sold to other nearby plants for that purpose. To a limited degree in the United States and Europe, sawdust and planer shavings are being compressed under high pressure into briquettes to be used as domestic fuel.

LUMBER. Lumber is the chief primary product of the natural wood industries of the world. Lumber is made in establishments ranging from the most primitive, in which boards are laboriously sawn out one at a time by hand, to the highly mechanized, mass-production sawmills of the west coast of North America and the Scandinavian countries.

The simplicity with which logs can be sawed into lumber makes possible a great variety of power sawmills of low cost, limited only by the ingenuity of the owner and the economic conditions under which he operates. Wind, water, steam, electricity, and internal-combustion engines—as may be available locally—furnish the power for these small mills. As a result, there are thousands of small sawmills throughout the world, but a much smaller number of medium and large mills. Thus, in Austria, with a forested area of about 34,000 square miles, there are more than 6,000 sawmills, operated by about 24,000 workers. A few are large, but most are very small. In the United States, approximately 90 per cent of the 53,109 sawmills reported in 1947 could be classified as small, producing in each case not more than one million board feet per year. Nearly 80 per cent of the total number produced less than 500,000 board feet per year. The 10 per cent of mills producing one million board feet or more per year, however, manufactured nearly 75 per cent of the total U.S. lumber output in 1947.

The Food and Agriculture Organization of the United Nations, in its 1954 *Yearbook of Forest Products Statistics,* gives the 1953 production of lumber by the countries reporting to it, as summarized in Table 5–III, columns 5 and 6. It will be seen that, of the total world production of lumber (including sawn crossties and timbers), estimated at 246 million cubic meters of solid wood, the United States produced about 38 per cent, and Canada about 7 per cent. The United States, however, consumes more lumber than it produces, for despite its great production it imports more lumber (chiefly from Canada) than it exports. Canada, on the other hand, although its per capita consumption of lumber is the highest reported, is the greatest lumber exporter, accounting for more than one third of the reported world exports of coniferous lumber. As shown in Table 5–V, Austria, Finland, and Sweden export from 65 to 85 per cent of the lumber they produce, while Canada exports 47 per cent of its much larger production. Other countries export less than 45 per cent.

TABLE 5–V

LUMBER PRODUCTION AND EXPORTS FROM CERTAIN NATIONS EXPORTING MORE
THAN 45 PER CENT OF THEIR LUMBER PRODUCTION, 1953 [a]

Country	Production	Exports	Proportion of Nation's Total Lumber Production
	Thousand cubic meters		*Per cent*
Austria	3,282 [b]	2,807	85
Finland	4,115 [c]	3,192	78
Sweden	6,900	4,478	65
Canada	18,153	8,506	47

[a] Based on FAO, *Yearbook of Forest Products Statistics, 1954,* Table 15.
[b] Includes sleepers.
[c] Excludes production from small sawmills.

The average annual per capita consumption of lumber, 1949-53, as estimated by FAO from data of selected reporting countries, is shown in Table 5–VI.

Tables 5–V and 5–VI fail to show any consistent relation between the percentage of lumber exported by a country and the amount consumed within it. For example, Austria, which exported 85 per cent of the lumber it produced, used less per unit of population than did the United Kingdom, which must import nearly all the lumber it uses. Canada is a high producer, a high exporter, and highest in per capita use of lumber, while the United States is a net importing country but a high producer and a high user. The unit consumption of lumber in various countries is obviously influenced by the habits and preferences of the local population, as well as by the amount of lumber the country produces.

TABLE 5–VI

ESTIMATED ANNUAL LUMBER ("SAWN WOOD") CONSUMPTION PER CAPITA
IN VARIOUS COUNTRIES, 1949-1953 [a]

Country	Cubic Meters per Capita
Canada	0.67
New Zealand	0.66
United States	0.59
Norway	0.50
Australia	0.41
Sweden	0.36
Denmark	0.29
Finland	0.24
Switzerland	0.23
United Kingdom, Netherlands	0.16-0.18
France, Ireland, Japan, Belgium, Yugoslavia	0.10
Austria, Chile, Portugal, Brazil	0.05-0.09

[a] From FAO, *Yearbook of Forest Products Statistics, 1954,* Table 44.

Each important lumber-producing country has both large and small sawmills, but the character of the mills and the method of sawing are greatly influenced by the size and quality of the logs available and by the market served. For example, production sawmills on the west coast of Canada and the United States, in parts of Australia, New Zealand, and in some other countries must be equipped to handle and to saw large logs. Logs from virgin timber in these countries often are from 2 to 6 feet in diameter and sometimes considerably larger. In such large logs, and many of the smaller logs from virgin timber, the outer portion usually contains a high proportion of clear wood that is free from knots and other defects, while the central portion is more knotty and defective. It is customary, therefore, in sawing logs of this character, to turn them frequently so as to obtain the highest proportion of clear boards, which are the most valuable. This custom of "sawing for grade" is the common practice in many countries, in both large and small sawmills, where the log quality and lumber markets make it profitable.

On the other hand, logs from plantation forests or "second growth" timber stands are not usually allowed to grow large enough to produce much clear lumber. The knots they contain commonly extend to the bark or near it, so that little clear material can be obtained by sawing. This is also generally true of logs from virgin timber where the species or the climate is such that they do not attain large size. With such logs there is no incentive to "saw for grade," and the common practice is to saw them into boards or timbers as quickly as possible, with the least amount of turning.

Types of Saws. The simplest sawmill, requiring the least investment, consists essentially of a circular saw, a saw carriage to move the log back and forth past the saw, and a source of power. Such mills can cut accurately, if properly constructed and well maintained, but a large percentage of them are so poorly maintained and carelessly operated that they produce much badly cut lumber and are thus wasteful of material. Although a top saw, in addition to the main saw, is needed for sawing large logs, most of these simple mills have only one saw, but they permit sawing for grade, if desired. Where logs are too small to saw for grade, and where fast production of standard-sized boards or timbers is desired, circular saws may be set in gangs so as to make two or more cuts simultaneously.

Band saws allow cutting for grade and size as readily as do circular saws, and may be used on large or small logs. They are more costly to install and maintain than circular saws, however, so they are not generally suitable for small, low-cost sawmills. Their use for lumber manufacturing is generally confined to larger mills cutting medium to large logs. They are widely used in North American mills and to some extent in other countries.

The sash-gang saw, or frame saw, is prevalent in European mills cutting small logs, and to a gradually increasing extent in North America and other countries is being used for the same purpose. This type of saw has numerous short blades set in a frame that operates with an up-and-down motion and cuts an entire log at once. The distances between the saws are adjustable to produce the lumber thicknesses desired. Since substantial time is required to change the adjustments, the logs are usually sorted for size, so that the mill can operate on logs of the same size for long periods. In the larger mills in Europe, frame saws are commonly operated in pairs; the first saw slabs two sides and may take an additional board from each side, leaving a standard-sized timber or "cant" in the center. This cant is then transferred to a second saw, which reduces it to boards.

Sash-gang saws are generally heavier and more costly than circular-saw installations, but cut a thinner "kerf," and thus waste less wood in the form of sawdust than do circular saws. Their cost, weight, and immobility limit their use for small sawmills in North America, although they may be found in many small mills in Europe. However, some portable sash-gang saws are coming into use along the Pacific coast. Sash-gang saws are commonly used as secondary saws in large sawmills in the western part of North America. In such mills, the circular or band "head saw," in breaking down the log, produces many large cants of standard thicknesses, which then move on to the sash-gang saw for reduction to boards. There are, of course, innumerable combinations of saws of the several types, according to the size and character of logs being cut, the size of the sawmill, the markets served, and the ideas of the owners or the designers of the sawmills.

Lumber for the world markets and lumber for domestic use in most lumber-producing countries is square edged and cut to standard thicknesses, widths, and lengths. In some European countries, however, particularly with hardwoods, logs cut into lumber for domestic consumption are often sawed into boards the full length and width of the log and then reassembled into the same relative position they had in the original log, without "edging" or squaring the edges. They are seasoned and sold in this form. The buyer or user then cuts up the boards to best advantage for his particular purpose.

Secondary Lumber Industries. Although lumber is a primary product and its manufacture constitutes one of the important economic activities of the world, the secondary industries that use lumber as their principal raw material account for a larger share of the world's business and provide employment for more people than does lumber production. The average percentages of lumber used in the United States for different major use classifications during the five-year period 1948 to 1952, inclusive, were estimated as shown in Table 5–VII, from which it is apparent that nearly three fourths of the lumber consumed in the United States is used for structural purposes of one kind or another. To a large extent it goes into residential and farm buildings, but there are numerous other structural uses. In other countries the percentages of lumber going into the various categories would probably differ widely from the figures given in the table.

TABLE 5–VII

UNITED STATES: LUMBER USED FOR VARIOUS PURPOSES, 1948-1952 [a]

	Per Cent
Building and construction	71.4
Boxes and crating	10.6
Industrial	12.5
Railroad	3.6
Export	1.9
TOTAL	100.0

[a] Extracted from *Lumber Industry Facts*, 1953, National Lumber Manufacturers Association, Table 41.

In its industrial application lumber goes into hundreds of products, which vary in character and percentage in different countries according to differences in national customs, preferences, and economics. In most countries large quantities of lumber are used for furniture and millwork. In Japan, for example, the wooden shoe or "geta" so generally worn accounts for possibly 7 per cent of the country's lumber consumption, while in most other countries people depend on shoes or sandals made of other materials. Table 5–VIII lists the estimated industrial lumber consumption in the United States in 1948 by principal products manufactured, but omits a great variety of products that used amounts smaller than 100 million board feet.

COOPERAGE. The production of wood kegs, barrels, and similar containers for liquids and solids dates from ancient times, and the cooperage industry still employs thousands of workers all over the world. Dependable statistics on the quantity of such containers produced or the amount of wood used in their production, however, are very limited and not up to date. Cooperage-type containers are not included in the estimates of Table 5–VIII. Estimates by the U.S. Forest Service indicated that about 746 million board feet (log scale) of timber were required in 1939 for cooperage in the United States. Of this amount, approximately half was for tight cooperage and half for slack cooperage. The use of both slack and tight cooperage was apparently on the decline, however, because of the substitution of metal, cloth, and paper containers for many of the products formerly shipped in kegs, barrels, and pails, and the present consumption of wood for cooperage is probably much less than in 1939.

TABLE 5–VIII

UNITED STATES: ESTIMATED INDUSTRIAL LUMBER CONSUMPTION, PARTIAL LIST BY PRINCIPAL PRODUCTS, 1948 [a]

Product	Lumber Used in 1948 (In Million Board Feet)
Containers (excluding cooperage)	3,993
Millwork	2,150
Furniture	1,948
Flooring	1,150
Car construction and repair	458
Pallets	221
Fixtures	172
Prefabricated houses and panels for homes	159
Caskets and burial boxes	155
Woodenware, novelties, miscellaneous	133
Handles	127
Motor vehicles	126
Radios, phonographs, sewing machines	122

[a] Extracted from *Wood Used in Manufacture,* 1948, U.S. Dept. of Agriculture, Forest Service, Table 16. Includes only items for which 100 million board feet or more were used.

VENEER AND PLYWOOD. The manufacture of veneer and veneer products, although consuming much less timber than does the manufacture of lumber, is nevertheless one of the world's important wood industries. Accurate comparisons between the world production of lumber and of veneer are not available, and comparisons within any single country do not correctly imply the world picture. In the United States estimates indicate that in 1948 more than ten times as much timber was used in lumber manufacture as in veneer manufacture.

The principal use of veneer is in the manufacture of commercial plywood, although large quantities go into the production of baskets, fruit boxes, shipping boxes, drums, trunks, and other products. Much veneer is also glued into doors, furniture, radio cabinets, and the like. Plants that manufacture plywood, baskets, boxes, and other containers commonly produce their own veneer, while the veneers used in furniture, radio cabinets, and generally for decorative purposes are more often produced in plants that manufacture the veneer only.

Veneer is manufactured by sawing, slicing, and rotary cutting, but mostly by the latter method, in which the veneer log is revolved on its axis while a heavy knife, parallel to the log axis, is pressed against it. The veneer peels from the log in a manner similar to the unwinding of a roll of paper. Rotary-cut veneer can be made as thin as $\frac{1}{100}$ inch but is commonly produced in thicknesses up to $\frac{3}{16}$ inch. Thicknesses of $\frac{1}{4}$ inch and sometimes up to $\frac{1}{2}$ inch can be produced, depending on the character and quality of the wood and the equipment. Rotary cutting is normally used for species and for purposes where beauty is not of major importance. Beautiful figure, however, is obtained in this way from some species, of which birch and birdseye maple are good examples. It is also obtained in the manufacture of figured veneer from walnut stumps, which are fastened eccentrically in the lathe.

In veneer slicing, the usual practice is to fasten a long block or flitch to a heavy frame that moves diagonally past a veneer knife, thus taking off slices of the desired thickness from the flitch. This method is particularly suitable for the rapid production of highly figured wood, for the flitch can be fastened in the frame in such a way as to produce the desired figure. As the veneer falls from the knife, it is usually reassembled in its original relative position in the flitch, and through subsequent drying, packaging, and storage is so handled that the veneer from each flitch is finally sold and shipped as a unit.

The slicing method is also used in the production of veneer for some kinds of boxes and for battery separators, in which case the knife usually moves instead of the wood. This permits faster cutting, because the wood blocks are fed continuously against the knife and it is not necessary to stop the cutting to fasten each new block into the frame, as is the case when the knife remains stationary. When veneer is cut with a moving knife, the blocks used are considerably smaller than are those common with the stationary knife, which may be as much as 18 feet long. While veneers of similar maximum thicknesses can be made by slicing or by rotary cutting, the former method may be used to produce somewhat thinner veneers.

In both rotary cutting and slicing, the veneer is bent sharply away from the log as it passes over the thick knife, and this may cause checks in the convex or outer face of the curve. The severity of the checks depends on the character and condition of the wood, the thickness of the veneer, and the skill of the machine operator. Checks cannot be entirely prevented except in very thin veneer, but they can be kept within usable limits by skilful operators working with good material.

The sawing method of cutting veneer avoids the knife checking, and is particularly suitable for species that do not cut well by knife. It is accomplished by moving a log or flitch on a carriage past a thin circular saw, all working very accurately. Sawed veneer can be produced commercially as thin as $\frac{1}{20}$ inch and, of course, also in considerably thicker dimensions. Veneer sawing is slow in comparison with the rotary or slicing methods and is seldom used with species that may be cut well by these. Sawed veneer can be produced from either green or seasoned logs or flitches, whereas green material only can be cut well with a knife.

Plywood, the principal product made from veneer, is produced by gluing sheets of veneer together. There are usually three or five sheets, with the grain of each sheet, or "ply," at right angles to the adjacent ones. For special purposes, other numbers of plies and arrangements of grain direction are used to a limited extent. The center sheet or "core" may be lumber, veneer, or even some form of fiberboard or particle board. Alternating the grain directions of adjacent plies makes plywood resistant to splitting in both directions and reduces its tendency to shrink and swell in length and width. These properties and its availability in thin sheets of large size make plywood attractive for innumerable uses.

Although plywood or veneered wood seems to have been used to some extent since the days of the early Egyptians, the glues originally employed in its manufacture were easily weakened by moisture and its use, for that reason, was necessarily confined to dry places. About the beginning of the twentieth century moisture-resistant glues made from casein or animal blood became available, and means were found for increasing the moisture resistance of animal glue with formaldehyde. It was not until after World War I, however, that the invention of modern waterproof synthetic-resin glues made it possible for plywood and other glued wood to retain their strength even when thoroughly wet. With the advent of these improved glues, the field of usefulness of plywood widened enormously and its production expanded rapidly.

Plywood is produced to some extent in all industrialized countries that have suitable timber and also in some countries where the veneer logs are mostly imported. The total world production of plywood in 1953 was estimated at 7,960,000 cubic meters, of which more than half was produced in the United States. Table 5–IX shows estimated plywood production, imports, and exports in 1953 for the principal producing countries that reported. Although the United States produced more than half of the world's plywood, it used more than it produced and exported very little. The production of plywood from Douglas fir on the west coast of the United States and Canada has grown phenomenally. The first Douglas-fir plywood is said to have been made commercially near Portland, Oregon, in 1905. Statistics on the production of Douglas-fir plywood in the United States begin with 1925, when 153 million square feet (calculated to $\frac{3}{8}$ inch thickness) were reported. By 1952 the production had expanded to 3,066 million square feet, or approximately twenty times the amount in 1925. Before 1937 the U.S. production of hardwood plywood was greater than that of Douglas-fir and other softwood plywood, but by 1952 it was estimated that more than twice as much softwood as hardwood plywood was produced, and most of this was of Douglas fir.

TABLE 5–IX

Country	Production	Imports	Exports
World	7,960	500	470
United States	4,500 *	130	8
U.S.S.R.	946	–	49
Western Germany	484	21	12
Canada	461	10	34
Japan	408	–	58
Finland	244	–	215
France	147	7	22
Italy	140	1	6
Brazil	80 *	–	–
Australia	69	–	1
Sweden	45	7	16
India	23	...	...
United Kingdom	34	147	1

[a] From FAO, *Yearbook of Forest Products Statistics, 1954,* Table 23.
... Not available.
– None or less than 0.5.
* Unofficial figure.

MINE TIMBERS AND PULPWOOD. The production of round mine timbers (pit props) and of pulpwood is in each case a big industry with respect to the quantities produced and their importance in world commerce and economics. The combined total of these two round products shown in Table 5–I is nearly a third as great as the indicated total production of saw logs, and much greater than that of other industrial wood. From Table 5–II it is evident that about seven times as much pulpwood as round mine timber was consumed. These figures, however, do not include sawed mine timbers, which are extensively used in some countries and are included in the figures for saw logs and lumber.

RAILROAD TIES. The production of wood railroad ties is a separate industry only to a limited degree. Railroad ties include bridge ties (special-sized ties used on bridges), switch ties used in sets of increasing length at the points where turnouts or sidings depart or switch off from the running track, and crossties used for the running track. In the United States, switch ties and bridge ties are sawmill products, usually made in connection with other items of lumber and timber. The majority of crossties are also produced at sawmills. In large sawmills ties are usually only one of the numerous items produced, but in small sawmills they may be the principal item manufactured, with lumber as a by-product. Many crossties are still made by hand hewing. Although this practice is gradually disappearing, at least one sixth of the nearly 42 million crossties treated in the United States in 1952 were hewed. Much of the tie hewing is done by farmers during slack seasons or by other part-time workers, and their ties are sold to the railroads directly or through tie-producing companies. Some species of wood are so straight-grained and split so readily that ties can be made from fairly large logs by splitting with hand tools. This method finds some use in the redwood forests of California, with some of the eucalypts in Australia, and possibly elsewhere. In India, Pakistan, and some other countries, many crossties are produced by hand sawing.

In the United States and Canada, and to a considerable degree in other countries, the railroad-tie industry is as much a part of the wood-preserving industry as it is of the lumber industry, for, in most countries, relatively few wood ties are used without preservative treatment.

Statistics on the world production of crossties are too incomplete and inadequate to be of much value, but they indicate large-scale production in Australia, Canada, Finland, France, West Germany, Japan, and Sweden. India is probably also a large producer. Tie production statistics in the United States are less complete than are statistics on the quantities used annually by the railroads (Table 5–X).

TABLE 5–X

UNITED STATES: WOOD RAILROAD TIES INSTALLED, 1937, 1942, 1947, AND 1952 [a]

Year	Crossties				Switch and Bridge Ties [d]
	Total	Class I Railroads [b]		Other Roads: Treated and Untreated [c]	
		Treated	Untreated		
	Number of ties in millions				*Million bd. ft.*
1937	53.8	38.2	10.9	4.7	192,500
1942	56.7	47.9	5.3	3.5	184,200
1947	43.3	37.9	2.3	3.1	145,100
1952	36.5	32.9	1.3	2.3	130,400

[a] Source: U.S. Forest Service compilation from Interstate Commerce Commission, *Summary Tables of Statistics of Railways in United States.*
[b] Includes crossties laid in new track and in replacement.
[c] Includes crossties laid in replacement only by Class II and III railroads and by switching and terminal companies.
[d] Estimate based on data from Class I roads adjusted by the ratio between number of crossties installed on Class I roads and total number of crossties installed, including treated and untreated.

POLES, PILES, AND FENCE POSTS. These products, although of great importance and produced in large volume, require relatively little processing. The pole, pile, and post industry, therefore, is largely a collection and merchandising industry, with little processing involved other than that done at wood-preserving plants. The estimated consumption of poles, piles, and posts in the United States is shown in Table 5–XI.

Poles. In Europe and North America few species have sufficient natural durability to be economical for use as poles without preservative treatment. As a consequence, most wood poles receive such treatment. In Australia a number of species have very durable heartwood with nondurable sapwood. Poles of these species have customarily had their sapwood removed from the portion in and near the ground. It is expected that this practice will gradually be replaced by the use of treated poles, in which, regardless of species, the sapwood will be made as durable as the heartwood, thus eliminating the necessity for removing the sapwood and permitting the use of poles of smaller original diameter.

Piles. These are similar to poles in size and shape, but probably average somewhat larger. Those employed for temporary construction where durability is not required need no processing except cutting for length and selection for size, and frequently they are used without removal of the bark. Piles that will be completely submerged in fresh water or mud, or will always be below the water table in land use, also require no special processing or protection. On the other hand, piles that will extend above the water or above the water table in the soil can deteriorate in the above-water zone from decay or insect attack, and for such service most species require preservative treatment for long life. Piles in salt water are subject to decay and insect attack above water and to marine-borer attack in the water, unless given appropriate protection.

With some species having durable heartwood, the practice has been to remove the sapwood by hewing or sawing to a square or octagonal shape. Piles imported by European countries from tropical countries have often been of this character. In North America, however, piles are almost invariably used in the original round form.

Fence Posts. Wood fence posts are used mainly in timbered countries. In countries without timber, and in many that have timber, wood fences and wood fence posts find relatively little use—hedges, ditches, and walls being used instead. In the United States and Canada, however, wood posts are employed in enormous numbers, and they find considerable use in Australia, Great Britain, and New Zealand. Posts are often made locally from durable species by part-time workers and receive no processing other than cutting to length or splitting to size. As the supply of naturally durable species decreases, less durable woods must be employed, and preservative treatment becomes more necessary. The principal industrial processing of wood posts is, therefore, confined to wood-preserving plants, and such plants treated more than 22 million fence posts in the United States in 1952. The number of posts handled at wood-preserving plants, however, is only a small fraction of the total number used each year in the more than 15 million miles of fence in the United States. Some of these posts are metal and some concrete, but the majority are undoubtedly still made of wood and used without preservative treatment.

THE WOOD-PRESERVING INDUSTRY. Attempts to prolong the life of wood by treatment with materials to prevent decay and insect attack date from ancient times, but the modern industry began with the patents of Bethell and others about 1830 to 1840. On all continents pressure impregnation of wood is now practiced, using a variety of preservatives that have been found effective for different purposes. Published statistics on the quantity and forms of material treated commercially each year are available only for the United States, where they have been published annually, beginning with 1909. It is known, however, that large amounts of poles, piles, railroad ties, building lumber, construction timber, and other wood products are treated in many countries of Europe, and in Canada, Mexico, India, South Africa, Japan, New Zealand, and other countries. In addition to the wood that receives pressure treatment, much wood is treated by nonpressure methods such as hot-and-cold-bath, soaking, and immersion treatments, for which statistics are not available. Table 5–XI is a summary for the United States of the quantities reported treated, almost entirely by pressure methods.

TABLE 5–XI

UNITED STATES: WOOD PRODUCTS REPORTED COMMERCIALLY TREATED, 1909, 1929, 1949, AND 1952 [a]

(In Million Cubic Feet of Material Treated)

Year	Total	Crossties	Switch Ties	Piles	Poles [c]	Wood Blocks
1909	75.9	62.1	b	4.4	0.7	3.0
1929	362.0	213.1	14.4	17.1	71.2	6.9
1949	290.6	120.1	18.9	11.0	106.2	2.3
1952	315.0	125.8	10.7	16.7	96.5	6.5

Year	Cross Arms	Construction Timbers	Lumber	Fence Posts	Miscellaneous
1909	0.4	5.3			0.05
1929	2.0	20.2	7.3	0.9	3.0
1949	1.4	6.4	23.8	5.9	2.6
1952	2.0	5.1	36.2	11.3	4.2

[a] Extracted from Henry B. Steer. "Wood Preservation Statistics 1952," *Amer. Wood Preservers' Assn. Proceedings*, Vol. 49, 1953, p. 317.

[b] Included in construction timbers.

[c] Includes both full-length pressure-treated poles and nonpressure (butt-treated) poles.

Coal-tar creosote, made by distillation from coal tar, is the principal wood preservative in the world and thus far the most dependable for general use against all wood-destroying organisms and all conditions of service. It is often diluted with petroleum oil for the treatment of timber to be used in land or fresh-water structures. Where petroleum is cheap, the dilution reduces the cost of the preservative materially without seriously reducing its effectiveness against fungi and insects, but the addition of petroleum to creosote destroys its effectiveness against marine borers. Coal tar is also used as a diluent for creosote, and the mixture is suitable for salt water as well as land use.

Numerous water-borne preservatives are also used throughout the world to give protection against decay and insects without the discoloration and disagreeable oiliness of wood that has been treated with creosote and its mixtures. Most of the present-day water-borne preservatives have appreciable resistance to leaching when used under wet conditions, but on the whole they are less effective for such uses than are the creosote preservatives. The water-borne preservatives find their greatest use in buildings and other structures where both cleanness and protection are desired.

The resistance of wood to flaming and burning may also be greatly increased by heavily impregnating it with suitable mixtures of water-borne, fire-retarding salts. The treatment is effective but too costly for general use and, therefore, not so widely practiced as is preservation against fungi and insects. For example, less than one million of the total of 315 million cubic feet of material treated in the United States in 1952 was treated with fire-retarding chemicals.

In the pressure-treating process the wood is run on tram cars into a large steel cylinder built to stand high internal pressures. The preservative is then admitted to the cylinder, and pressure, usually between 100 and 200 pounds per square inch, is applied by pumps until the desired quantity of preservative has been forced into the wood. The wood may be treated either in the green or seasoned condition. There are many variations in the details of the preparing or conditioning of the wood prior to the application of preservative pressure, in the amounts of pressure used, and in the methods of applying it, depending upon the preservative used, the species and condition of the wood under treatment, and the preservative absorption and penetration desired.

The principal nonpressure treatment in commercial use is the hot-and-cold-bath method, in which the wood is first heated in preservative or some other heating medium and then covered with a cool preservative and allowed to cool further while submerged. There are a number of variations in details depending upon the product treated, the preservative used, and the equipment available. Poles treated by the hot-and-cold-bath method are included in the data of Table 5–XI.

In the treatment of window sash, doors, and other items of millwork, a growing practice in the United States is to immerse the product for three minutes in a solution of pentachlorophenol in a volatile petroleum solvent, or to accomplish the same result by applying a vacuum and then flooding the wood momentarily with preservative and releasing the vacuum. Wood treated in this manner is not included in Table 5–XI, for no statistics are available.

Wood-Conversion Industries

Wood may be converted into other useful products by mechanical, chemical, or biological methods, or combinations of methods. Some wood pulp is made mechanically, some chemically, and some by a combination of the two. Sugar and some other chemicals are made from wood by

chemical methods, yeast and alcohol by chemical conversion followed by biological action. Other organic products can also be made by fermentation of wood sugar. Charcoal and other wood-distillation products are the result of chemical change brought about by heating without the use of additional chemicals. Lactic, butyric, and acetic acids have been made experimentally in substantial yields by direct fermentation of sawdust without intervening chemical treatment, although this conversion method is not known to be in commercial use. From the standpoint of volume of wood used, number of employees, value of products, and influence upon the world's economy, the most important of the wood-conversion industries is the pulp and paper industry. The magnitude of wood consumption by the pulp and paper industry as compared with that of the charcoal industry is roughly indicated in Table 5–II.

The pulp and paper industry is really two industries which overlap to such a degree that neither one is entirely distinct from the other. In addition, the fiberboard or building-board industry is closely related to the pulp industry. Some mills produce pulp only and sell it to other manufacturers. Some produce pulp for their own use only, in the manufacture of paper or other pulp products. Other mills produce pulp that they convert into building boards. Many mills produce paper only, from purchased pulp. Paper, in turn, is produced in a multitude of grades and qualities and converted into an almost unlimited number of end products.

THE WOOD-PULP INDUSTRY. Wood pulp may be made by strictly mechanical means, by cooking wood with chemicals, or by combinations of chemical and mechanical methods.

Mechanical Pulp. This is made almost entirely by pressing blocks of wood against huge grindstones revolving in the presence of hot water. This is the cheapest method of producing pulp and gives yields of 90 per cent or more, based on the dry weight of the wood. Approximately one third of the world's pulp is made in this manner. Most of it is used in the manufacture of newspapers, but substantial amounts go into other kinds of paper. Cheap power is a basic requirement in the profitable manufacture of mechanical or "groundwood" pulp, for power is the major product consumed, in addition to the wood itself. Groundwood pulp mills are usually located, therefore, where both wood and water power are abundant and relatively cheap.

The amount of power used per ton of pulp and the quality of the pulp produced are influenced by the species of wood used, the condition of the grindstone surface, and the operating conditions. Since paper made from groundwood pulp alone is too weak for most uses, stronger pulp must be added. Newsprint paper, for example, commonly contains between 15 and 20 per cent chemical pulp and the rest groundwood pulp.

Chemical Pulp. This is made by cooking wood chips under pressure in solutions of chemicals which dissolve out the lignin and some of the other soluble materials in the wood, leaving the cellulose fibers in a more or less

pure state. The yield of pulp is less than half of the original weight of the wood. The quality and usefulness of the pulp depend upon the species of wood, the cooking chemical used, and other cooking and processing details.

In the *sulfite* process, the cooking liquor consists of a solution of calcium, magnesium, ammonium, or sodium bisulfite plus sulfurous acid. This results in a strong, relatively light-colored pulp, which is adaptable to the widest variety of uses of any of the commercial wood pulps. One of its important uses is in mixture with groundwood pulp for the manufacture of newsprint paper. When especially purified, sulfite pulp is used in the manufacture of viscose rayon and other cellulose derivatives. The sulfite process is used mainly with light-colored, long-fibered, nonresinous softwoods like spruce, hemlock, and balsam, but some birch, aspen, and southern yellow pine are also employed.

The *sulfate* process uses an alkaline cooking liquor containing sodium sulfide and sodium hydroxide. It is adaptable to both resinous and non-resinous species and, in fact, can be used with almost any wood. In the United States the sulfate process is used principally in the manufacture of pulp from pine, but its use for other species is growing. Most grades of sulfate pulp are used for wrapping paper, bags, fiber shipping containers, and other purposes where high strength is important. The pulp can also be bleached and used for the manufacture of high-grade papers for many purposes.

In the *soda* process, also, an alkaline cooking liquor is employed, consisting of a solution of caustic soda. This method is used mainly for hardwoods, and the pulp produces a bulky paper with low strength but good opacity, when used alone. Mixed with longer-fibered pulps added for strength, soda pulp is used extensively for high-quality printing papers.

Semichemical Pulps. These are newer than the others and differ from them in being produced partly by chemical and partly by mechanical means. The wood chips are softened by partial cooking in chemical solution and then pulped by passing them between revolving discs or plates. The chief cooking chemical used is neutral sodium sulfite solution, but both alkaline sulfate and acid sulfite solutions may also be used. The yield of pulp depends upon the extent of the cooking and the severity of the processing, but is usually within the range of 70 to 80 per cent because much of the lignin is left with the fibers, in contrast with the strictly chemical processes that take out practically all of the lignin and, as pointed out, yield less than 50 per cent. The principal use for semichemical pulps is in the production of corrugating board for fiber boxes. Bleached semichemical pulps are being used also for high-quality white papers, including glassine, bond, book, magazine, and other grades. The semichemical process is especially suitable for pulping miscellaneous hardwoods, a characteristic which, together with the high yield and wide utility of the pulp, favors its increasing use.

A variation of the semichemical process consists in heating the wood in steam or water, followed by mechanical fiberization. These methods produce, with yields of 85 to 95 per cent, coarse pulps used mainly in the production of fiberboards, roofing felts, and similar products.

Dissolving Pulp Products. A relatively small but growing use for chemical wood pulps is for the production of highly purified pulps called dissolving pulps or high alpha-cellulose pulps. These are used in the manufacture of such products as rayon fabrics and tire cord, cellophane, absorbent tissue, lacquers, smokeless powder, photographic film, plastics, and a variety of cellulose chemicals. It is estimated that more than 700 thousand tons of dissolving wood pulp were produced in the United States in 1952, and more than 420 thousand tons in Canada. Other important producers are Sweden, Norway, Finland, Western Germany, Austria, Italy, and Japan.

Production and Consumption

The world production of wood pulp in 1952 (including that of U.S.S.R.), was estimated by FAO at 37.7 million metric tons. Of the world production reported to FAO (not including U.S.S.R.), about 35 per cent was mechanical, 29 per cent sulfite, and 36 per cent all others. The relative production of the principal pulp-producing countries and an indication of the growth of the industry are evidenced in Table 5–XII.

TABLE 5–XII

PULP PRODUCED IN THE PRINCIPAL PULP-PRODUCING COUNTRIES, 1937, 1946, 1953 [a]
(In Million Metric Tons)

Country	Pulp Produced		
	1937	1946	1953
United States	5.963	9.622	14.837
Canada	4.551	5.829	7.929
Sweden	3.524	2.736	3.223
Finland	2.191	1.195	1.929
Japan	0.901	0.206	1.507

[a] FAO, *Yearbook of Forest Products Statistics, 1952,* p. 10; *1954,* Table 28.

From year to year pulp production is strongly influenced by world economic conditions; hence the relative proportions of the total contributed by different countries as well as the proportions of the different kinds of pulp vary considerably.

The United States is not only the greatest producer but also the greatest consumer of wood pulp, for its pulp imports greatly exceed its exports. Canada and the Scandinavian countries produce much more pulp than they consume, and depend heavily on the export markets. The United States consumes about one half of the total world production of pulp. Consumption of wood-pulp and pulp products in different countries is indicated in Table 5–XIII.

TABLE 5–XIII

ANNUAL PER CAPITA CONSUMPTION OF WOOD PULP AND PULP PRODUCTS
BY COUNTRIES, 1949-1953 [a]

Country	Kilograms per Capita
United States	128
Sweden	81
Canada	77
Finland	75
Norway	67
Australia	48
New Zealand	48
Switzerland	41
Denmark	39
United Kingdom	39
Belgium	32
Netherlands	31
Western Germany	25
Austria	21

[a] From FAO, *Yearbook of Forest Products Statistics, 1954*, Table 44.

THE PAPER AND PAPERBOARD INDUSTRIES. The variety of papers and paper products manufactured is almost unlimited and continually growing. The greatest single product of the paper industry, however, is newsprint paper, which accounted for more than 40 per cent of the reported world production of paper and paperboard in 1952, as shown in Table 5–XIV.

TABLE 5–XIV

PRODUCTION OF DIFFERENT CATEGORIES OF PAPER, BY COUNTRIES REPORTING
TO FAO, 1950, 1952 [a]

Product	1950	1952	
	Million metric tons		*Per cent*
Newsprint	8.9	9.8	22
Other printing and writing paper ..	8.1	8.6	19
Other paper	11.4	11.5	25
Paperboard	15.3	15.6	34
TOTAL	43.7	45.5	100

[a] From FAO, *Yearbook of Forest Products Statistics, 1953*, p. 5.

Canada manufactured about half of the world's production of newsprint, and this product constituted about 80 per cent of the total Canadian paper and paperboard production. The United States absorbed about 93 per cent of the newsprint exported from Canada and more than 25 per cent of the Scandinavian exports.

Of the great variety of papers other than newsprint and paperboard, the United States manufactured about three fourths of the total world's production in 1951 and consumed about the same amount. These included wrapping, printing, bond, book, tissue, sanitary, and many other papers. Paperboard is used principally in packaging, as in fiber boxes, cardboard boxes, milk containers, and numberless other items.

Table 5–XV shows the total paper and board production in the United States in 1951 by principal categories. These categories can, of course, be further broken down into many subdivisions.

TABLE 5–XV

UNITED STATES: PAPER AND BOARD PRODUCTION BY MAJOR GRADE GROUPS, 1951 [a]
(In Thousand Short Tons)

Grade	Total U.S. Production in 1951
Total paper and board	26,048
Paper, total	11,624
Newsprint	1,108
Machine coated	1,113
Book	1,610
Fine	1,366
Coarse	3,627
Sanitary	1,244
Absorbent	128
Other	1,356
Paperboard, total	11,621
Container board	6,323
Bending board	3,272
Special paperboard	1,064
Other	962
Wet-machine board, total	148
Construction paper and board, total	2,655
Building paper and insulation	1,386
Building board	1,269

[a] From U.S. Dept. of Commerce, National Production Authority. Includes all paper and board production from wood pulp, waste paper, and other pulps.

BUILDING BOARD OR FIBERBOARD. This classification includes coarse fiber products such as hardboards, insulation boards, and similar products, largely used in building construction but also to an increasing extent for industrial products of various kinds. The estimated world production in 1953 was 2.62 million metric tons, of which hardboards, including semi-hardboards, constituted 48 per cent (see Table 5–XVI). In Europe the production of hardboards was twice as great as that of insulation boards. The reverse was true in the United States and Canada, where insulation-board production was more than twice that of hardboards. About one third of the reported production of hardboard and two thirds of the insulation board were manufactured in the United States.

Hardboards are made in large dense sheets from various kinds of wood pulp by the use of high temperatures and pressures in hot-plate presses. Insulation boards are much lighter in weight and less dense, and are dried with hot air in tunnel dryers, without pressure.

TABLE 5–XVI

PRODUCTION OF FIBERBOARD (BUILDING BOARD) BY PRINCIPAL REPORTING COUNTRIES, 1953 [a]
(In Thousand Metric Tons)

Country, Region	Hardboard	Insulation Board	Total
World	1270	1350	2620
Europe	600	280	880
Sweden	215	55	270
Finland	46	58	104
Norway	47	37	84
West Germany	51	14	65
France	44	12	56
Belgium	34 *	10 *	44 *
United Kingdom	18	26	44
Italy	34	3	37
Czechoslovakia	20 *	15 *	35 *
Poland	20 *	15 *	35 *
Austria	17	8	25
U.S.S.R.	70	70	140
United States	435	836	1271
Canada	49	128	177

[a] Based on FAO, *Yearbook of Forest Products Statistics, 1954*, Table 33.
* Unofficial figure.

CHARCOAL AND WOOD-DISTILLATION INDUSTRY. When wood is heated to high temperatures in air it burns, but in the absence of air it turns to charcoal, giving off much gas in the process. The gas consists mostly of water, but it includes acetic acid, methyl alcohol, various light oils, and tars, the proportions varying with the species of wood used and the temperatures maintained. Methyl alcohol and acetic acid made in other ways compete strongly with the wood products, and the commercial value of wood tars and other distillation products is limited. As a result, most of the value of the products of wood distillation lies in the charcoal, and most of the world's charcoal is produced without saving the by-products.

When the gaseous by-products are not to be saved, charcoal can be produced very simply by stacking the wood together, covering it with earth, igniting it in one or two places, and maintaining a slow heat by controlling the admission of air. After the wood reaches a temperature of about 500° F. an exothermic chemical reaction begins, which furnishes much heat and reduces the amount of air required to finish the carbonization. The time required to complete the charring process and cool the charge subsequently so that the charcoal may be removed without igniting when exposed to the air varies from three or four days to two or three weeks, according to the size of the charge and the character of the pit. Simple kilns made of brick, concrete blocks, or even metal, are often used instead of the earth covering. An ordinary five-cord concrete-block kiln can complete a charge in about eight days.

When the gases are to be condensed and saved, much more expensive equipment is required, such as steel ovens, tram cars, condensers, water pumps, and refining apparatus, which make the investment much higher than when the gases are wasted. Ovens of this kind in common use can carbonize a charge in about one day, but generally the preheating requires three days and the cooling three days in addition, making a total of seven days.

Statistics on charcoal production are incomplete and inadequate. Wood used for charcoal is sometimes reported with that used for fuel, and the amounts of charcoal produced are seldom reported. Table 5–XVII is a summary of the amounts of wood reported used for charcoal in 1952 in the countries that reported this item separately. The figures, even though not

TABLE 5–XVII

USE OF WOOD FOR CHARCOAL BY PRINCIPAL REPORTING COUNTRIES, 1953 [a]

Countries, Etc.	Thousand Cubic Meters
World	55,300 [b]
Europe	5,600 [b]
Italy	2,508
Portugal	1,040
France	420
Sweden	400
Greece	222
Yugoslavia	71
United Kingdom	70
United States	481
Canada	73
Honduras	2,500
Argentina	21,600
Colombia	2,000
Chile	470
French Morocco	404
Gold Coast	734
Iran	4,000
Japan	12,109
Philippines	1,653

[a] From FAO, *Yearbook of Forest Products Statistics, 1954*, Table 12. See also Table 5–II above.
[b] Does not include data for U.S.S.R. and certain other countries.

accurate, indicate that Argentina produces a large percentage of the world's charcoal. India is also a heavy producer, but no data on Indian production are available. Italy used about an eighth as much wood for charcoal as did Argentina. The U.S. charcoal production is estimated at about 335,000 tons. Charcoal is used mainly for domestic fuel and carbon disulfide manufacture. In Japan and certain other countries it is used to some extent for truck and bus fuel. In the United States much charcoal is used for recreational cooking at picnics and barbecues and on similar occasions. There are, of course, innumerable industrial uses for charcoal in metallurgical, chemical, and other manufacturing operations.

WOOD-HYDROLYSIS INDUSTRY. When wood is heated with acid under properly controlled conditions the celluloses and hemicelluloses are converted into sugars which can be separated and purified to produce glucose and xylose; or else the solution can be neutralized and fermented to produce alcohol, glycerine, yeast, citric acid, and a number of other products. The production of sugars from wood has been experimented with extensively in the United States and high yields have been obtained, but the process is not yet commercially successful in this country. It has found commercial use in Europe for the production of sugars, alcohol, and yeast —especially in Germany, France, and Switzerland. Production statistics, however, are not available.

Other Forest-Products Industries

A multitude of products other than wood comes from the forests, including naval stores, tannins, and cork, which are important articles of world commerce. Rubber could be included as a forest product of great economic importance, but most of the natural rubber is now being produced from plantations instead of from wild trees in the forest. Oils, gums, waxes, and resins in great variety are obtained from the forests of the world. Many fruits, nuts, spices, and other edible products originally obtained from wild trees are now produced from plantation trees of improved varieties and thus have become agricultural rather than forest products, but others are still wild-forest crops. Christmas trees have become an important wild-forest product in the United States and Canada although gradually coming in larger quantities from plantations. In parts of the United States and Canada where hard maple is plentiful, maple syrup and maple sugar are products of local importance and esteem. The list could be extended to include hundreds of products, although many of them have local rather than international importance.

THE NAVAL-STORES INDUSTRY. Turpentine and rosin are the two principal products now included in the term "naval stores," a term that dates from the time when all ships were made of wood. Turpentine and rosin are obtained by the distillation of the oleoresin or "pitch" that exudes from living pine trees when they are "tapped" or scarified. At present these products are also obtained by steam distillation and solvent extraction from chips of resinous wood, mainly pine stumps, that have been left in the ground until the nonresinous portions have rotted away. Substantial amounts of turpentine are also produced as a by-product in the sulfate pulping of pine chips, and a much smaller amount as a by-product from the destructive distillation of pine wood. Of the 1951 production of turpentine in the United States, it was estimated that 36 per cent was "gum" turpentine, 33.6 per cent wood turpentine (from stumps), 29.7 per cent from sulfate pulping, and 0.7 per cent from destructive distillation. Ten years earlier the percentages were 52.0, 34.6, 11.8, and 1.6. Of the 1951

U.S. rosin production, 39.4 per cent was from gum and 60.6 per cent mainly from solvent extraction. World statistics on turpentine and rosin production are shown in Table 5–XVIII, which, however, does not include data from the U.S.S.R. and a number of other turpentine-producing countries. Of the total production shown in Table 5–XVIII, the United States produced more than did the rest of the world combined. A large percentage of the production of each major producing country is exported. In addition to turpentine and rosin, pine oil, pine tar, and other naval-stores items are produced, and an increasing number of chemicals are being synthesized from the primary naval-stores products.

TABLE 5–XVIII

WORLD PRODUCTION OF TURPENTINE AND ROSIN, 1951 [a]

Country	Turpentine (Thousand U.S. gal.)	Rosin (Thousand lb.)
World	53,309	1,511,797
United States	34,856	1,086,888
Other countries	18,453	424,909
France	4,685	123,457
Portugal	5,122	147,691
Sweden	3,000	6,000
Spain	2,410	57,143
Mexico	1,600	52,000
Greece	1,058	27,122
Japan	428	10,496
Others	150	1,000

[a] *Naval Stores Review, International Yearbook*, 1952. Does not include statistics from U.S.S.R., China, and several other countries.

CORK. Commercial cork is the outer bark of a species of oak that grows mainly in countries bordering the western half of the Mediterranean Sea, particularly France, Portugal, Spain, and North Africa. Cork trees also grow in other countries in small quantities and have even been introduced into the United States, but are not industrially important there. Every eight or ten years the outer bark, usually one or two inches thick, is carefully stripped from the trees without damaging them or interfering with their growth or production of subsequent crops. The bark is air-dried for a few days and then taken to market and sold for manufacture into insulation, bottle stoppers, and cork compositions of various kinds.

Portugal, the world's largest producer of cork, accounts for about half of the world's estimated production of 310,000 tons, and cork and cork products are important items of export from that country. The United States uses almost one half of the world's cork crop.

TANNIN EXTRACTS. The production of tannin extracts for leather tanning amounts to a considerable industry throughout the world. The quebracho wood of South America produces more tannin extract than does any other single source. This wood, which is very heavy, hard, and high in tannin content, is chipped and leached to yield an extract that is highly valued by tanners. More than 250,000 tons of it were exported from Argentina and Paraguay in 1950. On a smaller scale, chestnut wood chips are extracted for tannin in the United States, Italy, and France. Commercial tannins are also derived from barks, fruits, and leaves as well as from the wood of plants. Wattle bark from Australia and South and East Africa is an important source. Many of the forest species of the United States contain substantial quantities of tannin in their barks, but in general only the barks of eastern hemlock, chestnut oak, and tanbark oak have found extensive commercial use in this country. Improvements in by-product utilization may in time bring into commercial use other barks that are available as waste in large amounts at sawmills, pulp mills, veneer mills, and other factories.

Tannin production in the United States has been decreasing for years, and importation increasing. In 1927 nearly 56 per cent of the vegetable tannins used in the United States were from domestic sources, but in 1950 domestic tannins constituted only about 15 per cent of the total and in 1952 the ratio was still lower. Most of the domestic tannin was obtained from chestnut wood, with much smaller amounts coming from oak and hemlock barks. Nearly 70 per cent of the tannins imported in 1950 were obtained from quebracho wood and about 19 per cent from wattle bark.[1]

Waste Utilization

In the conversion of trees into wood products, on the average much less than half of the tree gets to market in the form of finished products. The waste is usually greater in countries that are heavily timbered or where labor costs are high than where the reverse is true. The U.S. Forest Service in 1946 estimated that of the wood cut in or imported into the United States in 1944, 43 per cent reached the hands of the user, 22.5 per cent was used under the boilers of mills and factories that processed the wood, and 34.5 per cent found no use at all. This estimate did not include any bark, most of which finds no use or is burned as fuel.

The waste in producing fuel wood, mine timbers, and fence posts is relatively low in comparison with the waste in the production of lumber, hewed ties, and cooperage, for which the estimated losses are from 68 to 72 per cent. In the manufacture of chemical pulp, the lignin and other constituents dissolved out by the pulp liquor, and thus lost, amount to 50 to 60 per cent of the original pulpwood, although fuel values are received from a part of these liquors. Altogether, the total amount of lignin, bark, and wood in the United States that finds no use may exceed 100 million tons annually. As the Forest Service has pointed out, such waste could be considered equivalent to a neglected forest, a source of raw material of great

1 Jerome S. Rogers. "Potential tannin supplies from domestic barks," New England Wood Utilization Council, *Bull. no. 39*, 1952, p. 18.

potential value. The extent to which it can be used economically, how-ever, is limited by its accessibility to markets and the cost at which it can be made available to prospective users. Manufacturers can be expected to use wood residues, instead of roundwood or lumber, as their raw material only where it is financially profitable to do so. The wood-waste problem is not one of wilful wastefulness but one of economics and technical developments.

Since 1944 much progress has been made in the use of logging, veneer-mill, and sawmill wastes in the manufacture of pulp and building boards, and these uses seem to be growing steadily. More and more sawmills are removing the bark from their logs before sawing, which increases the ac-ceptability of the slabs and edgings from the logs for pulp manufacture. Matson [2] estimated that the equivalent of nearly five million cords of logging and mill residues is being used annually in the production of pulp chips, hardboards, and soft boards, chiefly in the Pacific Coast states.

There is also a newer and relatively much smaller use for sawdust, planer shavings, and other fine material: they are combined with resins and then, by means of heat and pressure, the mixture is converted into hard, smooth sheets that can be used like plywood, hardboard, and similar products, in the manufacture of doors, cabinets, toys, and numerous other things. The production of such "particle boards" is expanding.

Sawdust, shavings, and "hogged" sawmill waste are suitable for chemical processing, and it is known that a great variety of useful chemicals, such as sugars, acids, alcohols, yeast, and furfural can be obtained from them in good yields. Many of these products may in time be made profitably from wood residues but, for the moment, they do not offer attractive com-mercial possibilities in North America.

Many useful products can be made from waste bark. Douglas-fir bark, for example, is being ground up and segregated into a variety of products to which proprietary names have been given and which, through aggressive merchandising, find many uses. Douglas-fir bark also yields useful tannins and waxes, but not yet in commercial production. The bark of California redwood is being processed commercially into a fibrous insulating material and a by-product dust. It is improbable, however, that more than a small fraction of all the bark available can be used in such ways.

Wood flour, of which possibly 80,000 tons are produced annually in the United States, is made by grinding sawdust or shavings from acceptable species and sifting it to the degrees of fineness needed. It is used in the manufacture of linoleum, adhesives, certain molded plastic products, dynamite, and numerous other products where an absorbent filler is needed.

Small pieces of wood in standardized sizes and shapes are produced in substantial quantities from sawmill slabs and low-grade lumber and are sold to manufacturers of various products. Such material from softwoods

2 E. E. Matson. "Potential raw material supply for wood fiber products," *Jour. Forest Prod-ucts Res. Soc.*, Annual Proceedings Number, 1953, pp. 142–145.

is commonly called "cut stock," and that from hardwoods "dimension stock." Much skill and efficiency are required to produce these products from wood residues with the degree of accuracy and uniformity of dryness desired by the purchaser and at a profit to the producer.

Many other potential uses exist for products that can be made from the residues of sawmills and woodworking factories. The problem for the plants producing the residues is first to find markets for which their residues or the products made from them are suitable, and then to deliver the residues or the products to the user at a cost that is attractive to him and profitable to the producing plant. Although innumerable products can be made from wood residues, only a limited number can be made profitably.

Large owners of timberland who are operating on a sustained-yield basis and running their own manufacturing plants can make a variety of products and locate their plants so that the waste from one may be used conveniently as the raw material for another. In a number of notable instances, by integrating their industries in this way and by good management, large lumber manufacturers have eliminated their wood losses or reduced them to very low figures. Although the small sawmill operator is much more limited in his ability to use his residues, he can improve his machinery and methods so as to reduce the waste to the lowest practicable minimum. It may also be practicable in some localities for small, separately owned plants making different products so to integrate or group themselves that most of the residues from the primary breakdown of the log will find profitable use.

REGIONAL

6. ALASKA

Raymond F. Taylor

The prewar conception of Alaska as a land of ice, snow, gold, and dog teams has undoubtedly long since vanished. The much traveled G.I., the Alaska Highway's tourists, and the defense workers have discovered the country and spread the word that it is no longer entirely as Robert W. Service pictured it. Yet few notice the forests of the interior. Much of the land along the Highway has been burned, and only those who fly see the winding streams bordered by forests. But the tourist following the triangle route by steamer through southeastern Alaska to Ketchikan, Wrangell, Sitka, and Juneau, although he may be mainly interested in totem poles and glaciers, cannot fail to observe and wonder at the unbroken, little used, and dense forests of hemlock and spruce.

The Coastal and Interior Forests

The forests of Alaska are conveniently grouped in two broad natural divisions: the Coastal Forest and the Interior Forest, which meet only locally. For the most part these two great formations are separated by the Coast Mountains in southeastern Alaska, the St. Elias Mountains adjacent to the Gulf of Alaska, and the Chugach Mountains on the north side of Prince William Sound.

Extending from Dixon Entrance in southeastern Alaska to Cook Inlet in southwestern Alaska, the Coastal Forest occupies a region of heavy precipitation and moderate temperature. In its southern portion the principal forest type is western hemlock (*Tsuga heterophylla*)–Sitka spruce (*Picea sitchensis*), similar in many respects to that found on the coasts of Oregon, Washington, and British Columbia. Western red cedar (*Thuja plicata*) and Alaska yellow cedar (*Chamaecyparis nootkatensis*) are also encountered and locally may be abundant.[1] To the northward and westward the details of forest composition change, with certain species disappearing and the relative abundance of others becoming altered. Thus, western red cedar is not found north of Petersburg, and Alaska yellow cedar evidently reaches the northwestern limit of its range at Prince William Sound. Mountain hemlock (*Tsuga mertensiana*), a tree of alpine

[1] Sources for botanical nomenclature: Hultén (1941-50), Taylor and Little (1950). For complete references see below, p. 125.

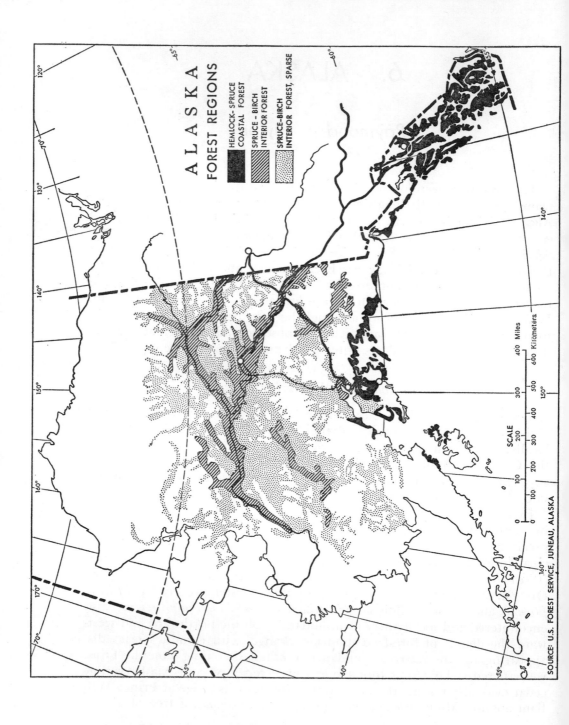

ALASKA
FOREST REGIONS

HEMLOCK- SPRUCE
COASTAL FOREST

SPRUCE – BIRCH
INTERIOR FOREST

SPRUCE-BIRCH
INTERIOR FOREST, SPARSE

SCALE

0   100   200   300   400 Miles

0   100   200   300   400   500   600 Kilometers

SOURCE: U.S. FOREST SERVICE, JUNEAU, ALASKA

habitats in southeastern Alaska, is occasionally seen, forming essentially pure stands, at sea level in Prince William Sound and along Turnagain Arm on the Kenai Peninsula. On Afognak Island, and on the north side of Kodiak Island, where the Coastal Forest may be said to reach its north-western limit, Sitka spruce is the sole dominant. The precise factors responsible for these differences in species composition within the belt occupied by the Coastal Forest are not known, but it is probable that they are principally climatic. It is also noteworthy, as one travels from southeastern Alaska northward and westward along the coast, that the rate of tree growth and the elevation of the timber line decrease and the proportion of the land area which supports noncommercial forest or is devoid of trees increases. In southeastern Alaska barren mountain tops and muskeg represent over half of the total land area; the proportion of nontimbered land increases to the north and west.

The Interior Forest occurs inland of the mountain ranges, previously mentioned, which sweep northward and westward in a great arc at a varying distance from the coast. It occupies the basins of the Susitna, Matanuska, and Copper Rivers, and the west side of the Kenai Peninsula, and covers tremendous areas from the Alaska Range northward and westward to the treeless arctic tundra. Greater diversity is seen in the Interior Forest than in the Coastal Forest. This results principally from forest fires and the occurrence over large sections of permafrost with attendant poor soil drainage. Fires account in large measure for the extensive stands of quaking aspen (*Populus tremuloides*) and Alaska paper birch (*Betula papyrifera* var. *humilis*) seen throughout most of the interior. In many sections permafrost at shallow depth, together with poor soil drainage, appears to be responsible for restricting the forest to comparatively narrow belts along streams. In areas long unburned, black spruce (*Picea mariana*) is the usual forest tree of the lowlands, while white spruce (*Picea glauca*) forms essentially pure stands on the uplands. But the proportion of the land area that bears forest stands is much less in the interior than in the Coastal Forest region.

THE COASTAL CLIMAX FORESTS. The 16-million-acre Tongass National Forest and the 5-million-acre Chugach National Forest include practically all of the commercially valuable forests along the coast. The average stand has a volume of only 20 to 25 thousand board feet per acre (4,000 to 5,000 cubic feet). This volume, which would be regarded with considerable enthusiasm in some of our northern states, has been too small to interest many Alaska sawmill loggers in the past. An annual cut of perhaps 10 million cubic feet compared to the immense resource (Table 6–I) seems small, but it must be remembered that little but saw timber has been cut in the past. Loggers have been seeking out pockets of large spruce and hemlock for many years, scorning the typical climax forest.

Of the climax forest type in southeastern Alaska three fourths consists of western hemlock, one fifth of Sitka spruce, and the remainder of western red cedar (south of Petersburg), Alaska yellow cedar, mountain hemlock (on the upper slopes), and occasionally other species, such as alpine fir (*Abies lasiocarpa*), amabilis or silver fir (*Abies amabilis*), and alder (*Alnus* sp.). Although stable as a whole, individual acres are in constant change, and are surprisingly all-aged.[2] Struggling young hemlocks, extremely tolerant trees, attempting to survive in small openings created by falling veterans, are overtopped by ancient trees that germinated when Marco Polo was in China. Yet the diameters at the base exceed two or three feet.

On the best habitats growth exceeds decay and death, but the poor sites barely maintain a stand of trees. These merge with scrubby stands and muskegs, where stunted mountain hemlock and lodgepole pine (*Pinus contorta*) manage to eke out a precarious existence in cold, wet, poorly aerated, and acid soil. Not that these species could not thrive on well-drained good sites—but they are confined to the muskegs because they cannot compete with western hemlock and Sitka spruce on the better habitats.

The stable climax of the coastal region, a rather decrepit forest with an unhealthy amount of rot and stag heads, may be nature's ultimate decision as to what can be maintained, but the subclimax—the type of stand that follows a catastrophe to the climax—is much to be preferred, if volume of wood is any consideration. The young stands that regenerate naturally after cutting, particularly if the acid humus is torn up and mixed with the mineral soil in logging, are even-aged, grow rapidly, and are relatively free from the diseases so prominent in the climax forest. Studies made 25 years ago, and recently checked, show that these thrifty young stands at 80 to 100 years of age, on sites of only average quality, contain double the volume per acre that is found in climax-forest stands whose dominant trees are 1,000 years old.[3] If they are not cut and reach an age of 300 to 400 years, then the process of breaking down into the climax begins. The overmature trees begin to fall prey to insects and disease. Veterans fall, creating openings too small to permit the development of spruce regeneration, and are replaced by slowly growing hemlocks. The forest composition gradually changes, Sitka spruce decreasing in numbers and western hemlock increasing. The latter species can apparently survive incredibly poor growing conditions for hundreds of years. Thus with the passage of time the healthy, rapidly growing young stand containing about 50 per cent Sitka spruce is transformed into a diseased, slowly growing climax stand containing perhaps 20 per cent spruce.

THE INTERIOR FOREST. The best white-spruce and Alaska paper-birch forests of the interior occur on the lower slopes in the valleys of the Yukon, Tanana, Kuskokwim, Susitna, and Copper Rivers, as well as along their main tributaries. Good soil drainage appears to be one of the requisites

2 Godman (1951).
3 Taylor (1934).

for the development of commercial stands. With an annual precipitation of only 7 to 20 inches, and the long summer days of intense solar radiation, the fire hazard is very high. Probably all forested areas in the interior have suffered from fire at one time or another, but since the gold rush period at the turn of the century the destruction by forest fires has been especially widespread. Almost every landscape bears unmistakable signs of fires in either recent or remote time.[4]

White spruce is the climax forest on well-drained upland soils. When destroyed by fire this species may immediately become re-established, but more commonly the first forest growth to appear is Alaska paper birch or quaking aspen, either in pure stands or in mixture. As succession occurs, the tolerant white spruce gradually enters the birch and aspen stands, where it develops first as an understory and later becomes dominant as the two pioneer species die out. Balsam poplar *(Populus tacamahaca)*, the cottonwood of the interior, is a pioneer species on recent alluvial outwash; locally it may enter upland areas that have been burned.

Poorly drained sites, if forested, usually support stands of black spruce; this species is better adapted for growth in cold, poorly aerated, wet situations than is white spruce. The black spruce is not confined to these unfavorable sites, however. Following repeated fires it may invade upland areas previously occupied by white spruce.

Repeated severe fires may transform areas which once supported forests of white spruce into a treeless expanse, with a vegetation cover of fireweed and grasses. Severe fires destroy all the forest floor—that is, all the unincorporated organic matter down to the mineral soil. A single severe fire—or repeated moderate surface fires—is usually followed by redevelopment of the forest stands.

The composition of a new stand is largely determined by available seed sources. Aspen or birch, pure or in mixture, are the most common "fire types," but occasionally the areas regenerate immediately to white spruce. Fortunately "weed species," such as the gray birch *(Betula populifolia)* in New England, do not occur in Alaska to invade the burned areas.

Extent and Volume of Forest Resource

Surveys in the Tongass National Forest of southeastern Alaska form the basis for fairly reliable estimates of the commercial forest and the volume of timber available. Less reliable estimates are available for the Chugach National Forest, situated on the shores of Prince William Sound in southwestern Alaska. Data relating to the interior are pretty much "expert guesses." As travel is mostly by plane, foresters have been able to make rough maps of a large part of the forested country. Information has also been drawn from reports of the United States Geological Survey and other government agencies. Figure 7, a synthesis of available information on forest distribution, shows the location and extent of the Coastal and the

[4] Lutz (1953).

Interior forests. The latter are separated into two areas: first, those bearing white spruce and Alaska paper birch of potential commercial value, and, second, sparsely timbered areas of woodland or tundra forest.

Table 6–I, giving the land area as broken down into classes, needs some interpretation. The estimate of 44 million productive acres of forest land in Alaska includes land capable of producing merchantable stands. The stands on another 89 million acres of sparse open woodland, semimuskeg, and scrub, may never be merchantable. The Coastal Forest, consisting almost entirely of the two national forests named above, accounts for about 4 million acres thought to be merchantable, chiefly for pulp timber. This includes coastal timber rising to 1,200- or sometimes 1,500-foot elevations and extending several miles back into the river valleys. The relatively open alpine forest above 1,500 feet is not included, nor are the comparatively open stands of short-boled trees at lower elevations. The latter are currently considered nonmerchantable, but this status may be changed by future economic conditions. All of the 4 million acres of merchantable forest are accessible from protected waterways.

TABLE 6–I

ALASKA: LAND AREAS AND GROWING STOCK ON PRODUCTIVE FOREST LAND

	Area (Thousand Acres)	Growing Stock (Thousand Cubic Feet)
Forest land, total	133,000	
With merchantable stands ...	44,000	
National Forests	4,000	16,500,000
Average stand per acre ..		4.1
Interior Forests	40,000	35,000,000
Average stand per acre ..		0.87
With nonmerchantable stands	89,000	
Cultivated land	15	
Grassland	38,985	
Other land	203,000	
TOTAL LAND AREA	375,000	

It is roughly estimated that 40 million acres of the Interior Forest are covered (or were before fires damaged them) by fairly dense white-spruce– white-birch stands, with their variations. Four million acres of the potentially productive part of the Interior Forest are classified as accessible from present towns, roads, and the Alaska Railroad. The remaining 36 million acres are termed inaccessible, although some of the area included is adjacent to navigable streams. If there were markets within any reasonable distance, such stands might be logged, but they are not accessible to present centers of habitation. Practically all the timberland in the interior is in the public domain or in some other form of public ownership.

The bulk of the useable growing stock of coastal Alaska (Table 6–I) lies in the Tongass National Forest. The Chugach National Forest contains some merchantable stands on the shores of Prince William Sound and along the eastern part of the Kenai Peninsula, but growth and volumes do not compare with those in the Tongass, and much of the Kenai area is more valuable for wildlife, recreation, and watershed protection than for growing merchantable timber. There are possibly 16.5 billion cubic feet, or roughly 92 billion board feet, in trees 8 inches in diameter and larger in the Coastal Forest. The bulk of this timber is in the two national forests.

The 40 million acres of merchantable growing stock in the Interior Forest (see Table 6–I) should have about 35 billion cubic feet of white spruce, white birch, aspen, and cottonwood. These volume estimates are based on sample plots measured during recent years and give the first information available on forest growth in the interior. The annual net growth, about 20 cubic feet per acre, is surprisingly good and could be increased under a forest-management program.

The climax forest of the coast varies from semiscrub, with an annual loss of volume, to the best sites, with a net annual growth of as much as 75 cubic feet per acre. It is estimated that in the climax forest as a whole, including a few small areas of fast-growing even-aged young stands, there may be a net increase of 5 cubic feet per acre annually. Sample plots measured in the interior spruce-birch type indicate a growth of approximately 20 cubic feet per acre annually. Most of these stands are even-aged and relatively young in comparison with the climax stands in the Coastal Forest. The drain from cutting is insignificant. The loss from fire, a large item in the interior but no item at all on the rain-soaked coast, cannot be computed.

Even now, with fire protection on the increase, approximately a million acres burn each year, many of the fires smoldering for months in black-spruce bogs and tundra. In the back country the suppression of fires is a most vexing problem. Difficulty of access and lack of local supplies and labor are problems to be faced in the majority of large fires. A glance at a map of Alaska would seem to indicate numerous towns in the interior, but actually many are little more than names. The territorial population of perhaps 128,000 people is concentrated in the coastal towns and in defense areas such as Fairbanks and Anchorage. Some of the fires are due to lightning, but the majority are caused by man.

For many years the Interior Forest has been regarded as consisting of slow-growing, stunted arctic stands of little or no value, either present or prospective. Yet the area of the Interior Forest, in the normal commercial sense of the term, that has remained unburned for a century or more is at least as large as the commercial forest land area of the Douglas-fir region of Oregon and Washington. The need for a forest survey to determine the quantity of timber, the location of the best stands, and of potentially productive but burned forest land, is evident. The forest resources of interior Alaska will one day be needed, and it is to be hoped that more than the charred remnants will then be available.

Growth Rates

Plans for utilizing the timber in the Tongass National Forest contemplate the eventual construction of four or five pulp mills, and a cut of approximately 800 million board feet each year, when all the mills are operating. After 25 years of effort by the Forest Service to interest pulp companies in the obvious value of these stands, one $50,000,000 plant has been constructed and actual cutting of pulpwood has begun.

An average cut of about 800 million board feet per year over an 80-year period, allowing for a slow start, would use up the present climax stand. With proper forestry practices according to the growth data, new rapidly growing stands would then be ready for cutting. During that period the stands regenerated on the areas cut for pulp timber would grow at an approximate average rate of 112 net cubic feet per acre yearly, resulting in some 16 to 18 billion cubic feet being available at the end of 80 years, some of it mature enough to use, if necessary. Thereafter the annual growth should be close to 336 million cubic feet per year on 3 million acres, or roughly 1.9 billion board feet per year in trees 7 inches and larger in diameter. If silvicultural practices such as thinning and pruning become economically possible, not only the growth but also the quality of the trees could be increased materially.

In the Interior Forest possible increased future growth depends on the control of fire and on increased utilization. With fire control but no increase in use of the stands, increased growth would merely be the reflection of added productive acres. With utilization, stands could be improved and growth increased.

Recent study of the interior stands shows their value as a source of considerable wood material. Of 58 sample plots in well-stocked stands having timber of merchantable size, the average volume per acre was 2,400 merchantable cubic feet,[5] or about 8,000 board feet.[6] The average age of the timber on the plots was 123 years. The rotation age, as indicated by these meager data, should probably be about 160 years, at which time the average diameter of the trees would be 8 to 12 inches. Such stands will have perhaps 3,900 cubic feet, or 15,500 board feet, per acre. At the rotation age 80 per cent of the trees would be 5 inches in diameter and larger, and 20 per cent would exceed 12 inches. Occasional 18- or 20-inch trees would be found.

In northern Maine and in Ontario stands of red spruce (*Picea rubens*), white spruce, and balsam fir (*Abies balsamea*) support a large pulp industry, yet volumes per acre are seldom as large as 3,000 cubic feet. In Finland, Norway, and Sweden stands of 1,500 cubic feet per acre are above average, yet the forests are one of the leading resources of Scandinavia and Finland.

[5] Trees 5-inch diameter and larger to a 4-inch top.
[6] Trees 7-inch diameter and larger to a 6-inch top.

Utilization of Forest Products

With a resource of more than 50 billion cubic feet and an annual cut before 1955 of perhaps 62 million board feet, it is obvious that the forests of Alaska can be considered only as in storage for future use. Unfortunately the storage is not very safe in the interior, where fires take such a toll. Cutting in the Interior Forest is relatively insignificant; more than 60 little mills, many operated part time only, cut less than 12 million board feet of lumber in 1951. In the Coastal Forest region 14 mills produce three fourths of the approximately 50 million board feet cut annually, the products being lumber, construction timbers, packing cases for canned salmon, and some railroad ties. The other one fourth of the cut consists of fish-trap logs and dock and wharf piling for local use. Since 1954 the cut has increased as a result of pulp-timber cutting.

The Ketchikan pulp mill, now operating, is the first to come to Alaska and will produce in the neighborhood of 350 tons of dissolving pulp per day. Other pulp mills may be expected in southeastern Alaska, if economic conditions remain favorable.

One of the conditions in purchasing stumpage from the national forests in Alaska is that the wood must be given primary manufacture in the Territory, in order to maintain and develop local industries. The opportunities for small wood-using establishments to supply furniture, small boats, oars, barrels, and tierces are obvious, yet they have not been developed to any extent, in spite of the fact that the high freight rates provide a ready-made tariff for the local producer. It is hoped that extensive cutting of pulp timber will make it possible to supply such industries with cheaper wood, and thus encourage their establishment.

A plywood plant, the first of its kind in Alaska, was recently built at Juneau, at a cost of over one million dollars. It employs about 180 men and produces several million feet of plywood per month, some of which is exported to the States. Before its establishment the only exports of forest products from Alaska were occasional small shipments of the better grades of lumber.

In view of the present insignificant exploitation of the immense timber resources of Alaska, a brief consideration of the actual wood consumption in the Territory is of interest. Unfortunately, reliable up-to-date facts are not available. Wood and wood products are shipped to Alaska by various routes, and since 1947 no Territorial or governmental agency has been responsible for recording such imports unless they originate in foreign countries. In 1947 Alaska imported almost $117,000,000 worth of all products, including close to $7,000,000 worth of wood and wood products. Exports totaling $129,000,000 in value consisted primarily of fish, furs, ores, and bullion. The $7,000,000 worth of wood products and lumber shipped in does not include wood products or other military and naval supplies and equipment for use by the United States Armed Forces, a large item in itself. It was estimated that in fiscal year 1951-52 Alaska Command Stations would use for maintenance and new construction 13,000 squares of cedar shingles, 72 million board feet of spruce and hemlock lumber, and 4.9 million board feet of birch lumber.

As only a few shingles are produced in Alaska, and since the cut of spruce and hemlock, including white spruce in the Interior Forest, has seldom exceeded 60 million feet per year, it is doubtful if much of the above was supplied by Alaskan mills. The opportunity for local production to meet local needs clearly exists, but the initiative seems to be lacking. Raw materials for a birch-products industry occur along the government railroad. The market is promising, and private groups have expressed interest from time to time, but so far nothing has come of it.

Other Industries in Relation to Forest Production

Other industries have an evident bearing on possible future demands for forest products.

According to the Alaska Development Board, the Territory has seven million acres of arable land, but an eminent soil scientist, long familiar with Alaska soil conditions, states: "Probably the land potentially arable under anything like foreseeable economic conditions is less than one million acres. Of this perhaps 15,000 acres is now (1950) cleared and farmed, not counting unimproved range." [7] It is probable that the latter estimate as to the area of potentially arable land is more in keeping with reality that the former. In the production of agricultural crops, as in the production of wood products, the crying needs in this undeveloped territory are for year-round industries to support a stable population and for the development of facilities for cheap transportation to markets. Agricultural products raised in the Matanuska Valley near Anchorage are sold in that city and at the Army bases. The same is true of farms near other large towns. The terrific cost of clearing land, the high cost of living, and the lack of adequate information on appropriate agricultural methods in this new country, also discourage any rapid growth of farming, although many of the technical problems are being solved by the Alaska Agricultural Experiment Station.

Other industries in Alaska include fur farming, trapping, and the tourist trade. The first is not on the increase, and trapping cannot safely be expanded, but the tourist business could be developed to a much greater extent. Mining is not the booming industry it once was, and Alaska's mainstay, the fishing industry, like mining, is seasonal. Almost all of the fishing and canning takes place during a few summer months, and nonresidents brought north for the season make up more than half the cannery workers. Often they live and eat in company buildings, drawing their pay in the States after the season is over.

[7] Kellogg (1951), 37-38.

Future Possibilities

Fishing and mining account for some 80 per cent of the value of the total production of the Territory. Hard times follow when either industry cannot operate at capacity. The utilization of the Coastal Forest for pulp timber will provide one year-round industry, and with the coming of enough pulp mills to utilize the allowable cut from the Tongass National Forest, southeastern Alaska should become a prosperous region.

In 1948 a federal forest research organization was established in southeastern Alaska to investigate methods of cutting pulp timber and other forest products, silvicultural procedures to be followed in developing new stands, and measures to be taken to insure the protection of salmon-spawning streams from logging damage. Research will keep pace with the problems that arise as pulpwood cutting progresses and will endeavor to provide the information necessary to keep the forest land fully productive. With an early start, it is hoped that mistakes like those made in the early days in the States may be avoided.

The future possibilities of forestry in the interior are not easily estimated. The first problem is to halt the forest fires. The Forestry Division of the Bureau of Land Management is making headway under immense difficulties. The Alaska Forest Research Center, co-operating with this agency, has studied the effect of fire on the forests and other vegetation, in order to supply basic information about damage to timber stands as well as to game, fur bearers, and other values.

Protection of the forests from fire will maintain for future use what is left of the resource, but only with an increased population will there be any possibility of building up the growing stock and improving the growth and composition of the stands. In spite of a constantly increasing world population, Alaska continues to be ignored as a land for permanent homes. Even the slight increase in Alaska's population during the past ten years is partly a reflection of defense activities. The development of Alaska is a highly complex problem, but progress is being made. Eventually the forests will contribute to the development of the Territory and to the economic growth of the United States.

SELECTED REFERENCES

GODMAN, R. M. 1951. A site classification and "quick-cruise" volume table for climax stands. U.S. Forest Service, Alaska Forest Res. Center, *Tech. Note 11.*

HULTÉN, ERIC. 1941-1950. Flora of Alaska and Yukon. *Lunds Universitets Arsskrift,* I-X, 37-46i.

KELLOGG, C. E. 1951. Soils of Alaska. *Nat. Res. Council. Bull.* 122:37-38.

LUTZ, H. J. 1953. Ecological effects of forest fires in the interior of Alaska. U.S. Forest Service, Alaska Forest Res. Center, *Tech. Note 5.*

TAYLOR, R. F. 1934. Yield of second-growth western hemlock–Sitka spruce stands in southeastern Alaska. U.S. Dept. Agr., *Tech. Bull. 412.*

———, and LITTLE, E. L., Jr. 1950. Pocket guide to Alaska trees. U.S. Dept. Agr., Forest Service, *Agr. Handbook No. 5.*

7. CANADA

George Tunstell [*]

There are more than 150 tree species native to Canada, of which 31 are conifers, commonly called "softwoods." Comparatively few of the 119 broadleaf species, commonly called "hardwoods," are of any great commercial value. The principal species in use today are listed below.

SOFTWOODS

Common Name	Scientific Name
White spruce	*Picea glauca*
Red spruce	*Picea rubens*
Black spruce	*Picea mariana*
Sitka spruce	*Picea sitchensis*
Engelmann spruce	*Picea engelmanni*
Douglas fir	*Pseudotsuga taxifolia*
Eastern white pine	*Pinus strobus*
Red pine	*Pinus resinosa*
Jack pine	*Pinus banksiana*
Ponderosa pine	*Pinus ponderosa*
Western white pine	*Pinus monticola*
Lodgepole pine	*Pinus contorta* var. *latifolia*
Balsam fir	*Abies balsamea*
Amabilis fir	*Abies amabilis*
Grand fir	*Abies grandis*
Eastern white cedar	*Thuja occidentalis*
Western red cedar	*Thuja plicata*
Yellow cedar	*Chamaecyparis nootkatensis*
Tamarack	*Larix laricina*
Western larch	*Larix occidentalis*
Eastern hemlock	*Tsuga canadensis*
Western hemlock	*Tsuga heterophylla*

HARDWOODS

Common Name	Scientific Name
Trembling aspen	*Populus tremuloides*
Largetooth aspen	*Populus grandidentata*
Balsam poplar	*Populus tacamahaca*

Sources for the above nomenclature:
H. P. Kelsey and W. A. Dayton. 1942. *Standardized plant names.* 2d ed. J. Horace Mc-Farland Co., Harrisburg, Pa.
Alfred Rehder. 1940. *Manual of cultivated trees and shrubs hardy in North America.* The Macmillan Co., New York.

* Prepared with the assistance of other members of the Forestry Branch, Department of Northern Affairs and National Resources, Canada.

HARDWOODS (Continued)

Common Name	Scientific Name
Black cottonwood	*Populus trichocarpa*
White oak	*Quercus alba*
Red oak	*Quercus borealis*
Sugar maple	*Acer saccharum*
Red maple	*Acer rubrum*
Yellow birch	*Betula lutea*
White birch	*Betula papyrifera*
Beech	*Fagus grandifolia*
White ash	*Fraxinus americana*
Black ash	*Fraxinus nigra*
Basswood	*Tilia americana*
White elm	*Ulmus americana*
Rock elm	*Ulmus thomasii*
Red alder	*Alnus rubra*

Forest Regions

The forests of Canada cover a vast area, extending from the Atlantic to the Pacific and from the Canada–United States boundary to the Arctic tundra. Wide variations in physiographic, soil, and climatic conditions are reflected in marked differences in the forests; eight more or less well-defined forest regions are recognized. The relative importance of these, on the basis of area, is shown in the following table. Figure 8 shows their geographic location.

Region	Per Cent of Forest Area
Boreal	80.1
Great Lakes–St. Lawrence	7.9
Subalpine	4.0
Montane	2.5
Coast	2.2
Acadian	2.0
Columbia	0.9
Deciduous	0.4

THE BOREAL FOREST REGION. This region covers the greater part of the land area of Canada, stretching unbroken from Newfoundland and the Atlantic coast of Quebec to Alaska. Along its southern side it follows the limits of the Great Lakes–St. Lawrence Region, then skirts the open grasslands of the Prairie Provinces, and terminates in the west in the foothills of the Rocky Mountains. To the north it is bounded by the limits of tree growth.

Temperatures in the region vary from a summer maximum of at least 90° F. to a winter minimum of at least −50° F. Precipitation ordinarily varies from 15 to 30 inches annually, although these amounts are exceeded in eastern Quebec.

The principal trees of the Boreal Forest are white and black spruce, balsam fir, poplars, white birch, and jack pine. Near the foothills of the

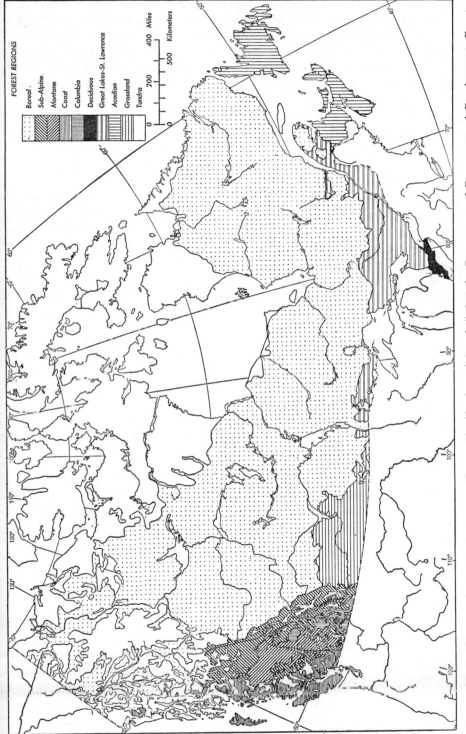

FIG. 8. Canada: forest regions. Based on map "Forest Classification of Canada," Canada, Department of Resources and Development, Forestry Branch, special edition, 1950.

Rocky Mountains the last species is replaced by lodgepole pine. In Quebec and Ontario, and as far west as a line running from Lake Winnipeg to Lake Athabaska in the Prairie Provinces, the region is underlain by the Canadian Shield. Although the Shield contains extensive tracts of good soil, formed from glacial or sedimentary deposits, most of the region is characterized by shallow soils. Considerable areas of bare rock testify to the disastrous results of forest fires followed by erosion. The forests of this part of the region are mainly coniferous, with black spruce and balsam fir as dominants, and are valuable chiefly for pulpwood. West of Lake Winnipeg, the same tree species are in evidence but in different proportions. Here the soil is deep and relatively fertile, and the characteristic forest is a mixture of poplar and white spruce.

Along the northern boundary of the Boreal Forest is an area of transition from the merchantable forests of the south to the treeless wastes of the Far North. The forests here are of no commercial value, although some have considerable local economic value since they provide cover for fur-bearing animals and wood for fuel and buildings for the scattered inhabitants of the area. White and black spruce, larch, and birch are the principal tree species, and these are usually of stunted growth because of the severity of the climate. In river valleys and other protected sites occasional clumps of trees of fair size are to be found.

Along the southern boundary of the Boreal Forest, but lying entirely within the Prairie Provinces, is a zone of transition between the true forest region to the north and the open grasslands to the south. Here aspen is the dominant tree and is in sole possession of most of the area. In southern Manitoba stands of bur oak *(Quercus macrocarpa)* are found, and elm, basswood, and ash occur singly or in small groups in river beds. Most of the area is farmed and much of the forest has been reduced to farm wood lots.

THE GREAT LAKES–ST. LAWRENCE FOREST REGION. This region, centering on the Great Lakes system and extending eastward down the St. Lawrence Valley, occupies a middle position both in location and in composition between predominantly coniferous forests to the north and deciduous forests to the south. Precipitation varies from an annual average of 25 inches in the west to 45 inches in the east, and the growing season is from 100 to 150 days. Good forest soils of sedimentary origin are common, but the region also includes southward extensions of the Canadian Shield.

The characteristic species are white pine, red pine, and hemlock, associated with the maples; yellow birch; and, in some sections, beech and basswood. Aspen, cedar, and jack pine are widely distributed, and spruce and balsam fir are common in certain localities. Among the less widely distributed hardwood species are white birch, elm, hickories *(Carya* spp.), white and black ash, bur, red and white oak, ironwood *(Ostrya virginiana),* and butternut *(Juglans cinerea).* The pine forests of the Ottawa Valley and Algonquin Park have been famous as one of the greatest of Canada's lumbering areas. Elsewhere in the region forests of mixed type predominate, with a considerable proportion of pure hardwood stands in more favored locations in the south.

THE SUBALPINE FOREST REGION. Essentially a coniferous forest, this region extends from the grasslands of the prairies and the western border of the Boreal Region up the eastern slopes of the Rockies to timber line. This same type of forest reappears in a narrow strip between the plateaus of the Montane Region and the mountain tops of the Coast Ranges.

In general, this forest formation occupies areas ranging in altitude from 3,500 to 6,000 feet. Rainfall is moderate, temperatures are low, and the growing season is short. The dominant tree species are Engelmann spruce, alpine fir (*Abies lasiocarpa*), and lodgepole pine. Less widely distributed are mountain hemlock (*Tsuga mertensiana*), alpine larch (*Larix lyallii*), and white-barked pine *(Pinus albicaulis)*.

THE MONTANE FOREST REGION. This region forms part of the Interior Dry Belt of British Columbia. It covers an extensive series of interior plateaus, valleys, and ranges from the United States border to the valley of the Skeena River. The climate is relatively dry, with low summer rainfall and moderate to high temperatures. Where it is very dry, as in the lower river valleys, the forest gives way to open grassland.

The principal tree species are ponderosa pine, Douglas fir, lodgepole pine, and aspen. In the north ponderosa pine disappears and associations of Douglas fir, aspen, and lodgepole pine become dominant. In the northeastern portion of the region, around Prince George, stands of Engelmann spruce and alpine fir grade into the forests of the Subalpine and Columbia Regions.

THE COAST FOREST REGION. This region includes the western slope of the Coast and Cascade Mountains and the islands along the coast. The climate is mild and equable, with heavy precipitation (40 to 200 inches annually), of which about 70 per cent falls during the autumn and winter months. These conditions are conducive to the luxuriant growth of coniferous forests and produce the largest trees and the heaviest stands in Canada.

The dominant trees are western hemlock and western red cedar, with Douglas fir in the south and Sitka spruce in the north. All four of these species, of which the most important commercially is Douglas fir, grow to large sizes and occasionally are found in stands running up to 100,000 board feet per acre. Conifers of lesser importance include yellow cedar, mountain hemlock, amabilis, grand and alpine firs, and western white pine. Of the broadleaved trees, alder is widely distributed, and Garry oak (*Quercus garryana*) and madroña (*Arbutus menziesii*) are found in the vicinity of the Strait of Georgia. Broadleaved maple (*Acer macrophyllum*) and vine maple (*Acer circinatum*) occur at low elevations in the south, and black cottonwood is found on alluvial soils in the valleys.

THE COLUMBIA FOREST REGION. Also known as the Interior Wet Belt of British Columbia, this region supports forests similar in composition to those of the Coast Region. The forests lie in the valleys of the Columbia and other rivers at elevations of from 2,500 to 4,000 feet, above the Montane Region and below the Subalpine. The precipitation varies from 30 to 60 inches. Actually the region should be mapped as a series of small "islands" and "stringers" surrounded by patches of subalpine forest; but it is impracticable to do this on a small scale. Some authorities consider the Columbia Region to be merely an extension of the Coast Forest Region. The division followed here has been adopted because of the complete physical separation of the two regions in Canada, and also because the climate is intermediate between that of the Coast and that of the Interior Dry Belt.

The principal species are Engelmann spruce, western red cedar, western hemlock, and Douglas fir. Among other species of considerable importance are alpine and grand firs, western white pine, and western larch. Lodgepole pine commonly replaces stands destroyed by fire. Black cottonwood is found on rich alluvial soils.

THE ACADIAN FOREST REGION. This region comprises Newfoundland, Prince Edward Island, Nova Scotia, and all of New Brunswick but the northwest corner. The maritime climate is favorable to tree growth, with annual precipitation averaging 40 inches. The forests are predominantly coniferous, especially in northern New Brunswick and Cape Breton Island. Mixed forests, interspersed with hardwood ridges, are more common in southern New Brunswick and Nova Scotia.

Among the conifers red spruce is the characteristic dominant, usually associated with balsam fir. White and black spruce, and white and red pine, are widely distributed. Jack pine occurs in pure stands on sandy plains. Hemlock, which is believed to have been much more important in the past, is still widely distributed. Other characteristic conifers are cedar and tamarack. Yellow birch, maple, and beech occur in fairly large quantities and usually occupy well-drained ridges. White birch, wire birch *(Betula populifolia)*, and poplar are found in association with conifers. Other hardwoods occurring are oak, butternut, basswood, ash, and elm.

THE DECIDUOUS FOREST REGION. This region, in Canada a small northerly extension of the great forest of the same type in the United States, occupies the southwestern portion of the Ontario Peninsula. Favorable climatic and soil conditions permit the growth of a number of tree species not found elsewhere in Canada, but the area is completely settled, and the forests are represented now only by wood lots, parks, and small wooded areas on the lighter soils. The characteristic trees are beech and sugar maple, together with basswood, red maple, and several oaks. Coniferous species are represented largely by scattered specimens of white pine, hemlock, and red juniper *(Juniperus virginiana)*. Among the less common hardwoods, which occur singly or in small groups, are hickories, black walnut (*Juglans nigra*), chestnut (*Castanea* spp.), tulip tree (*Liriodendron tulipifera*), magnolia (*Magnolia* spp.), mulberry (*Morus* sp.), sycamore (*Platanus occidentalis*), sassafras (*Sassafras albidum*), black gum (*Nyssa sylvatica*), Kentucky coffee tree (*Gymnocladus dioicus*), and a number of other species that find their northern limit in this region.

Forest Resources

Accurate information is lacking on the area of forest land in Canada and the volume of timber growing thereon. A five-year forest inventory program, initiated in 1951 by the federal government in co-operation with the provinces, should give much more reliable figures than are presently available. However, with reliable figures for some parts of the country, fairly satisfactory figures for other parts, unsatisfactory figures for still other parts, and little or no information for the remainder, the estimates set forth below should be accepted with caution; they are tentative and subject to revision on completion of the inventory now being made.

FORESTED AREAS. The total land area of Canada is 3,466,182 square miles. The forested area (exclusive of the Labrador portion of the Province of Newfoundland) is approximately 1,485,000 square miles, or 43 per cent of the total land area (Table 7–I). Excluding the northern territories, the total forested area is approximately 1,209,000 square miles, or 60 per cent of the land area of the provinces.

Because of adverse climatic or edaphic conditions, more than two fifths of the country's total forested area is classified as nonproductive—that is, as land incapable of producing crops of merchantable timber. Although these lands are of little significance to the forest industries, they do provide timber for local use, shelter game and fur-bearing animals, and conserve water supplies.

The productive forests cover approximately 826,000 square miles, or 24 per cent of the land area of Canada. Owing to the lack of transportation facilities and to other factors, only 70 per cent of the productive area, or 577,000 square miles, is considered to be accessible for commercial operations at the present time. Of this accessible area, about 60 per cent is occupied by trees of merchantable size and the remainder by young growth.

The productive but inaccessible forests of 249,000 square miles constitute a reserve for the future. Their development must await the advance of satisfactory means of transportation, the enhancement of their economic value as a result of continued exploitation of the accessible forests, and the expansion of markets for forest products. Owing to somewhat less favorable conditions for growth, the productive capacity of the inaccessible timber lands is expected to be less than that of the accessible areas.

TABLE 7-I

Canada: Areas of Forested Land, 1954

(In Square Miles)

	New-found-land	Prince Edward Island	Nova Scotia	New Bruns-wick	Quebec	Ontario	Mani-toba	Saskat-chewan	Alberta	British Colum-bia	Provin-cial Total	North-west Terri-tories	Yukon Terri-tory	Total Canada
Forested Land														
Productive	11,220	610	11,555	22,000	250,772	159,812	30,500	47,883	93,060	123,218	759,630	33,600	42,100	826,330
Accessible productive	11,220	610	11,555	22,000	191,227	129,778	23,476	21,342	54,000	86,253	551,461	11,700	14,200	577,361
Nonproductive	13,699	–	–	190	94,314	63,400	62,500	62,804	37,560	124,141	458,608	161,000	39,100	658,708
Total forested land	24,919	610	11,555	22,190	345,086	223,212	93,000	110,687	130,620	247,359	1,209,238	194,600	81,200	1,485,038
Total land area	37,013	2,184	20,743	27,473	523,860	348,141	219,723	220,182	248,800	359,279	2,007,398	1,253,438	205,346	3,466,182

Source: Canada, Department of Northern Affairs and National Resources. Amendments, 1955, to Forest and Forest Products Statistics. *Bulletin 106.* Ottawa.

VOLUME OF MERCHANTABLE TIMBER. The estimates shown in Figs. 9 and 10 of the volume of merchantable timber in Canada are based on trees with a diameter at breast height of 4 inches or over, and exclude the wood which would be left in stumps or tops. The volume of all species for the whole forested area totals 417,823 million cubic feet, of which

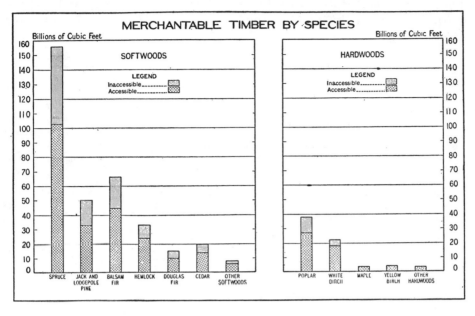

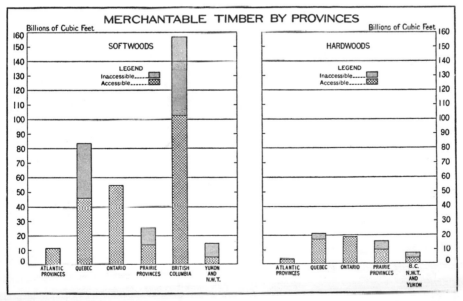

FIGS. 9 and 10. Canada: merchantable timber, by species and by provinces. From Canada: Dept. of Northern Affairs and National Resources, Forestry Branch, Economics Section, *Bull. 106, 1955.*

about 69 per cent is considered to be accessible. Most of this total volume
—some 347,559 million cubic feet—is softwoods, of which 67 per cent is
accessible.

For the accessible forest areas estimates have been compiled for merchantable timber on the basis of the size of the trees (Figs. 11 and 12).
The volume of accessible saw timber, trees 10 inches and over in diameter,
is 640,509 million board feet, and material 4 to 9 inches in diameter
totals 1,884 million cords.

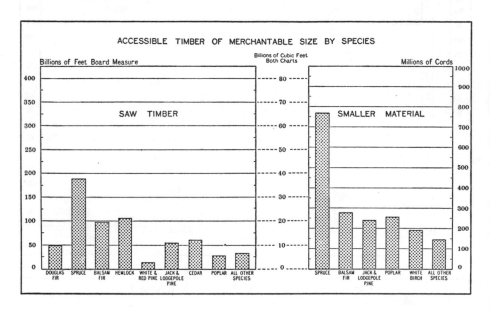

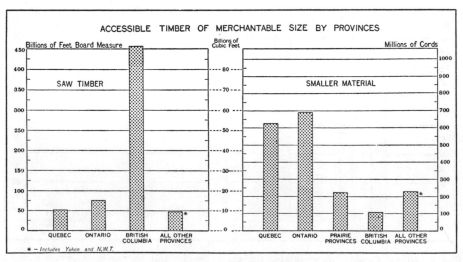

FIGS. 11 and 12. Canada: accessible timber of merchantable sizes, by species and by provinces.
From same source as Figs. 9 and 10.

FOREST OWNERSHIP. Approximately 73 per cent of the total forest area is owned by the provinces. Some 21 per cent (mostly in the Yukon and Northwest Territories) is owned by the federal government and the remaining 6 per cent is in private ownership. It has been the general policy of government to grant timber-cutting rights but to retain ownership of the land. About 15 per cent of the total forested area, or 221,090 square miles, is Crown lands under timber license. Naturally the licensed areas and those privately owned are in the more accessible regions.

The area of forest lands privately owned is 103,729 square miles, of which 35,594 are classed as farm wood lots. These wood lots comprise 13 per cent of the total area in occupied farms. They vary in size from 3 or 4 acres to 200 acres, or more. Furthermore, as they are predominantly in the south, their growth rate is considerably above average for the whole country. Wood produced on the farms makes an appreciable contribution to industry.

The predominance of Crown over privately owned land holds good in all but three provinces. In Prince Edward Island practically all forested land is privately owned, in Nova Scotia 73 per cent, and in New Brunswick about 50 per cent.

Forest Industries

For statistical purposes the forest industries of Canada are divided into five main groups: woods operations (logging), the lumber industry, the pulp and paper industry, the wood-using industries, and the paper-using industries (exclusive of printing trades). The principal statistics of these industries for the year 1952 are given in Table 7–II.

TABLE 7–II

CANADA: STATISTICS OF FOREST INDUSTRIES, 1952

Industry	Number of Employees	Salaries and Wages	Net Value of Production
		Million dollars	
Woods operations	149,318	488	662
Pulp and paper	57,803	225	584
Lumber	60,931	136	261
Wood using	69,537	164	273
Paper using	25,162	67	152
TOTAL	362,751	1,080	1,932

Forest industries in 1952 with a net value of $1,932,000,000 accounted for 14.1 per cent of the value of all industries.

WOODS OPERATIONS. East of the Rocky Mountains the lumber and the pulp and paper companies carry on their own logging operations. Some saw logs and appreciable quantities of pulpwood are cut by private owners or independent loggers who sell to the companies or on the export market.

Most of the wood is still floated to the mills on the rivers and lakes, but with the rapid development of roads an increasing quantity is being hauled by truck.

In British Columbia many independent logging companies still acquire cutting rights from the Crown and sell their logs on the open market. Their numbers are being sharply reduced, however, by the competition between sawmills and pulp mills seeking timber areas in order to ensure adequate future supplies. Heavy logging trucks have largely replaced the logging railroad in hauling logs to the coast, where they are rafted for transport to the mills.

The farm wood lots of Canada contribute an appreciable quantity of fuel wood, pulpwood, saw logs, posts, and other products.

A summary of the primary forest production is given in Table 7–III. The gross value of these primary forest products amounted to $816,000,000 in 1952, a considerable increase over 1946, when the volume was only 2,813 million cubic feet valued at $413,000,000.

TABLE 7–III

CANADA: PRIMARY FOREST PRODUCTION, 1952

Product	Quantity in Commercial Unit		Equivalent Volumes in Thousands of Cubic Feet
Logs and bolts	7,272,019	M. ft. b.m.	1,393,000
Pulpwood	14,102,394	Cords	1,199,000
Fuel wood	10,516,709	Cords	841,000
Posts	16,096,074	Number	19,000
Hewn ties	713,924	Number	4,000
Fence rails	4,694,624	Number	5,000
Round mining timber	49,435,386	Cu. ft.	49,000
Wood for distillation	40,027	Cords	3,000
Poles and piling	1,053,243	Number	16,000
Miscellaneous products	–		37,000
TOTAL			3,566,000

THE LUMBER INDUSTRY. The economic development of Canada has long been associated with that of the lumber industry. The early trade and manufactures of the country were mainly in timber and lumber. Coincident with the expansion of the lumber industry in the nineteenth century were the building of railways, wagon and motor roads, the improvement of inland navigation, and the expansion of northward and westward settlement. The lumber industry today compares favorably in importance with other major, newer manufacturing industries, such as pulp and paper, automobile manufacture, and the making of electrical apparatus and supplies. Statistics for 1952 show that lumber leads all other manufacturing industries in total number of persons employed, and stands fourth in net value of products and second in total wages and salaries paid. In the same year there were more than 8,200 active sawmills in Canada.

They are widely distributed across the country adjacent to stands of merchantable timber, in areas where markets have been developed.

In 1952, 16 per cent of the country's lumber was sawn in Quebec, 12 per cent in Ontario, and 54 per cent in British Columbia. Most of the larger mills are located on the Pacific Coast. This is significant, for it indicates fundamental differences in sawmilling practices east and west of the Rocky Mountains. The large trees in British Columbia required special machines for efficient handling. Massive machinery and large staffs have, in turn, required the building of permanent mills operating throughout the year. In contrast, the smaller trees of the eastern Canadian forests make it economically feasible to build smaller and comparatively inexpensive mills, which generally operate only in the summer and autumn seasons.

Output of the lumber industry in 1952 comprised 6,808 million board feet of lumber; 9,407 thousand ties; 2,425,000 squares of shingles; and 112 million laths, besides other products such as box shooks, staves, pickets, headings, and mine timbers. The gross value of all these products was $568,000,000.

THE PULP AND PAPER INDUSTRY. A notable feature of Canada's industrial development during the past half-century has been the spectacular rise of the pulp and paper industry to the pre-eminent position that it now holds. Pulp and paper mills lead all other manufacturing industries in net and gross values of production, in total wages and salaries paid, and in expenditures on fuel and electricity. Employment in the industry in 1952 totaled 57,803, making it the second largest employer in the country. The 128 mills in Canada manufacturing pulp and paper top the world in the production of newsprint and are second only to those of the United States in the production of wood pulp.

The Province of Quebec is the leading producer of both pulp and paper, manufacturing almost half the Canadian output of pulp and more than half the paper production. Ontario follows, producing 26 per cent of the pulp output and 27 per cent of the paper. British Columbia, New Brunswick, Newfoundland, Nova Scotia, and Manitoba account for the remaining production, in that order.

Wood pulp produced in Canada in 1952 totaled 8,968,000 tons, valued at $650,021,000. Mechanical pulps made up 58 per cent of the output and chemical pulps the remainder. The chief woods used for wood pulp are spruce and balsam fir, which together accounted for 85 per cent of the wood used by the mills. Jack pine, western hemlock, and poplar comprised most of the remainder.

Canadian production of paper and paperboard in 1952 amounted to 7,202,000 tons, valued at $838,105,000. Newsprint made up 79 per cent of this tonnage, and paperboard 11 per cent. Wrapping papers, book and writing papers, and tissue papers were the most important of the remaining products.

MISCELLANEOUS WOOD-USING INDUSTRIES. This group comprises some 13 industries, including concerns making furniture, veneers, plywoods, hardwood flooring, boxes, baskets, crates, coffins and caskets, and sash, door, and planing mills. The furniture concerns, the sash, door, and planing mills, and the veneer and plywood industries yielded 79 per cent of the $273 million net value of production for the group in 1952, when the net values for the main industries were as follows:

Furniture	$106,057,000
Sash, door, and planing mills	71,918,000
Veneer and plywood	38,437,000
Box, basket, and crate	13,483,000
Hardwood flooring	5,170,000
Coffins and caskets	4,625,000
All other wood-using industries	33,140,000

Depletion of Forest Resources

A study of the depletion of the Canadian forests must take into account not only utilization but waste, for a considerable amount of timber is lost each year through forest fires, insect infestations, and tree diseases.

Despite considerable progress in forest-fire protection, the losses from this source are still staggering. For the ten years 1943-52, the average annual number of fires was about 5,100 and the forested area burned each year amounted to roughly 2,400 square miles. The annual loss averages about 440 million board feet of saw timber and over one million cords of small material. In addition to this loss in timber, wildlife has been destroyed, recreational values reduced, soils impoverished, and watershed values impaired. Statistics show that lightning is responsible for about 17 per cent of these fires, that 75 per cent can be attributed to human carelessness, and the remaining 8 per cent to incendiarism or unknown causes.

Reliable figures are not available on the quantities of timber lost through the action of insects and diseases. Some conception of the magnitude of these losses may be gained from the fact that the spruce budworm infests thousands of square miles, that the birch "die-back" has already killed most of the yellow birch in the Maritime Provinces and has spread into Quebec and Ontario, and that the Dutch elm disease is now prevalent throughout the range of elm trees in Quebec. Some authorities place the annual loss of timber from forest insects and disease at 500 million cubic feet.

The figures on forest depletion presented in Table 7–IV involve a certain amount of duplication, for some of the dead or dying timber is cut for use and is thus included twice in the total. No attempt has been made to correct this error, for the estimate of losses from fire is not very reliable and that of losses due to insects and diseases is no better than an intelligent guess.

Although all the utilization and most of the wastage occurs on the present *occupied productive* forest area of approximately 267,000 square miles (or where commercial cutting is concentrated), it is from the *accessible productive* forest of 577,000 square miles that the forest production of the future will be obtained. Merchantable timber on the accessible productive forest is estimated at 288,232 million cubic feet, of which approximately 132,000 million cubic feet may be considered as located on the occupied area. The average annual depletion for the decade 1943-52 amounted to 1.3 per cent of the accessible productive volume or to 2.8 per cent of the volume on the occupied forest land. The depletion for 1952, however, shows an appreciable increase over the average, being 1.5 per cent of the accessible volume and 3.3 per cent of the volume on the occupied forest. These rates indicate that, whereas in many localities severe overcutting is taking place, the annual growth is not being used on the less accessible portions of the productive forest. This situation emphasizes the urgent need for increased protection and management of the commercial forests, if forest growth is to balance depletion.

TABLE 7–IV

CANADA: ANNUAL FOREST DEPLETION, 1943-1952 AND 1952

	Million Cubic Feet of Usable Wood		Percentage of Depletion 1952
	1943-52	1952	
Annual utilization	3,030	3,566	81.9
Annual wastage			
By forest fires	191	290	6.6
By insects and diseases ...	500	500	11.5
Total annual wastage ..	(691)	(790)	(18.1)
Annual depletion	3,721	4,356	100

Consumption and External Trade

Forest products have always played an important part in the development of Canadian trade. Although the country is a big consumer of wood and its products, it has a big surplus for export. The early lumber industry was founded on the shipment of squared timber and, later, pine and spruce deals to Great Britain, and lumber to the United States. Today exports of lumber amount to almost 50 per cent of the annual production and the pulp and paper industry disposes of over 75 per cent of its paper production in foreign markets.

Canada's favorable balance on commodity trading in wood products is significant, for it helps the country settle her debit accounts abroad. Credits from the sale of forest products amounted to $1,233,000,000 in 1952, while there was a deficit balance on trading account of all other commodities of $908,000,000. A comparison of these figures reveals the extent to which wood products are used to pay for imports. Table 7–V shows the relationship between production, exports, imports, and domestic use of four main groups of wood products.

TABLE 7–V

CANADA: PRODUCTION, EXPORTS, IMPORTS, AND APPARENT CONSUMPTION
OF FOREST PRODUCTS, 1952

Forest Product	Unit of Measurement	Production	Exports	Imports	Apparent Consumption
Primary	Million cu. ft.	3,565,529	294,131	20,562	3,291,960
	Thousand dollars	815,651	95,920	5,663	725,394
Lumber	Million ft. b.m.	6,807,594	3,339,658	151,778	3,619,714
	Thousand dollars	483,195	297,205	16,968	202,958
Wood pulp	Tons	8,968,009	1,940,582	54,589	7,082,016
	Thousand dollars	650,021	291,863	5,499	363,657
Newsprint	Tons	5,707,030	5,327,430	Nil	379,600
	Thousand dollars	600,516	591,790	Nil	8,726

PRIMARY FOREST PRODUCTS. All but 8 per cent of the primary forest production was utilized at home in 1952 to support the sawmilling, pulp and paper, and other industries. Pulpwood was the most important export item with a volume of 2,493,000 cords. The export of saw logs amounted to 52 million board feet. The volume of imports was less than one tenth the volume of exports.

LUMBER. A record was set in lumber production in 1951, with 6,949 million board feet; this declined in 1952 to 6,808, of which nearly 50 per cent was exported.

Exports of lumber to the United States, in million board feet, fell from an all-time high of 3,024 in 1950 to 2,168 in 1951, then rose again in 1952 to 2,252. Lumber exported to the United Kingdom rose sharply in 1951 to 896 million board feet from 276 million in 1950, and declined in 1952 to 857 million.

WOOD PULP. Of the wood pulp produced in 1952, nearly 22 per cent was exported. Nearly 82 per cent of these exports, or 1,588,978 tons valued at $225,082,376, went to the United States. Shipments to Great Britain, which are never very great, amounted to 210,684 tons.

NEWSPRINT. The production of newsprint reached an all-time high in 1952 of 5,707,030 tons valued at $600,515,960. Exports were 5,327,430 tons (or 93 per cent of the production), with all but 10 per cent going to the United States.

Canada's position in the newsprint market is pre-eminent, her exports accounting for over 80 per cent of world exports of newsprint. Over half the pages of the newspapers of the world are printed on paper made in Canada.

Forest Policy

The need for better forest management has been receiving increasing recognition by governments, by forest industries, and by the public at large. This has been brought about by an increased demand for forest products, followed by increased cuttings, which, in turn, have raised the fear that the drain on the forests may exceed the volume of wood added by growth. This concern for the future led to the appointment of a Royal Commission on Forestry in 1944 in British Columbia, in 1945 in Saskatchewan, in 1946 in Ontario, and in 1954 in Newfoundland, to study all phases of the forestry situation and to make recommendations. In the other provinces the forestry problem is being approached by different means.

Forests within the provinces are administered by the provincial governments. The federal government is responsible for the administration of forests in the Yukon and in the Northwest Territories and in national parks and Indian reserves, carries on research in forestry and in the uses of forest products, and provides assistance to the provinces in connection with certain forest activities. In view of this division of authority and responsibility, recent developments in forest policy and the status of forest management must be discussed separately for the federal government and each of the ten provinces.

FEDERAL FOREST POLICY. In 1949 the federal Parliament passed the Canada Forestry Act, authorizing the federal government to give the provinces financial assistance in carrying out approved programs of work. In 1951 assistance was offered to the provinces to initiate a five-year plan aimed at completing their forest inventories and reforesting vacant Crown lands. Agreements have subsequently been signed with most of the provinces. Federal appropriations under the Canada Forestry Act totaled $1,025,000 in 1951-52 and $1,225,000 in 1952-53.

NEWFOUNDLAND. This province, which includes the coast of Labrador, became confederated with Canada in 1949. The forests of Labrador are only now being surveyed for development, but on Newfoundland Island large areas are controlled under long-term leases by two pulp and paper companies. The provincial government is directly concerned with the administration of Crown forests (apart from the holdings of the paper companies) and particularly interested in insuring the wood supply necessary to the city of St. John's and the numerous small villages scattered along the lengthy coastline. Crown lands within three miles of the coast are reserved for local use. A forest protective association, supported jointly by the government, the pulp and paper companies, and the Canadian National Railways, is chiefly responsible for protection against forest fires on company and railway lands.

PRINCE EDWARD ISLAND. The forest policy of this small province, in which nearly all the forests are privately owned, is directed toward improving management on farm wood lots. A forest service, set up in the Department of Industry and Natural Resources in 1950, employs two foresters on nursery developments, planting, and extension forestry.

NOVA SCOTIA. The forestry situation in Nova Scotia differs in important respects from that in other provinces of Canada, largely because 75 per cent of the forests are privately owned. Ownership units range in size from a few acres in farm wood lots to large tracts controlled by major industrial companies. The province is actively engaged in a forest inventory which will be completed in 1957, in demarcating the boundaries of Crown forests which it controls directly, and in adding to the Crown forest area by purchase.

The most important forestry development during the postwar years has been the implementation of the Small Tree Act. Any operator who desires to cut a quantity of 50,000 board feet or more, and who wishes to cut any trees less than 10 inches in diameter at the stump, must file an application for permission to do so with the Department of Lands and Forests. The area is then inspected, and conditions governing the cutting are laid down by the Department. More than 1,300 applications were dealt with during the fiscal year 1951-52. This act gives a measure of control over operations on privately owned lands not to be found elsewhere in Canada.

NEW BRUNSWICK. Approximately one half of the forests in New Brunswick belong to the Crown, the remainder being privately owned. Since World War II the provincial government has engaged in a program of aerial photography and mapping over the whole province, which will be completed in 1957. Surveys of some of the more important forest areas have been made by the province, and the larger commercial forest owners have completed inventories of their holdings. Plans are being developed for rapid and inexpensive methods of preparing estimates of the forests at ten-year intervals. Licensees occupying Crown lands must have their forest management plans approved by the Minister of Lands and Mines. Management plans are also prepared by the Department. At the end of 1952, management reports covering 5,000 square miles, or nearly one half the total area of Crown forest in the province, had been submitted.

QUEBEC. For many years it has been the policy of the government of Quebec to require all large lessees of Crown lands to make inventories of their forests and to prepare long-term and short-term management plans covering their operations. Operators are also required to submit for approval detailed plans covering proposed operations for each year. The allowable cut is somewhat less than the estimated annual increment. In 1952 the total area of concessions (i.e., areas held under license or lease) was 80,000 square miles, and management plans covering 71,000 square miles were in force or in preparation.

The province advises and assists the owners of small forest properties, such as farm wood lots, and actively encourages them to improve the management of their properties. Inventories of unoccupied Crown lands are made by the provincial government and combined with information provided by commercial companies to give estimates for the forest resources of the province as a whole.

Fire protection on occupied Crown lands is carried on by associations of licensees, whereas protection of unoccupied forests is a function of the provincial Forest Protection Service.

ONTARIO. The Royal Commissioner appointed to examine the forestry situation in the province in 1946 assembled a small staff of expert assistants and personally investigated conditions in all the principal forest regions. One recommendation, which has been implemented, involved the establishment of an Advisory Committee to the Minister of Lands and Forests. This Committee studies problems raised by itself or referred to it by others. Also all forest legislation has been reviewed, revised, and consolidated.

Aerial photography, mapping, and inventory of 173,000 square miles —a major portion of the province—were undertaken in 1947 and are now completed. The Department of Lands and Forests has developed its own forest survey organization to interpret aerial photographs, make maps, and carry on a broad program of sampling in the field. The province is extending its inventory with federal assistance to a further 33,000 square miles of small but valuable holdings in the southern agricultural area, and to 69,000 square miles in the north.

Commercial companies operating parcels of Crown land of 50 square miles or more are required to prepare long-term and intermediate working plans, and to submit annual cutting plans for approval.

MANITOBA. The forest policy of this province was originally based upon an inventory of its resources prepared by the Dominion Forest Service shortly after the transfer of resources to provincial control in 1930. More accurate estimates of forest resources have been made from time to time, and the province is now completing a new inventory of its forests with financial assistance from the federal government. With the exception of one pulp and paper mill, forest operations are on a small scale, in comparison with those of the eastern provinces, and efforts are directed principally toward assuring continuing supplies of wood for small manufacturing industries and for individual consumers.

SASKATCHEWAN. During World War II, Saskatchewan's output of spruce lumber rose to levels which the available forest could not continue to support. Consequently the government has sharply reduced the allowable annual cut from Crown lands. Saskatchewan's Royal Commission report of 1947 stressed the extreme importance of improved fire protection, the need for a forest inventory, the need for intensive study of the feasibility

of selective cutting, and other measures likely to encourage natural regeneration of the desired species (notably spruce) and closer control of
cutting operations. Marketing of lumber sawn from timber cut from
Crown lands, other than Crown timber berths established prior to 1930,
is carried on by the Saskatchewan Timber Board. The inventory program
of the province is well advanced. The basic provincial survey covered
about 44,000 square miles, including the bulk of the accessible productive
forest area. The new federal-provincial agreement calls for a reconnaissance survey of an additional 103,000 square miles in the northern part of
the province and of 10,000 square miles in the settled portions south of
the main forest belt.

ALBERTA. The most notable postwar development in Alberta has been
the establishment of the Eastern Rockies Forest Conservation Board. This
joint board, supported by the federal and provincial governments, is responsible for protecting the eastern slopes of the Rocky Mountains, in
which rise the headwaters of the Saskatchewan River. Federal participa-
tion in the project is based on the fact that this river runs through Saskatchewan and Manitoba, as well as Alberta. Federal funds have been
provided to finance construction of roads and other improvements needed
in the protection program. Forestry operations on the area are carried
out by the staff of the provincial Department of Lands and Forests.

Aerial photography, mapping, and the preparation of a forest inventory for the greater part of the province, begun in 1949, were completed
in 1953. Further inventory work north of the 57th parallel of latitude has
been undertaken with federal assistance.

BRITISH COLUMBIA. Important modifications of the forest laws of the
province have been made as a result of the report of the Royal Commissioner, submitted in 1945. In 1947 the legislature of British Columbia
authorized the establishment of a new form of forest tenure known as a
Forest Management License, authorizing the Minister of Lands and Forests
to reserve specified areas of Crown lands in perpetuity for the use of any
person, provided he manages the forests so as to assure a sustained-yield
output. If the person already owns or holds certain timber lands within
the area prescribed, these are automatically included in the license. The
ultimate object is to insure sufficient supplies of timber, in perpetuity, for
established forest industries.

Royalties at regular rates are to be paid for all timber considered to be
merchantable at the time the license is issued. On all timber which attains
merchantable size after the license is issued, stumpage and royalty will be
paid at the rate of 16 per cent of the appraised stumpage value at the time
of cutting. Land rental is at the rate of one cent per acre, one sixth of the
regular rate. A number of forest management licenses have already been
issued, and applications for others are under consideration.

The province's inventory program covers all of the province—a total
land area of 359,000 square miles, of which 273,000 will be surveyed

to provincial inventory standards and 86,000 in the north will be covered by a reconnaissance survey.

Prospects for the Future

During the past quarter century a considerable acreage of forested land has been cleared for agricultural or other uses. A considerable area of forest has also been destroyed by repeated forest fires. Despite this reduction in the area of forests, the utilization of primary forest products has shown a substantial increase, from a little over $2\frac{1}{4}$ billion cubic feet of merchantable timber in 1925 to better than $3\frac{1}{2}$ billion in 1952. During this period there were many industrial changes. Some mills were forced out of business because of shortages of raw materials, but at the same time many new establishments were erected, some of them in locations where the forest resources had not previously been utilized. The most marked increase of primary forest products was in pulpwood, which in 1925 amounted to 5,092,461 cords and in 1952 had reached 14,102,394 cords. Increases in "logs and bolts," "fuel wood," and "other products" were less spectacular.

Canada will continue to be a leader in the production of forest products, because so much of her vast land area is better suited to forests than to anything else. Opinions differ as to the extent to which forest industries can be expanded, but all experts agree that, with better forest management and better silviculture, there is much room for development.

SELECTED REFERENCES

Annual Reports of the Forest Services of the federal and provincial governments.
Canada. Dept. of Resources and Development. Forestry Br. 1952. Canada's forests, 1946-50. Report to Sixth British Commonwealth Forestry Conference, 1952. Ottawa.
———. 1952. Forest and forest products statistics, Canada. *Forestry Br. Bull. 106.* Ottawa.
———. 1952. Wood is wealth; Canada's forest economy, 1938-1949. *Forestry Br. Bull. 105.* Ottawa.
HALLIDAY, W. E. D. 1937. A forest classification for Canada. *Forestry Br. Bull. 89* (reprinted 1950). Department of Resources and Development, Forest Research Division, Ottawa.

8. THE UNITED STATES

H. R. Josephson and Dwight Hair

Originally forests covered the entire eastern half of the United States in an almost unbroken area extending from the Atlantic seaboard to the central Great Plains. West of the Great Plains, forests occurred in more isolated groups, chiefly in the mountainous areas where rainfall is more abundant. Altogether, these forests once covered more than 900 million acres. Today about 622 million acres of forests still remain in the continental United States, and forests in Alaska total some further 140 million acres. In the western United States and Alaska these forests have for the most part escaped the plow and remained undeveloped for other uses, primarily because of rough topography, poor soils, or adverse climate. Large areas of eastern forest land, however, were once under cultivation and have reverted to forest after being abandoned by agriculture.

The forests of the United States represent one of the world's greatest concentrations of commercial timber species. Softwood forests containing woods of world renown, such as Douglas fir (*Pseudotsuga taxifolia*),[1] redwood (*Sequoia sempervirens*), white pine (*Pinus strobus*), ponderosa pine (*P. ponderosa*), and southern pines, represent an estimated 11 per cent of the world's total softwood forest area. Hardwood forests made up of species such as oak (*Quercus*), maple (*Acer*), birch (*Betula*), and gum (*Nyssa*) represent about 5 per cent of the total world area of hardwoods.

Forest Types

The present-day forests of the United States contain about 845 native tree species, including more than 165 commercial species, which occur in 18 major forest types. The variety of tree species in these forests is due to extremely varied conditions of climate, topography, and soils, conditions reflected, for example, in the semitropical hardwoods of the deep South, the forests of stunted pine and juniper over much of the arid West, the extensive forests of oak and hickory throughout most of the East, and the dense Douglas-fir and redwood forests on the West Coast.

About two thirds of the nation's forests are in the eastern United States. These are predominantly hardwood forests, except in the extreme South, where pines are abundant, and in the North where spruce (*Picea*), fir

[1] For sources of botanical nomenclature in this chapter see p. 182.

(Abies), and pine predominate. Even in the great southern pine region about half the timber is made up of hardwood species.

In the western United States the forests are largely comprised of softwoods, with very limited mixtures of hardwoods such as aspen *(Populus)*, alder *(Alnus)*, oak, and maple. Over large portions of the West, the forests occur only at the higher altitudes, and they are generally interspersed with treeless valleys and deserts, and with barren outcroppings of rock at the highest elevations.

The forests of the United States may be classified into a number of major types (Fig. 13), reflecting the prevalence of key species, as follows:

LONGLEAF-SLASH PINE AND LOBLOLLY-SHORTLEAF PINE. These two forest types, extending from New Jersey to Texas, are dominant in the famous southern pine region, which still supplies about one third of the timber cut and more than half of the pulpwood used by the pulp and paper industry in the United States.

In the southeastern portion of this great area the pine forests contain chiefly longleaf *(Pinus palustris)* and slash pine *(P. caribaea)*. These produce turpentine and rosin for the world's largest naval stores industry. They also provide the raw material for large pulp mills and thousands of sawmills. On dry, sandy sites longleaf pine usually dominates, and the stands are generally parklike in character, with a ground cover of coarse grasses and low shrubs. Loblolly *(Pinus taeda)* and pond pine *(P. serotina)* prevail in moister areas. Slash pine is common along the Gulf Coast; because of its rapid growth and high quality this is a favorite species in both public and industrial tree-planting programs. The dominant species of the inland pine forests are loblolly and shortleaf *(P. echinata)* pines, but here and there Virginia pine *(P. virginiana)* or pitch pine *(P. rigida)* is important.

Throughout the southern pine forests various hardwoods—red oak *(Quercus borealis* var. *maxima)*, white oak *(Q. alba)*, sweetgum *(Liquidambar styraciflua)*, yellow poplar *(Liriodendron tulipifera)*, and hickory *(Carya)*—are important elements and in many localities are more abundant than the pines. Along the slopes of the Appalachian Mountains southern red oak *(Q. falcata)* and chestnut oak *(Q. prinus)* are predominant, while in eastern Texas and Arkansas post oak *(Q. stellata)* and blackjack oak *(Q. marilandica)* are common species. In all, more than ten species of pines and a considerably larger number of hardwood species make up a variety of distinct local types in this region.

The composition and pattern of the southern pine types is a changing one, largely reflecting the activities of man. Thus, millions of acres of pine forest have grown up through natural reseeding of abandoned lands once farmed for cotton and other field crops. Over large areas formerly occupied by pine, on the other hand, hardwoods are encroaching as a result of increasing protection from fire and the general practice of cutting the preferred pines more heavily than the associated hardwoods.

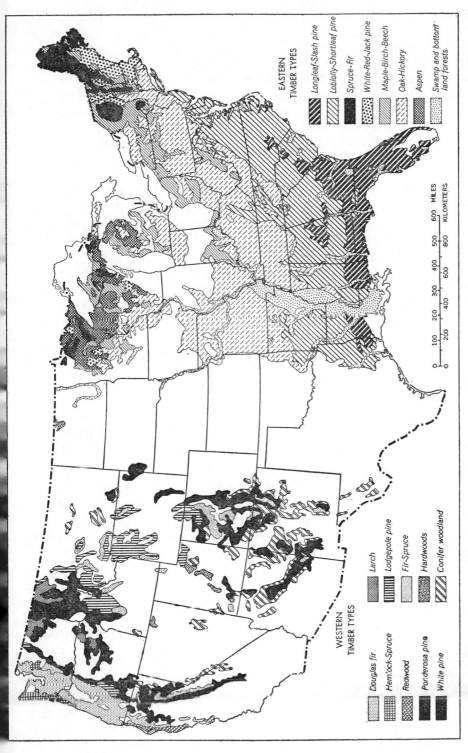

EASTERN TIMBER TYPES

Longleaf-Slash pine
Loblolly-Shortleaf pine
Spruce-Fir
White-Red-Jack pine
Maple-Birch-Beech
Oak-Hickory
Aspen
Swamp and bottom land forests.

WESTERN TIMBER TYPES

Douglas fir
Hemlock-Spruce
Redwood
Ponderosa pine
White pine
Larch
Lodgepole pine
Fir-Spruce
Hardwoods
Conifer woodland

FIG. 13. United States: major forest types. Areas not typed may have some commercial timber, usually covering less than 10 per cent of the land. Extensive areas of chaparral and other noncommercial forests not shown. Based on map "Areas Characterized by Major Forest Types in the United States," U.S. Department of Agriculture, Forest Service, 1949. From the National Survey of Forest Resources.

SWAMP AND BOTTOM-LAND HARDWOODS. In the bottom lands of the South there are dense hardwood forests made up of blackgum *(Nyssa sylvatica)*, swamp *(N. biflora)* and water tupelo *(N. uniflora)*, lowland oaks, red maple *(Acer rubrum)*, cottonwood *(Populus)*, sycamore *(Platanus occidentalis)*, cypress *(Taxodium)*, and a variety of other trees, shrubs, and vines. Along the more northerly rivers cottonwood, elm *(Ulmus)*, ash *(Fraxinus)*, and maple predominate. These bottom lands, which are periodically subjected to flooding, are generally productive forest sites. Bottom-land forests, particularly in the great Mississippi delta, contain a large part of the high-grade hardwood timber resources remaining in the United States.

In most of the river bottoms there are considerable variations in stand composition, reflecting minor differences in elevation and flooding. On low ridges, where soils are better drained and aerated, sweetgum, over-cup oak *(Quercus lyrata)*, water oak *(Q. nigra)*, hickory, black ash *(Fraxinus nigra)*, and various other species occur.

Swamp forests are found in sizable areas near the coast and along the sluggish streams of the Coastal Plain. Outstanding examples are in the Dismal Swamp, the Okefenokee Swamp, and along numerous bayous and sloughs of the lower Mississippi. Cypress and water tupelo often grow in pure stands in these forests.

Subtropical vegetation appears along the swamps and marshes in Florida and southern Texas, but in areas so small as to be of negligible commercial importance. Mangrove *(Rhizophora mangle)* is the most representative species in the stands, forming dense thickets extending for many miles along the coast in brackish waters. Royal palm *(Roystonea regia)* and thatch palm *(Thrinax)*, Florida yew *(Taxus floridana)*, wild fig *(Ficus)*, palmetto *(Sabal)*, buttonwood *(Laguncularia racemosa)*, seagrape *(Coccoloba uvifera)*, and blackwood are also common in these subtropical forests.

OAK-HICKORY. Forests characterized by various species of oaks and hickories form a broad belt across the eastern United States north of the southern pine region, extending from the Mississippi valley into New England. This hardwood forest belt was originally continuous and of great luxuriance, but a large part of it has been cleared for agriculture. The remaining forests consist chiefly of second-growth stands, including former croplands that have reverted to forest and extensive areas depleted by cutting, grazing, and repeated fires.

The oak-hickory forest is made up of many localized types and merges imperceptibly into the adjoining southern pine and northern hardwood types. In the Ozark region and adjacent lands of the Mississippi valley, white oak, black oak *(Q. velutina)*, and hickory are dominant species, with such common associates as black walnut *(Juglans nigra)*, American elm *(Ulmus americana)*, white ash *(Fraxinus americana)*, and post oaks. In the Appalachian mountain and plateau regions, chestnut oak, hickories, and yellow poplar *(Liriodendron tulipifera)* are usually the dominating species. A large number of other species, however, especially maple and pine, make up a considerable part of the forests. American chestnut (*Castanea dentata*) was formerly dominant in large parts of this area, but the chestnut blight has practically eliminated this useful tree.

MAPLE-BIRCH-BEECH. The northern hardwood type, characterized by maple, beech (*Fagus grandifolia*), and birch (*Betula*) occurs mainly throughout the Lake states and eastward through Pennsylvania, New York, and New England. Southern extensions of the type are also found on the upper slopes of the Appalachian Mountains. The maple-birch-beech type is one of widely varying combinations, often including a variety of other species such as eastern hemlock (*Tsuga canadensis*), spruce (*Picea*), balsam fir (*Abies balsamea*), eastern white pine, aspen, basswood (*Tilia*), and northern red oak. In many areas this type has taken over sites formerly occupied by such softwoods as pine and spruce.

ASPEN. Extensive areas of aspen and birch have developed in the Lake states, and to a lesser degree in the northeast, as a result of logging operations and repeated fires. Aspen is usually a short-lived species and ultimately may be largely displaced by other species, such as maple and balsam fir.

NORTHERN PINE. Eastern white pine, red pine (*Pinus resinosa*), and jack pine (*P. banksiana*), occurring either in mixtures or pure stands, are found on the drier sites throughout the Northeast and the Lake states. Vast areas of virgin eastern white- and red-pine forests throughout the "north woods" of these regions have been the backbone of the great softwood lumber industry since colonial times, but as a result of logging and fire only remnant areas of these once magnificent forests remain today; throughout the range of these species, most pine sites have been taken over by aspen, birch, or other northern hardwoods. On sandy soils in the Lake states grow extensive areas of jack pine, a useful pulp species.

FIR-SPRUCE FORESTS OF THE EAST. The fir-spruce forests of the Northeast and the Lake states regions are an extension of the great belt of subarctic forests that covers much of Canada. Small areas of fir-spruce are also found at high elevations in the Appalachian Mountains.

On low lying, poorly drained sites, where the soil is a muck or a peat, this type is made up of black spruce (*Picea mariana*), balsam fir, northern white cedar (*Chamaecyparis thyoides*), and tamarack (*Larix laricina*). On the better drained uplands it consists of a combination of red spruce (*Picea rubens*), balsam fir, eastern hemlock, birch, and maple. Both spruce and fir are preferred pulping species and utilization of forests of this type is in general more intensive than that of the intermingled northern hardwood types.

FIR-SPRUCE FORESTS OF THE WEST. The fir-spruce forests of the West are high-altitude forests, occurring in scattered localities in the Rocky Mountains at elevations up to 11,500 feet and in limited areas in the Cascade Mountains of Oregon and Washington. These forests are composed mainly of Engelmann spruce (*Picea engelmanni*), Colorado blue spruce (*Picea pungens*), true firs (*Abies*), and mountain hemlock (*Tsuga mertensiana*). In the central Rocky Mountains, from 7,500 feet to timber line, Engelmann spruce and alpine fir (*Abies lasiocarpa*) predominate. In the northern Rocky Mountains of Idaho and western Montana, the Engelmann spruce descends to lower levels, and alpine fir in pure stands or mixed with mountain hemlock forms the higher-altitude stands.

Bristlecone pine (*Pinus aristata*) and whitebark pine (*P. albicaulis*) are common in the western fir-spruce forests, often occupying the most exposed and rocky ridges just below timber line. Although commercial use of the fir-spruce forests of the West has so far been limited, they are of great importance for watershed protection and for recreation.

WESTERN WHITE PINE AND LARCH. Western white pine (*P. monticola*) occurs in commercial stands confined almost entirely to northern Idaho. Occupying the moister sites below the zone of Engelmann spruce, it is usually associated with western red cedar (*Thuya plicata*), western hemlock (*Tsuga heterophylla*), and grand fir (*Abies grandis*). It usually is not a climax type, but tends to pass by stages into the western-red-cedar and western-hemlock types. Western white pine is an outstanding commercial species, and a large lumber industry has been based upon it. The future of the species is threatened, however, by the white-pine blister rust, which has reached serious proportions locally.

Bordering upon the western-white-pine type and frequently intermingled with it are extensive forests of western larch (*Larix occidentalis*) and Douglas fir (*Pseudotsuga taxifolia*). Western larch frequently acts as a pioneer species in the development of western white pine, occupying the ground soon after fire or logging. To date, cutting of western larch or Douglas fir in the Rocky Mountains has been somewhat limited, although potentially both species are of considerable commercial importance.

DOUGLAS FIR. The Rocky Mountain form of Douglas fir is found with the western larch type, as just mentioned, and also in other scattered areas throughout the Rocky Mountains. But it is in western Oregon and Washington that Douglas fir attains its greatest size and value in the world-famous forests of the Pacific Northwest. Although often found in in this region in nearly pure stands, it appears even more frequently in mixtures with western hemlock, western red cedar, and true firs. In California, Douglas fir occurs mixed with redwood (*Sequoia sempervirens*) in some areas and with ponderosa pine (*Pinus ponderosa*), sugar pine (*P. lambertiana*), true firs, and incense cedar (*Libocedrus decurrens*) in others.

The Douglas-fir forests of the Pacific coast are in an almost ideal area for forest growth. Long growing seasons, heavy precipitation, and suitable soils produce rapid growth and dense stands, which presently and potentially are among the economically most important forests in the

United States. The Douglas-fir region of Washington and Oregon, comprising only 26 million acres of commercial forest land, contains nearly 31 per cent of the remaining saw timber in the United States and provides about one fourth of the total saw timber cut.

HEMLOCK-SPRUCE. Closely associated with the Douglas-fir forests in Oregon and Washington is the hemlock-spruce type, in which western hemlock, or Sitka spruce (*Picea sitchensis*), or both together predominate. This type is found mainly in the fog belt along the Pacific coast and in small areas in the Cascade Mountains. The type is of commercial importance as a source of pulpwood and lumber, and yields limited amounts of exceptionally high-grade spruce.

REDWOOD. Among the more famous forests of the country are the redwoods of northwestern California. This type occupies a narrow belt about 400 miles in length and averaging about 20 miles in width. On fog drenched flats and river bottoms it forms pure stands, often with more than a million board feet per acre—the heaviest stands of timber in the world. Mixtures of redwood with Douglas fir, white fir (*Abies concolor*), tanoak (*Lithocarpus densiflora*), madroña (*Arbutus menziesii*), and alder are common. Southward, redwood is limited to well-watered sites within reach of ocean fogs, usually as stringers along narrow canyons. Climatically the redwood belt is one of frequent fog and extended periods of rain. The redwood forests sustain an important lumber industry and a growing plywood industry based largely upon the intermixed Douglas fir.

PONDEROSA PINE. Ponderosa pine is the most extensive western type, occurring throughout the Sierra Nevada Mountains in California, east of the Cascades in Oregon and Washington, and at intermediate altitudes through the Rocky Mountains. In California ponderosa pine is often intermixed with a number of other important species. Sugar pine is an important and valuable component of the type in many areas. Mixtures of pine, Douglas fir, true firs, incense cedar, and California black oak (*Quercus kelloggii*) are also characteristic of this area, where scattered groves of giant sequoia (*Sequoiadendron gigantea*), the oldest and largest of the world's living trees, are also found. In most other parts of its range, ponderosa pine occurs in somewhat purer stands than it does in California.

Ponderosa pine is in general the most drought-resistant of the western commercial timber types. Rainfall in the pine belt is sparse—20 to 30 inches annually—with fairly short growing seasons and large seasonal fluctuations in temperature. The pine forests are usually fairly open, and the herbaceous vegetation and browse plants that occur as an understory and in nontimbered patches and meadows constitute an important grazing resource. Ponderosa pine is the third most important commercial tree in the United States from the standpoint of lumber production, being exceeded in importance only by Douglas fir and southern pine.

LODGEPOLE PINE. Lodgepole pine (*Pinus contorta*) is common at all middle altitudes in the Rocky Mountain region and in limited parts of the Cascades in Oregon and Washington. The stands are characteristically pure, reflecting a tendency to seed-in heavily after fires. Owing to its inaccessibility and relatively small size, lodgepole pine is of limited commercial use.

HARDWOODS AND CONIFER WOODLANDS. In addition to the principal commercial timber types described above, large tracts in the western states are covered with other types of hardwood or coniferous woodland. Some local areas of aspen, cottonwood, and alder have been classified as commercial, but generally they are of limited importance for timber production, although their value for watershed protection and grazing is often substantial. Piñon pine (*Pinus cembroides*) and juniper constitute the most extensive of these types at lower altitudes throughout the western interior, merging with ponderosa pine at higher altitudes and with sagebrush (*Artemisia tridentata*) at lower. These open forests are extensively grazed by livestock.

Chaparral, or forest of stunted hardwood trees and shrubs, occurs most typically in southern California and at certain places in the Rocky Mountain area. In it more than 100 different tree and shrub species are found, including Gambel oak (*Q. gambeli*), mountain mahogany (*Cercocarpus*), manzanita (*Arctostaphylos*), and chamise (*Adenostoma*). Although of practically no commercial importance, these forests are extremely valuable for the protection of watersheds.

Classes of Forest Land

The forests of the United States cover about 622 million acres, or 32.7 per cent of the land area of the continental United States. About three fourths of the forest area, or nearly 460 million acres, is classified as "commercial" forest land, capable of producing timber of commercial quantity and quality, and available now or prospectively for commercial timber use (Table 8–I).

TABLE 8–I

UNITED STATES: FOREST LAND AREAS BY CLASS OF LAND, 1945 [a]

(In Thousand Acres)

Region	Total Forest Land	Commercial Forest Land [b]	Noncommercial Forest Land	
			Reserved for Parks, Etc.	Unproductive
North	175,473	166,282	4,239	4,952
South	220,661	185,184	1,296	34,181
West	225,933	108,075	6,968	110,890
TOTAL ..	622,067	459,541	12,503	150,023

[a] Source: Forest Service, U.S. Department of Agriculture.

[b] Land capable of producing timber of commercial quantity and quality, and available now or prospectively for commercial use.

The remaining 162 million acres, "noncommercial" forest land, include about 12.5 million acres of timberlands withdrawn from commercial timber use and reserved for parks, game reserves, etc., plus some 150 million acres of unproductive or inaccessible lands incapable of economic timber production. These noncommercial forests are largely made up of high alpine forests and certain other woodlands at lower elevations in the western United States. Although commercially unproductive for timber, many of these forests are valuable for watershed protection, recreation, and livestock grazing.

Character of Forest Cover

When the first white settlers came to this country, an area of more than 900 million acres was covered with virgin forest in what is now the continental United States. Clearing for farms and cities, cutting for timber products, and uncontrolled fires have reduced the forest cover to only about two thirds of the original area. Moreover, these remaining areas of forest have been drastically changed in character.

About 44 million acres of forest—or less than 10 per cent of the total commercial forest area—were classed as old-growth saw timber in 1945 (Table 8-II and Fig. 14). These virgin stands were located almost entirely in the West, where they still cover more than a third of the commercial forest land. Although these remnant old-growth stands are for the most part of lower quality than the virgin stands that had previously been cut, they still represent a heavy concentration of valuable timber.

TABLE 8-II

UNITED STATES: CHARACTER OF FOREST COVER ON COMMERCIAL FOREST LANDS BY REGION, 1945 [a]

(In Thousand Acres)

Region	Total	Old-Growth Saw Timber [b]	Young-Growth Saw Timber [b]	Pole Timber, Seedlings, and Saplings	Poorly Stocked and Denuded
North	166,282	2,159	46,890	88,401	28,832
South	185,184	767	90,334	59,609	34,474
West	108,075	41,381	17,373	37,865	11,456
TOTAL .	459,541	44,307	154,597	185,875	74,762

[a] Source: Forest Service, U.S. Department of Agriculture.
[b] Includes areas characterized by timber large enough for saw logs (lumber) and in sufficient volume per acre for economic operation.

Second-growth saw-timber stands cover about 155 million acres, or about a third of the total commercial forest area. Nearly 90 per cent of these stands are in the East. In most of them individual trees are relatively small and the volume per acre is low. In the South, for example, second-growth stands average only about 3,700 board feet per acre.

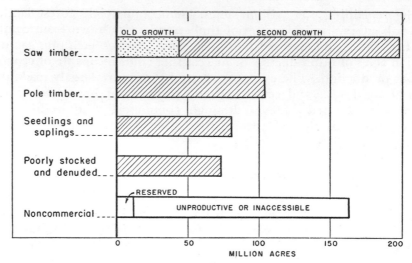

FIG. 14. United States: forest land areas by character of forest. Source for this diagram and Figs. 15-20, 22, and 23, U.S. Department of Agriculture, Forest Service, National Survey of Forest Resources, Reports, 1946-1950.

Areas supporting pole-timber trees, seedlings, and saplings totaled about 186 million acres in 1945, or 40 per cent of the commercial forest area. Additional poorly stocked and denuded lands aggregated about 75 million acres, or 16 per cent of the commercial forest area, most of it in the East.

Timber Volumes

Timber volumes on commercial forest lands in the United States, including all trees 5 inches or larger in diameter at breast height, totaled about 469 billion cubic feet in 1945 (Table 8–III). Roughly two thirds of this was in trees of saw-timber size, i.e., of sufficient size and quality

TABLE 8–III

UNITED STATES: VOLUME OF TIMBER ON COMMERCIAL FOREST LANDS, 1945 [a]

Region	All Timber [b]			Saw Timber [c]		
	Total	Softwood	Hardwood	Total	Softwood	Hardwood
	Million cubic feet			*Million board feet*		
North	101,379	25,542	75,837	233,159	68,259	164,900
South	127,728	59,161	68,567	340,287	195,842	144,445
West	239,901	236,283	3,618	1,043,276	1,036,847	6,429
TOTAL .	469,008	320,986	148,022	1,616,722	1,300,948	315,774

[a] Source: Forest Service, U.S. Department of Agriculture.
[b] Sound trees above 5.0 inches d.b.h. to a minimum top diameter of 4.0 inches inside bark.
[c] Trees suitable for conversion into lumber.

for manufacture into lumber. The balance was in trees of pole-timber size. Softwood species, located chiefly in the West, made up about two thirds of the total timber volume. The remaining third consisted of a wide variety of hardwood species, almost all in the East.

The volume of saw timber originally standing in the forests of the United States probably exceeded 8,000 billion board feet, but in 1945 it was estimated that they contained only 1,617 billion board feet (Table 8–III), half of it in old-growth stands in the West and the other half in second-growth stands.

Saw-timber stands in the United States are unequally distributed. The West, with less than one fourth of the total commercial forest land, has about two thirds of the total saw timber. Somewhat more than half of the total saw-timber volume is concentrated on 14 per cent of the nation's commercial forest land in the states of Washington, Oregon, and California. The East has three fourths of the commercial forest land, but only about a third of the total saw timber.

Douglas fir is the most abundant saw-timber species in the United States, accounting for more than one fourth of the total volume (Fig. 15).

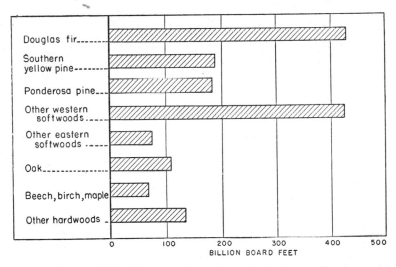

Fig. 15. United States: volume of saw timber by species.

Other western species, chiefly ponderosa pine, the true firs, western hemlock, sugar and white pine, redwood, spruce, larch, and lodgepole pine, together make up nearly 40 per cent of all saw timber in the United States. Shortleaf pine is the most important Eastern species, comprising about 12 per cent of the nation's volume of saw timber. Oaks constitute the predominant hardwood species, with about 7 per cent, and other hardwoods make up about 12 per cent of the total saw-timber volume.

The quality as well as the volume of the timber resources in the United States has been declining steadily, owing to the general practice of cutting the best and the largest trees and the preferred species, and to inadequate protection from fire and other destructive agents. Such reduction in quality began during Colonial times, with the culling of eastern forests for white-pine ship masts and oak ship timbers. Even today the lumber, pulp and paper, and other forest industries generally cut the better species and better quality trees. In the East, inferior hardwoods have consequently been encroaching on the more valuable softwood stands. Wood-using plants have been compelled to use smaller and smaller logs, with consequent lower productivity. Users of quality products, such as tight cooperage and ship timbers, are faced by increasingly serious raw-material supply problems. In all regions and industries it has become more and more difficult to procure quality timber.

A portion of the standing timber resources in the United States is not currently available for use because it is of low quality, scattered in small blocks, or in inaccessible locations. Much of the remaining old-growth timber in the West cannot be reached without construction of access roads to open up the "back country," particularly in the National Forests.

Timber Growth and Drain

The annual growth of all trees 5 inches or more in diameter was estimated at 13.4 billion cubic feet in 1944 (Table 8–IV). This was only slightly below an estimated rate of drain aggregating 13.7 billion cubic feet.

TABLE 8–IV

UNITED STATES: ANNUAL GROWTH OF TIMBER ON COMMERCIAL FOREST LANDS, 1944 [a]

Region	All Timber			Saw Timber		
	Total	Softwoods	Hardwoods	Total	Softwoods	Hardwoods
	Million cubic feet			*Million board feet*		
North	4,643	972	3,671	8,318	1,992	6,326
South	6,397	3,522	2,875	19,949	12,923	7,026
West	2,330	2,262	68	7,034	6,933	101
TOTAL .	13,370	6,756	6,614	35,301	21,848	13,453

[a] Source: Forest Service, U.S. Department of Agriculture.

Although total growth and drain were thus nearly in balance, there was a 21 per cent deficit in the more important softwoods and a 17 per cent surplus of hardwood growth (Fig. 16). Moreover, there was a pronounced deficit of quality timber; about 80 per cent of the total drain was in saw-timber trees, principally softwoods of relatively large size, but most of the growth was in small and low-grade trees, including many inferior hardwoods.

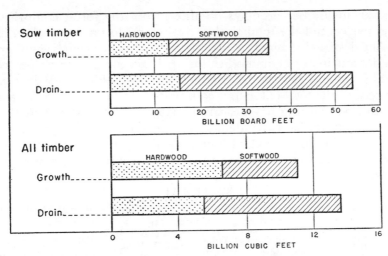

F<small>IG</small>. 16. United States: annual drain of saw timber and of all timber on commercial forest lands, 1945.

Saw-timber growth is estimated at 35.3 billion board feet for 1944. Saw-timber drain, however, totaled 53.9 billion board feet, or more than 50 per cent over growth (Table 8–V and Fig. 16). This represented a net depletion of more than 1 per cent of the nation's growing stock of saw timber. Since most forest products are cut from trees of saw-timber size, the deficit in saw-timber growth is of great significance.

TABLE 8–V

U<small>NITED</small> S<small>TATES</small>: A<small>NNUAL</small> G<small>ROWTH</small> <small>AND</small> D<small>RAIN</small> <small>OF</small> S<small>AW</small> T<small>IMBER</small>, 1944 [a]

(In Million Board Feet)

Region	Total			Softwoods			Hardwoods		
	Growth	Drain	Deficit	Growth	Drain	Deficit	Growth	Drain	Surplus or Deficit
North	8,318	9,004	— 686	1,992	2,986	— 994	6,326	6,018	+ 308
South	19,949	24,902	— 4,953	12,923	15,639	— 2,716	7,026	9,263	—2,237
West	7,034	19,987	—12,953	6,933	19,905	—12,972	101	82	+ 19
T<small>OTAL</small>	35,301	53,893	—18,592	21,848	38,530	—16,682	13,453	15,363	—1,910

[a] Source: Forest Service, U.S. Department of Agriculture.

The 1944 rates of timber growth were considerably below the levels deemed necessary to meet future requirements for timber products in the United States. The U.S. Forest Service has estimated that, to meet these future requirements, the United States would have to grow at least 18 billion cubic feet of timber annually, including about 72 billion board feet of saw timber.

The various timber products obtained from the forest comprise more than 90 per cent of the total timber drain, and losses due to fire, insects, and other destructive agents a little less than 10 per cent. Lumber is by far the largest item of commodity drain; it accounted for 74 per cent of the total volume of saw-timber products cut from U.S. forests in 1950 and 63 per cent of the total cubic-foot commodity drain (Table 8–VI and Fig. 17). Pulpwood cutting has steadily increased in importance as the pulp and paper industry has expanded, and in 1950 made up 14 per cent of the cubic-foot drain. Fuel wood, although declining in importance, made up 11 per cent, and the remaining 12 per cent represented a wide variety of items.

TABLE 8–VI

UNITED STATES: PRODUCTION OF TIMBER PRODUCTS AND ASSOCIATED DRAIN ON FORESTS, 1950 [a]

Product	Unit of Measure	Volume Cut	Roundwood Volume Cut	Drain [c]	
				All Timber	Saw Timber
		Million units [b]	*Million cubic feet*		*Million board feet*
Lumber	Board feet	37,950	5,313	7,590	38,863
Pulpwood	Cords	21	1,556	1,656	5,586
Veneer logs	Board feet	2,730	355	546	2,795
Fuel wood	Cords	60	1,332	1,332	2,220
Cooperage	Board feet	690	103	163	811
Mine timbers	Cubic feet	100	100	100	140
Hewn ties	Pieces	12	72	130	588
Poles	Pieces	7	89	93	327
Piling	Linear feet	32	22	24	96
Posts	Pieces	230	166	184	184
Miscellaneous	Cubic feet	250	250	275	600
TOTAL OF ALL PRODUCTS		–	9,358	12,093	52,210

[a] Source: Forest Service, U.S. Department of Agriculture.
[b] Not including 3 billion board feet of net lumber imports and nearly 12 million cords equivalent of imported pulpwood, wood pulp, and paper.
[c] Net volume of live timber cut on commercial forest lands, including logging residues.

A considerable part of the wood cut or destroyed in logging operations is not converted into usable products. Unutilized logging residues amounted to 2.9 billion cubic feet in 1944, with an additional 0.2 billion cubic feet used for fuel. Logging residues were especially concentrated in the Douglas-fir region of the Pacific Northwest, but more than half the total residues in 1944 were widely scattered throughout the eastern United States, mainly in the form of hardwood tops and defective logs. Although progress has since been made in reducing residues by more efficient wood utilization, tremendous quantities of wood residues are still available for use. Additional unused plant residues at manufacturing plants, such as sawmills and furniture and other manufacturing plants, amounted to 1.1 billion cubic feet in 1944, with an additional 1.8 billion cubic feet used for fuel. Unutilized residues of all kinds represented about 33 per cent of the total wood cut in the United States in 1944. An additional 1.6 per cent was used for fuel. Thus only 51 per cent of the total drain appeared in manufactured products.

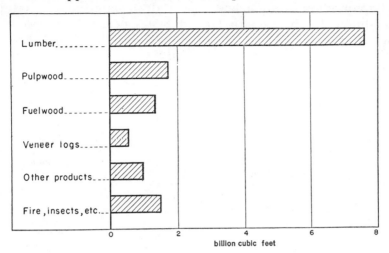

FIG. 17. United States: drain of timber from commercial forest lands, by products and destructive agents, 1950.

Losses due to destructive agents were estimated at about 1.5 billion cubic feet annually during the decade ending in 1944, with insects and disease accounting for most of this loss of timber of merchantable size. Conspicuous examples of serious diseases which have caused heavy losses in U.S. forests are the chestnut blight and the white-pine blister rust. Important insect enemies of the forest include the bark beetles which attack the important softwood species of the West and South, the hemlock looper, and the spruce budworm. Fire losses totaled nearly 0.5 billion cubic feet of timber annually in the decade ending in 1944. Moreover, in addition to these direct losses of timber, fire also destroys millions of trees of less than 5 inches in diameter and thus reduces future timber production. By impairing soil fertility fires have also lowered timber growth rates over extensive areas.

Ownership of Forest Land and Timber

The early land policy of the United States was to convert the public domain to private ownership. This policy continued until about the beginning of the twentieth century, when concern for future water and timber supplies led to the reservation of lands for National Forests and to basic changes in other land policies. Since the Weeks Law of 1911, federal purchases and land exchanges have added to the National Forest areas proclaimed from the public domain. In addition, millions of acres of forest land have reverted to states and counties for nonpayment of taxes, particularly during the depression years of the 1930's.

In 1945 about three fourths of all commercial forest land was in private ownership (Table 8–VII and Fig. 18), about 19 per cent under federal ownership or administration, and 6 per cent in state, county, and municipal holdings. In the western United States nearly 60 per cent of all commercial forest land is still owned by the federal government and administered chiefly as National Forests. In the East, only 7 per cent is federally owned.

TABLE 8–VII

UNITED STATES: OWNERSHIP OF COMMERCIAL FOREST LAND, 1945 [a]

(In Thousand Acres)

Region	All Ownerships	Federally Owned or Managed			State, County, and Municipal	Private
		Total	National Forest	Other		
North	166,282	11,143	9,451	1,692	19,471	135,668
South	185,184	14,227	10,177	4,050	2,209	168,748
West	108,075	63,783	53,866	9,917	5,543	38,749
TOTAL	459,541	89,153	73,494	15,659	27,223	343,165

[a] Source: Forest Service, U.S. Department of Agriculture.

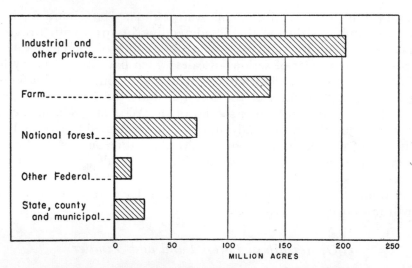

FIG. 18. United States: ownership of commercial forest land.

Private forest lands are characteristically held by small owners. In 1945 about three fourths of all the private forest land was in holdings of less than 5,000 acres, with more than half of the area in farm woodlands. Most of the rest was held by absentee owners. Medium and large-size holdings of 5 to 50 thousand acres made up 10 per cent of the private commercial forest lands, and larger holdings 15 per cent. Altogether there are more than four million owners of commercial forest land in the United States.

In 1944 lumber and pulp companies owned roughly 51 million acres. Although pulp companies have since acquired considerable forest land—chiefly from other large private holdings—lumber and pulp companies still control only about 13 per cent of the nation's commercial forest land, compared with 30 per cent in farms and 57 per cent in all other holdings. Thus these principal forest industries depend primarily on other private and public holdings for the bulk of their raw-material supplies.

Private owners held about 57 per cent of the total saw-timber volume in 1945. One fourth of the private saw timber was on farms, mainly in the East; the rest was in industrial and other private holdings.

Although federal lands made up only 19 per cent of the total acreage of commercial forest land in 1945, these lands support about 39 per cent of the total saw-timber stand. Most of this timber is in the National Forests, mainly in the West. Timber in state and local public holdings amounts to about 4 per cent of the total saw-timber stand.

Management of Forest Lands

Poor timber-cutting practices and inadequate protection against fire and other destructive agents are the primary reasons why timber growth in the United States is far below the productive capacity of the land. In 1944, for example, cutting practices were classed as "good" or better on only 8 per cent of the private forest land; on 28 per cent cutting was classed as "fair" and on 64 per cent as "poor" or "destructive." [2] Cutting practices were generally better on public holdings.

The character of cutting varied greatly, depending on the size of the property. Large private owners managed their land much better than did the small owners who hold the bulk of the private forest land. Relatively good cutting practices were found on pulp-company and large lumber-company holdings.

Considerable progress has been made in protecting the forests from fire and to a lesser extent from insects and diseases. During the past forty years fire protection has been extended to most public lands and to

[2] "Good" cutting requires that the cut be made in accordance with the demands of good silviculture and that the land be left in possession of desirable species in condition for vigorous growth in the immediate future. "Fair" cutting means cutting practices which will maintain on the land any reasonable stock of growing timber in species that are desirable and marketable. "Poor" cutting leaves the land with a limited means for natural reproduction, often in the form of remnant seed trees on broad areas otherwise clear-cut of all merchantable timber. In second-growth forests, poor cutting robs the stand of minimum-size merchantable trees in stages of rapid growth. Such cutting often causes deterioration of species with consequent reduction in both quality and quantity of forest growth. "Destructive" cutting leaves the land without timber values and without means for natural reproduction.

about 85 per cent of the private and state forest lands requiring it. The use of plows, tractors, and other mechanical equipment for fire fighting is steadily increasing.

Some 66 million acres of forest land, chiefly in the southern United States, were still without organized fire protection at the end of 1950. More intensive fire protection is also needed on a large part of the privately owned forest land.

Forest Products and Uses

Although use of the forest resources for timber products is of major importance, other functions of forest lands—notably for watersheds, recreation, wildlife, and grazing of livestock—are also of great significance.

FOREST PRODUCTS

The timber industries of the United States are among its leading manufacturing industries and form a major segment of the world's forest economy. The United States produces and consumes more wood products than does any other nation: more than half of the pulp and paper and about 40 per cent of the lumber produced in the entire world are consumed in the United States.

Manufacturing plants using wood as a principal raw material employ about 8 per cent of all manufacturing employees in the United States and account for about 6 per cent of the total value added by manufacture. Timber industries give direct employment to more than one million workers in the United States and pay out more than two billion dollars in annual wages. A far-flung logging industry, tens of thousands of wood-using plants, thousands of wholesale and retail establishments, transportation systems, and a large segment of the construction industry all depend upon timber.

LUMBER. Since Colonial days the forests of the United States have been important sources of lumber, as well as of fuel wood, cooperage, naval stores, and numerous other forest products. By 1799 lumber production had reached 300 million board feet annually, cut largely from the forests of New England. During the nineteenth century the center of lumber production gradually shifted from New England to the Lake states, which by 1869 accounted for 28 per cent of the total cut of 12.8 billion board feet. With rapid depletion of timber in the Lake states region, the center of the industry then shifted to the southern United States, reaching a peak there about 1909. Subsequently the center of lumber production shifted to the last great reservoir of virgin timber, the West. In 1950 western forests supplied 49 per cent of the total production of lumber, compared with 38 per cent in the South and 13 per cent in the North.

Total annual lumber production in the United States increased steadily to a peak of about 46 billion board feet in 1906 and 1907. Thereafter the trend was downward, reaching a depression low of about 13.5 billion board feet in 1932. Production during the 1940's, however, recovered to an average of about 35 billion board feet per year (Fig. 19).

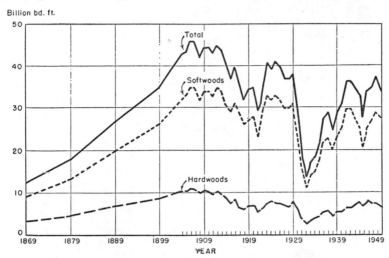

FIG. 19. United States: lumber production, 1869-1949.

Softwoods have made up about 80 per cent of the total production of lumber in the United States (Fig. 19). Southern yellow pine for a long time was the most important softwood cut (Fig. 20), with production averaging about 9 billion board feet annually during the last decade. Production of Douglas-fir lumber has steadily increased, however, and by 1950 was first in importance, with an annual production of about 10 billion board feet. Production of ponderosa-pine lumber also increased to about 4 billion board feet annually.

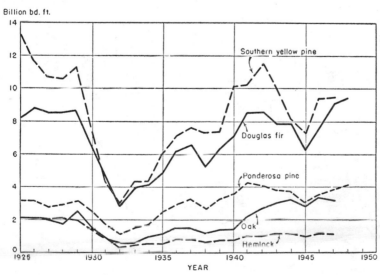

FIG. 20. United States: lumber production by species, 1925-1948.

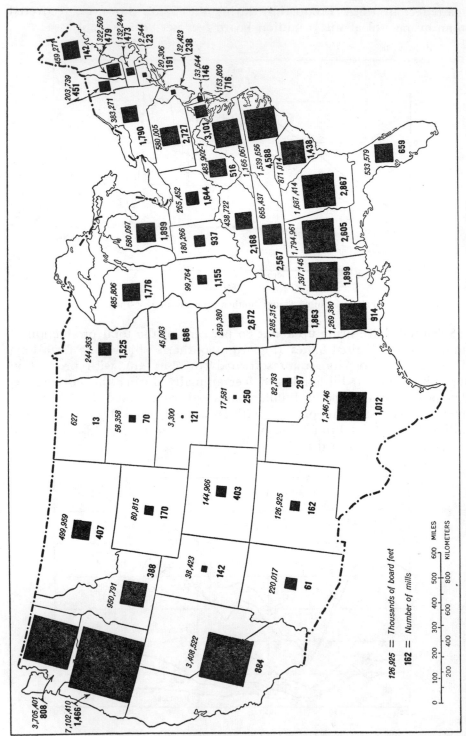

FIG. 21. United States: lumber production by states, 1947. Source: U.S. Census of Manufacturers, 1947.

126,925 = *Thousands of board feet*

162 = *Number of mills*

Among the hardwoods, various species of oaks have been of chief importance, accounting for about 45 per cent of the total hardwood lumber produced in 1950. Other important hardwood species cut for lumber include red gum (sweet gum), yellow poplar, maple, tupelo, cottonwood, beech, elm, birch, basswood, and ash.

Although widely dispersed throughout the United States, the lumber industry is centered principally in the three Pacific Coast states and in the South (Fig. 21).

There are more than 60,000 sawmills in the United States, varying in size from small plants producing a few hundred feet of lumber a day to enormous installations turning out over a million board feet a day. About 90 per cent of the active mills, comprising mainly small portable outfits, are located in the East. Lumber production, however, is concentrated in a relatively small number of plants, located chiefly in the West. Here, for example, in 1947, 1,104 mills (about 2 per cent of all active mills), each cutting more than 5 million board feet annually, accounted for 49 per cent of the total lumber produced. About 34 per cent of the active mills in 1947 produced about 93 per cent of the total lumber cut.

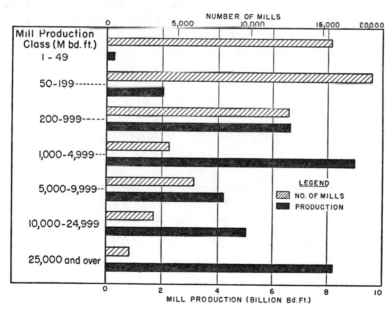

FIG. 22. United States: number of sawmills and annual production by mill-production classes, 1947.

The liquidation of large private timber holdings has brought about a steady decline in the number of large sawmills in the United States. Scattered tracts of timber in the East, chiefly second growth, provide the raw material for increasing numbers of the small portable sawmills that more and more characterize the lumber industry. Many of these small mills waste timber, owing to poor or inadequate equipment and inability to utilize slabs and other mill waste. Most small operators have little interest in the timber tracts that they purchase for liquidation; hence their cutting practices are generally poor. In the older forest regions the problem of maintaining large and efficient sawmills is complicated by shortages of suitable timber, by the typical pattern of intermingled small ownership, and by strong competition from other wood-using industries, particularly the pulp and paper industry.

Mechanization of production has been of considerable importance in the lumber industry, particularly in logging operations. By 1950, more than half of the logs produced were skidded from the forest with tractors, and about one fifth of the total by cable operations; only about a quarter of the saw logs produced were skidded with animals. Chain saws have largely replaced hand saws: in 1950 about 70 per cent of the saw logs cut in the United States were felled and bucked with power saws. Furthermore, truck hauling of saw logs from woods to plants has largely displaced railroads: in 1950 about 63 per cent of the saw logs produced were handled by truck and only 31 per cent by rail, with a small amount moved by water.

Lumber Imports and Exports. Lumber has always been an important element in the foreign trade of the United States, and in the late 1920's, lumber exports exceeded 3 billion board feet a year. The depression of the 1930's, however, and large domestic demands during World War II have caused exports to drop to less than one billion board feet annually (Fig. 23), while during the past twenty years lumber imports have increased and now exceed exports by a substantial margin.

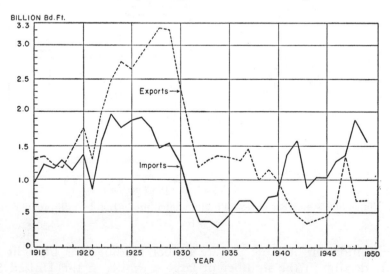

FIG. 23. United States: exports and imports of lumber, 1915-1949.

Most of the lumber exports from the United States have been softwoods, including spruce, southern yellow pine, Douglas fir, and western hemlock, but oak and other hardwood lumber have also been important, particularly in the markets of the United Kingdom and other European countries.

Softwoods, derived largely from Canada and Mexico, have made up most of the lumber imported into the United States. The chief hardwood imports have been fine cabinet woods from tropical areas such as the Philippines, West Africa, and Latin America.

Lumber Consumption. Consumption of lumber in the United States during the postwar years has averaged about 36 billion board feet a year. In 1950 about 42 per cent of the total lumber used entered into urban residential construction, 12 per cent into farm construction, and 21 per cent into construction of factories, commercial structures, etc.– a total of 75 per cent for all construction uses. The importance of lumber in residential construction is indicated by the fact that 82 per cent of the residential structures in use in 1940 were built of wood.

Lumber used for shipping purposes (e.g., for boxes and crates, dunnage and car blocking, pallets, and reels) amounted to about 6.4 billion board feet in 1950, or roughly 15 per cent of the total lumber used. During World War II, however, annual lumber requirements for such purposes reached a peak of more than 14 billion board feet.

The third major use of lumber is for factory products such as furniture and fixtures, agricultural implements, and vehicles. Total consumption of lumber for this purpose in 1950 amounted to about 3.8 billion board feet, or about 10 per cent of the total lumber used. Hardwoods supply most of the lumber required for factory products, while softwoods are mainly used in construction and shipping.

PULP AND PAPER. Among the wood-using industries in the United States next in importance to that of lumber is the large and rapidly expanding pulp and paper industry. Pulpwood produced from U.S. forests in 1950 amounted to 1,600 million cubic feet (Table 8–VI) and accounted for about 14 per cent of the total commodity drain. Total pulpwood consumption in 1950 was about 3,000 million cubic feet, of which about 230 million came from Canadian timberlands and the balance from domestic production and stocks. In addition, the United States pulp and paper industry imported the equivalent of about 10 million cords of wood in the form of wood pulp, newsprint, and other paper.

During the past three decades production of wood pulp, paper, and board in the United States has increased roughly fourfold (Fig. 24). In 1950 approximately 29 million tons of paper and paperboard were consumed, including about 24.4 million tons from U.S. mills and 4.6 million from foreign mills, chiefly Canadian.

Consumption of wood pulp in 1950 totaled 17.1 million tons, of which about 14.9 million were derived from U.S. plants and 2.2 million from Canadian and Scandinavian mills. About 0.6 million tons of this pulp was used in the production of rayon, cellophane, and plastics. The remaining 16.5 million tons of wood pulp, together with 8 million of waste paper and 1.4 million of other fibers, were used by U.S. mills in producing paper and board.

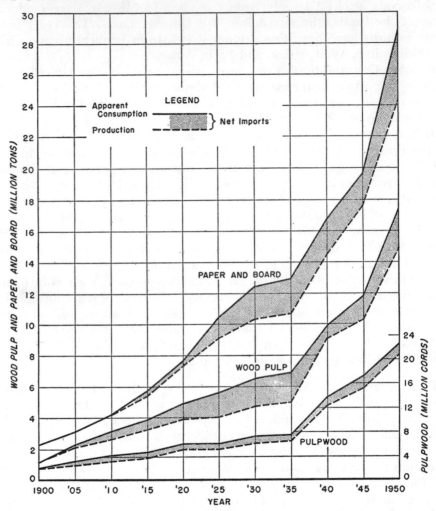

FIG. 24. United States: production and apparent consumption of pulpwood, wood pulp, and paper and board, 1900-1950. Data from U.S. Depts. of Commerce and Agriculture. Compiled by Division of Forest Economics, U.S. Forest Service, 1952.

There were more than 300 wood-pulp mills in the United States in 1952, with a total capacity of 51,400 tons of wood pulp per day (Fig. 25). Sixty-five mills producing sulfate or kraft pulp had about half the total capacity of the U.S. pulp industry, 67 sulfite mills had 18 per cent of the total, and 94 groundwood mills 17 per cent. The remaining 16 per cent was in 25 semichemical plants, 19 soda mills, and 36 plants producing defibrated and other miscellaneous forms of wood pulp.

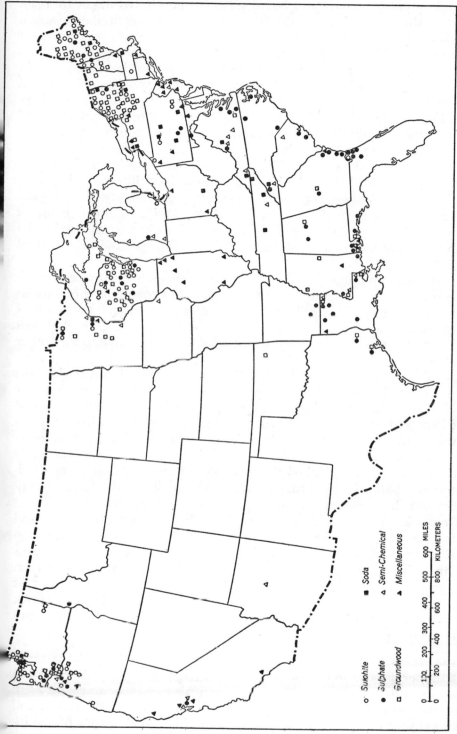

FIG. 25. United States: distribution of wood-pulp mills. Compiled by Division of Forest Economics, U. S. Forest Service, from Lockwood's *Directory of the Paper and Allied Trades*, 1952, and other sources.

There were 665 paper and board mills in the United States in 1947. Most of these were integrated with pulp mills, although there were a number of nonintegrated mills which depended upon purchases of domestic or imported wood pulp and other fibrous materials.

The pulp and paper industry in the United States developed first in New England, which had the advantages of ample supplies of preferred species, such as spruce and fir, abundant water, and proximity to markets. The industry in this region consists mainly of sulfite and groundwood mills. Subsequently the industry expanded to the Lake states, where it drew upon timber resources similar to those in the Northeast, and somewhat later it spread to the Pacific coast, where western hemlock, spruce, and true firs provided the basis for a substantial sulfite pulp industry. During the 1930's there began a phenomenal expansion of the kraft pulp and paper industry in the pine region of the South, based upon use of southern pines, and to a minor degree of various hardwood species; by 1950 the South had about half the total pulp-mill capacity in the United States.

Of the wood pulp produced in the United States, about 85 per cent is from softwood species and 15 per cent from hardwoods. The quantities of hardwoods used for pulp have been steadily expanding as the result of increased competition for the scarcer softwoods and of the development of improved processes for producing semichemical, sulfate, and other forms of pulp from hardwood timber.

In spite of the great size of the U.S. pulp and paper industry, imports are substantial and growing. In 1950 the United States imported nearly 5 million tons of newsprint, or 83 per cent of the total consumption of this item and more than twice the quantity imported in 1930. Imports of wood pulp, amounting to 2.4 million tons in 1950, have shown somewhat less of an increase, and pulpwood imports have been relatively stable (Fig. 24). The United States exports the equivalent of approximately one-half million cords of pulpwood, chiefly in the form of container board, wallboard, wrapping paper, and fine papers.

Domestic production is about equally divided between paper and board. Container board alone accounted for 24 per cent of the total 1950 production, and box board, building boards, and other types of boards for an additional 27 per cent. Coarse papers, including wrapping paper, bag paper, shipping sacks, etc., together accounted for 14 per cent of the 1950 production. Other items of large importance included book papers, fine papers, building papers, sanitary papers, newsprint, and groundwood papers.

VENEER AND PLYWOOD. Veneer logs and bolts rank third in importance as a timber product in the United States. In 1950 about 2.7 billion board feet (0.4 billion cubic feet roundwood equivalent) of logs and bolts were consumed by the approximately 750 plants which make up the veneer and plywood industry of the country. About half the total output of the industry consists of softwood plywood manufactured by about 70 relatively large plants in the western United States, whereas the other half includes numerous forms of hardwood veneer and plywood manufactured by the remaining plants, located chiefly in the East. Many of these eastern mills are integrated with other manufacturing plants producing furniture, containers, and other products.

Output of the softwood plywood industry has been increasing with great rapidity. In 1950, for example, production was more than twice that of 1940. Production of hardwood veneer and plywood, in contrast, has been increasing rather slowly.

Imports and exports of plywood and veneer are relatively insignificant except for certain tropical hardwoods, such as mahogany (*Cedrela* sp.), which are used in the manufacture of face veneers.

Veneer and plywood are used for a wide variety of purposes, notably in building construction and in the making of shipping containers and other factory products. Possibly two thirds of the softwood plywood produced is employed in construction as sheathing, subfloors, concrete forms, etc. Somewhat more than half of the hardwood veneer goes into baskets, hampers, wire-bound boxes, and other containers. Other hardwood veneers and softwood plywoods are used for furniture, cabinets, and various fabricated products.

OTHER TIMBER PRODUCTS. In 1950 other forest products cut in U.S. forests aggregated about 2.1 billion cubic feet, or roughly 20 per cent of the total production of timber products. Fuel wood was the most important of these. About 20 million cords of fuel wood were cut from sound living trees on commercial forest lands. An additional 40 million cords, used by domestic consumers and by sawmills and other manufacturing plants, were obtained from manufacturing waste, dead and cull trees, and miscellaneous sources such as fence rows. The use of fuel wood in the United States has been declining steadily, however, and may be expected to decline further, as the result of higher incomes, of the extension of gas, oil, and electric lines, and of urbanization.

The cooperage industry is still important in the United States, although the level of production is only about half that of 1929 and one third that of 1909. Approximately 690 million board feet of timber, much of relatively high quality, was used in the production of tight and slack cooperage in 1950. A downward trend in the use of cooperage reflects not only a shortage of high-quality timber, but also the substitution of steel, fiber, and other containers.

It is estimated that approximately 230 million fence posts, requiring 166 million cubic feet of timber, are still produced in the United States for use on farms and along rights-of-way.

Round and split timbers used in mining amount to about 100 million cubic feet annually, more than 80 per cent of them in coal mines. There has been considerable substitution of sawn lumber in certain areas, and occasional substitution of steel and concrete posts, but mine timbers still represent an important use of wood.

Hewn railroad ties cut in 1950 totaled about 12 million, or one fourth of the total ties installed by U.S. railroads in that year. Most of these hewn ties were of southern pine and oak. Use of hewn ties has been declining as a result of greater use of sawn ties, and total tie consumption has been reduced by greater use of wood preservatives.

Approximately 7 million utility poles are produced annually for electric power and communication lines, and one fourth as many trees are cut for use in harbor development, bridge construction, and building foundations.

A variety of miscellaneous logs and bolts—about 250 million cubic feet in 1950—are also used in the form of farm timbers and manufactured products such as shingles, laths, shoe lasts, spools, novelties, excelsior, box shook, and distillation products.

Production of the different timber products in the United States has varied considerably. Use of certain products, such as fuel wood and cooperage, has been declining, while consumption of products such as pulpwood and veneer logs has been increasing. Future requirements for timber products seem likely to increase as a result of population growth and the development of the nation's economy. To supply these potential future requirements plus a margin for exports, new uses, and security against unexpected losses, the President's Materials Policy Commission estimated in 1950 that the United States should aim to grow 18 billion cubic feet of timber annually, including 72 billion board feet of saw-timber-size material. Meeting this growth goal will require a one-third increase over the recent level of all-timber growth and a doubling of saw-timber growth.

NONTIMBER PRODUCTS. For more than a century the United States has been the world's largest producer of naval stores. Production in 1949 totaled approximately 673 thousand barrels (50 gallons) of turpentine, 2 million drums (520 pounds net) of rosin, and 191 thousand drums (520 pounds net rosin equivalent) of tall oil. Current production of turpentine and rosin is somewhat below the peak achieved in the early 1900's, but the production of tall oil, a by-product of the kraft pulp industry of comparatively recent origin, has increased tenfold since the period immediately before World War II.

Originally all naval stores were obtained from the crude gum of long-leaf, slash, and certain other pines, but in recent decades "wood" naval stores, distilled from stumps obtained on logged-over areas, have accounted for an increasing part of the total output. Since 1934 production of wood naval stores has approximately tripled, and in 1950 approximately 62 per cent of the turpentine production and 54 per cent of the rosin output came from the wood naval-stores plants of the United States.

Since its beginnings the naval-stores industry has relied upon foreign markets as an outlet for a major part of its production. Exports have shrunk, however, and in 1950 only 29 per cent of the turpentine production and 40 per cent of the rosin were shipped to foreign markets. Turpentine is largely used in paint and chemicals and rosin mainly for paper sizing, paints, chemicals, and soap.

Maple sugar and syrup represent a unique and important product of forests in the northern part of the United States and adjoining regions in Canada where sugar maple is a prominent species. In 1950 about 262,000 pounds of maple sugar and 2.0 million gallons of maple syrup were produced in the United States.

More than 21 million Christmas trees are cut in the United States each year, and an additional 9 million trees are imported from Canada. Most of these trees are cut from northern forests, with spruce, balsam fir, and Douglas fir as the preferred species.

Other important products are tannin extracts obtained from dead chestnut wood, sumac *(Rhus),* oak bark, and various other sources. Cascara bark *(Rhamnus purshianus)* is used in medicines. Edible nuts and seeds, wild fruits, pine litter, Spanish moss *(Tillandsia usneoides),* and ornamental plants are also of some importance locally.

WATERSHED PROTECTION

In many parts of the United States the most important function of the forest is the protection of watersheds. Some of the National Forests, especially in areas such as southern California, were established principally for the protection of irrigation and domestic water supplies, and purchase of eastern National Forests was initially authorized for the purpose of watershed protection. In the West, where water supply is particularly critical, high-altitude forest lands, which receive much of their precipitation in the form of snow, are the primary sources of water. Although the pressure for water is somewhat less in the more humid East, consumption of water for domestic use and for power and navigation is nevertheless enormous. Much of the water in the East also comes initially from forest land. Indeed, by supplying water and reducing floods and erosion the forests perform important functions in all parts of the United States.

FORAGE

A major function of the forest lands in the West and South is the production of forage for cattle, sheep, and other livestock. About 350 million acres, or more than half of the total forest-land area, produces forage in sufficient quantities to be used by livestock. More than one million cattle and horses and three million sheep are grazed on the National Forests alone for a part of each year.

In some areas forage occurs in meadows and other small openings in forests, while elsewhere livestock use the shrubs and herbaceous plants growing under forest cover. Nearly half of the total forest range lies west of the Great Plains, with the open forests of ponderosa pine, piñon juniper, and oak particularly important. Most of the forest grazing in the East is in the southern pine stands. In the eastern hardwood forests grazing is generally undesirable.

The grazing of forest ranges is usually a seasonal operation, particularly in the West, where forest ranges carry livestock during periods of the year when forage is not available at lower elevations. In general, in the West livestock put on their heaviest gains during the season when they are grazed on forest ranges.

RECREATION AND WILDLIFE

Recreation has come to account for a major use of forest lands in the United States. The number of visits to the National Forests alone totaled more than 27 million in 1950. Heavy recreational use was also made of the National Parks and of state and private forest lands throughout the United States. Millions of dollars have been invested in hotels, resorts, summer homes, camp grounds, ski lifts, and other facilities in forested areas. Recreational use varies from brief outings in local forests to extended pack trips in the remote mountain ranges of the West.

Many species of wildlife live in the forests and furnish both recreation and food to millions of people. It is estimated that 95 per cent of the deer, bear, and other big game, and at least a quarter of the smaller game and fur-bearing animals, live in forest areas. There are more than 2.8 million deer, as well as other big-game animals, in the National Forests alone. In 1942 forest game supplied more than 100 million pounds of dressed meat, as well as large quantities of fur and hides. These measurable economic values, however, are far surpassed by the intangible benefits of recreational enjoyment of wildlife.

Forest Policies and Programs

The United States has sufficient forest lands to grow all the timber the nation is likely to need, while continuing to serve other necessary functions. At the present time this growth is not being achieved. Current forest growth is substantially below current levels of drain and considerably below the output required to meet potential needs. Saw-timber growth, for example, is less than one half of a reasonable growth goal. Millions of acres need reforestation. Protection against fires, insects, and diseases is still far from satisfactory. With certain notable exceptions, cutting practices on private forest lands do not tend to maintain or build up timber growth. The problem of increasing growing stock to support a higher level of growth is complicated by the need of sustaining current levels of output of timber products. The task is also complicated by the need of balancing timber supply and use regionally as well as nationally.

Realization of the necessity for better conservation of forest resources has brought into existence a number of forestry programs, some of which will be briefly described.[3]

Fire Protection. In the last half of the nineteenth century a number of states enacted laws providing penalties for setting forest fires, and in 1891 fire control was initiated on the federal forest reserves. Not until the Weeks Law of 1911, however, did Congress authorize an effective program involving federal-state co-operation for the control of forest fires on state and private lands. This was later materially expanded by the Clarke-McNary Act of 1924. Since the inauguration of this federal-state co-operative program, public agencies have organized protection on about 85 per cent of the 427 million acres of state and private forest land that require it, as well as on most federal forest lands. Forest industries and other private owners have also spent large sums for the protection of private lands and have initiated educational programs which have substantially strengthened state and federal forest-fire prevention and control.

Fire protection is not yet adequate, however. Some 63 million acres, mainly in the South, were still without it at the beginning of 1952. In addition, more intensive fire protection is needed on much of the state and private land in organized protection districts, and on many public forest holdings.

Protection Against Insects and Disease. Protection of forests against insects and disease has long been recognized as a matter of public interest, but before 1947 the government dealt only with individual outbreaks as they occurred. Most of these efforts were directed toward the control of western-pine bark beetles, white-pine blister rust, and the gypsy moth. The Forest Pest Control Act of 1947, however, authorizes direct federal action and co-operation with states and other agencies in detecting outbreaks of insects and diseases and in suppressing them promptly on a nation-wide basis on both public and privately owned forest lands. The need for such efforts is indicated by the fact that, during the 20-year period ending in 1940, western pine beetles destroyed approximately 25 billion board feet of ponderosa pine in California, Oregon, and Washington alone.

Education and Technical Assistance. For many years foresters of the Federal-State Agricultural Extension Service have been arousing the public to the need for forest conservation and demonstrating methods of forest management and utilization. In 1951 approximately 78 extension foresters were employed in 46 different states and territories. The value of on-the-ground technical assistance and guidance to individual forest owners has also been impressively demonstrated by the federal-state program authorized by the Norris-Doxey Act of 1937 and the Co operative Forest Management Act of 1950. By 1950 there were 227 co-

[3] See also *Forests and National Prosperity.* U.S. Department of Agriculture, Miscellaneous Publication 668, 1948.

operative forest-management assistance projects in 36 states, each served by a resident forester. These provide technical services in cutting, woodland management, and marketing to local farmers and other small owners of forest land. Certain technical services are also made available to farmers through Soil Conservation Districts.

In recent years forest industries have also undertaken to promote good forestry practices. In 1950 approximately 100 industrial foresters provided management assistance to small owners. The American Forest Products Industries, the Southern Pulpwood Conservation Association, the Western Pine Association, and others have adopted aggressive forestry programs for aiding forest owners. The "Tree Farm" program originated by these organizations now covers some 23 million acres of private properties dedicated by the owners to timber growing. The "Keep Green" program is also an effective aid in forest-fire prevention. The number of foresters engaged in private forestry work is estimated at close to 3,700, of which about 3,100 are employed by forest industries, the balance being either self-employed as private consultants or employed by associations.

Both public and private agencies will have to expand their educational and technical services still further, however, if most of the small landowners, who own in the aggregate about three fourths of all private forest lands and supply a major portion of the raw material used by the forest industries, are to be reached.

Conservation Payments. Payments made to farmers under the agricultural conservation program represent still another means of encouraging good forestry practices on private lands. These payments have been made for tree planting, fencing of woodlands against livestock, timber-stand improvement, construction of fire breaks, improved naval-stores production, and the like.

Forest Planting. The Clarke-McNary Act of 1924 authorized the federal government to co-operate with the states in the production and distribution of forest and shelter-belt planting stock. This program has been directed largely to the problem of restoring forest cover on the more than 62 million acres of private forest land that has been denuded or is so poorly stocked as to be practically nonproductive. Since 1924 about 1.5 billion trees have been distributed at nominal cost under this program, with the states carrying the main part of the expense. In addition, pulp companies and other wood-using industries have planted or distributed millions of trees. In all, about 5.6 million acres of plantations have been established on private and state lands and 2.1 million acres on federal lands.

Forest Credit and Insurance. Forestry is the only major form of land use in the United States for which suitable long-term credit facilities are not generally available. A system of credits to enable owners, for example, to consolidate timber holdings, improve their stands, and carry young timber to maturity, would be an important aid to forest conservation. Only a limited amount of forest-fire insurance is now available to reduce the risks inherent in forest enterprises and facilitate the granting of credit.

Forest Taxation. The general property tax has long been considered an important obstacle to commercial timber growing, and nearly thirty states have enacted special forest tax laws to encourage improved management and stability of ownership of forest lands. Many of these provide for taxes levied at the time of harvesting. The New Hampshire tax law of 1949 defers tax levies on timber and substantially reduces tax burdens for owners meeting certain standards of forest practice.

Forest Research. Well-organized and continuing research on all phases of forestry and forest-products utilization is basic for the promotion of forest conservation. The Forest Service of the U.S. Department of Agriculture has played a leading role in forest research through nine regional forest and range experiment stations and a Forest Products Laboratory at Madison, Wisconsin. Many states also conduct research in forestry and forest products, chiefly through the agricultural experiment stations and forestry schools, and considerable private research on wood utilization is conducted by various forest industries. Federal expenditures for forest research in 1951 totaled about $5,000,000, as compared with about $20,000,000 of state and private expenditures. All phases of forestry research still need to be strengthened.

Management of Public Forests. About one fifth of the commercial forest lands in the United States—or 89 million acres—is in federal ownership, and an additional 27 million acres is in state and local government holdings. In 1950 these public lands provided about 10 per cent of the total output of forest products. In view of the concentration of the remaining timber on National Forests the contribution of the public forests will undoubtedly increase in the near future. The cut from public lands also may be further increased by the installation of new wood-using plants in southeastern Alaska.

Timber on federal lands, and on many state and local public lands, is generally cut in accordance with sustained-yield management plans which provide for future timber crops. The Sustained Yield Unit Act of 1944 authorized co-operative management of federally owned and private forest lands, in order to insure permanent timber production.

The varied resources of the National Forests are managed by the Forest Service under a decentralized system of operation calling for 11 regional foresters, 150 forest supervisors, and 750 district rangers. Each district ranger administers the timber, range, water, wildlife, and recreational resources on an area that frequently exceeds a quarter of a million acres.

More intensive management of the National Forests and other public holdings would add substantially to present and future timber supplies. This would call for increased investments in the construction of access roads to open up undeveloped areas of timber, and for the strengthening of forest-fire controls, more intensive protection against insects and diseases, improvement of young timber stands, and the planting of denuded or idle areas.

During the past fifty years the United States has developed comprehensive forestry programs based upon federal, state, and private co-operative efforts. By a strengthening of these programs the forest lands can be made to produce the timber and other forest products and services that the United States is likely to need in the future.

SOURCES FOR BOTANICAL NOMENCLATURE

ABRAMS, LEROY. 1923. *Illustrated flora of the Pacific states.* 3 vols. Stanford University Press, Calif.

GLEASON, H. A., *et al.* 1952. *The new Britton and Brown illustrated flora of the northeastern United States and adjacent Canada.* 3 vols. New York Botanical Garden, New York.

KELSEY, H. P., and DAYTON, W. A. 1942. Standardized plant names. 2d ed. J. Horace McFarland Co., Harrisburg, Pa.

The present chapter was already in press when a thousand-page document on the forests of the United States was published by the U.S. Forest Service; *Timber Resource Review* [*Preliminary Review Draft*], Washington, D.C., 1955 (see review by Erhard Rostlund in the *Geographical Review,* **46** (1956):409-411).

9. MIDDLE AMERICA

Leslie R. Holdridge

Middle America seems a suitable collective name for the area comprising Mexico, Central America, Panama, and the West Indies. Within this region are located ten of the twenty Latin American Republics, as well as French, British, and Dutch possessions and small territories of the United States of America. The region roughly approximates a parallelogram tilted northwest and southeast, extending over about 25 degrees of latitude and 58 degrees of longitude. The eastern and western edges of the parallelogram are washed by the Atlantic and Pacific Oceans, respectively, with the Caribbean Sea and the Gulf of Mexico filling in the huge irregular areas between the West Indies and the continental land mass. The land area within the region adds up to slightly over 2½ million square kilometers or one million square miles.

Physical Geography

The physical geography of the region is extremely complicated. The sea is everywhere significant; only in northern Mexico are there areas at any appreciable distance from marine transportation. Mountains, however, are the one dominant land-surface feature. Except for the Yucatán Peninsula and limited coastal and valley areas, broken country predominates. Large navigable rivers are practically nonexistent, and fresh-water lakes are limited in number and usually small in area.

The climate of Middle America is the result largely of three factors: the temperature of the adjacent seas, the direction of the prevailing winds, and the mountains. In the extreme northwest corner of the region, the Pacific Ocean bordering the peninsula of Lower California is cold, so that the prevailing northwest winds bring little moisture to northern Mexico down to about latitude 20°N. Since the winds of northeastern Mexico come from the south in the summer and from the north in the winter, rather than on-shore from the warm waters of the Gulf of Mexico, they, too, are dry, and the arid zone extends all the way across northern Mexico.

In the West Indies and on the mainland south of Yucatán the persistent trade winds carry moisture inland from the warm seas, so that the forests of the eastern slopes are generally luxuriant. Dry seasons are practically nonexistent. During the rainy season, convectional storms bring abundant rain to the Pacific slopes of the mountains and to the inner valleys, but during the dry season the strong easterly winds bring little precipitation. This combination of mountains and winds is responsible for the sharp differentiation between vegetation on eastern and on western slopes that is general throughout the West Indies, southern Mexico, Central America, and Panama.

Middle America, as a whole, contains 2.08 and 2.12 per cent of the world's land surface and population, respectively. Population density, which exerts a profound influence on the forests, is greatest in the West Indies, which, with less than 10 per cent of the land area of Middle America, carry nearly one third of the population.

Forest Belts and Formations

Two sets of factors are responsible for the composition of the Middle American forests: floral origin and migration, which account for the presence of specific families and genera; and climatic, edaphic, and other factors, which influence the distribution of the elements of the flora.

The vegetation of Middle America is essentially a mixture of North American and South American floras, although there are also many species that are endemic or confined to the region. On the continent, the northern flora is dominant down to the Nicaragua–Costa Rica lowlands; southwards, the flora is predominantly South American. The northern flora is dominant also throughout the Greater Antilles and in the Lesser Antilles as far south as Guadeloupe and Dominica. From there on, the South American influence becomes progressively stronger, and in Trinidad the flora is essentially that of the adjacent continent.

Owing to the complex pattern of climate and soils, as well as to the heterogeneity of the plant communities, it is extremely difficult to classify the Middle American flora in terms of plant associations. Hence, to avoid confusion, we shall define the forests by climate alone, as formations or with reference to life zones.

Most of Middle America's forests are tropical. The only part of the region in the Warm Temperate Zone [1] is northern Mexico, and here there is little true forest. Northern Mexico includes a small area of true desert and much desert bush, thorn steppe, and savanna or dry forest. Only above 2,000 meters is precipitation sufficient to support a moist forest with associations of oaks and pines, but the areas that attain these elevations are very restricted. Along the coasts there are a few small areas of low subtropical thorn forest. All of these extratropical formations are of relatively little significance in the total forest picture of the region.

In the Middle American tropics one encounters as much temperature variation from sea level to the highest mountains as one would in travel-

[1] As here conceived, the latitudinal belt bounded at mean sea level by the annual isotherm of 12° C. in the south and by the line marking the occurrence of killing frosts more than once every three years in the north.

ing from the heat equator to the poles: correspondingly one finds a wide range in vegetation, equivalent to that of the latitudinal zones. The range in precipitation is smaller, but it is sufficient to result in a fairly wide range of formations within altitudinal belts.

TROPICAL BELT. Five forest formations in the Tropical Belt range in elevation from about 800 meters down to near sea level.

Thorn Forest. Where precipitation is less than 500 millimeters per year, stunted thorn forest is found. It is of little importance to man because of the poor quality of the timber it supplies and of the extremely restricted areas in which it occurs. There is thorn forest near Gonaïves in Haiti, in a small portion of the Zacapa valley in Guatemala, and possibly in some of the southern valleys in Mexico. A good example is the *Cercidium praecox* [2] association of the Zacapa valley.

Very Dry Forest. This is a fairly extensive formation, found in the western portions of some of the Greater Antilles, along the coast of Yucatán, in Curaçao, and in the Zacapa valley in Guatemala, where the rainfall ranges from approximately 500 to 1,000 millimeters per year. Specific examples in the Greater Antilles are the Guanica Insular Forest in Puerto Rico and the vegetation of the Cul de Sac Plain and Savane Desolé, just south of Gonaïves in Haiti. The forest is relatively low, mainly deciduous, but in some coastal areas contains a considerable proportion of evergreen trees with small leathery leaves.

The broadleaf species making up this forest in general produce hard, heavy woods, many of them very durable. Legumes and spiny trees are common, while cacti also flourish. The hardwoods have long been heavily exploited for railroad ties, firewood, and a wide variety of other uses. This has favored the cacti and spiny shrubs and trees, so that the physiognomy of the present residual stands is close to that of a thorn forest. Agriculture in the forest region is confined to the irrigable plains, with a small amount of shifting cultivation and grazing elsewhere.

The very dry forest is almost everywhere characterized by *Acacia farnesiana*, *Bursera simaruba*, and *Guaiacum sanctum*.

Dry Forest. This lowland tropical formation, which receives between 1,000 and 2,000 millimeters of rainfall a year, formerly supported some of the richest forest stands of Middle America. Environmental conditions favor the growth of large trees, and the associations are generally composed of a high percentage of valuable timbers. Large areas along the Pacific coast, the northern half of Petén in Guatemala, much of the Yucatán Peninsula, and much of the lowlands of the West Indies fall within the life zone of this forest, although most of the actual forest has been cleared or culled.

Important timber trees in this formation are Spanish cedar (*Cedrela mexicana*), mahogany (*Swietenia* sp.), *Bombacopsis quinatum*, *Entero-*

---

[2] Sources for botanical nomenclature: Record and Hess (1943), Standley (1920-26). For complete references see p. 200.

lobium cyclocarpum, Hymenaea courbaril, Andira inermis, Pithecello-bium saman, Platymiscium sp., *Chlorophora tinctoria, Sideroxylon* sp., *Astronium graveolens, Dalbergia* sp., *Sweetia panamensis, Bucida bur-ceras, Achras zapota, Cybistax donnell-smithii, Tabebuia chrysantha, Lysiloma latisiliqua,* and *Haematoxylon campechianum.* Indeed, the dry forest includes the majority of the precious woods that have figured so prominently in the export trade. Few species cover the whole area, however, and local variations are often significant. Cleared land in the area produces the major part of the sugar cane, cotton, sisal, henequen, and beef cattle of Middle America.

Moist Forest. The most extensive lowland natural forest stands which remain in Middle America belong to this formation. In contrast to the dry forest they are predominantly evergreen; they are also many-storied, more luxuriant, and composed of a greater number of species. Typical species are *Cordia alliodora, Carapa guianensis, Guarea* sp., *Prioria copaifera, Hieronyma* sp., *Anacardium excelsum, Minquartia guianensis, Aspidosperma* sp., *Vitex* sp., *Pentaclethra macroloba, Virola* sp., *Calo-phyllum brasiliensis, Terminalia* sp., *Vochysia* sp., *Dialium guianensis, Tabebuia pentaphylla, Ochroma lagopus,* and *Manilkara* spp. Variations in the make-up of the stands reflect special soil conditions, e.g., *Pinus cari-baea* on gravelly and sandy soils in much of northeastern Nicaragua, and a *Curatella-Byrsonima* association on infertile scattered savanna soils. The moist-forest region is important for the production of bananas, abacá, African oil palm, rubber, and cacao, all of which are largely confined to alluvial plains.

With the supply of high-grade species in the dry forest running low, the demand is increasing for the generally poorer timbers of the tropical moist forest. For example, industrial users of wood for veneers are becom-ing more and more dependent upon this formation.

Wet Forest. This is a formation of limited extent, occurring on the lower eastern slopes of some of the Caribbean islands and in northeastern and southwestern Costa Rica. Its associations have not been studied sufficiently to determine the most characteristic mainland species. In the Antilles, *Dacryodes excelsa* and *Talauma* are timber-tree components of the wet forest.

SUBTROPICAL BELT. The Subtropical Belt lies above that of the tropical forests just described. Normally it extends from between 600 and 700 meters to between 1,400 and 1,500 meters above sea level, although it drops down to lower elevations in the Greater Antilles and in the north-ern continental part of Middle America. Its forests are generally less use-ful for timber than are those either below or above it, but they are of great importance for watershed protection and the regulation of stream flow.

Dry Forest (Savanna). The area once covered by this formation was settled early by man, and little is known of the nature of the original forest. In Guatemala, where the life zone of this forest is extensive, an ecological survey shows that over 11 per cent of the country (12,700 square kilometers) was formerly covered by this formation. *Ipomoea arborea* is a characteristic dry-forest species.

Moist Forest. The areas covered, in this case, are important for both agriculture and forestry. They possess the best climate for coffee, and most of the fertile soils are being used for that crop. Since in Middle America coffee is grown under shade, coffee plantations are essentially forests which provide rather satisfactory protection for the soils and produce large quantities of firewood from the pruning and occasional changing of the shade trees.

On the mainland, within Nicaragua, *Pinus oocarpa* and *Quercus* sp. form an important forest association. In Honduras this association covers approximately one fifth of the area of the country. Northward the same forest type occurs in Guatemala, British Honduras, and in parts of Mexico. Throughout the area the present stands are being heavily cut and frequently burned, so that they are becoming rapidly depleted. They could be highly productive if properly managed and protected.

Wet Forest. This formation occurs at high elevations in the West Indies and over extensive areas on the mainland. It includes some species valuable for timber, of which Lauraceae are among the best. Because of high precipitation and rugged terrain most of the area covered by this forest type should be set aside in reserves for watershed protection.

Rain Forest. This formation is found on some of the exposed eastern mountain peaks in the Antilles and to a limited extent in western Guatemala and on the mountains of Costa Rica. Because of its small area, the rain forest is not important except for local watershed protection.

LOWER MONTANE BELT. This third altitudinal belt, adjacent to and extending upward from the Subtropical Belt, comprises an elevational range of approximately 1,000 meters. The forests are largely coniferous and are of great importance to forestry in mainland Middle America. Very little of the belt is represented in the West Indies, except on the island of Hispaniola.

Dry Forest. Little remains of the dry forest of the Lower Montane Belt, except for some stands of *Pinus montezumae*. This is because many of the areas in the belt—the valley of Mexico City and other highland valleys in Mexico and Guatemala—were selected as good sites for settlement by pre-Columbian Indians. The best soils have been used chiefly for the growing of corn and wheat, and the total area of the formation is small.

Moist Forest. The more extensive tracts of moist forest occur mainly in Mexico, Guatemala, and at high elevations in Hispaniola and Cuba. In the Antilles, the most important species is *Pinus occidentalis*. On the mainland the principal pines are *Pinus pseudostrobus, P. tenuifolia,* and *P. patula*. On the borders of the forest region, these may be mixed with *P. oocarpa, P. montezumae,* or *P. rudis* Endl., and throughout the region they are often associated with various species of oak. It is much easier to maintain pine as a subclimax forest here than in the subtropical moist forest.

There is considerable agriculture in this forest region. Some of the flat valley floors have been in continuous cultivation for centuries. The hillsides, also, are all too often cultivated, but usually only for a few years at a time.

Wet Forest. A wide variety of forest associations is found in the wet-forest zone. *Cupressus lusitanica* is prominent on ridges and slopes and appears to be a fire subclimax; it occurs from Mexico to Honduras and makes an excellent timber. The hardwood association in northern Central America and Mexico contains many temperate-region genera such as *Pinus, Ilex, Alnus, Cornus,* and *Viburnum.* In Costa Rica, huge white oaks, *Quercus copeyensis* and *Q. tomentocaulis,* form magnificent stands, while associations similar to those of northern Central America grow on richer soils.

Lower Montane Rain Forest. This formation is limited to Costa Rica. Its most common dominant tree that has been studied is *Ocotea austinii* C. K. Allen, which produces a timber of medium value.

MONTANE BELT. The Montane (or fourth altitudinal) Belt reaches to an elevation of approximately 1,000 meters above the upper limit of the Lower Montane Belt. It occurs to a limited extent in Panama, Costa Rica, and Guatemala, and more extensively in Mexico. Agricultural land use within it is restricted mainly to the grazing of sheep and cattle and the cultivation of a few potatoes.

Moist Forest. In Costa Rica the moist forest of this belt is very limited, with *Quercus costaricensis* Liebm. the only large tree. In Guatemala *Juniperus standleyi* Steyerm. forms scattered stands on dry hills surrounding open prairie in the driest parts of the formation. In Guatemala and Mexico *Pinus rudis* Endl. occupies the intermediate areas, and *Pinus ayacahuite,* a true white pine, covers the wettest areas. *P. rudis* Endl. is often severely attacked by *Dendroctonus* beetles.

Wet Forest. In southern Central America the wet forest is of little value for timber. Some of the characteristic species are *Buddleia alpina, Escallonia poasana,* and *Myrrhidendron.* In Guatemala and Mexico there are stands of *Abies guatemalensis* and *Abies religiosa.* Here both *Pinus ayacahuite,* which is also characteristic of the moist forest, and the firs are large trees and produce good softwood lumber. The fir forests in Mexico are important to the local pulp and paper industry.

SUBALPINE BELT. The forests of this fifth altitudinal belt, which extends upward from the Montane Belt for approximately 500 meters, are of little commercial interest because they are found only on the highest mountain peaks in Costa Rica and Mexico. In the latter country *Pinus hartwegii* forms open stands of medium- to small-sized trees on high, relatively inaccessible mountain slopes. In Costa Rica the association is a low bush, including some paramo plants from South America.

Above this belt the alpine and nival belts are found on the highest peaks in Mexico, but all of these areas are above the timber line.

History of Use

In pre-Columbian times, the Indians made relatively little impression on the natural forest. Since the early European settlers were more interested in precious metals than in agriculture, forest clearing progressed slowly for some time after the discovery of America. Eventually, however, the European demand for sugar, rum, indigo, cochineal dye, cacao, and other agricultural crops reached significant proportions, and the clearing of land for agriculture, especially in the Antilles, expanded rapidly. Most of the timber was burned on the ground, but much precious wood was exported to Europe and later to the United States. The introduction of coffee into the Western Hemisphere had a far-reaching effect on the mountain forests, although fortunately the combination of coffee plants and shade trees maintained a cover almost equivalent to that of a natural forest. Clean-tilled crops, such as ginger, were conducive to erosion.

The heavy drain on precious woods for export to Europe and North America, together with continued clearing for plantation and subsistence crops for a rapidly increasing population, led to the destruction of most of the accessible forests in the West Indies. With Antillean tropical hardwoods exhausted, northern buyers turned to Central America and Mexico for timber, and exploitation of the mainland forests has continued, with little letup, to the present.

Until World War II, however, the export trade in valuable hardwoods had little over-all effect on the natural forests. Only the most precious woods would repay the cost of logging and transportation; hence, cutting was very selective and resulted primarily in the reduction of a few valuable species, while the forest as a whole remained substantially intact.

The main cause of forest reduction, until quite recently, has been rapid agricultural expansion. Bananas, for example, have replaced extensive areas of lowland forest, and subsistence agriculture effectively destroyed much of the original mainland forest. The major part of the timber resources of the cleared forests in Middle America has either rotted on the ground or been burned.

Until World War II the mainland areas of Middle America still seemed to many to have inexhaustible supplies of timber. In the Antilles, however, good southern hard pine and Pacific coast lumber could be imported more cheaply than lumber of similar quality could be secured from the remaining limited forest areas. As a striking example, a Haitian summer lodge built at 5,000 feet above sea level and 50 miles from the coast was lined and sealed with southern yellow pine from the United States, even though it was located in the heart of a magnificent pine forest.

World War II changed this situation considerably. Lumber shortages in the United States curtailed shipping, and high prices largely shut off imports of coniferous lumber into Middle America. Local people turned again to the remaining forests, this time with increased attention to the second-class woods, which had not previously been heavily exploited. This trend has continued since the end of war.

The Middle American countries without timber have to depend increasingly on their near neighbors in the region for forest products. Cuba takes heavy supplies of construction and cabinet woods from the mainland areas of Middle America. El Salvador receives most of the timber that she needs from Honduras and Nicaragua. Wood from Middle America is exported to Venezuela and is shipped southward along the Pacific coast as far as Peru. Postwar exports to North America and Europe have also increased, as timber buyers from temperate zones are now willing to buy a larger number of species.

Increasing internal demand, however, has been the most important drain on the countries of the region. Most of these have more than doubled their population within the present century, and local consumption of timber has increased considerably. World War II gave an impetus to local wood industries which will further increase wood consumption.

Forest Industries and Products

The forests of Middle America provide fuel for the population and labor and income for a tremendous number of workers. As the majority of the products moves without either control or tabulation, statistical data are practically nonexistent, and few people in Middle America are aware of how important the forest industries are to the economy of their countries.

FUEL AND ROUNDWOOD. In most of these countries the quantity of wood consumed in the form of fuel and roundwood far surpasses the volume of sawn timber. Such uses have received little attention, but they play an important part in any survey of forests and forest products.

In Guatemala, for example, logs cut for sawn lumber in 1949 amounted to 140,000 cubic meters, while during the same year the consumption of firewood and charcoal was approximately ten times as much. If the quantity of unsawn wood used locally in the construction of fences and common adobe houses could be estimated, the figures would be even more striking. Guatemala City's 200,000 inhabitants consume firewood and charcoal valued at about $1,000,000 a year.

In Haiti the local production of less than 15,000 cubic meters of sawn lumber annually is sufficient to supply the local market without resort to imports. However, with a total population larger than that of Guatemala, a comparable consumption of firewood would amount to about 1,500,000 cubic meters, so that Haiti may be using approximately 100 times as much wood for firewood and charcoal as for sawn lumber. As long as the annual increment of growth exceeds the needs of the population for fuel, the use of roundwood is a salvage operation that does no damage to the forests. As soon as the forests are considerably reduced, however, the taking of wood for fuel not only depletes the remaining forests but also seriously drains the growing stock and cuts down future timber supplies. There can be no doubt that this is now the situation almost everywhere in Middle America.

LUMBER INDUSTRY. After fuel and charcoal production, the milling of dimension stock is the second largest wood-using industry in Middle America. Because of the general depletion of the forests in the Antilles, the major part of the industry is now located on the mainland. Although there are various combinations, logging and extraction methods follow three general patterns depending on climatic conditions and the stage of agricultural development in various areas.

Logging operations for the extraction of large logs of precious woods from little-developed localities or virgin forests are usually seasonal. This type of logging is typical of the Atlantic coastal region of Central America, the Petén region of Guatemala, and the Darien Province of southeastern Panama. In Darien, for example, logging operations for the extraction of mahogany and Spanish cedar start in November, near the end of the rainy season. The first operations comprise the scouting or locating of individual trees, the setting up of camps, and the assembling of tractors and trucks. As soon as the weather permits, the trees are felled and the logs are yarded at several truck-loading points in the forest. A network of truck roads extending from a location on a river or estuary to the various yards is built with the aid of bulldozers. When the dry season is well advanced, work is centered on trucking the season's crop of logs to the water. This job must be completed before the rainy season. Once the rains start, usually in April, the logs are rolled into the water, fastened together in strings or rafts, and floated or hauled by tug boats or launches to deep-water points where they can be boomed directly into the holds of ocean freighters.

In drier regions and in the coniferous forests, better soil conditions permit year-round tractor hauling and trucking, except during occasional short periods. Under such conditions, which are prevalent in the coniferous forests of northern Central America, Mexico and Hispaniola, most of the larger mills carry on continuous operations based mainly on dry-land transport only. Tractors and trucks have largely replaced oxen.

For smaller mills in the wetter and more agriculturally developed regions, operations are also carried out throughout the year. Oxen transport the logs to all-weather roads or railroads, whence they are hauled to the sawmill. In parts of Costa Rica's Atlantic lowlands, oxen haul the logs to narrow-gauge tramways. Here the logs are loaded on to small mule-drawn tramcars and hauled to the main railroad lines. Wherever ox transport is used, the logs are usually first squared and pointed at one end to ease their hauling over rough terrain. This has to be done, even though a considerable loss of clear lumber from each log is involved.

The sawmills of the region differ greatly in terms of machinery, efficiency, and daily output. Circular saws are generally used in the smaller mills, while band saws are more commonly used in the larger mills and are on the increase. Most of the larger mills have additional equipment in the form of edgers, cutoff saws, and planers, but, because of cheap labor, the turning of logs on the carriage and the moving of sawn lumber in the yard is still unmechanized, and many layouts are inefficient in the matter of saving labor. In isolated regions, pit-sawing by hand is still practiced for local needs.

In recent years the logging of precious woods for export has probably declined. The greatest gains in the industry have taken place in the pine forests of northern Central America. According to an FAO survey, the annual production of pine lumber in Honduras in 1953 and 1954 amounted to about 500,000 cubic meters, of which an estimated 80 per cent was exported. The forest service of Costa Rica surveyed the output of sawmills in both 1951 and 1953 and found that the milling for local needs had increased from less than 200,000 to more than 250,000 cubic meters during that two-year period.

PULP AND PAPER INDUSTRY. Mexico has three pulp and paper mills in operation, which produce paper for the internal market. Although two of these mills purchase considerable raw material from other sources within the country, all three have been tied in to specific forest blocks or *unidades*. These cover an aggregate area of about 203,000 hectares in the states of México, Puebla, Morelos, Jalisco, and Colima, and yield annually about 314,000 cubic meters of round material for the factories (pine, 260,000 cubic meters; fir, 54,000 cubic meters). In addition to these, one other *unidad* of 202,731 hectares has been established in the state of Chihuahua, from which part of the yield will be assigned to a projected paper mill. The possibility of setting up paper mills in Central America has been studied by FAO, and we may look forward to important developments in this field.

One small pulp mill utilizing raw material from a large plantation of *Bambusa vulgaris* was established in Trinidad before World War II. With the change in economic conditions following the war, the operation was considered unsatisfactory and the factory was dismantled and shipped to India.

PLYWOOD AND VENEER PLANTS. The last decade has seen a rapid development of this industry, with the establishment of plants in Mexico, Guatemala, Honduras, and Panama. Two large plants in Guatemala and Panama, as well as a smaller recently established mill on the north coast of Honduras, produce mainly for the export market, but the Mexican industry is supported by a good local market. Mexico has four establishments, one large plant in the State of Durango using pine, and three other plants in the southeastern tropical lowlands. Of the latter, two are large plants located at Colonia Yucatán and at Campeche, and the third is a smaller mill at Zoh Laguna.

In addition to the production of plywood and veneer within the region, a considerable quantity of lumber is exported from Middle America for manufacture into veneer in other countries. Mahogany, Spanish cedar, primavera (*Cybistax donnell-smithii*), and cativo (*Prioria copaifera*) have been the principal species used, but a demand is building up for other species as well.

FURNITURE INDUSTRY. Most of the countries of the region have well-developed local furniture industries. Although the majority of the shops are small, with only a few workmen, in the aggregate they employ a very appreciable amount of labor. Most of the furniture is made of solid lumber from the high-grade species that are not attacked by termites. These same shops usually turn out window sashes, doors, and other articles of turnery, carving, or inlay for the tourist trade. Where these are attached to sawmills, much wood that would otherwise be wasted is used for such articles. A recently established plant at Colonia Yucatán, Mexico, utilizes short-length lumber and other materials from the sawmill and woods that were previously wasted, to make up furniture parts, which are crated and shipped unassembled to furniture manufacturing plants in the United States of America.

Simpler furniture is often the product of home industries. A good example of this is the manufacture of beds, chairs, and tables of white-pine lumber in the farm homes around Totonicapán, Guatemala. Each farmer may be permitted to cut one or two trees a year from the communal forests. With the help of his family, he works this lumber into furniture, which is later sold in local markets throughout the country.

OTHER WOOD INDUSTRIES. Mexico has developed one plant at Ciudad Valles for the fabrication of compressed wallboards ("Fibracel"). This product, intended primarily for export, is made from a mixture of about 27 hardwoods which are harvested from second-growth forests now being cleared for agricultural development. Saplings, 5 to 19 centimeters in diameter, are chipped and put through the manufacturing process.

The practice of kiln drying and the preservative treatment of lumber are still limited. Air drying is the usual process employed for reducing the moisture content of the lumber utilized within the region. One dry kiln is operated by a private company which exports balsa lumber from Costa Rica, and kilns are essential parts of the various plywood plants in the region and of the Fibracel factory at Ciudad Valles.

Mexico is trying to stimulate the establishment of timber-treating plants as part of its policy of reducing the drain on the nation's forests, but elsewhere in the region few preservative-treatment plants are in operation and these are run mainly by large private corporations which treat railroad ties and other lumber products for their own use. An example of such a plant is that of the Tela Railroad Company in Honduras, which treated 50,000 cubic meters during 1953.

Large quantities of wood in the round, or hewn or split by axe, are used locally for house construction, fence posts, telephone and telegraph posts, and railroad ties. Except where treating plants are available, railroad ties and communication-line posts consist of highly durable but untreated timbers. As durable timbers diminish, farmers turn more and more to the use of living fence posts, for which certain nondurable species such as *Erythrina* and *Spondias* may be employed. Living telegraph posts of *Spondias* have been observed in areas in Haiti where timber is scarce. Few data are available on the consumption of wood for these uses, but large volumes are involved.

The construction of truck and auto-bus bodies and ox-carts is important locally. Costa Rica is noted for its attractive ox-carts, with fancy designs painted on the bodies and solid wheels.

The match and matchbox industry is represented in most of the countries, although the total amount of wood used is relatively small. The species commonly employed are *Didymopanax morototoni* and other woods of the Araliaceae, *Bursera simaruba, Pinus* sp., and *Simaruba glauca* for matches, and Lauraceae for boxes.

In addition to these industries, the manufacture of coffins, tool handles, etc., increases the use of lumber and provides employment. These minor products are of special interest to the silviculturist, for they provide outlets for mixed-forest species not otherwise in demand.

MISCELLANEOUS FOREST PRODUCTS. In addition to lumber and fuel wood, other products of Middle America's forests yield an income. The most important is chicle gum from *Achras zapota,* produced mainly in Mexico and Guatemala. In 1948 chicle was the third product by value of exports from Guatemala, with a total value of over $2,500,000. The market for chicle has declined in recent years, however, owing to competition of gums from other sources and to the development of synthetic materials for chewing-gum bases.

On the so-called "Balsam Coast" in El Salvador, the gum from *Myroxylon balsamum* var. *pereirae* Harms has been collected for centuries and exported for use in ointments and proprietary preparations. Gum from *Liquidambar styraciflua* is collected in Nicaragua and Honduras. The fragrant resin from *Protium* trees is sold in local markets for incense.

Rubber from wild *Castilloa* trees is used locally in making raincoats, and during the two world wars it was collected for export. *Pinus occidentalis* and P. *oocarpa* are tapped by crude methods for naval stores in several countries, and furnish raw materials for local use.

Palms furnish many products. In Guatemala *Chamaedorea* flowers are a common vegetable. In Costa Rica *Euterpe* palm hearts from the forest are sold in large quantities for salads, and *Bactris utilis* fruits are common in the markets. Palms provide leaves for thatching, fibers for hat manufacture, and nuts for oil. In both Cuba and the Dominican Republic the hard outer layer of the trunks of royal palms is used commonly for siding and floors in rural houses.

Wild ipecac is collected from the forest floor in Nicaragua and Costa Rica. Christmas trees and other decorative plants are collected once a year. Vines for wickerwork, bark for fiber, orchids, and *Philodendron* cuttings are other products of the forests of Middle America.

Tannin barks, which are collected for local tanneries, merit special mention. Mangrove barks are used extensively, along with the barks of other species, such as *Byrsonima crassifolia, Rapanea guianensis, Pinus ayacahuite, Quercus* sp., and *Piptadenia peregrina.*

Present Condition of the Forests

The tropical forest is a dynamic, persistent entity which is very difficult to eradicate permanently. True, it has fallen back continuously before the increasing populations of Middle America, yet wherever man has relaxed his activities, it springs up anew. Succession progresses rapidly, especially in the areas of higher rainfall, and untended pastures and abandoned agricultural clearings revert to forest within a few years.

In the West Indies, where there are dense concentrations of populations and the forests have long been subject to heavy abuse, the percentage of forest cover averages at least 30 per cent of the total area. Mexico's forest acreage approximates 15 per cent, but this relatively low figure is due to the extensive areas in northern Mexico that are not climatically adapted to producing a natural forest cover. Central America and Panama show a much more favorable balance, with approximately 60 per cent of their total area still forested. Twenty-two per cent of the total area of Middle America is forested, but, if the warm-temperate region of Mexico be eliminated, forest cover in the truly tropical portion of Middle America would be considerably higher than 22 per cent.

Just as there is a marked difference between the subregions of Middle America in the percentages of forest cover, so there is a corresponding difference between the countries or islands making up the subregions. The same is true of sections within countries. To a marked degree there is, naturally, a close positive correlation between the density of population and the degree of reduction of forest areas, although rough topography and soils of poor fertility are factors deterrent to clearing even in heavily populated regions.

The condition of the remaining forests, however, is of much greater significance than is the actual percentage of forest cover. The forests of the dry regions have, by and large, been reduced and culled much more extensively than those of the wetter regions. This is because agriculture developed sooner and faster in the drier regions, fires are more destructive, the associations contain a higher percentage of durable and valuable timbers that are in demand, and succession or redevelopment of the forest cover proceeds at a slower pace. Thus the dry forests of the Pacific coast of mainland Middle America have been greatly reduced; only isolated sections remain that have not been culled rather heavily of the better species.

The major blocks of virgin or lightly culled forests on the mainland are located mainly on the wetter lowlands and on mountain slopes facing the Caribbean Sea. From the Isthmus of Tehuantepec in Mexico, these forests broaden out through the State of Chiapas into Campeche, Yucatán, and Quintana Roo, and extend into British Honduras and northern Guatemala. The Petén, the Zona Reina of the Department of Huehue-tenango, and parts of Alta Verapaz and Izabal form a huge block of virgin or only lightly culled forest in Guatemala. Only in the Department of Izabal and in northern Honduras do plantations of abacá and bananas and settlements along the railroads break the continuity of this forest. Further south, it dominates the eastern watershed to the Colombian border, except for parts of eastern Costa Rica and northeastern Panama, where cacao, banana, and abacá plantations cover fairly extensive areas. Aside from these openings, only the Canal Zone, a few coastal towns, and occasional spills of settlement across the Continental Divide from the highland break the continuity of the forest. A few fairly extensive forests west of the Continental Divide in southern Costa Rica and eastern Panama, the highland coniferous forests of northern Central America and Mexico, and this forest on the Atlantic slopes of the lowlands are the greatest remaining blocks of virgin forest in Middle America.

In the West Indies, only Trinidad, Dominica, and the Dominican Republic still retain high percentages of forest cover, but these forests constitute a very small proportion of the total land surface. Clearing of lowlands has been almost complete in the Antilles, except for areas of very low rainfall, or of very rough topography, such as the "cockpit," or broken limestone region, of central Jamaica. As on the mainland, the drier forests have been culled more heavily, and the major remnants of forests are located on the eastern slopes or ends of the islands, where the moisture-laden trade winds strike the mountains.

Drain far exceeds growth in the forests of Middle America. In agricultural regions cutting generally surpasses growth on what are mostly second-growth stands. Along the fringes of the agricultural regions, logging and clearing for new settlement add up to a drain on the remaining natural forest stands that greatly exceeds the compensating annual increment in the second-growth areas. Since the virgin forest does not increase in volume but merely balances new growth with mortality, as a timber reserve it is being reduced year by year.

Growth is not only inadequate in quantity but inferior in quality. Much of the increment on the second-growth stands consists of inferior species. Middle America is thus faced with a constantly diminishing reserve of timber and with an increasing proportion of inferior species in the remaining stands.

Development of Forestry

The status of forestry in a nation is a reflection both of the attitude of the people toward the forest and of the economic condition of the forest. As long as forest lands are extensive and forest products cheap, few people will be interested in forestry. But when part of a country has been deforested, the inhabitants of the impoverished areas may become sufficiently forestry-conscious to urge protective measures for the whole country. In large countries, this movement can be effective because it gathers strength long before the natural forest is entirely gone. In smaller countries, like most of those of Middle America, particularly where education is deficient, such movements may never develop effectively before all of the original forest stands are finished or considerably altered.

The first countries to develop effective forestry movements were Mexico, the one large country in the region, and the European territorial possessions which were able to draw upon the experience and resources of the mother countries. But even here forestry came very late. No significant movements were in progress before the twentieth century, when timber shortage first appeared to be a real possibility. Within the past few decades, however, most of the Middle American countries have taken some steps toward forest control.

All too often, however, the small countries have tried to pattern their forestry organizations and legislation along the line of those of larger nations with different problems and greater resources. Inadequately financed and poorly trained staffs try ineffectively to enforce complex and unsuitable forestry laws, and overemphasis on law enforcement and police action often tends to create in the popular mind a negative attitude toward forestry.

Forestry has often been interpreted to mean merely reforestation. Considerable sums have been spent in Middle America in operating forest nurseries and distributing planting stock. This is an expensive and technically difficult form of forestry, especially with the hardwood species of lowland areas; and public distribution of plants and seeds to private landowners has not generally brought satisfactory results.

Despite these difficulties, Middle American forestry today is making considerable progress. Increasing demands and diminishing supplies force more and more people to recognize the necessity for forest conservation. Growing numbers of technical foresters are developing local techniques to fit local conditions and are exchanging information between various parts of the region.

The forestry work of the Colonial Forest Service in the British possessions and of the Insular and United States Forest Services in Puerto Rico has effectively advanced regional understanding of forest management.

The Tropical Forest Experiment Station in Puerto Rico edits and publishes a trilingual forestry journal, *The Caribbean Forester,* for the dissemination of forestry information throughout the region. The Institute of Inter-American Affairs, the Office of Foreign Agricultural Relations, and the Forest Service of the United States Government have all contributed technical assistance to forestry in Middle America. The Food and Agricultural Organization of the United Nations has sent foresters to Mexico, Guatemala, Honduras, Nicaragua, and Haiti. The Technical Cooperation Program of the Inter-American Institute of Agricultural Sciences, a subsidiary of the Organization of American States, has two foresters in the region.

Technical training in forestry is advancing. Cuba has operated a practical school for forest guards just outside Havana for many years, and Mexico has long offered courses in forestry in the universities. International programs provide fellowships for study abroad. The Tropical Forest Experiment Station in Puerto Rico gives short-term on-the-job training. The Inter-American Institute has helped to operate short training courses and seminars, and now offers graduate studies in forestry at Turrialba.

These local developments are particularly important, because they provide the forester with opportunities for studying floras and forestry conditions most like those that he will face in his own country. Techniques and methods developed locally are increasingly used in public and private forestry. One of the most interesting of these is the system of *unidades* now in operation in Mexico. Under this system, a block or set of blocks of forest land, together with a forest industry, such as a pulp factory, is set up as a working circle or *unidad.* The area may comprise government, company, communal, or privately owned lands. The government forest service plans and administers cutting operations. Prices for products are determined by factory officials in conjunction with landowners. The *unidad* factory agrees to accept, and the property owners agree to sell, all of the lumber produced in the area. Since cutting schedules are devised so as to build up the growing stock, this system assures a sustained yield for the factory and a continued income for the owners. This combination of regulation with technical guidance for the benefit of all parties concerned is well suited to local conditions.

Landowners throughout the area are evincing an increasing interest in forestry and a more favorable attitude toward government regulation and assistance, primarily because the present markets for wood and wood products make it economically feasible and desirable to carry on silvicultural operations. The United Fruit Company is conducting active reforestation projects in Honduras and Costa Rica. Private landowners in Guatemala are managing their forests and planting trees in order to maintain certain areas in sustained-yield forestry.

Agriculture and forestry are frequently combined. Trinidad has long used the *taungya* system for establishing teak plantations. Shifting cultivators in El Salvador are encouraged to plant *Gliricidia sepium* seeds with their last crops of corn, thus bringing a valuable wood crop into a rotation with agricultural crops. The combination of shade trees with coffee and cacao produces large amounts of firewood throughout most of the region. Costa Rican dairy farmers have planted a considerable acreage of *Alnus acuminata* trees in combination with pasture and grass to be cut and carried to the stables. This is a fast-growing tree, and such plantations already contribute approximately one million board feet, or 2,360 cubic meters, of lumber per year.

Future Trends

The continuing rapid rise in population, together with an increased demand for agricultural land and timber products will greatly reduce the remaining natural forests of Middle America in the next few decades. The decline of public timber resources may be expected to stimulate the practice of forestry on private lands as well as the demand for government forest extension services.

Industrial developments within the region will increase the drain on the forests, but in the long run will stimulate forestry, as most industries need sustained yields for profitable long-term operations. Industries will stimulate the trend toward the utilization of many species and products little used at present. The chemical industry, in particular, will probably utilize vast amounts of cellulose, which is supplied in great abundance by the trees of Middle America. The forests of the region may well become important sources for proteins to supplement livestock rations and human diets.

While both the supply of forest products and the condition of forest stands will continue to deteriorate for some time in the future, these very factors, in the long run, will stimulate the future development of forestry. Paralleling these trends will come greater recognition of proper land utilization, and many areas now devoted to agriculture will be reforested once more for the public good. In sum, forestry seems destined to play an increasingly important role in the life and economy of Middle America.

SELECTED REFERENCES

BEARD, J. S. 1946. *The natural vegetation of Trinidad.* Oxford. University Press, London.

BOURNE, W. C., et al. 1946. *Preliminary survey of conservation possibilities in El Salvador.* Servicio Cooperativo Interamericano de Salud Pública, El Salvador.

GILL, TOM. 1931. *Tropical forests of the Caribbean.* Tropical Plant Research Foundation, in co-operation with the Charles Lathrop Pack Forestry Trust, Washington, D. C.

HOLDRIDGE, L. R. 1947. "Determination of world plant formations from simple climatic data," *Science,* 105 (2727):367-368.

———, et al. 1950. *The forests of Guatemala.* (Unpublished report prepared by the Inter-American Institute of Agricultural Sciences, Turrialba, Costa Rica, and El Instituto de Fomento de la Producción de Guatemala, Guatemala City.

JAMES, PRESTON. 1942. *Latin America.* Odyssey Press, Inc., New York.

MERKER, C. A., et al. 1943. *The forests of Costa Rica.* U.S. Dept. of Agriculture, Forest Service, in co-operation with Office of the Co-ordinator of Inter-American Affairs, Washington, D.C.

REARK, J. B. 1952. Forest ecology of the Reventazón Valley. (Unpublished thesis, Inter-American Institute of Agricultural Sciences, Turrialba, Costa Rica.)

RECORD, S. J., and HESS, R. W. 1943. *Timbers of the New World.* Yale University Press, New Haven.

STANDLEY, P. C. 1920-1926. Trees and shrubs of Mexico. *Contributions from the U.S. National Herbarium,* 23:1-169, 171-515, 517-848, 849-1312, 1313-1721.

United Nations. Food and Agriculture Organization. 1950. *Report of the F.A.O. Mission for Nicaragua.* Washington, D.C.

United Nations. 1950. *Statistical Yearbook, 1949-50.* New York.

United States Department of Agriculture. Forest Service. 1938-1951. *The Caribbean forester,* vols. I-XII, quarterly. Tropical Forest Experiment Station, Río Piedras, Puerto Rico.

VERDOORN, FRANZ, ed. 1945. *Plants and plant science in Latin America.* Chronica Botanica Co., Waltham, Mass.

ZON, R., and SPARHAWK, W. N. 1923. *Forest resources of the world,* vol. II. McGraw-Hill Book Co., Inc., New York.

10.   SOUTH AMERICA

William R. Barbour

The total forested area of South America amounts to 860,800,000 hectares, or about 49 per cent of the total land area.[1] Of the forested area,
about 35 per cent is classed as "accessible" and 65 per cent as "inaccessible." Since a large part of the South American forests remains virtually
unexplored, the above figures must be regarded as approximations only.

Forests are often thus classified as "accessible" and "inaccessible." The
former group includes those forests that are sufficiently near to centers of
population and well enough served by railways, rivers, or other means
of transportation to make possible the marketing of forest products. The
term "accessible" is relative; a forest might be accessible for products of
such high value, or low volume and weight, that they could stand a heavy
transportation cost, but nonaccessible for bulkier and less valuable forest
products. Moreover, accessibility changes with the development of transportation facilities, the growth of population, the depletion of the forests,
and an increased demand for products. Eventually, all of the forest areas
of South America will probably become accessible.

Forest Species and Forest Types

South America has extremely diversified climates and forests. There
are trees that can grow under almost arctic conditions at the extreme
southern end of the continent, and others that are at home in equatorial
jungles; some thrive at sea level and others at timber line at heights of
4,000 meters; some in regions where the rainfall exceeds 10 meters (400
inches) every month of the year, and others in semideserts with a rainfall
of 25 centimeters (10 inches) confined to a short portion of the year; and
there is a diversity of species on various soils.

It is not known how many species of trees grow in the forests of South
America, but certainly they number in the thousands. But of these thousands, by far the greater number consist of trees so small and scrubby, so
scarce, or so limited in their range that they do not appreciably affect the
economy of the continent. Less than 200 species constitute the great bulk
of the South American forests.

---

[1] United Nations. Food and Agriculture Organization. *Yearbook of Forest Products Statistics, 1954,* Table 45.

In the appendix to this chapter (pp. 219-230, below), the more important of these trees are classified and described according to the principal uses made of their woods.

The forests of South America may be grouped by types as follows: (1) Tropical Broadleaf Evergreen, (2) Tropical Broadleaf Deciduous, (3) Mountain Broadleaf Evergreen, (4) Temperate Coniferous and Broadleaf, (5) Araucaria ("Pine"), (6) Dry Scrub Forests, and (7) Mangrove Swamp Forests. The areas without natural forests are open grasslands, such as the llanos of the Orinoco country and the pampas of Argentina, dry treeless uplands in the interior of Brazil, deserts along the Pacific coast in Peru and Chile, treeless alpine regions high in the Andes, and subarctic icy regions at the southern tip of the continent.

Except for the araucaria and mangrove swamp forests, climate rather than species composition determines the types listed above. In fact, the same or similar species of trees are often found in more than one forest type.

(1) TROPICAL BROADLEAF EVERGREEN FORESTS ("RAIN FOREST"). This forest type is sometimes referred to as "rain forest," since the amount and distribution of rainfall are the limiting factors in its occurrence. The type occurs where temperature conditions are tropical, usually at low and middle elevations, and where there is a heavy rainfall distributed throughout the year, with no pronounced dry season. The forest is composed of broadleaf trees and palms (no coniferous trees), and the trees retain their leaves throughout the year.

Tropical broadleaf evergreen forests are dense and usually have heavy stands of timber. Such forests are typically three-storied. The upper story is composed of forest giants often 6 to 8 feet in diameter and 150 feet, or more, high. Beneath this is an intermediate story of smaller trees up to 3 feet in diameter and 100 feet high; and below this, an understory of small trees that can grow in heavy shade. The forests are usually hung and interlaced with vines that climb to the tops of the highest trees and seem to bind the whole formation together. Under such a forest it appears to be twilight even at midday.

The rain forest is the most abundant and widespread type in South America. Its greatest extent is in the Amazon River basin. Vast, largely unbroken, and as wild and little-explored as any region in the world, it extends from the Amazon basin through most of French Guiana, Surinam, and British Guiana, and westward past the mouth of the Orinoco River in Venezuela.

A smaller area of rain forest lies in a narrow belt along the seaward side of the coastal ranges of Brazil from about latitude 5° to 30°S. Another patch surrounds the upper portions of Lake Maracaibo in Venezuela, and still another is found in the basin of the Magdalena River in Colombia. A ribbon of rain forest also stretches along the Pacific coast from the Panama border to Guayaquil in Ecuador.

The number of tree species in the rain forest runs into the thousands, and the composition of the forest varies greatly from one region to another. Nearly all the mahogany (*Swietenia* sp.) [2] in South America and all of the *Hevea* type of rubber are confined to this type, as are the brazil-nut trees (*Bertholletia excelsa*) and many cabinet woods. Except along the coast and for varying distances back from the main rivers, this forest type has been little exploited. Much of it is unexplored or has been seen only from the air. There are treeless areas within the forest, and other areas where palms are the only trees, but such areas have not been accurately mapped. The tropical broadleaf evergreen forests of South America constitute the greatest untapped natural resource in the continent.

(2) TROPICAL BROADLEAF DECIDUOUS FORESTS. These forests occur where there is a pronounced annual dry season, during which many or all of the trees shed their leaves. There is generally no sharp dividing line between this type and the preceding one; they are most easily distinguished one from another in the dry season.

Deciduous tropical forests do not have as heavy stands of timber as do the evergreen broadleaf forests. The trees often reach large diameters but are not very tall and usually are wide-spreading. Leguminosae are common. Usually there is a heavy ground cover of wild pineapple, shrubs, and herbaceous growths.

The largest extent of tropical broadleaf deciduous forests is in Brazil, behind the maritime belt of evergreen broadleaf forest and extending westward across the upper portions of the watershed of the Paraná River almost to the Paraguay River in eastern Paraguay. A smaller area is found in southern Brazil south of the araucaria forests, and others occur on the upper watershed of the São Francisco River and in Matto Grosso at the head of the Paraguay River in Brazil and Bolivia. There are also forests of this type in Venezuela, on the seaward side of the coastal range both east and west of Caracas.

Both the soils and the climates in these regions are well adapted to agriculture and, as a result, large areas of forest have been cleared. Most of the coffee in Brazil is grown on land that was formerly deciduous forest. These deciduous forests have suffered much from uncontrolled exploitation and from devastating forest fires in the dry seasons.

(3) MOUNTAIN BROADLEAF EVERGREEN FORESTS ("CLOUD FOREST"). This type occurs high in the Andes in a belt of varying width from central Bolivia to Venezuela. It is sharply cut off on the west by treeless regions, but on the east merges gradually into the tropical broadleaf evergreen forests of the Amazon basin.

In general, the trees are small in diameter and not very tall, but grow in dense stands. They usually occupy such rough terrain and are so re-

[2] Source for botanical nomenclature: S. J. Record and R. W. Hess. 1943. *Timbers of the New World*. Yale University Press, New Haven.

mote from civilization that they have been little exploited; the only well-known product is quinine, from the wild *Cinchona* trees.

(4) TEMPERATE CONIFEROUS AND BROADLEAF FORESTS. This type is found in southern Chile, extending at some points across the Andes into Argentina. The forests extend practically unbroken from latitude 35° S. to and beyond the Straits of Magellan. Cold, wet winters predominate throughout this region.

The hardwoods of this type are mainly species of the genus *Nothofagus*, the southern-hemisphere equivalent of the beech of the north. Mingled with the hardwoods are several conifers. The forests are usually quite dense, with heavy stands of timber of good quality, but owing to the sparse population and lack of transportation they have been little exploited.

(5) ARAUCARIA ("PINE") FORESTS. This type is differentiated by its species of trees rather than by its climatic aspect. It consists of two separate portions, in both of which the prevailing timber is of the genus *Araucaria* of the Coniferae. Araucaria, often referred to as "Brazilian," "Paraná," or "Chilean" pine, yields a useful general-purpose wood much like the yellow pine of the North Temperate Zone. The edible seeds of the araucaria, collected when the trees are felled, are an important article of commerce in Chile.

Much the largest area is located in southeastern Brazil, in the States of Paraná, Santa Catarina, and Rio Grande do Sul, with small and unimportant extensions into Uruguay, eastern Paraguay, and the Argentinian Territory of Misiones. In this araucaria forest there is a mingling of hardwoods, of which the most important is embuia (*Phoebe porosa*). The araucaria forests of Brazil have been and are now being heavily exploited, both for use in the country and for export. Lumbering in these forests is carried on by modern methods and on a larger scale than in any other South American forests.

In the Brazilian araucaria forests the original understory consisted largely of shrubby trees of yerba maté or Paraguay tea (*Ilex paraguariensis*), and very extensive plantations of this plant, whose product is so universally used in southern South America, have been established for many years. More recently, plantations of true tea (*Thea sinensis*) have been started. Other areas have been cleared for pasture and farming, and the araucaria forest has shrunk so much that it may soon be unable to supply its local and export markets.

The other and much smaller area of araucaria forest is located on both sides of the Andean divide, mainly in Chile, near latitude 40° S. The trees are found in pure and usually open stands. Exploitation has not been heavy because of the rough terrain and the sparse population. It is not probable that much araucaria lumber from this forest will ever be exported, for Chile, so much of whose area is treeless, will consume all the lumber that the forest can produce.

(6) DRY SCRUB FORESTS. This xerophytic type of forest is found in areas of limited and seasonally concentrated rainfall, or in areas of adequate rainfall but of salty, alkaline, or porous soils.

The largest area, in eastern Brazil, merges on the west into the vast treeless plains of the Brazilian Highlands. Another large area comprises the Gran Chaco, in northern Argentina and western Paraguay; in this section, where the scrubby nature of the trees is due more to alkaline soil than to a lack of rainfall, red quebracho (*Schinopsis* spp.) is by far the most important tree because of its great value as a source of tanning material. Another dry scrub forest covers the coastal region in western Venezuela and the Guajira Peninsula in Colombia. Here divi-divi (*Libidibia coriaria*) is the most important species, although some areas can support cactus only. A somewhat similar forest occupies the coast of Ecuador and Peru south of Guayaquil.

(7) MANGROVE SWAMP FORESTS. Mangrove swamps occupy shallow salt-water belts of varying width on the Atlantic side of South America from about the Tropic of Capricorn to latitude 10° S. and again from latitude 3° S. along the coasts of Guiana and Venezuela to Trinidad. Mangrove swamps are also found west of Caracas to the Peninsula of Paraguaná, and west of the Guajira Peninsula to the Panama border. On the Pacific coast, although not so well developed, this type is found more or less continuously from Panama to Guayaquil.

In these forests the trees grow in dense stands on land that is under water at high tide. Tangles of arching and interlacing aerial roots make such forests almost impenetrable. The main species is red mangrove (*Rhizophora mangle*), with *Avicennia* and *Conocarpus* interspersed. The bark of all these species of mangrove is rich in tannin, which, despite its poor quality, is used locally by the leather industry and is exported to some extent. Mangrove wood is hard, heavy, and durable and is used for firewood, charcoal, posts, crossties, and piling. In the future these mangrove forests will probably be utilized much more heavily than they are today.

The Forests of South America by Countries

In this section the forests of each South American country will be described briefly. Statistical data concerning forest areas, fellings, and foreign trade are presented in Tables 10–I and 10–II.

COLOMBIA. Tables 10–I and 10–II imply that Colombia ranks fourth among South American countries in both total forest area and production (fellings) and second in area of accessible forests.[3] The figure 62,000 hectares for accessible forests is at present much too high. Well over half of the forest area is still in public ownership. From Table 10–II it may

---

[3] The statements here and later regarding the ranks of the several countries are based on Tables 10–I and 10–II and hence are approximate only, since the figures in the tables represent the situation at different dates.

be seen that the exports and imports of forest products are small in comparison with the total production. Most of Colombia's timber imports are of coniferous sawn lumber.

TABLE 10–I

SOUTH AMERICA: FOREST AREAS, *ca.* 1953 [a]

			Forest Areas			Population
			1,000 Hectares	Per Cent of Total Land Area	Accessible Forests (1,000 Hectares)	
Argentina	1953[b]	1953[b]	70,000	25	60,000	18,379,000
Bolivia	1938	1950	47,000	44	6,000	3,019,031
Brazil	1954	1950	480,195	57	120,048	51,944,397
British Guiana ..	1952	1953	18,100	91	3,600	465,416
Chile	1953	1952	16,360	22	6,895	5,930,809
Colombia	1953	1954	69,000	62	62,000	12,381,160
Ecuador	1953	1952	12,000	44	2,500	3,348,365
French Guiana ..	1954	1954	8,500	96	1,500	27,863
Paraguay	1952	1954	20,906	54	6,272	1,530,000
Peru	1952	1950	70,000	62	15,000	8,492,873
Surinam	1953	1952	11,721	84	1,000	238,000
Uruguay	1951	1953	486	3	486	2,550,000
Venezuela	1951	1950	36,500[c]	41	12,000[c]	5,034,838
Total			860,000	34	297,300	

[a] Areas copied, percentages calculated, from Food and Agriculture Organization of the United Nations, *Yearbook of Forest Products Statistics, 1954*, Table 45, pp. 122-123. Population from *The Statesman's Yearbook, 1955*.

[b] The first date after each name refers to the forest data, the second date to the population.

[c] Unofficial figure; includes brushlands.

As the forests are opened up and the demand for more kinds of products increases, Colombia will probably become a large exporter.

The Guajira Peninsula and regions west of it along the Caribbean comprise an arid section, occupied by dry scrub forests containing little or no timber of saw-log size but yielding tanning material from divi-divi pods and mangrove bark.

West of this dry region, occupying portions of the watershed of the Magdalena River, is a belt of tropical broadleaf evergreen forest. Much of this is readily accessible and has been heavily exploited, and portions of it have been cleared for agriculture. The same type of forest reappears along the Pacific coast from Panama to Ecuador. Most of this region is sparsely settled and the forests have not been greatly exploited. Near the mouth of the Atrato River there are heavy forests of cativo (*Prioria copaifera*) and other species that will eventually provide export products. A belt of mountain broadleaf evergreen forest follows the Andes range and its bifurcations, but gives way at the highest elevations to treeless páramos.

East of the Andes the northern drainage basin of the Orinoco River in Colombia consists of treeless llanos, with narrow strips of timber along the watercourses. South of the llanos dense and virtually unexplored tropical broadleaf evergreen forests extend across the divide to the northern tributaries of the Amazon.

TABLE 10–II

SOUTH AMERICA: PRODUCTION (FELLINGS) AND FOREIGN TRADE IN FOREST PRODUCTS, *ca.* 1953 [a]

	Fellings					Foreign Trade in Forest Products			
	Total Fellings	Sawlogs, Veneer Logs, and Logs for Sleepers	Pulpwood and Pit Props	Other Industrial Wood	Fuel Wood (Including wood for charcoal)	Volume		Value	
						Exports	Imports	Exports	Imports
	Thousand cubic meters roundwood equivalents							*Thousand U.S. dollars*	
Argentina	15,960	1,930	150	1,080	12,800	8	1,270	968	61,514
Bolivia	7,531[b]	114[b]	14[b]	6[b]	7,400[b]	90[b]	20[b]	...	...
Brazil	(94,920)	4,800[c]	120[d]	...	90,000	1,660	1,250	38,170[e]	77,124[e]
British Guiana	338	159	–	9	170	170	20	1,633	918
Chile	5,743	2,008	265	260	3,210	250	190	9,362	8,370
Colombia	6,463	1,125	215	3	5,120	30	170	67[e]	...
Ecuador	836	←————200*————→			636	...	...	...	...
French Guiana	40	30	–	–	10	1	–	63[b]	...
Paraguay	1,800[e]*	300[e]*	–[e]	–*	1,500*	280[b]	7[b]	...	...
Peru	1,347	34	18	–	1,295	8	580	384[f]	10,347
Surinam	315	115	–	–	200	50	30	2,093	75
Uruguay	608[e]	66[e]	–[e]	12[e]	530	...	340[e]	...	...
Venezuela	(328)[g]	292[g]	–	2[g]	34[g]	–	240	57[f]	15,345

( ) Incomplete figure.
– None or less than half the appropriate unit.
... Not available.
* Unofficial figure.
[a] Based primarily on: Food and Agriculture Organization of the United Nations, *Yearbook of Forest Products Statistics, 1954*, Tables 1, 40, 41, 43, with additional data from the same, *1951*, Table 38; *1953*, Tables 40, 42.
[b] 1951.
[c] Excludes logs for sleepers.
[d] Excludes pit props.
[e] 1952.
[f] 1950.
[g] Recorded fellings only. Total fellings in 1948 estimated at 814,000 cubic meters, in 1950 at 273,000 (*ibid. 1949*, Table 1; *1951*, Table 1).

Around the main centers of population, such as Bogotá, Medellin, and Cartagena, so much land has been cleared for agriculture and the remaining forests have been so heavily exploited that sometimes even firewood is scarce. Apart from plantations of eucalyptus, especially around Bogotá, little has been done in Colombia to protect the existing forests or to reforest denuded areas. Although the forest resources of the country as a whole are very great, a large part of the forests, especially those lying east of the Andes, are so inaccessible and remote from markets that they add nothing to the economy of the country and probably will not for many years.

Principal Commercial Species.

CABINET WOODS: Gateado, Albarco, Balaústre, Cabima, Tananeo, Roble Colorado, Mahogany.

SPECIALTY WOODS: Lignum-vitae, Black Palm.

GENERAL-UTILITY WOODS: Espavé, Carreto, Apamate, Acapro, Tolú, Canalete, Almácigo, Guayabo, Jabillo, María, Maní, Cativo, Samán, Carapa, Cedro, Balata.

TANNIN WOODS: Mangrove, Divi-divi.

ESSENTIAL OILS, DRUGS, ETC.: Anime, Cinchona, Coca, Tonka Bean, Copaiba, Ivory Nut, Panama Hat Palm.

VENEZUELA. Venezuela ranks about sixth among the South American countries in total forest area and fifth in area of accessible forests. She has long imported relatively large quantities of lumber, mainly squared timbers of yellow pine which are re-sawed into boards in the country. Much of this goes to the oil fields. In terms of value, "paper, paperboard, and manufactures thereof" accounted for two thirds of the imports in 1953. Exports of forest products are of minor importance.

Venezuela is divided into three main geographical regions: the basin of the Orinoco River, including the llanos and the Guiana hinterland; the eastern range of the Andes which continues past Caracas as a relatively low coastal range; and the Maracaibo lake basin.

Much of the territory drained by the Orinoco consists of treeless llanos, with occasional narrow strips of timber along the streams. The llanos gradually merge on the south and southeast into heavy tropical broadleaf evergreen forests, dense and almost uninhabited, which can be entered only with great difficulty along rapid-infested rivers.

The coastal range contains a belt of deciduous forest which adjoins the llanos. The eastern range of the Andes bears mountain broadleaf evergreen forests; much land has been cleared for upland agriculture in this zone. An area of dry scrub forest occupies the region lying northeast and northwest of Lake Maracaibo. Around the head of Lake Maracaibo, bordered on the south and west by high mountain forests, lie tropical broadleaf evergreen forests which have not been completely explored owing to inaccessibility and hostile Indians.

Until recent years, little afforestation was done in Venezuela except for plantations of mahogany and other species along the rights of way of the railroads near Caracas. Forestry work has been inaugurated too recently to show much result. As in many other tropical countries, it is a "feast or a famine" in Venezuela: near the centers of population the forests have been so depleted that even firewood is becoming scarce, while in the less accessible regions the forests remain almost untouched. Except, perhaps, for a few woods for special purposes, Venezuela could and should be self-supporting in forest products and should have a large exportable surplus.

Principal Commercial Species.

CABINET WOODS: Gateado, Angelino, Albarco, Coffee Wood, Tananeo, Roble Colorado, Mahogany.

SPECIALTY WOODS: West Indian Boxwood, Vera, Black Palm, Lignum-vitae.

GENERAL-UTILITY WOODS: Caracolí, Carreto, Apamate, Saqui-saqui, Canalete, Jabillo, María, Courbaril, Samán, Carapa, Spanish Cedar, Balata.

TANNIN WOODS: Mangrove, Divi-divi.

ESSENTIAL OILS, DRUGS, GUMS, ETC. Anime, Tonka Bean, Balata, Copaiba, Courbaril.

BRITISH GUIANA. While the three European colonies on the Caribbean rank first among the South American countries in terms of the ratio of forest land to total land area (French Guiana, 96 per cent; British Guiana, 91 per cent; Surinam, 84 per cent; Table 10–I), they rank last in terms of production (Table 10–II).

Except for a strip along the coast and a few smaller settlements inland, most of British Guiana is covered with tropical broadleaf evergreen forests.

While much of the forest lands remains virtually unexplored, more is known of the composition of British Guiana's forests than of that of other tropical American countries, because the colony has maintained an active forestry service for many years. The country is more than self-supporting in forest products, exporting shingles, firewood, and other products to the British West Indian islands and veneer logs to Europe. The best known forest product is greenheart, which, because of its relative immunity to teredos, has been largely used for piling and other marine structures. As the country is further developed, exports should increase.

Exports of forest products from British Guiana are principally sawn lumber, saw logs and veneer logs, charcoal, and fuel wood. The imports consist mainly of paper and paper products, sawn lumber, barrels and barrel staves.

Principal Commercial Species.

CABINET WOODS: Purpleheart, Roble Colorado, Brownheart, Letterwood.

SPECIALTY WOODS: Greenheart.

GENERAL-UTILITY WOODS: Caracolí, Fotui, White Cedar, Washiba, Laurel, Pequia, Dalina, Jabillo, María, Maní, Houmirí, Cabbagebark, Wallaba, Courbaril, Mora, Crabwood, Spanish Cedar, Virola, Beefwood, Simaruba, Cèdre gris.

OTHERS: Mangrove, Tonka Bean, Balata.

SURINAM. Forest conditions in Surinam are much like those in British Guiana. Except for a strip along the coast, the country is covered with dense tropical broadleaf evergreen forest, much of which has not been explored. The species of trees are about the same as in British Guiana. There are very heavy pure stands of possentrie (*Hura crepitans*) near the coast. *Virola* is abundant and is being exported in the form of veneer logs. Crabwood or *Carapa* abounds in the western part of the colony. Manbarklak is valued for its resistance to teredo damage.

Surinam has a department of forestry which has done valuable work classifying the forest species and investigating the possibilities of various woods.

In 1953 Surinam exported 14,000 cubic meters of saw logs and veneer logs, 5,000 of sleepers, and 9,000 of veneer and plywood. That same year her imports of forest products consisted principally of paper and paper products, with a small quantity of sawn lumber and fiberboard. It is probable that exports from Surinam will increase and that the country will always have an exportable surplus.

FRENCH GUIANA. French Guiana has the highest ratio (96 per cent) of forested area to total land area of any South American country, but also by far the lowest production. The colony is almost entirely covered with tropical broadleaf evergreen forests, mostly unexplored and devoid of transportation facilities except for the rivers.

The kinds of timber are about the same as in British Guiana and Surinam. Best known are the cabinet wood satiné, and bois de rose femelle, which yields an essential oil used in the perfume industry. Occasional small amounts of *Carapa* and *Simaruba* are cut for export. Some timber is cut for charcoal and firewood. In the future French Guiana may develop an important export trade in forest products.

ECUADOR. Ecuador is divided into three zones: the upper watersheds of Amazon tributaries east of the Andes, the Andean ranges, and the slopes and plains between the Andes and the Pacific Ocean. Unfortunately, no figures are available on the exports or imports of forest products for this country.

The Amazon forests are of the tropical broadleaf evergreen type and have not been completely explored. They are as a whole extremely inaccessible, their only outlet being by the long voyage down the Amazon. Along the upper slopes of the Andes there are mountain broadleaf evergreen forests, greatly denuded by the shifting agricultural population. In this high mountain forest much cinchona bark was collected during World War II.

The lower western slopes of the mountains, and the plains below, have tropical broadleaf evergreen forests in the northern part of the country and dry scrub forests in the south. Much land has been cleared for cacao and sugar cane cultivation. This belt, especially the valley of the Guayas River, is rich in balsa. During World War II some 95 per cent of the world's supply of balsa came from Ecuador.

Principal Commercial Species.

CABINET WOODS: Amarillo, Sándalo.
SPECIALTY WOODS: Balsa.
GENERAL-UTILITY WOODS: Sisín, Caracolí, Laurel, Mora, Tangaré, Spanish
  Cedar, Sande, María, Guayacán, Guachapelí.
OTHER: Mangrove, Mora (fustic), Copal, Cinchona, Caucho, Divi-divi,
  Ivory Nut, Panama Hat Palm.

PERU. Although Peru and Argentina are closely tied for second rank among the countries of South America in terms of total forest area, approximately 85 per cent of the forest area of Argentina is reckoned as "accessible," whereas the ratio for Peru is only about 21 per cent. In Peru by far the greater part of the fellings are for fuel wood and charcoal.

Peru has three geographic zones: the upper Amazon basin, the Andes, and the slopes and plains between the mountains and the Pacific. The country east of the Andes is covered with dense tropical broadleaf evergreen forests, most of which are wild and inaccessible. Mahogany occurs here in very large quantities and some of it is exported down the Amazon.

Originally clothed—except for treeless alpine portions—in mountain broadleaf evergreen forests, the Andes have been thickly settled since the days of the Incas, and many of their forests have disappeared. In some sections even firewood is scarce. Eucalyptus has been planted to a considerable extent. Cinchona is an abundant understory tree in these mountain forests, and great quantities of its bark were collected during World War II as a source of quinine.

Except for a small area of dry scrub forest adjoining Ecuador, all of the western portion of Peru is treeless and very arid. Some tree plantations have been made where irrigation water is available. Since Peru's forests east of the Andes have their only feasible outlet down the Amazon River, the heavily settled portions of the arid coast have to import nearly all their lumber.

In 1952, Peru exported 10,000 and, in 1953, 3,000 cubic meters of sawn hardwood lumber. The value of the imports of forest products in 1953 was about 270 times that of the exports! About three fifths of the value of the imports in 1953 was accounted for by sawn softwood and railway sleepers [4] and about a quarter by newsprint and other paper products.

Principal Commercial Species.

CABINET WOODS: Walnut, Mahogany.
GENERAL-UTILITY WOODS: Figueroa, Spanish Cedar.

BOLIVIA. Slightly more than one eighth of Bolivia's forested area is rated as accessible. Although Bolivia ranks about third among the South

---

[4] There were unusually heavy imports of these two items in 1953 (in 1,000 cubic meters: softwood sawn wood, 1952, 61; 1953, 159; sleepers, 1952, 13; 1953, 159) FAO, *Yearbook of Forest Products Statistics, 1954*, Table 39.

American countries in production of forest products, 98 per cent of the production in 1952 was for fuel wood and charcoal. Both exports and imports are of minor importance. Exports in 1951 included some 50,000 cubic meters of fuel wood and 20,000 of hardwood logs (probably for the most part mahogany shipped down the Amazon). Imports, brought inland by rail from the port of Arica in Chile, consist mainly of paper products and sawn lumber.

With the western range of the Andes forming its western boundary, all of Bolivia drains eastward into tributaries of the Amazon and Paraguay Rivers. The country's two main topographic features are the high Bolivian Plateau and the slopes and plains east of the plateau. The greater portion of the plateau region is treeless. In northern and northeastern Bolivia, especially on the upper waters of the Madeira River, a tributary of the Amazon, there are wild and largely unexplored tropical broadleaf evergreen forests. It is reported that this region contains a great deal of mahogany.

Along the eastern slopes of the eastern Andean range, at high elevations, there are mountain broadleaf evergreen forests. Farther south, where the mountains are lower and the climate is drier, lies a belt of tropical broadleaf deciduous forest, and this type also occurs in the northeastern corner of the country, in the headwaters region of the Paraguay River. A small portion of the southeastern corner of Bolivia lies within the dry scrub forest of the Gran Chaco. This section has wax palms, quebracho, quebracho blanco, algarroba, etc., none of which is exploited.

Until transportation is opened up between the centers of population in the plateaus and the forests to the east, Bolivia's forests will be of little benefit to her. The plateau country is too bleak to permit the successful growing of trees in plantations. The per capita consumption of forest products in Bolivia is probably among the lowest in the world.

CHILE. Chile ranks about eighth among the South American countries in total forest area, sixth in area of accessible forest, fifth in production of forest products (1953), but perhaps second only to Brazil in the value of her exports of forest products. The exports in 1953 were predominantly sawn lumber (hardwood, 73,000 cubic meters; softwood, 62,000), plus a small quantity of railway sleepers (9,000 cubic meters). The imports consist mostly of wood pulp, newsprint, and other paper products, some sawn lumber for use in the treeless north, and quebracho tanning extract from Argentina.

The northern third of Chile is desert. The central third was formerly partially forested but now is mainly devoted to agriculture. The southern third is nearly all forested except for cold wastes beyond the Straits of Magellan. There is an area of araucaria forests at about latitude 42° S., but with this exception Chile's forests are temperate-zone mixed broadleaf and deciduous forests.

Most of Chile's requirements for forest products are supplied within the country, mainly from the araucaria and mixed temperate forests. Lack of transportation facilities and the inaccessibility of the southernmost forests have hindered large-scale commercial exploitation; the most accessible forests have been heavily overexploited. Chile probably never will be an important exporter of lumber, but with proper care of her forests should be practically self-supporting.

Forest fires do tremendous damage in Chile's forests. It is estimated that they destroy annually over four times as much timber as is used by the Chileans.

Principal Commercial Species.

GENERAL-UTILITY WOODS: Chilean Pine, Alerce, Lahuán, Lingue, Ciprés, Raulí, Coihué, Roble.

TANNIN WOODS: Lingue, Algarrobillo, Ulmo.

OTHERS: Winter's Bark, Quillay.

BRAZIL. Brazil, by far the largest country in South America in both area and population, ranks first in nearly every category shown in Tables 10–I and 10–II. Her total forested area is somewhat greater than that of all the rest of South America put together, and she probably possesses more than two fifths of the total area of accessible forests on the continent. In 1953 total fellings came to about six times the figure for Argentina which ranked second in this respect, and exports of forest products may well have exceeded in volume the combined volume of those of all other South American countries.

Topographically, Brazil may be divided into five main regions: the Amazon Basin, the Paraná-Paraguay Basin, the Guiana Highlands, the Brazilian Highlands, and the Coastal Plain.

The Amazon Basin includes more than one third of Brazil and is one of the world's least explored and least developed regions. The greater part is occupied by seemingly endless tropical broadleaf evergreen forests. Inland from many of the main rivers and at the headwaters of the southern tributaries of the Amazon are treeless areas whose limits have not been accurately determined. With the exception of *Hevea* rubber, whose production is much less than it was before plantations were developed in the Far East, and some mahogany from the western tributaries of the Amazon, few forest products come from the Amazon Basin. Large areas of mangrove swamps occur at the mouth of the Amazon and extend along the coast.

Much of the Paraná-Paraguay Basin in Brazil is covered with tropical broadleaf deciduous forests, and a part of the araucaria pine forests is within this drainage system. The territory at the headwaters of both of the rivers is mainly treeless, though there is some tropical broadleaf deciduous forest at the head of the Paraguay.

The Guiana Highlands in northern Brazil form a largely unexplored tract, part of it covered with tropical broadleaf evergreen forests, part with treeless savannas, and part with intermingling belts of forest and savanna. Very little forest produce comes from this region.

The Brazilian Highlands, lying east of the Paraná-Paraguay Basin and the southern portion of the Amazon Basin, are bordered on the east by an escarpment that separates the highlands from the Coastal Plain. Much of this highland region is treeless, although there are dry scrub forests in its northeastern part and farther south there are areas of tropical broadleaf deciduous forests. Most of the araucaria pine forests are in the highland zone. The accessible portion of the forests of the Brazilian Highlands have been heavily exploited for many years.

The Coastal Plain forms a belt of varying width from about latitude 7° to 30° S. Almost all of this plain was originally covered with high-quality tropical broadleaf evergreen forests, with mangrove swamp forests along the shore. The upper slopes of the interior escarpment are covered in the north by dry scrub forests and in the south by tropical deciduous broadleaf forests. In former days this plain yielded the greater part of the cabinet woods, especially rosewood, for which Brazil is noted. Large portions of the plain and the slopes of the escarpment are now cleared for agriculture, and it is in this region that most of the population of Brazil lives today.

In some of the heavily populated portions of Brazil, forest products, even firewood, have become scarce, but in most of the country, owing to lack of labor, lumbering equipment, and transportation facilities, forest exploitation is in its infancy.

In Brazil federal regulations control the cutting of timber, though they are not universally enforced, and the country is intensifying its program of reforestation. Eucalyptus, grown in plantations in many sections, is used mainly for fuel and railroad sleepers. Except for a few specialized products, Brazil will doubtless continue to be self-sufficient in forest products and will have an increasing exportable surplus. In the realm of hardwoods (broadleaf woods) Brazil's resources are the greatest of any country in the world. This resource will grow in importance as research and experiments determine the technological qualities of many common woods that are not much used at present.

The principal exports of forest products in 1953 were (in thousands of cubic meters, roundwood): saw logs and veneer logs, 27; sleepers, 16; veneer and plywood, 2; poles, piling, and posts, 1; (in thousands of cubic meters of sawn wood): sawn lumber, 954. Most of these exports went to the neighboring countries of Uruguay and Argentina. The imports consist predominantly of wood pulp, newsprint, and other paper and paper products.

Principal Commercial Species.

CABINET WOODS: Gonçalo, Peroba, Embuia, Jequitibá, Araraúba, Rosewood, Kingwood, Cabreuva, Oleo Vermelho, Pau Roxo, Vinhatico, Ibiráro, Acapú, Mahogany, Páo Rainha, Páo Amarello.

GENERAL-UTILITY WOODS: Paraná Pine, Urunday, Quebracho Blanco, Peroba, Lapacho, Ipé, Louro, Freijo, Guayabí, Pequía, Araça, Urucurana, María, Moumerí, Ibirá, Sapupira, Jatahy, Angelim, Braúna, Angico, Algarroba, Cangerana, Andiroba, Cedro, Guariuba, Ucuhúba, Massaranduba, Marupá, Muiraúba, Cedro Rana.

TANNIN WOODS: Quebracho, Mangrove, Cebil, Barbatimão.

EDIBLE PRODUCTS: Pequia, Brazilnut, Paradise Nut, Paraguay Tea, Cumarú.

NONEDIBLE PRODUCTS: Pará Rubber, Jatahy, Ucuhúba, Carnaúba, Oiticica, Piassaba.

PARAGUAY. Paraguay ranks about seventh among the South American countries both in total forested area and in the area of accessible forests. Accurate up-to-date data are not available for production, exports, and imports; FAO figures for 1951 and 1952 are presented in Table 10–II.

Paraguay is divided into two parts by the Paraguay River. East of the river there is a belt of level country, in part naturally treeless and in part cleared for agriculture along the river, behind which lies hilly country, an extension of the Brazilian Highlands, largely covered with dense tropical broadleaf deciduous forests. Here, excellent stands of valuable species have been only slightly exploited, owing to lack of transportation. Rafts of logs of such species as Spanish cedar are floated down the Paraná River to markets in Argentina.

West of the Paraguay lies the Gran Chaco. This section of Paraguay is flat and mostly treeless and swampy for some distance back from the river. The little-known region farther west consists of belts and patches of rather scrubby timber separated by treeless savannas. Here rainfall is lacking during parts of the year and the soil tends to be alkaline.

In this Chaco section of Paraguay, quebracho is much the most important tree. Formerly, quebracho logs were exported on a very large scale to Argentina, the United States, and Europe for manufacture into tannic acid. More recently, several quebracho tannin plants have been established in Paraguay and the export of quebracho extract has largely replaced the export of logs.

Paraguay's quebracho forests, which have been her most important forest resource, have been badly abused by indiscriminate cutting and lack of protection against forest fires. Since quebracho grows very slowly and does not reseed freely, there is danger that this source of income to the country will decline.

Owing to Paraguay's isolation (all imports must come through Argentina, with a heavy transportation charge up-river), imports of forest products are very scanty and consist mainly of paper and paper products. Paraguay is of necessity self-supporting in such forest products as lumber.

She can, and very likely will, export increasing amounts of logs of species that are in demand in Argentina and Uruguay, but probably will not develop an export market—except for quebracho—outside of the continent.

Principal Commercial Species.

CABINET WOODS: Incienso, Ibiráro.

SPECIALTY WOODS: Palo Blanco.

GENERAL-UTILITY WOODS: Urunday, Quebracho Blanco, Lapacho, Peterebí, Guayabí, Ibirá, Curupay, Algarroba, Cangerana, Cedro, Mora.

TANNING MATERIALS: Quebracho, Curupay.

OTHERS: Palo Santo (fragrant resin), Paraguay Tea, Algarroba (pods for cattle feed), Carnaúba.

URUGUAY. Uruguay, in area the smallest republic in South America, also has by far the smallest forest area and lowest ratio of forested area to total area. Production is mostly for fuel wood and charcoal. Posts, poles, and other timber, for farm use largely, come from plantations of algarroba, eucalyptus, poplar, and other species.

Uruguay is for the most part treeless, a northeastward extension of the pampas of Argentina, varied in the north by low ridges or spurs from the Brazilian Highlands. Along some of the rivers, especially in the northern and eastern parts of the country, there are forest belts with species similar to those in adjacent portions of Argentina and Brazil. Some products from these forests, mainly cedro and lapacho logs, are floated down the Uruguay River to Montevideo.

Even with intensive forest management, Uruguay can hardly hope ever to be self-supporting with respect to, and much less an exporter of, forest products. The best that can be expected is that her small area of natural forests, plus forest plantations, will continue to fulfill her needs for fuel wood and farm timbers.

Exports are practically nil but imports are relatively heavy. Uruguay obtains cabinet woods from Paraguay and Argentina, and large quantities of Paraná pine lumber from Brazil.

ARGENTINA. We have seen that, while Argentina vies with Peru for second place among the South American countries in terms of total forested area, she has a much greater area of accessible forest. This helps explain why her production (fellings) is more than ten times that of Peru (Table 10–II).

Argentina is divided into four main physiographic regions. The subtropical northern plain, the Gran Chaco, consists of dry scrub forests mingled with treeless areas. This is the home of the red quebracho, the world's most important source of tanning material. Most of the quebracho was formerly exported in log form for conversion in factories in the United States and Europe, but now there are some twenty tannin-extract factories in Argentina and the export of quebracho logs has almost ceased. Mingled with the red quebracho in the Chaco are other timbers, including quebracho blanco and algarroba. Considerable quantities of red quebracho and algarroba are used for sleepers and paving blocks.

In the part of the subtropical region that lies in the Province of Corrientes and the Territory of Misiones there are excellent tropical broadleaf deciduous forests, which yield logs that are floated down the Paraná and Uruguay Rivers to Buenos Aires and Montevideo.

The Pampas in central Argentina and in Patagonia to the south are treeless. The Andean region along the western boundary of the country contains some timber, mainly in the extreme southern portions, where the temperate coniferous and broadleaf forests of Chile cross the divide into Argentina. Owing to their inaccessibility, these forests are very little exploited.

Tree plantations, principally willow (*Salix*), poplar (*Populus*), and other fast-growing species, have been established on a quite large scale in some of the treeless portions of Argentina. Argentina, however, will continue to be a "have not" country in forest resources. Even with careful conservation (which is not in effect at present), it will have to import the greater part of its required forest products, especially softwood lumber— mainly Paraná pine from Brazil—and paper products. Although furniture and plywood industries have been established in Argentina, they will not be able to expand materially without depending largely on imported raw materials.

Argentina's exports of forest products in 1953 were valued as follows in U.S. dollars: wood and lumber, $605,000; paper, paperboard, and manufactures thereof, $340,000; wood manufactures, $23,000. Imports of forest products, of which the total value was about sixty times that of the corresponding exports, were as follows: wood and lumber (largely softwood lumber from Brazil and Chile), $44,572,000; wood pulp (from Finland and Sweden), paper and paper products (mostly from Sweden), $12,-090,000; wood manufactures, $4,852,000.

Principal Commercial Species.

CABINET WOODS: Walnut, Incienso, Ibiráro, Tipa.

SPECIALTY WOODS: Palo Blanco.

GENERAL-UTILITY WOODS: Chilean Pine, Alerce, Urunday, Quebracho Blanco, Lapajo, Peterebí, Guayabí, Roble, Guindo, Ibirá, Curupay, Algarroba, Cangerana, Cedro, Mora.

TANNIN WOODS: Red Quebracho, Curupay.

OTHERS: Mora (fustic dye), Winter's Bark, Palo Santo (fragrant resin), Paraguay Tea, Algarroba (pods for cattle feed), Quillay (soapbark).

The Future for South America's Forest Resources

South America is developing rapidly and her population is expanding. As a continent, she has ample forest resources for the future, both for domestic use and for export, but these resources are not evenly distributed. The scarcity of forest products close to centers of population will in the future be aggravated and it will be more and more necessary to develop transportation facilities to make use of forests that are at present inaccessible.

Exportation outside the continent has in the past been largely confined to a few cabinet woods and special products such as quebracho extract. This type of exportation will not increase materially and in some instances may be curtailed. Future exports will consist mainly of common general-utility woods, which can supplement the waning supplies of hardwoods in the North Temperate Zone. This process has already begun: a number of woods that formerly were little used even in the countries where they grow, are now finding markets in the United States and Europe. Much remains to be done, however, in determining the qualifications of such woods for various uses and in educating consumers as to their potentialities.

Most of the countries of South America are in the favorable position of still being able to lock the stable before the horse is stolen. If they put conservation practices into effect before it is too late, their forest resources can be of very great and growing importance, not only to South America itself, but to all the world.

APPENDIX

COMMERCIAL TREE SPECIES OF SOUTH AMERICA
(CLASSIFIED ACCORDING TO USE)

Explanation. The figures in parentheses indicate the forest types in which the trees are mainly found (as numbered on pages 202-205 above). The abbreviations designate the countries in South America where they principally grow.

I. *Trees Destroyed by Utilization*

A. Wood the Principal Product

1. CABINET WOODS

Woods that are hard enough to resist abrasion, that do not warp, and that are easy to work and finish, especially those with beautiful color or grain, are greatly in demand by manufacturers and users of furniture as cabinet wood. Generally these were the woods first exploited in South America and are the best known today, but overexploitation has made many of them scarce. Although in general the demand for cabinet woods seems assured, changing styles greatly affect the demand for different woods. Two generations ago, for example, rosewood was the de-luxe furniture wood; today the demand is for "blond" woods, and rosewood is much less used than formerly. Mahogany, on the other hand, holds its popularity because of its beauty of grain and other good qualities, though in response to the whims of fashion it may end up bleached to almost white or darkened to almost black.

ANACARDIACEAE
  Astronium spp. Diomate, Gateado, Gonçalo. (1, 2, 6) Col., Ven., Braz.
      Brown or reddish, streaked with black. Hard and heavy. Sometimes sliced into veneers for fine furniture.

BIGNONIACEAE
  Paratecoma peroba. Peroba. (1, 2) Braz.

JUGLANDACEAE
  Juglans spp. Nogal (Walnut). (3, 6) Col., Ven., Peru, Arg.
      Most of the walnut in South America is found at high elevations, except in Argentina. Some of it is soft and light-colored, but some is equal in quality to the black walnut of the North Temperate Zone.

LAURACEAE
  Ocotea caracasana. Angelino. (1) Ven.
  Phoebe porosa. Embuia. (5) Braz.
      Embuia grows in southern Brazil mixed with so-called Brazilian pine. Known to the export trade as Brazilian walnut. There is a heavy local demand, and the supply is diminishing.

LECYTHIDACEAE

Cariniana spp. Bacú, Albarco, Jequitibá. (1) Col., Ven., Braz.
Formerly exported from Colombia as "Colombian mahogany." Abundant
in parts of Brazil. Reddish-brown, medium weight, easy to work.

LEGUMINOSAE

Centrolobium spp. Balaústre, Amarillo, Araraúba. (1) Col., Ven., Ec., Braz.
Orange-brown with dark streaks. In local demand for fine furniture.

Copaifera spp. Cabima, Copaiba. (1) Col., Ven., Sur., Braz.
Coppery brown, fairly hard and heavy. In local demand for furniture.

Dalbergia spp. Rosewood, Jacarandá, Kingwood. (1, 2) Braz.
Brown with purplish-black markings. Long known as a de-luxe furniture
wood, but much less popular today than in past generations. Also used for
inlays, turnery, etc. Three centuries of exploitation have greatly depleted
accessible supplies.

Libidibia spp. Coffee Wood, Granadillo. (6) Ven., Col.

Myrocarpus frondosus. Cabreuva, Incienso. (1, 2) Braz., Arg., Par.
Esteemed in Argentina for fine furniture and turnery.

Myroxylon balsamum. Tolú, Sándalo, Oleo Vermelho, Incienso. (1, 2) Col.,
Ven., Ec., Braz., Par., Arg.
Reddish brown, very hard and heavy. Exported from Brazil as Oleo
Vermelho.

Peltogyne spp. Purpleheart, Tananeo, Páo Roxo. (1) Col., Ven., Guianas,
Braz.
Deep purple, hard and heavy. In some demand for inlay and cabinet work.

Plathymenia reticulata. Vinhatico. (1) Braz.
Yellow-brown, moderate hardness and weight. Used locally for cabinet
work, parquet flooring, etc.

Platymiscium spp. Roble Colorado, Macacaúba. (1) Col., Ven., Guianas,
Braz.
Reddish-brown, usually striped. Fairly hard and heavy. Works well.
Sometimes known as Panama redwood. Exported for furniture and turn-
ery. A good wood that probably will increase in importance.

Pterogyne nitens. Ibiráro. (1) Braz., Par., Arg.
Reddish-brown, resembling mahogany. Hard and heavy. Commercially
important in Argentina.

Tipuana tipu. Tipa. (2) Bol., Arg.
Yellowish-brown, medium hardness and weight. Liked in Argentina for
cabinet work.

Vouacapoua spp. Brownheart, Acapú. (1) Guianas, Braz.

MELIACEAE

Swietenia macrophylla. Mahogany, Caoba. (1) Col., Ven., Braz., Peru, Bol.
Mahogany is the world's most important cabinet wood. It has been used
for centuries and has never lost its popularity. Flesh-pink when freshly cut,
it darkens naturally to the typical "mahogany" color, but is usually stained
to expedite darkening. It is also bleached to produce "blond" mahogany.
No other cabinet wood has such a variety of grain and figure. Of medium
hardness and weight, it is easy to work and holds its place well, and in
every respect is ideally adapted for cabinet work. Used mainly as thin
veneers over other wood, but also in the solid form. Limited quantities are

found in western Venezuela and in portions of Colombia and Ecuador, but the main South American supply occurs in a belt along the upper reaches of the southern tributaries of the Amazon in Brazil, Peru, and Bolivia. Since this region is inaccessible and not fully explored, the definite range and total quantity of mahogany there are not known. It is probable that this Amazon region contains more mahogany than does all the rest of tropical America.

MORACEAE
  Brosimum spp. Satiné, Muirapiranga, Páo Rainha. (1) Col., Ven., Braz., Peru, Bol.
    Rich golden-red, very hard and heavy. Not abundant.
  Piratinera spp. Letterwood, Snakewood. (1) Guianas.
    Reddish-brown with peculiar dark markings. Very hard and heavy. Scarce and expensive. Used for inlays and miscellaneous turnery.

PROTEACEAE
  Roupala spp. Carne de Vaca. (1) Braz.
    Dark brown with conspicuous oaklike rays. Hard and heavy. Used locally for furniture.

RUTACEAE
  Euxylophora paraensis. Páo Amarello. (1) Braz.
    Deep yellow. Fairly hard and heavy. A favorite wood in Brazil for parquet flooring and furniture. Not much export demand.

2. SPECIALTY WOODS

Specialty woods are those that, because of certain qualities, are adapted to special uses. With the development of synthetic products, however, the demand for most specialty woods is decreasing.

BOMBACACEAE
  Ochroma spp. Balsa. (1, 6) Ven., Braz., Ec.
    Balsa is the lightest commercial wood in the world, sometimes lighter than cork, for which it may be substituted in life rafts, insulation, etc. It is the favored wood for model airplanes. The world demand for this wood began during World War I and reached its maximum during World War II, when great quantities were exported from Ecuador. Balsa is now giving way for technical purposes to such products as rock wool and fiber glass. Balsa is one of the fastest-growing woods in the world; it springs up like a weed on abandoned farmland and yields saw logs in five years.

FLACOURTIACEAE
  Gossypiospermum praecox. West Indian Boxwood, Zapatero. (6) Ven.
    Most abundant in the area around Lake Maracaibo. The principal boxwood of commerce, used for rulers, engravers' blocks, and turnery. The supply is not too abundant.

LAURACEAE
  Ocotea rodiaei. Greenheart. (1) Br. G., Sur.
    Its great resistance to teredo (seaworm) attack has led to a world-wide use of this wood for marine piling, locks, and other salt-water construction, especially in the tropics. Sometimes used for flooring and general construc-

tion. Greenheart is the principal timber exported from British Guiana, but exports have recently been decreasing.

LECYTHIDACEAE

Eschweilera spp. Manbarklak. (1) Sur.
A wood similar to greenheart, but harder and heavier.

PALMAE

Astrocaryum spp. Black Palm. (1) Col., Ven.
The "rind" of this small palm is extremely hard and strong and is used for canes, fishing rods, etc.

RUBIACEAE

Calycophyllum spp. Palo Blanco. (1) Arg., Par.
Used in Argentina for turnery. A similar wood, called lemonwood, is exported from the West Indies for the manufacture of archery bows. Suited for many of the uses of hickory.

ZYGOPHYLLACEAE

Guaiacum spp. Lignum-vitae, Guayacán. (6) Col., Ven.
Most of the lignum-vitae of commerce comes from the West Indies and Central America, but the tree is also found along the arid coasts of Colombia and Venezuela. Lignum-vitae is one of the hardest and heaviest woods in the world, and was formerly much used for pulleys, bowling balls, and bearing blocks for propeller shafts, but synthetic products have captured much of its market.

3. GENERAL-UTILITY WOODS

By far the greatest number of the forest trees of South America fall into this category. Without any special beauty of color or grain, they are good ordinary woods, comparable to the oak, ash, birch, maple, and gum of the temperate zone. They are used locally to an increasing extent, but are seldom exported, and in a sense are "forgotten" woods, not appreciated as they should be. As South American populations grow and the demand for wood increases, they should more and more come into their own, and many of them are so abundant that even increased local usage should permit large-scale exportation. Much research is needed, however, to determine the technical characteristics of these woods and their adaptability to industrial processes.

ANACARDIACEAE

Anacardium spp. Espavé, Caracolí. (1) Ven., Col., Br. G., Ec., Braz.
A very large and abundant tree. Wood grayish to yellow or light brown, fairly light and soft, with a tendency to cut "woolly." Used for general construction, boxes, dugout canoes, etc.

Astronium urundeuva. Urunday, etc. (1, 6) Braz., Arg., Par.
Heartwood dark red, very hard, heavy, and durable. Used locally for bridge timbers and heavy construction. Not exported.

APOCYNACEAE

Aspidosperma quebracho-blanco. Quebracho Blanco. (6) Arg., Par., Braz.
Found in the Gran Chaco mixed with red quebracho. Wood brownish or pinkish; hard, heavy, and strong. Used locally for heavy construction and fuel.

ARAUCARACEAE

Araucaria araucana. Chilean Pine, Pino. (5) Chile, Arg.

This wood, which resembles the yellow pines of the North Temperate Zone and has similar uses, is found usually in pure stands on both sides of the Andean range in Chile and Argentina. It is of good quality and is used for general construction, interior trim, etc. Owing to the inaccessibility of the forests, its exploitation is not yet highly developed. Local markets, mainly in Chile, will absorb the total cut.

Araucaria angustifolia. Paraná Pine, Brazilian Pine, Pinheiro, Pino. (5) Braz., Arg., Par.

This tree, whose wood resembles that of Chilean pine, grows in southern Brazil and extends into eastern Paraguay and the Territory of Misiones in Argentina. The stands are mixed with embuia and other hardwoods. This wood is exploited to a greater extent than any other in South America, and with modern logging equipment and sawmills. It is used throughout southern Brazil, whence it is exported to Argentina and Uruguay in large quantities. Some has been exported to the United States and Europe. These pine forests have been badly treated; there has been great waste in logging and much loss from forest fires. Unless better care is taken of them the supply of Paraná pine lumber will not continue to meet the demand.

BIGNONIACEAE

Jacaranda spp. Fotui, Caroba. (1) Col., Ven., Guianas, Braz.

Wood yellowish or grayish, light and soft, not durable. Used locally for boxes, match sticks, cheap construction, etc.

Tabebuia spp. Acapro, Washiba, Ipé, Lapacho. (1) Col., Ven., Br. G., Braz., Arg., Par.

Wood olive-brown, very hard, heavy, and durable. Used, especially in Argentina, for heavy construction, carpentry, and vehicles.

Tabebuia pentaphylla and spp. Apamate, White Cedar, Roble, etc. (1) Col., Ven., Guianas.

Wood light brown, of medium hardness and weight. Resembles ash in appearance. Used for construction, carpentry, interior trim, etc. A good wood, not as much appreciated as it should be.

BOMBACACEAE

Bombacopsis spp. Tolú, Saqui-saqui. (2) Col., Ven.

Wood reddish-brown, fairly light and soft, durable. Easy to work. Used for carpentry, exterior siding, and interior trim. Excellent for wooden vats. There is a potential export market.

Ceiba pentandra. Ceiba, etc. (1, 2) Col., Ven., Braz.

One of the largest of tropical trees. Fruit pods yield kapok. Wood very light, soft, perishable. Suitable for plywood corestock, and has been exported to a small extent.

BORAGINACEAE

Cordia spp. Canalete, Peterebí, Louro, Freijo. (1, 2) Widespread throughout South America.

Patagonula americana. Guayabí, etc. (1, 2) Arg., Uru., Par., Braz.

The two above genera have similar wood, which is light yellowish-brown, medium in hardness and weight, durable, resistant to termites. Highly valued locally for general construction, interior trim, furniture, cooperage, etc. Exported to a small extent as "Brazilian walnut." The local demand will probably in the future absorb most of the available supply.

BURSERACEAE

Bursera simaruba. Almácigo, Indio Desnudo. (1, 3, 6) Col., Ven.
Wood whitish, light, soft, not durable. Suitable for boxes, match sticks, cheap construction.

CARYOCARACEAE

Caryocar spp. Pequia, etc. (1) Guianas, Braz.
A yellowish, tough and strong wood, used locally for boat construction, heavy timbers, etc.

COMBRETACEAE

Terminalia spp. Guayabo, Araça, etc. (1) Col., Ven., Guianas, Braz.
Woods vary from yellow to brownish-red, moderately heavy and strong, often striped. General construction, furniture, rotary veneer.

CUPRESSIACEAE

Fitzroya cupressoides. Alerce. (4) Chile, Arg.
Found in dense forests in southern Chile and across the Andes into Argentina, alerce has a reddish light-weight wood of excellent quality. It is utilized in Chile for shingles, carpentry, and general construction, but only in small quantities, for the forests are mainly inaccessible.
Pilgerodendron uviferum. Ciprés, Lahuán. (4) Chile.
In southern Chile to Tierra del Fuego. A first-class coniferous wood, suitable for construction, interior trim, and flooring, but not extensively utilized at present.

EUPHORBIACEAE

Hieronyma alchorneoides. Dalina, Urucurana, etc. (1) Guianas, Braz.
A hard and heavy reddish wood, used for general construction.
Hura crepitans. Ceiba, Jabillo, Possentrie. (1, 2) Col., Ven., Guianas.
A very large tree, sometimes occurring in dense pure stands. Wood cream colored to light brown, fairly light and soft, smooth grained. Not durable. Suitable for general construction, plywood, etc.
Sapium spp. Caucho, etc. (1) Ven., Col., Guianas, Braz.
Wood light and soft, light colored, not durable. Used as rough lumber.

FAGACEAE

Nothofagus spp. Guindo, Ñire, Lenga, Roble, Raulí, Coihué. (4) Chile, Arg.
Found in the southern Andes. Corresponds to the beech of the North Temperate Zone. Fairly hard and heavy, color from pale brown to bright red. Used for general construction and flooring. Though abundant, much of the timber of this genus occupies inaccessible sites in regions with a small population and therefore is little used.

GUTTIFERAE

Calophyllum brasiliense. María, Palo María, Edaballi. (1) Col., Ven., Guianas, Braz.
An important tree locally, but not much exported. Wood reddish-brown, fairly hard, and heavy. Used for local boat building, heavy construction,

flooring, etc. Suitable for veneer for plywood, maría will probably increase in importance, both for local use and for export.

Symphonia globulifera. Maní, etc. (1) Col., Ven., Guianas, Braz.
Resembles maría, but olive-green in color. Usually grows in swamps.

HUMIRIACEAE

Humiria spp. Houmirí, etc. (1) Guianas, Braz.
Wood dark red, heavy, hard, and strong. Used in heavy construction.

LAURACEAE

Persea lingue. Lingue. (4) Chile.
In southern Chile, often in pure stands. Wood pale brown, of medium hardness and weight. Used locally for interior trim, furniture, etc.

There are in South America many other species of the Lauraceae, whose botanical nomenclature is very much confused. The woods vary from yellow to brown or red, are usually of medium hardness and weight, and are suitable for general construction and interior trim.

LEGUMINOSAE

Andira spp. Angelin, etc. (1) Col., Ven., Guianas, Braz.
Wood yellowish to brown, hard and heavy, durable.

Apuleia leiocarpa. Garapa, Ibirá. (1, 2) Braz., Uru., Arg.
Wood yellow, hard, and heavy, used locally for construction, interior trim, flooring, etc.

Bowdichia spp. Sapupira. (1) Braz.
Wood dark brown, very hard and heavy. Used locally for carts, etc.

Dicorynia spp. Angélique. (1) Fr. G.
A large and abundant tree. Wood brown, hard and heavy, durable. Used for construction, etc.

Eperua spp. Wallaba, Ipé, etc. (1) Guianas, Braz.
Especially important in British Guiana, usually occurring in dense pure stands. Wood reddish-brown, fairly hard and heavy. Used for construction, shingles, cooperage, etc.

Hymenaea courbaril. Courbaril, Jatahy. (1) Ven., Guianas, Braz.
Wood reddish-brown, quite hard and heavy. Used for carpentry and general construction.

Hymenolobium spp. Angelim. (1) Braz.
Large and abundant tree with brown, hard, and heavy wood. Used for heavy construction.

Melanoxylon brauna. Braúna. (1) Braz.
Wood dark brown, very hard and heavy, used for bridge timbers, etc.

Mora spp. Nato, Mora. (1) Col., Ven., Ec., Guianas, Braz.
Usually in pure stands in swamps. Wood reddish-brown, hard, and heavy.

Piptadenia spp. Angico, Curupay, etc. (1, 2) Braz., Arg., Par.
Wood reddish-brown, very hard and heavy. Used for heavy construction.

Prioria copaifera. Cativo. (1) Col.
In pure stands on the lower drainage of the Atrato River in Colombia. Formerly considered worthless but now exported on a large scale from Costa Rica for plywood. A good example of a "forgotten wood" that is now finding a world market.

Prosopis spp. Algarroba. (2, 6) Braz., Uru., Arg., Par.

Wood dark brown, hard, heavy, and durable. Used locally for fence and house posts and general construction. Has been used for paving blocks.

Samanea saman. Samán, Lara, etc. (1, 2) Col., Ven.

A very large tree with brown wood resembling walnut. Used locally for general construction and furniture.

MELIACEAE

Cabralea spp. Cangerana. (1) Braz., Uru, Arg., Par.

Wood deep red, of medium hardness and weight. Used for construction and furniture.

Carapa guianensis. Crabwood, Carapa, Andiroba, Tangaré, Figueroa. (1) Col., Ven., Guianas, Braz., Ec., Peru.

Large trees, often found in dense pure stands. Wood reddish-brown, of medium hardness and weight, grain varies from fine to coarse. Another neglected wood that is gradually coming into its own, both for local use and for export to the United States and Europe. Used as a substitute for mahogany in the furniture trade, and for flooring.

Cedrela spp. Cedro, Spanish Cedar. (1, 2, 3) All of South America except Chile.

The most important timber species in South America for local use; also exported to some extent. Wood pinkish-brown, light to medium in hardness and weight, very durable and resistant to termites. Works easily and holds its place well. The favorite wood for interior trim in houses, it is also used for furniture, although rather soft for that purpose.

MORACEAE

Chlorophora tinctoria. Mora. (2, 6) Arg., Par., Braz.

Wood deep yellow, very hard, heavy, and durable.

Clarisia insignis. Guariúba, etc. (1) Braz.

Wood yellow-brown, of medium hardness and weight. Used for general construction.

MYRISTICACEAE

Virola spp. Virola, Becuiba, Ucuhúba. (1) Guianas, Braz.

Trees large and abundant. Wood reddish-brown, of medium hardness and weight. Used locally for general construction, exported for plywood.

SAPOTACEAE

Manilkara spp. Beefwood, Balata, Massaranduba. (1) Col., Ven., Guianas, Braz.

Wood dark red, very hard, heavy, and durable. Used for heavy construction.

SIMARUBACEAE

Simaruba spp. Simaruba, Marupá. (1) Guianas, Braz.

Wood light lemon-yellow, light and soft. Used locally for general carpentry and exported to some extent.

VOCHYSIACEAE

Qualea spp. Cèdre gris, Muiraúba. (1) Guianas, Braz.

Vochysia spp. Eta-balli, Grignon, Cedro Rana. (1) Guianas, Braz.

Qualea and *Vochysia* have similar wood, pinkish-brown, light and soft. Used locally for carpentry, suitable for plywood.

B. Wood Not the Principal Product

1. TANNING MATERIALS

ANACARDIACEAE

Schinopsis spp. Quebracho. (6) Arg., Par., Braz., Bol.

Quebracho provides one of the world's most important tanning materials, especially for heavy leather. The dark-red, extremely hard, heavy, and durable wood of this tree contains 20 per cent or more of high-quality tannin. Formerly exported in log form, nearly all is now made into tanning extract in modern factories located in northern Argentina and in Paraguay, which produce nearly the entire world's supply. Uncontrolled exploitation, forest fires, and clearing for agriculture have made heavy inroads on this forest resource, and little or nothing is being done to encourage conservation or reforestação. This is especially unfortunate because as yet no satisfactory substitute has been found to take the place of quebracho tannin. Quebracho wood is also largely used for sleepers and other products where great durability is a desideratum.

AVICENNIACEAE

Avicennia marina. Black Mangrove, Mangle. (7) Col., Ven., Guianas.

Found in coastal swamps. Bark used locally for tanning.

COMBRETACEAE

Conocarpus erecta. Button Mangrove, Botoncillo, Mangle Blanco. (7) Col., Ven.

Found in coastal swamps in association with red mangrove. Tannin in bark.

GUTTIFERAE

Rheedia spp. Madroño, Bacury. (1) Col., Ven., Guianas, Braz.

The bark is rich in tannin and is used locally.

LAURACEAE

Beilschmiedia berteroana. Ulmo. (4) Chile.

Persea lingue. Lingue. (4) Chile.

The bark of the two above woods is used locally for tanning.

LEGUMINOSAE

Piptadenia spp. Angico, Cebil, Curupay. (1) Braz., Arg., Par.

The bark is an important local source of tannin.

Stryphnodendron barbatimao. Barbatimão. (6) Braz.

A small scrubby tree found in dry regions in Brazil. The bark contains up to 40 per cent of high-quality tannin. Important locally.

RHIZOPHORACEAE

Rhizophora mangle. Red Mangrove, Mangle. (7) Col., Ven., Sur., Braz., Ec.

Found usually in pure stands in salt-water swamps. While mangrove tannin is not of the highest quality, it is extensively used locally and is exported to some extent.

2. DYES

Tropical dyewoods, once very important articles of commerce, have been largely superseded by synthetics.

LEGUMINOSAE

Guilandina spp. Brazilwood, Brasiletto. (1) Braz.
This tree gave its name to the Republic of Brazil. Its wood yields a bright-red dye, but it is no longer used to any great extent for that purpose. The wood is favored for violin bows.

MORACEAE

Chlorophora tinctoria. Mora, etc. (1, 2) Col., Ven., Ec., Braz., Arg.
The wood yields the dye known as fustic, but has been almost entirely superseded by anilines.

3. ESSENTIAL OILS, DRUGS, GUMS, ETC.

BURSERACEAE

Protium spp. Anime, Copal. (1) Col., Ven., Guianas, Ec., Peru, Braz.
The bark contains a fragrant resin used medicinally and for incense.

LAURACEAE

Aniba rosaeodora. Bois de Rose Femelle. (1) Fr. G.
The wood contains a volatile oil that is distilled out and exported for use in the perfume industry.

RUBIACEAE

Cinchona spp. Quinine, Cinchona. (3) Col., Ec., Peru.
The original source of quinine was the cinchona tree growing on the high slopes of the Andes. The drug is found in the bark. Plantations in the Far East entirely superseded the native source, but, with the cutting off of the usual supplies during World War II, determined efforts were made to supply the demand from the Andean forests. Substitutes are rapidly taking the place of quinine for the treatment of malaria.

WINTERACEAE

Drimys winteri. Winter's Bark, Canelo. (4) Chile, Arg.
Found in the extreme southern portions of South America. The bark was formerly important in the treatment of scurvy, but is now used locally only.

ZYGOPHYLLACEAE

Bulnesia sarmienti. Palo Santo. (6) Arg., Par.
The wood contains a fragrant resin used for incense in churches.

II. Trees Not Destroyed by Utilization

A. Edible Products

1. SEEDS, NUTS, ETC.

ARAUCARIACEAE

Araucaria araucana. Pino, Piñones. (5) Chile, Arg.
The large seeds found in the cones have a good flavor and are popular in Chile.

CARYOCARACEAE

Caryocar spp. Pequia, etc. (1) Guianas, Braz.
The nut kernels are edible and yield an oil used in cooking.

LECYTHIDACEAE

Bertholletia excelsa. Brazilnut, Castanha. (1) Braz.

One of the largest trees in the Amazon region. The well-known nuts, nearly all obtained from trees growing wild, are a very important article of commerce.

Lecythis spp. Paradise Nut, Sapucaia. (1) Guianas, Braz.

The nuts, even tastier than brazilnuts, are exported to some extent.

2. FRUITS, PODS, LEAVES, ETC.

AQUIFOLIACEAE

Ilex paraguariensis. Paraguay Tea, Yerba Maté. (2, 5) Arg., Par., Braz.

The leaves are important as a source of the tea used universally in southern South America and exported to some extent. While part of the yield is from wild trees, most now comes from extensive plantations, mainly in southern Brazil.

ERYTHROXYLACEAE

Erythroxylon coca. Coca, etc. (3) Col., Peru, Bol.

A shrub or small tree that grows wild in the high Andes and is also cultivated in plantations. Leaves used locally as a stimulant and as a source of the drug cocaine.

LEGUMINOSAE

Coumarouna spp. Tonka Bean, Sarrapia, Cumarú. (1) Col., Ven., Guianas, Braz.

Seeds exported in large quantities as a source of coumarin oil, used in the perfume industry and to flavor tobacco products.

Prosopis spp. Algarroba. (2, 6) Braz., Arg., Uru., Par.

Samanea saman. Samán. (1, 2) Col., Ven.

Rich in carbohydrates and proteins, the pods of the above two trees are used for cattle feed.

B. Nonedible Products

1. RUBBER

EUPHORBIACEAE

Hevea brasiliensis. Pará Rubber, Seringueira. (1) Braz.

For many years Brazil was the sole source of the Pará type of rubber, but gradually the world's markets were captured by plantation rubber from the Far East and Africa. There was considerable exploitation of wild rubber in Brazil during World War II, and plantations have been established, but the supply is inadequate; Brazil has to import natural rubber for its expanding rubber industry, and is considering the establishment of synthetic rubber factories.

MORACEAE

Castilla spp. Caucho. (1) Braz., Ec., Peru.

Once a rather important source of rubber but now largely superseded by plantation *Hevea* rubber.

SAPOTACEAE

Manilkara spp. Balata. (1) Col., Ven., Guianas.

The source of balata rubber, valuable for certain special uses.

2. TANNIN

LEGUMINOSAE

Libidibia coriaria. Divi-divi. (6) Col., Ven.
   Found only in very arid regions. Its twisted pods yield a high-quality tannin. An important article of export.

3. WAXES, OILS, GUMS, ETC.

LEGUMINOSAE

Copaifera spp. Cabima, Copaiba. (1) Col., Ven., Sur., Braz.
   Yields, by tapping, the copaiba balsam of commerce.
Hymenaea courbaril. Courbaril, Jatahy. (1) Ven., Guianas, Braz.
   Exudations from the bark yield the copal of commerce.

MYRISTICACEAE

Virola spp. Virola, Ucuhúba, etc. (1) Guianas, Braz.
   Great quantities of seeds are used locally and exported as a source of oil for soap, etc.

PALMAE

Copernicia cerifera. Carnaúba. (2) (6) Braz., Par., Arg.
   Wax found encrusted on the young leaves is the source of the important carnauba wax of commerce.

ROSACEAE

Licania rigida. Oiticica. (1) Braz.
   The seeds yield an oil used in paints and varnishes.
Quillaja spp. Palo de Jabon, Quillay, Soapbark. (4) Arg., Chile.
   The bark contains saponin.

4. OTHER

BOMBACACEAE

Ceiba pentandra. Ceiba. (1, 2) Col., Ven., Braz.
   The pods yield kapok, but the kapok of commerce comes mainly from the Far East. Artificial products, such as foam rubber, are gradually taking the market from kapok.

CYCLANTHACEAE

Carludovica palmata. Panama Hat Palm, Jipijapa. (1, 6) Col., Ec., Peru.
   Fiber from the young leaves is used to make Panama hats, the industry being centered in Ecuador.

PALMAE

Attalea funifera Mart. Piassaba. (1) Braz.
   Fiber is obtained from young leaf stems.
Phytelephas spp. Ivory Nut. (1, 6) Col., Ec., Peru.
   The extremely hard nuts are used to make buttons.

11. NORTHERN EUROPE

K. Thorsten Streyffert, Alf Langsaeter, and Eino Saari

THE REGION AS A WHOLE

K. Thorsten Streyffert

The three Scandinavian countries, Sweden, Norway, and Denmark, are often, together with Finland, considered a unit. Denmark, however, differs noticeably from the others with regard to both climate and soil. A relatively milder climate brings Denmark within the borders of the West-European hardwood region, whereas the other countries lie almost completely within the North-European conifer region. The rocks are also essentially different. Denmark's soils rest primarily on Cretaceous and younger sedimentary formations, the rest of the area almost entirely on much older and more resistant formations. Highly cultivated and densely populated, Denmark—like western Europe generally—does not have large enough forests to meet her own domestic demands for forest products, whereas the rest of Scandinavia and Finland, with their vast forests, form the most important export area in the world for lumber, pulp, and paper.

Forest Regions

The primary division of the territory into a Conifer Region and a Hardwood Region is shown on Figure 26. As may be seen, the latter region includes Denmark and the southernmost coastal areas of Sweden. The border between the two regions coincides with the southern border of the spontaneous occurrence of spruce (*Picea abies*).[1]

THE CONIFER REGION. The Conifer Region is the westernmost part of a larger conifer forest which extends eastward across northern Europe and Siberia. The predominant trees are Scots pine (*Pinus silvestris*) and Norway spruce (*Picea abies*). Except for a few introduced species, other conifers are missing. Some hardwoods have made more or less conspicuous inroads into the conifer forest. The northern limit of the oak (*Quercus robur*), which runs through southernmost Finland, mid-Sweden, and the southern coastal areas of Norway, separates the Conifer Region into a northern and a southern zone.

[1] Source for botanical nomenclature: A. R. Clapham, *et al. Flora of the British Isles.* Cambridge University Press, London, 1952.

The milder climate, which permits the occurrence of oak, gives the forests of the southern zone a more vigorous appearance and a more rapid growth than are found in the northern zone. Formerly the forests of the northern zone were old and overmature, whereas those of the southern zone, owing to the denser population, had been largely cut and replaced by young and middle-aged stands. The contrast, however, has become less marked, as the working of the northern forests has progressed.

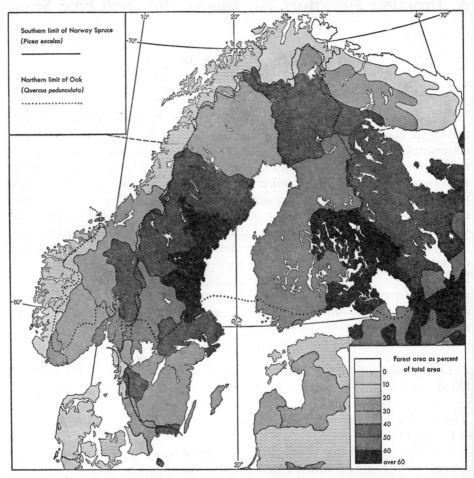

Fig. 26. Scandinavia and Finland: (*a*) distribution of forest areas, and (*b*) limits of Norway spruce (*Picea abies* or *excelsa*) and oak (*Quercus robur* or *pedunculata*)—(*a*) based on plate "General View on the Percentage of Forests in Europe." *Weltforstatlas*, Hamburg, 1951; (*b*) based on data supplied by the author.

The most abundant hardwoods of the Conifer Region are birches (*Betula pubescens, Betula verrucosa*, and a multitude of hybrid species), which, together with aspen (*Populus tremula*), occur throughout the region. Other less hardy hardwood species enter the forest flora in the south—linden (*Tilia vulgaris*), maple (*Acer platanoides*), elm (*Ulmus procera*), ash (*Fraxinus excelsior*), oak (*Quercus robur* and *Q. petraea*), and, in the extreme south, beech (*Fagus silvatica*). These less resistant hardwoods occupy the more fertile soils (clays, etc.), a preference that becomes more marked the farther north we go. As a consequence, the hardwoods were cut first when the land was cleared for cultivation, thus intensifying the coniferous character of the forests. Small, isolated patches of these less hardy hardwoods, relics of an earlier warmer climate, occur in certain climatically favored areas (e.g., on the south sides of the mountains) far to the north of their present normal habitat.

Much of Scandinavia lies above timber line—500 to 700 meters in northernmost Sweden and about 900 meters in mid-Sweden, but lower in Norway because of proximity to the ocean. At least two thirds of Norway is above timber line; of Sweden, the proportion is only 14 per cent. Most of Finland, however, is flat and forested.

The precipitation in the Conifer Region varies greatly. The Atlantic-facing mountains of Norway receive an annual precipitation of more than 2,000 millimeters. The west winds carry warm, moisture-laden air from the North Atlantic Drift. The Norwegian forests correspond in this respect to the coastal forests of Alaska, although most of the mountain-sides facing the Atlantic are now barren, because the trees were cut long ago for export, and grass and heather have taken their place. The mountains between Norway and Sweden are lower than the ranges that separate the Alaskan coastal forests from the interior and, hence, northern and central Sweden have better conditions for forest growth than does the Alaskan interior. The annual precipitation in these parts of Sweden averages about 500 millimeters, and even here the climate is influenced by the North Atlantic Drift. The influence of the Russian land mass, however, is also great in northern Sweden, where the climate appears to be transitional between a typically oceanic and a typically continental climate.

The annual precipitation of 500 millimeters in northern and central Sweden, on the other hand, is barely enough for optimum forest growth despite the fact that the winter precipitation is in the form of snow, which, when it melts, increases the water supply in the soil at the beginning of the vegetative period.

The abundant precipitation and mild temperature in large parts of Norway cause spruce to predominate over pine; in Sweden the two species are about equal in importance; in Finland, with a more continental climate, pine predominates over spruce. Soils, also, influence the distribution of tree species; thus, the sandy heaths of northernmost Sweden and Finland favor pine rather than spruce.

Most of the Conifer Region is covered by stony moraines, unsuitable for cultivation but satisfactory for conifers. The lower parts of Sweden and Finland, however, were covered by the sea during and after the melting of the ice sheet. Sand and clay were deposited, and the latter, more especially, has favored cultivation, which now extends over virtually all such deposits. In all, however, the cultivated area within the Conifer

Region is less than 10 per cent of the total area below timber line. Swamps and marshes within the Conifer Region cover an area even larger than that under cultivation and are especially frequent in the northern parts of Sweden and Finland. Many of them have been drained and planted for forests.

While forest fires still were frequent a hundred years ago, they are now rare—indeed, only a few hundred hectares are lost annually in Sweden from this cause. An extensive fire-warden system helps to reduce the extent of the fires, but even more effective is the greater care now taken by people in their handling of fire in the woods, since these have grown into a valuable asset.

THE HARDWOOD REGION. The Hardwood Region of Scandinavia is part of a much larger region of hardwood forests that covers most of western and central Europe. The dominating hardwood is the beech, but oak, ash, elm, and linden are also abundant. The hardy hardwoods, such as birch and aspen, are less common.

Conifers seldom grow naturally in this region. Scots pine (*Pinus silvestris*) probably was native in Denmark, but is now found there only where planted by man. Other conifers, especially Norway spruce and several North American species, have been planted extensively. These species ordinarily grow well here, but attacks of fungi and insects have recently caused much damage.

Most of the land in the Hardwood Region is used for cultivation; in Denmark, for example, only 8.6 per cent of the total area is forested. Where forests exist, the mild climate and fertile soils account for a high production of wood per hectare, and forestry is as intensive and well developed as anywhere in the world. Sizable imports of forest products are necessary, however, because of the small area in forest.

In all, about half of the forested area has been planted by man, a large part of it with conifers, and the change from hardwood to conifers continues because the latter are more profitable. Particularly noteworthy are the conifer plantations in western Jutland, on originally bare sands and heaths.

Forest Resources

More reliable and detailed statistics on the extent of the forests, the volume of standing timber, and the annual growth are available for Norway, Sweden, and Finland than for any other country, since these forests have been made the subject of inventories or surveys covering the whole of each country, the so-called national forest surveys. Work of this sort was started in an experimental way in a county of Sweden in 1911 to find out whether the method of surveying individual forest holdings could be applied to the forests of a whole country, although with a much greater distance between the survey lines. This being established, the first national survey was begun in Sweden in 1923. The same method was also applied in Finland and Norway, and several other countries have taken up the idea in different ways. By now two or three national forest surveys have been carried out in each of the three countries, rendering it possible to make interesting comparisons between the data from successive surveys.

These surveys have supplied not only the basic data mentioned above but also many supplementary data concerning the distribution of forest areas according to age and site classes, the distribution of the standing timber according to diameter classes, different species of trees, etc.

Data from these surveys on forest area and on the volume of standing timber and growth have been brought together in Table 11–I. This shows that the total forest area of Scandinavia and Finland is 51.5 million hectares, or about half of the total land area. However, the forest area of Denmark is insignificant, about one tenth of the total land area. It should also be noted that forests occupy only one fifth of the total land area of Norway, owing largely to the fact that two thirds of that country is above timber line. In Sweden, on the other hand, forests cover well over half, and in Finland nearly three quarters, of the total land area.

TABLE 11–I

SCANDINAVIA AND FINLAND: FOREST AREA, WOOD VOLUME, AND ANNUAL INCREMENT [a]

	Total Land Area	Productive Forest Area		Wood Volume [b]		Annual Increment [b]	
		Total	Per Cent of Total Area	Total	Per Hectare	Total	Per Hectare
	Thousand hectares			*Million cubic meters*	*Cubic meters*	*Million cubic meters*	*Cubic meters*
Denmark	4,240[c]	438[e]	10.3[c]	60[d]	142.0[d]	1.75[d]	4.7[d]
Finland	30,500	21,800	71.7	1,491	68.2	45.00	2.0
Norway	30,851	6,100[e]	19.7	390	64.0	12.00	2.0
Sweden	41,087	22,900	56.1	1,820	79.4	51.50	2.2
TOTAL	106,678	51,538	48.1	3,761	73.1	110.25	2.2

[a] Except as otherwise indicated, based on national forest surveys of Finland (1951-53), Sweden (1938-51), Norway (1919-31, 1937-).

[b] Figures for wood volume and increment apply to coniferous trees that have reached breast height and to hardwoods that have reached a diameter of at least 5 cm. at breast height. Volume inclusive, increment exclusive, of bark.

[c] *World Forest Resources,* United Nations Food and Agriculture Organization. Rome, 1955; pp. 60–61.

[d] Estimate.

[e] Does not include 1.4 million hectares of forest land above the coniferous timber line.

The volume of standing timber (inclusive of bark) amounts in the aggregate to nearly four billion cubic meters in Scandinavia and Finland, a large order of magnitude. The volume of standing timber per hectare, however, is comparatively low, between 64 and 79 cubic meters in Norway, Sweden, and Finland, though considerably higher in Denmark. This low volume per hectare is not solely a consequence of the northerly position of these countries. It can also be ascribed in part to former cutting methods which did not take into account the conditions necessary for regrowth. The same circumstances, and also to some extent the surplus of old-age classes with slow growth, serve to explain the low annual growth per hectare. In Norway, Sweden, and Finland this growth is remarkably even, the average for each country being between 2.0 and 2.2 cubic meters (exclusive of bark). In this respect Denmark, with her milder climate and well-tended forests, and an annual growth estimated at 4.7 cubic meters per hectare, far surpasses the other Nordic countries.

As the present old and often carelessly logged-over stands are replaced by the younger, well cared-for stands now on their way, the annual growth will tend to rise. Indeed, comparison of the results of successive forest surveys shows that this tendency is already apparent. Thus, in Finland, the third national forest survey of 1951-53 showed an annual growth of 45 million cubic meters as compared with 41 million disclosed by the second survey (1936-38) within the present political boundaries of Finland. In Sweden the first survey in 1923-29 gave 47.7 million as against 51.5 million cubic meters at the second survey in 1938-51. So far as the second forest survey has progressed in Norway it confirms this general tendency.

That much can still be accomplished in raising the annual growth is generally recognized in the Nordic countries, where great endeavors now are being made to increase the sustained yield from the forests.

FOREST OWNERSHIP. Table 11–II shows the distribution of the forests according to ownership.

TABLE 11–II

SCANDINAVIA AND FINLAND: AREAS OF STATE FORESTS, OTHER PUBLIC FORESTS, AND PRIVATE FORESTS, *ca.* 1952 [a]

(Thousand Hectares)

	State Forests		Other Public		Private		Total	
	Area	Per Cent	Area	Per Cent	Area	Per Cent	Area	Per Cent
Denmark	86	25	23	7	239	68	348	100
Norway	445	7	477	8	5,178	85	6,100	100
Sweden	4,344	19	1,217	5	17,387	76	22,948	100
Finland	7,400	34	380	2	13,890	64	21,670	100

[a] Data for Denmark supplied by Professor P. Moltesen; for Norway by A. Langsaeter, Chief Forester; for Finland by Professor E. Saari; data for Sweden from *Statistical Yearbook of Forestry*, 1954, Stockholm.

Private forests predominate in all four countries. Except in Norway, however, the state-owned forests are also important. The state forests are found mostly in areas of sparse population, which are mainly in the less productive north. Hence, the economic importance of the state forests and the profits they yield are less than the high percentages of state forest land might lead one to expect. During the last ten or twenty years, the total area in state forests, particularly in Sweden, has been increased by the purchase of woodlands in the better located regions.

Farmers own most of the private forests. However, the lumber and pulp companies also own substantial forest areas. In Sweden, these companies have acquired about 25 per cent of the forest area. Although the percentage is smaller in Finland and Norway, it still helps to regulate and stabilize the supply of raw material for the forest industries of these countries, thus lessening their dependence upon other forest owners.

In the early years of this century laws were passed prohibiting the purchase of forest lands by the companies. This was done in order to keep the ownership of forest lands in the hands of the farmers who are dependent upon the income from their forests.

FOREST MANAGEMENT. For almost a hundred years the state and other public forests have been under the supervision of trained forest personnel. The management has aimed at securing a sustained yield, and the forestry work, which has gradually increased in intensity and efficiency, by now has reached a high standard. All of these forests are managed according to working plans based upon scientific principles.

Of the owners of the private forests, only the pulp and lumber companies have been in a position to operate their holdings in a similar way. These company-owned forests are also under the supervision of trained personnel, are managed according to working plans so as to insure a sustained yield, and are on a par with the state forests with respect to forestry practice. Forests of this type occupy in the aggregate about 8.5 million hectares, or 17 per cent of the total forest area, in Scandinavia and Finland. As the company-owned forests, together with the state and other public forests, occupy about 22 million hectares, a substantial portion of the forests in the Nordic countries is well managed under the supervision of trained forest personnel.

The remaining forests, more than half of the total forest area, belong mainly to the farmers and to a lesser extent to big estates. The management of the farmers' forests has been favorably influenced by the forest policies of the Nordic countries. Of fundamental importance is the fact that, according to the law, the forest owners must care for regrowth after cutting. Besides this, trained personnel is furnished to supervise forestry work and to act in a generally advisory capacity by giving courses in all lines of forestry and forest utilization to the forest owners and by arranging for meetings, excursions, publicity, etc. Subsidies are also granted for certain kinds of forestry work.

First inaugurated in Sweden under the forest law of 1903, this "new deal" in forestry has since then been followed up in different ways in the other Nordic countries. The results are evident in the generally good condition of the farmers' forests, although there are still great variations

in the levels of forestry attained. On the whole, these forests also are managed on a sustained-yield basis, and simple working plans are being
adopted.

ECONOMIC USE OF THE FORESTS AND THEIR PRODUCTS: ANNUAL CUT.
Aside from use as pasture, which is being increasingly curtailed because
grazing prevents regeneration, the forests of Scandinavia are used almost
exclusively to supply wood. By far the greater part of the yearly cut is
manufactured into lumber, pulp, paper, wallboards, and plywood. A
substantial amount, however, is used for firewood, especially on the farms.
Coal and oil, which have to be imported, meet most of the demand for fuel
for industry and transportation, and, besides, for an ever-growing number
of homes, especially in the cities and towns. But the importance of the
forests was made evident during World War II, when imports of coal and
oil were interrupted.

A greater demand than is now made upon the forests for wood of small
dimensions and for hardwood would be welcome. Such wood ought to be
cut out in thinnings, but it cannot now be used for industrial purposes.
To find a market for it is one of the most serious forestry problems of the
region.

A small part of the annual cut is used for poles, posts, and railway ties,
and a certain amount is also exported as pulpwood and pit props.

Table 11–III shows the volume, by countries, of industrial wood and
fuel wood cut in 1952 and 1953. If we compare the total volume of fellings

TABLE 11–III

SCANDINAVIA AND FINLAND: VOLUME OF INDUSTRIAL WOOD AND FUEL WOOD CUT
ANNUALLY, *ca.* 1952–1953 [a]

(Millions of Cubic Meters Without Bark)

	Industrial Wood [b]		Fuel Wood [c]		Total Cut	
	1952	1953	1952	1953	1952	1953
Denmark	1.4	1.4	0.7	0.6	2.1	2.0
Finland [d]	17.5	22.1	9.4	8.7	26.9	30.8
Norway [e]	9.5	7.3	2.5	2.1	12.0	9.4
Sweden [e]	33.7	27.9	8.0	7.9	41.7	35.8
TOTAL	62.1	58.7	20.6	19.3	82.7	78.0

[a] Source: FAO, *Yearbook of Forest Products Statistics, 1954*, pp. 20–22.
[b] Saw logs, veneer logs, logs for sleepers, pulpwood, pit props, etc.
[c] Includes wood for charcoal.
[d] Figures are for years 1952-53 and 1953-54 and do not include all the cut.
[e] Years 1951-52 and 1952-53.

in each of these two years (82.7 and 78.0 million cubic meters) with the
figure for the annual growth (110 million cubic meters) given in Table
11–I, we obtain an apparent surplus of growth over cut of between about
27 and 32 million cubic meters. Although part of this surplus is offset

by waste in logging and losses from windfall and insect pests, there still remains an actual surplus of growth over cut, which explains the increase in the volume of standing timber that has taken place in Scandinavia and Finland according to the national forest surveys.

Forest Industries

Table 11–III shows that Sweden and Finland lead in the cutting of industrial wood; Norway is next and Denmark last. Most of this wood is consumed by the forest industries within these countries.

As might be expected, sawmills and pulp factories completely dominate the wood industry. Together, they consume the greater part of the raw material that is industrially processed, whereas the manufacture of wallboard and plywood, though important, absorbs only a small part.

Approximately the same amount of wood is used in the manufacture of wood pulp as in that of lumber. Indeed, in no other region except Canada does the wood-pulp industry consume so large a proportion of the raw material. Conditions in Scandinavia and Finland are similar to those in eastern Canada. While the trees do not reach the same size that they do in more favorable climates, they yield wood well suited for pulp, and the supply of water power is abundant and accessible. Furthermore, good markets for pulp and paper are found throughout Europe and also in the other continents.

The mechanical wood-pulp industry is comparatively well developed in Norway, partly because spruce, which predominates there, presents the best raw material for this kind of pulp, and also because of Norway's abundant water power.

About 40 per cent of the wood pulp produced is manufactured into paper and cardboard in Scandinavia and Finland. The rest of the pulp is exported, especially to paper mills in western Europe and the United States, a situation for which protective tariffs on paper are partly responsible. The paper industry of Scandinavia and Finland, however, produces, first of all, newsprint, which usually can be imported into other countries free of duty. It also produces other standardized papers for export, such as wrapping papers, which do not demand so close a contact between manufacturer and consumer as do papers for books and other specialized purposes.

The interruption of shipping from Finland and northern Scandinavia during the winter months makes it harder to find markets for paper than for wood pulp. This is because the paper consumers demand immediate delivery of paper that is not standardized and prefer continuous deliveries of standardized paper. The paper mills are therefore located farther south so that year-round shipments can be made. Norway has an advantage in this respect, since her Atlantic coast is free from ice throughout the year. In Finland one harbor, Turku (Åbo), is kept open by icebreakers, and this makes a certain amount of export possible at all times. Shipping on the Gulf of Bothnia, however, is interrupted by ice every winter.

Because it is difficult to convert all pulp into paper, the pulp industry has developed other high-grade pulp products. A large part of the sulfite pulp, after further processing, is exported for use as a raw material in the manufacture of viscose.

The pine and spruce forests of Scandinavia and Finland also produce first-rate lumber for millwork—lumber for which they are famous throughout the world. Indeed, an excellent balance has been reached in these countries between sawmilling and pulp production. The larger enterprises usually operate both sawmills and pulp factories and thus facilitate an economical use of the raw materials. Waste from the sawmills is much used in the manufacture of sulfate pulp.

Cheap water transport, natural harbors, and good industrial sites have contributed largely to the success of Scandinavia and Finland in competition on the world's markets for lumber, wood pulp, and paper. Most of the northern manufacturing plants are located at the mouths of the rivers, down which the timber is easily floated—the least costly method of transport, especially over long distances. The cost of floating the timber an average of 130 kilometers is hardly more than that of hauling it on a snow road an average of three kilometers from the place of cutting to the river-bank.

A terminal moraine crosses southern Finland from west to east. It forms a gigantic barrier that dams the water to make a vast lake system to the north. Large wood industries are located at the mouths of three rivers which cut through this barrier. Finland's largest wood industries, at the mouth of the Vuoxen, the river furthest to the east of the three, were turned over to Russia after World War II, along with valuable forests in Karelia.

There are practically no important rivers in southern Sweden, where the dense net of railroads and roads is used to transport the forest products. The manufacturing plants are therefore not only smaller than those farther north where the rivers are more plentiful, but are located in the interior rather than on the coast, since it costs more to transport logs than it does to transport finished wood products, pulp, and paper.

Movement of logs by trucks has become more common during the last twenty years and is now the principal means of transport in the areas without rivers. Networks of roads are being built into the forests today. Trucks are also being used to an increasing extent even in the river areas, especially where the hauling distances to the rivers are great. Trucks also transport wood that is not suitable for floating—notably hardwoods, such as birch and aspen. In Finland, however, large quantities of birch veneer timber are floated, although special devices are required to facilitate the floating of this wood.

FOREIGN TRADE. Scandinavia and Finland constitute the world's most important export area for forest products. Round timber was shipped from Norway's west coast as early as the eleventh century, and from 1600 until well after 1800 Norway led Europe in the export of sawn wood, although her eastern neighbors, with larger forest areas, have since surpassed her. From west to east, Norway, Sweden, Finland, and Russia have, one after the other, developed far-reaching forest industries. Certain reasons for this have been pointed out in the preceding sections. The great size of the forests in relation to the population makes possible large surpluses for export, even though the domestic consumption of wood per capita is one of the highest in the world. In Norway, Sweden, and Finland there are 3.0 hectares of forest land per capita, whereas in western and central Europe the ratio is only 0.3 hectare. Ease of transport makes the cutting and removal of lumber relatively cheap, and the location of the Nordic countries on the Atlantic and Baltic coasts, together with well-developed merchant marines, facilitates exports not only to western Europe but also to distant markets.

Total exports of the principal forest products from Norway, Sweden and Finland are shown in Table 11–IV for the years 1952 and 1953. As

TABLE 11–IV

NORWAY, SWEDEN, AND FINLAND: VOLUME OF EXPORTS OF CERTAIN FOREST PRODUCTS, 1952-1953 [a]

	Norway		Sweden		Finland	
	1952	1953	1952	1953	1952	1953
Coniferous saw logs and veneer logs (1,000 cu. m. [r])	4	–	48	61	699 [b]	272 [b]
Pit props (1,000 cu. m. [r])	145	114	1,000	552	1,653	588
Coniferous sawn wood (1,000 cu. m. [r])	23	136	3,111	4,376	2,711	3,112
Pulpwood (1,000 cu. m. [r])	12	2	183	216	2,631	1,431
Wood pulp (1,000 m. t.)	533	610	1,630	2,163	865	991
Veneers and plywood (1,000 cu. m. [s])	1	1	13	17	222	216
Newsprint (1,000 m. t.)	132	132	208	207	392	402

[a] Source: FAO, *Yearbook of Forest Products Statistics, 1954*, pp. 98-99.
[b] Includes other roundwood.
cu. m.: cubic meters.   [s]: sawn wood.
[r]: roundwood.   m. t.: metric tons.

previously mentioned, Denmark cannot meet her need for forest products from her own limited forest area, well managed as it may be. In 1953 Denmark had to import 148,000 standards of lumber, 68,000 tons of wood pulp, and 127,000 tons of paper and board, besides minor quantities of other forest products. These imports were almost wholly derived from the other Nordic countries.

Future exports from the region as a whole will depend essentially upon the future yield from its forests. In view of the obvious tendency toward an increase in the volume of standing timber as well as in the annual growth, as confirmed by the national forest surveys, it seems only reasonable to expect that exports of forest products will continue to increase and that the region will thus contribute an increasingly large proportion of what will be required to meet the world's growing needs of forest products.

PROGRAMS, POLICIES, AND RESEARCH. Forest programs, policies, and research in the three Scandinavian countries and in Finland have moved along generally parallel lines. Each country has sought to combine rational use of the forests with reasonable profits from their exploitation, through practical forestry laws, through research, educational, and advisory services, and through programs of economic assistance, and, in so doing, these countries have been pioneers.

SWEDEN

K. Thorsten Streyffert

The forests of Sweden have long buttressed the development of Swedish industries. The famous iron industry, which as early as 1700 accounted for 40 per cent of the world's export trade in steel, depended on the reduction of the ore with charcoal. Wood tar, until 1700 the chief source of lubricants and indispensable in shipbuilding, was practically a Swedish monopoly. During recent decades, milled lumber, pulp, paper, and other forest products have accounted for about half the value of Sweden's total exports.

During the period of growing industrial expansion of the second half of the nineteenth century, a rapid increase took place in the production and export of lumber, with a consequent increase in the cutting in the forests. This roused again the old fears of forest depletion, which eventually resulted in the Forest Law of 1903, the cornerstone of Swedish forestry legislation. The law made regeneration after cutting compulsory, and its effects are clearly apparent in the young forests that now cover the cutover areas.

The practice of cutting forests while they were still growing vigorously caused serious losses until a law was passed in 1917 which forbade cutting in young forests except by way of thinning. Little more could be accomplished by legislation in this respect, and the Forest Law of 1948 contains no essentially new provisions.

However, forest laws alone will not advance forestry. While regulations may prevent abuses and maintain certain minimum standards, the voluntary co-operation of the many small and large forest owners is essential for any real progress in forestry. This applies particularly to the smaller forests, which have no trained staffs of their own.

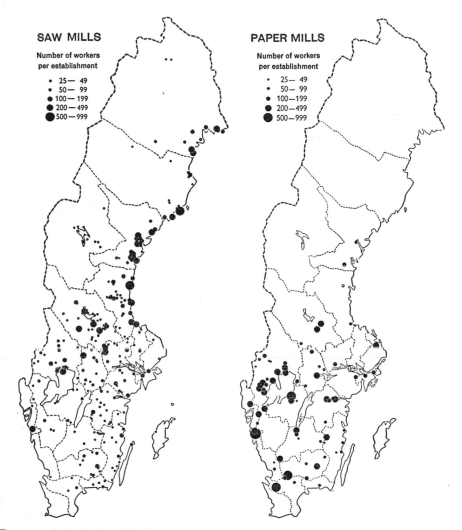

FIGS. 27 and 28. Sweden: distribution of sawmills and paper mills. Based (with Figs. 29 and 30) on maps in *Sveriges Skogar och Skogsindustrie*, Kooperativa Forbundets Bokvorlag, Stock-holm, 1950.

The indisputable progress in forestry in Sweden and the other Scandi-navian countries springs from the fact that the smaller forest owners' interest has been aroused and their access to trained forest personnel has been facilitated. In Sweden this was accomplished by the Law of 1903, which delegated a considerable degree of autonomy to local boards and extended membership on them to representatives of the forest owners.

The most important task of these county forestry boards has been to keep trained personnel at hand and to awaken the interest of the owners through education and information services. At present, most of the wood cut for sale from the farmers' wood lots is marked for cutting by this personnel, a matter of great importance, since half of the forests, including the best situated, belongs to the farmers. Financial assistance is also given—up to 40 per cent of the cost—for drainage operations, the replanting of old bare lands, and the building of truck roads.

The national forest surveys, originally inspired by the fear of forest depletion, have become valuable instruments for the forming of forest policies, because of the clear pictures they give of forest conditions in general and of the volume of timber and growth. Special interest has been attached to comparisons of the second with the first forest inventories, which have revealed changes in the volume of standing timber as well as in a number of other important respects. In the period averaging 14 years between the inventories in northern Sweden (covering 15.3 million hectares) the volume of standing timber more than 10 centimeters in diameter at breast height (with bark) was reduced from 946 to 925 million cubic meters, i.e., by 2.2 per cent. On the other hand, during the period averaging 20 years between the inventories in southern Sweden (covering 7.6 million hectares) the corresponding volume of standing timber increased from 552 to 690 million cubic meters. For Sweden as a whole this meant an increase in the total volume of standing timber of 117 million cubic meters, or 7.8 per cent.

To facilitate the adaptation of the forest industries to the changes in the volume and composition of the standing timber in different parts of the country, felling programs have been worked out on the basis of data from the forest inventories. The program for the country as a whole shows a possible yearly cut during the present decade (1950-60) of 32.4 million cubic meters of timber (not including firewood), of which 30.2 million cubic meters will be available to the forest industries in the form of saw logs and pulpwood. These data do not include hardwood, which is less important than softwood as a raw material for the forest industries of Sweden. The actual consumption of saw logs and pulpwood by the forest industries was only 27.0 million cubic meters in 1950 but has increased somewhat since then.

It is calculated that the possible yield will continue to increase in the long run as a result of the intensified forestry now practised.

The national forest surveys have made the people of Sweden as a whole more forest-minded, more interested in increasing the productivity of their woodlands.

A serious problem today in Sweden, as in the other Nordic countries, is the growing scarcity of forest labor. In order to operate with the reduced labor force, a great movement toward increasing the efficiency of forest work has been started by the big pulp and lumber companies, in cooperation with the State Forest Service, and a new and extensive line of research work has been organized to this end. As a result, logging is becoming increasingly mechanized and transportation methods are being much improved.

The main center of research work in the field of forestry is the State Forest Research Institute at Stockholm. This was founded in 1902

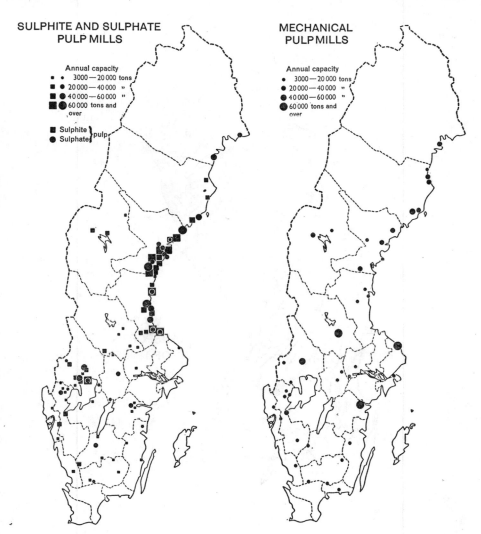

FIGS. 29 and 30. Sweden: distribution of pulp mills.

and has become of increasing importance as forestry has grown more intensive and placed correspondingly higher demands on its research workers. An interesting field of research pertains to forest genetics, which aims at producing new and more fast-growing races of our forest trees, a matter of special interest to Sweden, with its comparatively slow-growing forest trees.

The Royal School of Forestry at Stockholm was founded in 1828, and is thus one of the oldest forest schools in the world. In addition to higher forest education, it has made notable contributions to research in forestry.

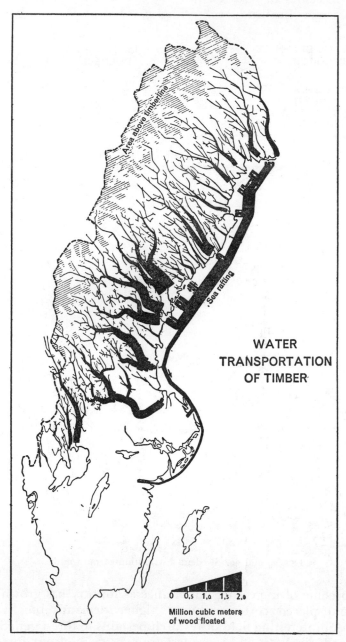

FIG. 31. Sweden: water transportation of lumber. Based on map in Flottingen i Sverige fram till år 1935, *Sv. flottledsförb årsb. 1938*, 3023–3170.

NORWAY

Alf Langsaeter

Norwegian timber and other forest products were exported to the countries around the North Sea as early as the Viking age. At first this trade was confined to round timber, but changed little by little to hewn boards and, when sawmills were first established toward the end of the sixteenth century, to sawn boards and planks.

The forests also provided both the countryside and the growing towns with increasing quantities of fuel wood and timber for building purposes. From the beginning of the seventeenth to the middle of the nineteenth century the important Norwegian iron industry used wood in the form of charcoal. The forests nearest to a port or to the consumer were the first ones to be utilized, but gradually the area of cutting was enlarged, partly because of rising prices of timber and partly because of the devastation of the easily accessible forests.

Thus, two different patterns of forest exploitation were developed, depending on local needs. Near the iron works charcoal burning led to clear-cutting. Where conditions for natural regeneration were good, dense even-aged forest grew up, but where conditions were difficult a long time elapsed before the felled areas were covered with more or less uneven-aged young forest. In a few places, as for instance near the copper mines at Röros, these cuttings did great damage, causing the pine forest to degrade to poor birch forest or barren land.

Where sawn timber was to be utilized, it paid to cut only the large trees. The method of cutting in the primeval forests was therefore necessarily selective, and the small trees were left standing until they reached a suitable size.

In the 1870's a new industry, the manufacture of pulp, started. Development was at first slow. Since 1900, however, this industry has been of essential importance, and today practically all of Norway's exports of forest products consists of mechanical and chemical pulp and paper. Nearly all of the production of the sawmills is consumed by the home market.

Smaller sizes of timber, which formerly had little value or were not worth producing at all, are now being utilized. This has caused a relative increase in the price of small-sized timber. The fact that it has become worth while to cut the smaller sizes has, in turn, made it possible, during the last thirty to fifty years, to improve the forests by better cutting practices.

In 1863 and 1908 laws were passed to prevent destructive cutting in exposed forests, especially at high elevations or near the coast. The cutting of trees of less than a certain minimum size was often prohibited unless the trees were marked for felling by authorized persons. The reduction in the difference in price between the small and the large sizes of timber changed the methods of exploitation. The earlier selective method based on the size of the tree gradually gave way to more suitable methods of selective cutting, in which increment was the deciding factor in the choice of the trees to be felled.

The fundamental principle of the Forest Protection Act (passed 1932) is that the private owner is free to run his own forest property as he wishes as long as he observes the provisions of the act. In younger forests, cutting is prohibited except when necessary for the development of the stand. In older forests, cutting must not be done in such a way that natural regeneration is harmed or prevented.

Each parish and each county has its own local supervisory forestry board to enforce the law. Trained personnel, consisting of both parish and county forest officers, is employed to assist these boards. The district forest officers' primary task is to control the way in which the private owner treats his forest, but great stress is also laid on information and guidance.

The private forest owner is charged a silvicultural fee of 2 per cent of the gross value of the timber he cuts for sale or for industrial purposes. The local forestry board enters this fee on a bank account for each forest, and the owner gets his fee back after establishing that he has made silvicultural improvements costing the corresponding amount.

A certain part of the timber price is dedicated by a provisional act to future investments. The amount is decided for a year at a time and has varied from one to nine kroner per cubic meter. This sum also goes back to the forest owner, provided certain improvements in his forest are accomplished, such as building roads for timber transport and houses for forest workers, making maps and working plans, etc.

The government also gives direct financial aid for building motor-vehicle roads in the forests and for silvicultural work, the amounts depending on the yearly budget. During the last few years, the grants have amounted to 25 per cent of the cost of the silvicultural work and 15 to 30 per cent of the cost of the roads, with a maximum of 50 per cent. The silvicultural and the investment fees, the subsidies, and the forest laws have together brought a marked improvement in the care of private forests. The method of selective cutting will be gradually abandoned in favor of a method of rational thinnings of the younger forest and appropriate cuttings for natural or artificial regeneration in old stands. This method will improve the natural regeneration and give a higher yield per acre of forest land.

During the years 1919-31 a government survey of the timber volume of the growing stock and of the increment was undertaken for each county in turn. Another survey was begun in 1937 and by now has covered more than half of the forests. This new survey is still going on, and in all the counties resurveyed the time between the first and the second survey has been more than twenty years. The results show that both volume and increment have been increasing in the interval between the surveys, the increase in increment being between 15 and 20 per cent.

Along the western and northern coasts of Norway large areas well suited for forestry are at present either barren or covered with hardwoods of little value. Most of the land belongs to private owners. The government is establishing nurseries and attempting to increase the owners' understanding of afforestation through education, guidance, and planning. It also gives direct financial aid, half of the cost, to private owners whose plantations are approved by the forest authorities.

Superior forest personnel—both for public and private forestry—is trained at the Norwegian Agricultural College at As, near Oslo. The average number of graduates is thirty every second year, and the length of the course is three years. The students must have passed courses at a preparatory forestry school to obtain admission. At present there are four of these schools, with courses lasting from a year to a year and a half, and the average number of forest technicians trained amounts to 120 per year. Some education in forestry is also given at the agricultural schools, and there is also a school for forest workers.

Forest research work, carried on by the Norwegian Forest Research Institute at As, the Forest Research Station of Western Norway in Bergen, and the Norwegian Agricultural College, has contributed much toward the development of Norwegian forestry during the last twenty or thirty years.

FINLAND

Eino Saari

Forests and the exports of forest products have always played an important role in Finnish industry. New problems arose in Finland's forests in the latter part of the nineteenth century. During the preceding decades, although forest owners had been free to manage their forests much as they pleased, sawmills had been strictly regulated. Steam-driven sawmills were forbidden until 1857, but by 1861 all such regulations were abandoned, and in the ensuing decades large new mills were constructed in rapid succession, the rafting of timber became general for long hauls, and cutting was greatly increased and carried far back into the wilderness. Finally, toward the end of the century, the establishment of many new pulp and paper companies, together with a growing demand for pit props for export, led to the widespread cutting not only of saw timber but also of small timber.

Without restrictions on cutting, fear of the devastation of the forests became acute. A law forbidding ruthless destruction was passed in 1886, but was weakly enforced. A new law was finally passed in 1917, prohibiting all cutting that would endanger natural regeneration and also any cutting of young vigorous coniferous forest except for thinning. To enforce this law a Commission was established in each county, and in this way an effective war against destruction was begun.

The prohibitions concerning coniferous pine forests were extended in 1928 to young vigorous broadleaf forests. The administration of the private forests was tightened. Eighteen district forestry boards were created to enforce the law and do forestry extension work among the farmers. Each board was obligated to hire at least one forester and the necessary number of forest technicians, who had had two years of training in a ranger school. To co-ordinate the work of these district boards and to serve in central agencies, two previously existing forestry associations were selected to function as semi-official central organizations in the forest extension work, Tapio for the Finnish-speaking districts and Skogskultur for the two Swedish-speaking districts. These appoint one member of each district board. Since the other members are appointed by the local farm organizations, each board is essentially a self-governing body representing the private forest owners.

All this is under the Forest Service, an independent office subordinate to the Ministry of Agriculture. The main task of the Forest Service, which was founded in 1851, has been to manage the state forests.

The general opinion in Finland has long been that laws alone cannot preserve forests without their owners' co-operation. This is particularly important in a country where the greater part of the forest land belongs to farmers. Forestry extension work was begun at the end of the nineteenth century. The local work, until 1928 in the hands of the local farm organizations, has since then been carried forward by the district forestry boards and the two central organizations. Their intensive labors have made the Finnish farmer, who usually is also a forest owner, more interested in forestry than ever before.

Since 1928 the Government has appropriated funds toward the improvement of the private forests, thus enabling owners to get plans, expert assistance, plants, and seeds free of charge, and to arrange for loans at nominal interest or to receive direct grants. The forest owners have made particular use of such funds to drain swampy ground and, during recent years, to improve logging roads. There are differences of opinion, however, as to whether forestry in Finland needs such subsidies under present circumstances.

Important in Finnish forestry are the forest owners' own associations. The first local organizations of this sort were founded at the beginning of this century. Their most useful function is to employ forest technicians who have had two years' training at a lower forestry school. In 1950 a law was enacted requiring each forest owner to pay an annual fee of 2 to 6 per cent on the taxable income from his forest toward financing the work of the local forestry associations, the aim being to secure the widest possible distribution of these organizations with their trained staff. Thus, each forest owner contributes his share toward the employment of forest technicians.

In the early twenties, the forest owners became much interested in co-operative sales organizations and other forms of industrial co-operation.

At this time a central association, the Metsäkeskus Osakeyhtiö, was founded, and a number of local groups were established soon afterwards, especially in the sawmill industry. Although the depression forced many of these to close, the central organization and some of the local groups are still in operation. Early in the thirties, moreover, the political central organization of agricultural producers founded a company for the sale of wood, reorganized later into a co-operative wood-sales organization with farmers as members. This group, which some 60,000 forest owners have joined, has worked especially in the field of the roundwood export business. In 1953 a joint stock company was established, with farmers as shareholders. Its purpose is to manage a forest-industries enterprise with pulp mills, a paper and cardboard factory, a sawmill, a woodworking factory, a chemical industry, etc., and its own forests.

Ever since the middle of the nineteenth century, the question of whether or not the forests of Finland were being overworked has been discussed. No definite answers could be given to this question until after the two extensive national forest surveys of the early twenties and late thirties. These have shown that increment and drain were about equal in the thirties, but that to increase the volume of wood available for future cutting, it would be necessary to decrease the rate for at least twenty years. This actually happened during World War II, and the third national forest survey (1951-53) showed an increase in both growing stock and growth.

Employers must furnish their forest workers with housing complying with certain minimum standards. Partly as a consequence, there has been a marked improvement in housing and other circumstances of the forest workers' lives. The government sets standard wages.

The extensive surveys mentioned above were made by the Forest Research Institute (founded in 1917). This institute has the following subdivisions: silviculture, forest biology, forest mensuration and inventory, forest technology, forest economy, soil research, and marshland research. Directly under the Department of Agriculture, the Institute is not connected with the Forest Service. The Evois Forest Institute was founded in the 1850's for the advancement of higher education in forestry. In 1908 this training was transferred to Helsinki University in the capital and since then, like agriculture, has had a college of its own. An elementary school in forestry was founded in 1876 and several similar schools have since been opened. The courses in these usually take two years and include both practical and theoretical studies. Some of the private forest companies have recently opened their own schools.

The forest industry has also set up special research institutes for the study of wood chemistry, paper manufacture, and the scientific management of logging operations. The government's technical research institute carries on studies of wood.

12. THE BRITISH ISLES

Richard St. Barbe Baker

The British are traditionally a forest people and from time immemorial have venerated their trees. The fruits of the forest and the wildlife that thrived in its shelter gave the early Britons food and strength, and the sturdy, deep-rooted oak has lent its character to the islanders who later used its solid trunk to build the ships that have made them famous as a maritime folk.

Diverse geological formations and soils, a maritime climate, and varied microclimates combine to give the British Isles a capacity for growing a great variety of trees. At the end of the Ice Age, the southern parts of the islands were largely covered with broadleaf forests, primarily of oak (*Quercus*),[1] ash (*Fraxinus*), beech (*Fagus*), hornbeam (*Carpinus*), willow (*Salix*), hazel (*Corylus*), holly (*Ilex*), and yew (*Taxus*), with juniper (*Juniperus*) growing best on the chalk. Nearly the whole of the north was covered by a natural mixture of pine (*Pinus*) and silver birch (*Betula verrucosa*), parts of which still survive as the Ancient Caledonian Forest at Rothiemurchus (from the Gaelic, *rath an mor guibhais*, "plain of the great pines") and at Ardlui on Loch Lomond. Pre-Roman Britain, viewed from the air, would probably have appeared as a continuous forest, with only a few open spaces on chalky downlands.

In ancient Britain the protecting trees were regarded as deities or dwelling places of spirits, as aristocrats of the plant world, stronger and worthier than grasses or shrubs. They were worshipped as the guardians of fertility and there was a widespread fear of injuring them. Before a noble tree was felled, a ceremony of placation was held and the tree's permission sought. This was the Era of Mythology, but, as the centuries went by, man reached an Era of Exploitation when trees were valued in terms of money and the accumulated wealth of the centuries was ruthlessly plundered. Today we are at the end of that period, which, in its most intensive form, has lasted less than a century. Two major wars have stripped our islands of much of their protective tree cover, thus so lowering the water table that in a dry season the capillary attraction on many a farm is insufficient for the growing of good crops. Let us hope that we are now entering an Era of Ecology, a period when man will seriously

---

[1] Source for botanical nomenclature: A. R. Clapham, T. G. Tutin, and E. F. Warburg. *Flora of the British Isles*. Cambridge University Press, London, 1952.

253

study his relationship to the natural environment. In Great Britain we are faced with an uphill task. We bear the sins of our forefathers, who reaped where they had not sown.

The British Forests Since the First World War

During World War I several hundred thousand acres of our forests were sacrificed. The German U-boats reduced imports to almost nothing, and our stocks of timber were nearly exhausted. For years, thoughtful people had urged the government to adopt a progressive forestry policy, but not until after the war was an effective forestry act passed. The task of the Forestry Commission, founded in 1919, was to plant as many trees as possible against a similar national emergency. The first thought was for pit props, to keep the coal mines productive in the event of imports again being drastically reduced. Early progress was good, and by 1939 the Commission was administering close on 500,000 acres of woodlands, of which 370,000 represented new plantings; but, unfortunately, we had not recovered from the damage of the first war before another came, and it was yet more devastating. Considerably more than a million acres of mature woods were felled.

These were not the only occasions in history when the woodlands of Great Britain have been decimated. They suffered under the onslaughts of the charcoal burners before coal was used for smelting, and as long ago as 1664 John Evelyn uttered this warning in his famous *Sylva:*

> After due reproofs of the late impolitic waste and universal sloth amongst us, we should now turn our indignation into prayers, and address ourselves to our better-natured countrymen, that such woods, as do yet remain entire, might be carefully preserved, and such as are destroyed, sedulously repaired. . . . Truly, the waste and destruction of our woods has been so universal that I conceive nothing less than an universal plantation of all sorts of trees will supply, and will encounter the defect.

In 1938 close on £64,000,000 worth of timber in one form or another and of wood pulp, most of it from Norway, Finland, and France, was imported into England, representing about 96 per cent of our supplies. These sources of supply were temporarily lost to us after the fall of those countries, yet Britain continued to require 3,000 tons of timber per day. The epic story of how this large quantity was provided cannot be told here, but British landowners gave generously of their woods to meet the needs of war. Our King himself set a fine example by allowing nine tenths of his woodlands in the Duchy of Cornwall to be sacrificed. During the war most of the Commission's woodlands were still too young to yield pit wood, let alone larger timber; 98 per cent had to come from privately owned estates. Even so, the Forestry Commission supplied no fewer than 50 million cubic feet of timber.

The census of woodlands carried out by the Forestry Commission in 1947-49 showed that there were in Great Britain nearly 3.5 million acres of woodland, amounting to about 6.1 per cent of the total land surface. Productive woodland amounted to about 2.5 million acres.

In terms of ownership the British forests may be classified thus:

1. National Forests under the Forestry Commission.
2. The ancient Crown forests, also under the supervision of the Forestry Commission.
3. Privately owned forests.
4. Forests owned by municipal bodies.

The Forestry Commission directly controls rather less than one third of the total forest area. By far the greater part is privately owned, despite death duties which have tended to break up wooded estates. Fellings in these private woods are now regulated by the Forestry Commission, which also insists on the early replanting of most cleared areas and provides grants and technical advice to aid such work.

In spite of the wholesale planting of coniferous forests by the Forestry Commission, hardwoods and conifers are in about equal proportion. The main types of forest crop can be roughly classified as follows: (1) full-grown hardwoods, (2) full-grown softwoods, (3) coppice under standards, (4) copsewood, (5) hedgerow trees and shelter belts.

The forest products in great demand now are pit props for the mines, sleepers for the railways, and standard building material. The annual output of pit wood is estimated at 39,441,600 cubic feet. There is also a large demand for packing cases and boxes in a country so largely depend-ent on its exports. Indications are that pulpwood and fiberboard will play an increasingly important part in the utilization of home-produced timber. In Great Britain 9,385,200 cubic feet of sawn softwood were pro-duced in 1954 and 27,720,000 of sawn hardwood. The bulk of the timber used by Great Britain is still imported from other countries, the Do-minions, and the Crown Colonies. In 1954 this amounted to 484,000,000 cubic feet, exclusive, of course, of a very large quantity of wood pulp. Great Britain, indeed, is one of the largest importers of timber in the world and cannot be expected to be self-supporting. With the Common-wealth, however, she could not only be self-supporting but could provide a surplus for other countries.

In the British Isles the so-called "indirect benefits" of the trees are more important than the "direct." The trees tend to equalize the tem-perature, both of the soil and of the atmosphere, and to reduce extremes in summer and winter. They reduce the relative humidity of the air and, in some cases, the total amount of dew or rainfall. They absorb and retain the moisture in the soil, especially in the upper layer of humus. By retarding the runoff after heavy rains they protect the surface soil from erosion and prevent disastrous floods of the kind that plague us, now that we have denuded the earth of much of its vital tree cover. Trees equalize the flow of water during the seasons. They assure pure water for springs and brooks by filtration through their humus and roots. They help purify the air of excess carbon dioxide.

In these islands, our woods and hedgerow trees afford considerable shelter to farms and cattle from the winter gales. The well-wooded estates provide cover for partridges and pheasants and add to the amenities of country life, and the economic uses of the forests and woodlands are legion. As John Evelyn wrote, "It is certain and demonstrable that all arts and artisans whatsoever must fail and cease, if there were no timber and wood in a nation. For he that shall take his pen and begin to set down what act, mystery or task belonging anyway to human life, could be maintained and exercised without wood, will quickly find that I speak no paradox. . . . We had better be without gold than without timber."

The Natural Forests of Great Britain

THE NEW FOREST. Of the few remaining natural forests in Great Britain, the New Forest, in the southern county of Hampshire, is one of the largest and finest. It was formed in 1079 by William the Conqueror, thirteen years after the Battle of Hastings. He named it the New Forest because it was a new addition to the many forests which the Crown had appropriated in early feudal times. The original name for this rather wild tract of country was Ytene, which means the furzy waste or gorse-land.

The Anglo-Saxon kings had continued the Roman tradition that the forests of England should be treated as common hunting grounds. Hence the punishments of maiming, and even death, for hunting in the royal forest caused much local hatred for the Norman kings. The superstitious believed, therefore, that it was not just a coincidence that one of William the Conqueror's younger sons was gored to death by a stag, or that his nephew was killed when his horse dashed him against a tree. And the events of that August night in 1100 are still thought by many to be a mystery. Was it really an accident that King William Rufus was stuck in the heart by an arrow from the bow of Sir Walter Tyrell?

The New Forest lies in a broad shallow basin, filled with gravel, sand, and clay, and is surrounded by low chalk downlands to the north and west and by Southampton Water and the Solent to the east and south. There are no steep hills in the area; the highest point is only 420 feet above sea level. There are three main surface forms with associated distinctive types of vegetation: infertile and flat-topped gravel plateaus and sandy plains forming heathlands, clays and loams forming the woodlands, and broad areas of low-lying, boggy marshland. The portion of the New Forest still owned by the nation covers an area of 65,000 acres, or about 100 square miles, of which only about 28,000 acres rank as productive woodland. Although certain plantations are enclosed by stout fencing, most of them are open for the public's enjoyment. Large open stretches of wild and lonely country are inhabited by deer and forest ponies, and in the autumn months, when the acorns and beech mast are on the ground, black pigs may be seen roaming about. Unfortunately, the deer, like the foxes, are still the victims of an occasional hunt. The badger can be found lurking around his burrow after dark, if one has the patience to sit in a hide and wait for him. It is a great boon to the city-worn Englishman to have such a large and beautiful parkland near at hand.

The oak and the beech are the most outstanding natural trees of the New Forest, but, contrary to general belief, the beech is now nearly as important as the famous oaks. A few ancient oaks are still preserved, but the majority that are left standing are not very old. Great inroads were made into the old, slow-growing oak stands for building the wooden ships of the British navy. About the time of the Napoleonic wars, the forest oaks suffered another great loss, when more than 4,000 full-grown trees were laid low by a violent hurricane.

The beech trees were not cut down as much as the oaks, and there are some particularly fine trees at Mark Ash, near the center of the forest. The former forest people, and the gypsies, used the beech leaves for filling mattresses, the mast for feeding their pigs, and pollarded branches for deer browse. The wood was used extensively for charcoal. Pollarding and charcoal burning were restricted by an act in 1698.

Other trees for which the New Forest is well known are the yews and the hollies. Some of the finest yews are to be seen at Sloden, and the holly grows into a fair-sized tree in some parts of the forest. Of the coniferous trees now grown in the forest, the Scots pine (*Pinus sylvestris*) is the only one that is a native of the British Isles. Scots pine provided a large proportion of the 12 million cubic feet of timber cut from the New Forest during the last war. The first fir trees introduced into the forest were planted at Ocknell Clump in 1776. The Douglas fir (*Pseudotsuga taxifolia*) was introduced into Britain about 125 years ago, and in the Boldrewood Enclosure in the New Forest there is a plantation nearly a hundred years old, with trees up to 155 feet in height and 12 feet in girth. With the Forest Act of 1851, the Crown was empowered to enclose and plant 10,000 acres of land in the New Forest. Extensive enclosures were therefore made in order to increase the forest's capacity for timber production, and several hundred acres of oak and Scots pine were planted. Each enclosure had its own woodman's cottage, many of which are still occupied by foresters and game keepers.

In 1851 the former offices of Lord Warden, Ranger, Woodward, and Regarder were abolished, but the office of Verderer remains to this day. The New Forest is administered from the old Verderer's Hall in the Queen's House at Lyndhurst, near the geographical center of the forest. Here the ancient Court of Swainmote and Attachment still meets to administer the heath grazing rights.

The enclosures that were made following the 1851 Act were not very popular with the general public. Many fine trees were needlessly cut down and serried ranks of oak, larch, and fir were planted in their place. This led to the formation of the New Forest Association, which undertook to protect the natural beauty of the forest. Later, the Act of 1877 provided that not more than 16,000 acres should ever be enclosed at one time and that the ornamental woods should be carefully preserved. Under the latest New Forest legislation—the Act of 1949—the Forestry Commission is empowered, with the consent of the Verderer, to plant a further 5,000 acres. The Commission is therefore doing a great deal of planting in the New Forest. It is also carrying out various silvicultural experiments in its nurseries. Small areas, called quadrats, are set aside, where a census is kept of the existing species of trees and of new ones that are being regenerated by the natural action of the wind and the birds. Whenever a large area of woodland is felled, a few healthy and mature mother trees are left standing to foster natural regrowth. This saves labor and greatly adds to the forest's charm. In certain localities natural regeneration has taken place in large bomb craters made during the last war, and these are being specially observed.

At present the New Forest is regarded as completely available for public enjoyment and there is a happy co-operation between the Forestry Commission, the inhabitants of the forest, and the Council for the Preservation of Rural England.

KIELDER FOREST, A NATIONAL FOREST PARK. Other forests are now springing up in many parts of the country. Perhaps the largest of these is Kielder Forest (70,000 acres). This carries some 40,000 acres of growing trees and is, at present, the most ambitious scheme on which the Forestry Commission is engaged; yet it is only one of a group of forests whose development will change the economy of a wide area from the Scottish border to the River Tyne. There are also several neighboring forests on both sides of the border, totaling, with Kielder, 130,000 acres. With Kielder, these have recently been declared a National Forest Park. Several modern villages are being built hereabouts for the forest workers and their families.

The formation of Kielder Forest began in 1926 and continued slowly at first, at the rate of only 100 acres a year, but, as new techniques were developed, from 1932 onward the average annual planting was 1,500 acres and today it is nearly double that. In Kielder the turf-planting system is widely used: the trees are planted in the overturned turf, following deep ploughing of the land, which ensures adequate drainage. Raised thus above the level of the thick grass or heather and provided with a moist yet well-drained bed, the young tree is given a good start in life. The species generally used are Sitka spruce (*Picea sitchensis*) and the common, or Norway, spruce (*Picea abies*), the first from the Pacific Northwest and the second the traditional Christmas tree. Sometimes for silvicultural reasons Scots pine (*Pinus sylvestris*) and the North American lodgepole pine (*Pinus contorta*) are mixed with these. Both Japanese larch (*Larix leptolepis*) and European larch (*Larix decidua*) have a place on the steep hillsides, with Douglas fir (*Pseudotsuga taxifolia*) in the more sheltered pockets. The Douglas fir grows with great rapidity in sheltered situations and often reaches a very large size, growing even faster than in its native Oregon or British Columbia. The giant fir (*Abies grandis*), planted in amenity belts, is also a rapid grower. A few western hemlock (*Tsuga heterophylla*), Lawson's cypress (*Chamaecyparis lawsoniana*), and western red cedar (*Thuja plicata*) may be found, besides mature indigenous trees such as alder (*Alnus glutinosa*), birch (*Betula verrucosa*), and rowan (*Sorbus aucuparia*)—thick with blossom in spring and scarlet with berries in autumn—and also gean (*Prunus avium*), or flowering wild cherry, which makes a good nurse tree, since it is very light-demanding and is therefore easily suppressed by more rapidly-growing shade-bearing species. Lower down in the valleys grows scrub, with willows, mostly sallow (*Salix caprea*), ash (*Fraxinus excelsior*), and wych elm (*Ulmus glabra*). Oak (*Quercus robur*) and beech (*Fagus sylvatica*) have also been planted, while the common sycamore (*Acer pseudoplatanus*) is gradually seeding itself naturally and reaching considerable size.

The worst enemy of the forest is fire. In 1948 a blaze burned nearly 700 acres in Kielder within two hours, spreading at times at a rate of 15 acres per minute, so that most of the damage was done before the fire-fighting equipment could be brought into action. Fine, dry, windy weather is the most dangerous, and if it occurs when the woods are full of holiday-makers, as during Bank-Holiday or Easter periods, the forest staff have sleepless nights. Another problem is the maintenance of effective drainage, for without this the roots become waterlogged and tree growth is checked. Trees can easily be "drowned," or their root holds become weakened. On exposed uplands, moreover, wind damage may be serious.

The plantations of Kielder Forest have now reached an age when thinnings are being undertaken, and by 1975 it is estimated that the output will reach 1,205,000 cubic feet per year, worth possibly £60,000. The highest elevation above sea level is at 1,975 feet and the highest regular planting at 1,250 feet, although experimental planting is being undertaken up to 1,500 feet. The rainfall averages about 50 inches a year.

OTHER NATIONAL FOREST PARKS. Kielder Forest, as we have seen, is part of a newly established National Forest Park. The first park of the kind to be formed in England and Wales was the Forest of Dean, established in 1938. It covers 29,000 acres of well-wooded hill country in Gloucestershire and Monmouth, including the whole of the ancient Royal Forest of Dean, plus the famous woods of the Wye Valley from Symonds Yat down to Tintern Abbey and Chepstow.

In North Wales, the Snowdonia National Forest Park occupies 21,000 acres, mainly in the valleys and on neighboring uplands of the River Conway and its tributary streams, the Llcdr, Llugwy, and Machno. There are many miles of attractive walks through the young woods of Gwydyr Forest and the surrounding moorlands of the Snowdon foothills, and there is an excellent camp at Beddgelert Forest, close to the western slopes of Snowdon.

To the west of the English Lake District is the small Forest Park of Hardknott. In Scotland, the Argyll National Forest Park extends from the neighborhood of Dunoon for 17 miles up the western shores of Loch Long to Arrochar, where there are public camping grounds. It covers 58,000 acres and includes the summit of Ben Ime (3,818 feet) and the rock climbs on the Cobbler.

The Glen Trool Forest Park in Ayrshire, Kirkcudbright, and Galloway, covers 110,000 acres, including the summit of the Merrick (2,764 feet) and several hill lochs. A lovely camping site is available close to Loch Trool.

The Glen More Forest Park near Aviemore, in Inverness-shire, has an area of 12,500 acres and rises from the shores of Loch Morlich to the summit of Cairngorm (4,084 feet). There is a camping center at Glen More Lodge.

Forestry Work in the United Kingdom

Forestry work like that at Kielder is continuing in many parts of England, Scotland, and Wales, and also in Northern Ireland, where the Ministry of Agriculture is responsible. When suitable land is acquired, it has to be surveyed in detail to determine its physical characteristics and extent and its silvicultural possibilities. The experienced forester rarely has to resort to digging test holes, for he can gauge the depth and nature of the soil by observing the wild herbage and existing tree growth on the site. Elevation, prevailing winds, the force and direction of gales, moisture and its distribution over the seasons, temperatures, and the occurrence of frost—all the influences that go to make up the local climate must be observed and taken into consideration before the choice of species is made and the plans of management prepared. Such knowledge is essential, for, however skilled the forestry officer or "working-plan" officer, all his work may be wasted unless he is familiar with every detail of local information accumulated by experience over the years. There is, indeed, some truth in the saying that a forester is born, not made. Certainly many of the qualities that characterize a good British forester have been handed down from father to son. For success, he must have an intuitive awareness of the land and sympathy with nature's way. The choice of species for a new forest is a large problem and often involves momentous decisions, especially when it is necessary to select admixtures of various species that will compete healthily with each other in the early stages, and combine to clear the ground of weeds and later to allow the most valuable species to form the final crop and to develop without too much competition. Knowledge of the root systems of different species is important; thus there should be as little competition as possible between the pear-shaped, the heart-shaped, and the flat-shaped patterns. These three may be advantageously mixed in order to lift the water table and keep the water in circulation, provide the right combination of minerals for plant food through leaf-fall, and reduce competition between neighboring trees, especially when planted along equidistant lines.

Although landowners of the past used to plant trees for their grandchildren, present-day forestry is practically a new industry for the country. It will give us the opportunity of making the most of men, money, and land. We already visualize 50,000 employed directly in the management of forests now being planted, and these, in turn, should give work for 200,000 more in wood-using industries. As we grow more timber, we shall save shipping and at the same time bring into production large areas of barren land and steep hillsides where today bracken is insidiously encroaching. The Forestry Commission is rendering a great service to the country by halting the drift of men from the countryside to the towns. It is hoped that before long the reverse process will set in, and more and more people will be restored to the countryside which their fathers forsook for the lure of the big cities.

Tree Cover in Wales

Geologically speaking, the flora of Wales is comparatively new, for it is probable that most of the land was covered by ice during the last glaciation and that most, if not all, of the plants have reached Wales since then. Perhaps the first trees to arrive were silver birches, followed by Scots pine; then came hazel. With the improvement of the climate, other broadleaf trees came in and, in due course, oak forests covered the lowlands and mounted well up on the hillsides. Then there was a time when the climate deteriorated, peat-forming plants invaded the upper slopes, and the broadleaf forests were again restricted to the lowlands, as they are today. Many forests were swept away for burning charcoal for use in the smelting of iron ore before coal was used for this purpose. More recently, the forests near the mines have suffered because they provide the necessary pit wood.

The climax vegetation of much of Wales, as, indeed, of the greater part of Great Britain, is a "deciduous summer forest," dominated by trees that shed their leaves in winter. The various subassociations or forest types, according to Welsh botanists, include Damp Oakwood, in which the dominating species used to be the common oak (*Quercus robur*), although this has all but disappeared or been replaced by fresh plantings. The second type, the Durmast Oakwood, dominated by *Quercus petraea*, is the typical woodland of the steeper slopes on the older siliceous rocks. Owing to constant fellings and grazing, this has been reduced to scrub, which represents 15 per cent of the tree cover in Wales. The third type is dominated by the ash (*Fraxinus excelsior*), usually on Carboniferous limestone in South Wales. On the Lias limestone of Glamorgan the field maple (*Acer campestre*) is associated with the ash and oak. The fourth consists of the Beechwoods, dominated by *Fagus sylvatica,* which occur on Carboniferous limestones and on the Old Red sandstone near Cardiff. This forest type marks the western limit of beech as a native tree in Europe. The last type is that of the Alder-Willow, dominated by *Alnus glutinosa,* together with various willows, chiefly *Salix caprea* and *Salix atrocinerea.*

When, toward the end of the fifteenth century, the English Parliament passed a number of acts designed to encourage timber growing for the Navy, a form of silviculture was established which survived till the twentieth century. Under this system, about 17 standards to the acre were grown, with coppice in between. The object was to grow trees with widely ramifying branches in order to provide the knees and heels used in building ships, both men-o'-war and merchant vessels. When steel took the place of wood for shipbuilding, this system was no longer needed, and so the oak-with-coppice type has been gradually converted into high forest. However, little encouragement was given to landowners to plant, owing to the quantities of imported timber that came from the Baltic and other countries, and during World War I more than half the woodlands of Wales were sacrificed. Since then the Forestry Commission has been seeking to create national forests and villages for forest workers in Wales and to assist the owners of privately owned woodlands. Attention is mainly directed to the establishment of new coniferous forests.

Monmouth, the best wooded county in Wales, has a tree cover of 12.8 per cent, and Anglesey, the worst, has but 1.2 per cent; the average for the whole of Wales is 5 per cent of the total land area. High forest covers 44.5 per cent of the total woodland area; coppice and coppice with standards, 14 per cent; scrub, 13.8 per cent; felled or devastated areas, 24.5 per cent; while uneconomic and amenity woods and shelter belts account for 3.2 per cent.

There are many remarkable trees in Wales, which compare well in age and size with any to be found elsewhere in the British Isles. The oldest are yews—of which more than forty are known for their size and antiquity. Among the exotics is the European silver fir (*Abies alba*) which has been cultivated in Great Britain since 1603. The tallest known, at Aberpergwm, has been measured at 145 feet in height by 13 feet 2 inches in girth. The largest Douglas fir (*Pseudotsuga taxifolia*) in the British Isles (at Powis Castle, Welshpool) has reached the remarkable height of 168 feet and is 11 feet 7 inches in girth at 4 feet from the ground.

The Sitka spruce (*Picea sitchensis*) at Stanage Park, Radnorshire, probably one of the oldest and largest in Great Britain, was planted in 1845 and in 1931 was 128½ feet high and 13 feet 2 inches in girth at 5 feet from the ground. Many common or European larch trees (*Larix decidua*) are grown in Wales, both by private owners and by the Forestry Commission. Valued for its strength and toughness, the larch offers high resistance to compression and is preferred above all timbers for pit wood in mines, for it grows straight, is not too heavy, and bends before it breaks, thus giving warning to the miners whose lives depend upon its endurance.

Scots pine *(Pinus sylvestris)*, which, as we have seen, was one of the first trees to introduce itself to Wales after the Ice Age, with the white birch *(Betula verrucosa)*, used to cover extensive areas. The tallest Scots pines in Wales are at Penpont, near Brecon, where several are over 120 feet in height.

The common walnut *(Juglans regia)* is cultivated throughout Wales. An avenue of these at Gwernyfed Park, Breconshire, is a quarter of a mile long with trunks averaging ten feet in circumference. A sweet chestnut tree *(Castanea sativa)* near Dynevor Castle, Carmarthenshire, is 115 feet high and 18 feet in girth.

The finest oaks in the British Isles are to be found along the Welsh borders, outstanding among them being those of Powis Castle. The largest, when measured in 1925, was found to be 105 feet high and 24 feet in girth and was said to contain 2,062 cubic feet of timber. It was a hybrid between the two native species, *Quercus petraea* and *Quercus robur*. A giant oak, also at Powis Castle, though not so tall, girthed 31 feet.

The common beech *(Fagus sylvatica)* has been found growing wild in practically every county of Wales and has also been widely planted for shelter. The old beeches at Llantarnam Abbey, Monmouthshire, are probably the largest in Wales. The tallest is 110 feet high and the biggest has a girth of 16 feet.

I have recorded the foregoing trees to show that Wales is pre-eminently a tree-growing country and, at the same time, to suggest that the native broadleaf species may yet make their contribution to the well-being of the country where they thrive so well.

Forestry in Scotland

The Forestry Commission now has more than one million acres of land in Scotland. Of this area some 355,000 acres are under plantations. The separate forest units number 193 and are well distributed throughout the country. The balance of the land includes areas still being grazed but to be planted as soon as conditions permit, ground which is given over to forest nurseries, a good deal of unplantable land such as mountain tops, and also a considerable amount of other land which will remain permanently in agriculture.

Among the largest and most picturesque of the Commission's forests is that of Loch Ard, between Aberfoyle and the Trossachs. This covers some 32,000 acres, of which more than 12,000 acres have been planted to date. Another is Inverliever, beside Loch Awe in Argyll, one of the first areas to be afforested by the Crown in Scotland. Work began there in 1907, and some 5,000 acres have been planted to date.

In the north, on the southern shore of the Moray Firth, lies Culbin Forest (7,500 acres), which has been formed on reclaimed drifting sand dunes. The whole of the drifting sands have now been fixed and are rapidly becoming productive woodlands.

The principal trees planted in the Commission's forests are conifers. The native Scots pine (*Pinus sylvestris*) is high on the list, but on the peaty, moister slopes of the western hills Sitka spruce (*Picea sitchensis*) has been found most successful, and Norway spruce (*Picea abies*) has been planted in large quantities. Other conifers are the three larches—the European (*Larix decidua*), the Japanese (*Larix leptolepis*), and a cross between the European and the Japanese larch; Corsican pine (*Pinus nigra* ssp. *laricio*); and Douglas fir (*Pseudotsuga taxifolia*) which was introduced from British Columbia by David Douglas, a young botanist, in the late 1820's.

Nearly all the tree plants required are raised from seed in the Commission's nurseries, the largest of which are situated at Newton (near Elgin), Kirroughtree (near Newton Stewart), Ledmore (near Perth), and Tulliallan (near Alloa). At the last-named there is a small but important seed-extraction station, where most of the home-grown seed supply is obtained from cones collected from selected trees all over Scotland. Other seed comes from abroad—some from Europe, some from the west coast of North America, and some even from Japan.

A feature of Scotland's forestry is the establishment of villages with forest holdings. The average number of men employed by the Forestry Commission has risen to 15 per 1,000 acres planted, from only 2 or 3 per 1,000 acres who were given work when the land was under other uses—as, for example, when it carried sheep, deer, or grouse. At the present time about 25,000 are employed in the forests and perhaps 100,000 in subsidiary industries such as sawmilling.

There should be no conflict between forestry and agriculture; in fact, one should be the handmaiden of the other. It has been found that work in the woods has enabled landowners to tide over hard years by providing seasonal employment. The future prosperity of Scotland will be largely bound up with its forests and its "white coal," the water power that will come from a more adequate tree cover.

Forestry in Northern Ireland

Down to the beginning of the seventeenth century much of Ulster was clothed with primeval forests, and traces of great trees may still be found in deep peat in all parts of the province. The clearance of the forests resulted from colonization. As the land became settled the forest was pushed back, reckless exploitation was the order of the day, and it was not until 1903 that there was a definite turning of the tide of deforestation. In that year the state forestry program was inaugurated, with the setting up of a Forestry Branch of the Department of Agriculture and Technical Instruction and the acquisition of Avondale (in County Wicklow) as the first forestry center and training school in Ireland. The two world wars made further inroads into the remaining stands of trees and brought home the importance of adequate strategic reserves of growing timber. The British Forestry Commission, which, as we have seen, came into being in 1919, for a time absorbed the Irish forestry department, which had started out along the same road 16 years earlier. When the Government of Northern Ireland was formed in 1921-22 it assumed the responsibility for forestry in that country, and its new Ministry of Agriculture became the forest authority, working with powers and duties similar to those conferred on the Forestry Commission by the Forestry Act of 1919. At this time the forest estate totaled some 4,000 acres, of which about 700 acres had already been planted; the staff consisted of one inspector and 25 men. Since then the Ministry's reforestation program has steadily developed. In the 1920's the annual state planting rate averaged some 400 acres. It then rose and during the 1930's and war years (1939-45) averaged 1,000 acres and since the war has stood between 2,000 and 2,500 acres. As a consequence, there is now a total planting area of about 40,000 acres and a staff of nine inspectors and more than 1,000 regular employees. The 2,000-2,500 acres-per-annum rate is necessary to achieve the 50-year target that has been set of 150,000 acres of productive state forest. It is proposed that 95 per cent of the trees planted should be softwoods, of which Sitka spruce (*Picea sitchensis*) will be the dominant species.

Wherever practicable, hardwoods are planted either in pure stands or in mixture with conifer nurse trees. In the latter case the conifers are removed as the crop matures, so that by the time the last conifers are removed at an age of about 60 or 70 years, a full crop of hardwoods is left to grow on to maturity at about 130 years. During this second phase of the rotation the normal practice is to underplant the hardwoods with shade-bearing conifers, so that two crops of conifers and one of hardwoods are produced in each rotation. While the exact proportions of the various species used vary from year to year, they approximate the following percentages: spruce 61 (Sitka spruce 54, Norway spruce 7) larch 14, pine 13, Douglas fir 6, other conifers 1½, hardwoods 4½ (divided fairly evenly between oak, ash, and beech to the extent of 3½ per cent, the remaining 1 per cent comprising a number of minor species).

The Ministry's oldest plantations first reached the thinning stage in the early years of World War II, and there are now some 9,000 acres at various stages of thinning. Recent shipments of logs produced by the thinnings have been as follows (in tons): 2,800 (1950), 4,800 (1951), 9,400 (1952), 14,700 (1953), 17,500 (1954).[2] The medium-diameter logs are used as pit wood, those of larger diameter as sawable wood (suitable, however, for small scantlings only), and those of smaller diameter for fence posts and pulping.

2 Ministry of Agriculture, Northern Ireland. *Forestry in Northern Ireland,* 1955.

Forestry in Eire

Nowhere in the British Isles is tree growth so rapid as in Ireland, with its mild, humid climate, and geologists and archeologists have recently established the fact that the "Emerald Isle" ·was once covered with vast forests, which in the course of time have been gradually reduced. Among these were extensive oak forests, the most famous of all being that of Shillelagh in Wicklow, from which, I am told, is derived the name formerly given to an oak stick and now wrongly transferred to blackthorn. There is a tradition that the oaks of Shillelagh provided the roof timbers both of Westminster Hall and of the Chapel of King's College, Cambridge. According to Hayes in his *Practical Treatise on Planting* (1794), the finest trees in Shillelagh were cut down in the time of Charles II and exported to Holland for the support of the Stadt House, under which hundreds of thousands of piles were driven. In 1692 iron forges were introduced and the ruin of the wood was all but completed. However, a few great trees were still being felled there at the end of the eighteenth century. It is recorded that, in 1731, 2,150 oak trees were standing in the deer park of Shillelagh but in 1780 only 38 remained. There were other forests of mighty oaks, of which single specimens girthed over 40 feet and it was common for oaks to reach a height of 120 feet or more. In the shadow of oak groves St. Columba founded the monasteries of Derry and Durrow (names derived from "drew," meaning an oak).

In seventeenth-century Ireland there was almost unrestricted felling both for burning charcoal for the iron-smelting industry and for clearings for agriculture. Perhaps initially in response to an appeal by John Evelyn, extensive planting was undertaken by landowners from 1760 to 1880, by which time about 350,000 acres had been planted; but from then onward planting declined, while felling increased. The first forestry school in Ireland, opened at Avondale in 1904, was the beginning of the present Irish Forestry Service. Albeit, progress was slow until early in the 1930's, when a rapid expansion began, only to be checked by World War II. A fresh impetus was given to forestry in 1948, when a contingent of about one hundred Men of the Trees,[3] with English foresters, went to Eire at the invitation of the President. Open discussions were held on tree problems, and, in conference with the newly appointed Minister of Lands, a figure was arrived at that might be regarded as the minimum tree cover for safety, namely 10 per cent of the total land area.

[3] The Society of the Men of the Trees, founded in 1922, encourages forest protection and the planting of trees in all lands, and advises on all tree and forestry questions. Already it has been instrumental in planting millions of trees in many countries, and each year representatives join a Summer School and Trees Conference in one country or another. On this occasion the President of Eire was acting as host to the delegates.

The Forestry Commission and the forestry societies, together with the Men of the Trees, have produced a number of publications to interest the public in forestry. As these may be of special interest to visitors to Britain, I should be only too pleased to send lists of them to intending visitors.

It is now coming to be accepted that a great new forest industry can be built up in Ireland. But the day of the hardwoods appears to have passed, and only conifers find favor in official eyes. It is argued that, like any other crop, a tree crop must be judged on its exploitation value, and so 95 per cent of the timber and pulpwood used today is softwood. Already state forests are becoming productive and Irish timber compares favorably with imported products. A recent report by the Department of Lands, which is responsible for forestry, stated that 28 new forests had been established between 1950 and 1953, bringing the total area under productive forests to more than 200,000 acres. The actual area planted in that period amounted to 36,852 acres, or more than 12,000 a year. The number of state forests has now reached 165. The planting program for 1955 allowed for 13,500 acres with 24,000,000 transplants and a labor force of 4,500. A recent survey made by an expert from the Food and Agricultural Organization of the United Nations has supported a finding of a previous survey by the Forestry Service that an area of 1,200,000 acres would be suitable for afforestation "if it could be acquired." The crucial problem would seem to be the acquisition of the land. Once this problem has been solved, the government should have no difficulty in reaching its target of 25,000 acres a year. That would mean that the forests would be run on an average rotation of 48 years.

13. WESTERN EUROPE[*]

David Lowenthal

Civilization has largely deforested many parts of the world; western Europe is distinctive in the large proportion of its forests that have been transformed, rather than destroyed. Nevertheless, the impact of man over the past two or three millennia, and particularly in the past five centuries, has profoundly affected the west-European forests.

The forest flora that reoccupied western Europe after the Pleistocene glaciation was far less diversified than the Tertiary flora had been, for the Alps interposed a formidable barrier to the survival of many species during the ice ages and impeded the re-establishment of other species later on. Pine, birch, and hazelnut, mixed with oaks, elm, basswood, and hornbeam first dominated the postglacial landscape. After about 4000 B.C., as the climate grew colder, these forests were invaded by beech and then by fir and other conifers, which occupied the mountains and other locations where the hardwood associations found soil or climate uncongenial. Even so in most of western Europe hardwoods remained paramount, and the landscape that confronted Neolithic man was essentially a vast oak-beech forest, broken here and there by grasslands where soils were too poor or sites too exposed to support trees, by pine woods along the Atlantic and North Sea coasts, and by fir, spruce, and larch in the Alps and at high altitudes elsewhere.

Less than one fourth of western Europe is now wooded (Table 13–I), and the forests have changed greatly. Half of them are now coniferous, and much of the remaining broadleaf area is no longer high forest but coppice, particularly in France and Belgium. Exotics have been added to the original assemblage, while many native species have lost ground, although in general there is less diversity than before man's impact was felt. Individual forests are also more uniform in size and age composition; even-aged and monocultural stands have replaced much of the natural mixed forest.

Two factors are principally responsible for these changes: clearing for settlement and cropland (significant since the Pax Romana), and the demand for forest products for fuel and, especially in the recent past and

* The American Geographical Society and the writer are especially indebted to Professor P. Silvy-Leligois, of the École Nationale des Eaux et Forêts, Nancy, France, for permission to make use of certain unpublished materials prepared by him.

TABLE 13-I

WESTERN EUROPE: FOREST DATA, 1953 [a]

	France	W. Germany	E. Germany	Switzerland	Belgium	Luxembourg	Netherlands	West Europe [b] Total
Forest area								
1. 1,000 hectares	11,407	6,732	2,749	950 [c]	601	81	250	22,770
2. Per cent of total area	20.7	28.1	25.6	23.8	19.9	31.4	7.6	22.1
3. Hectares per capita	0.3	0.14	0.16	0.2	0.07	0.3	0.02	0.17
4. Coniferous (per cent of total forest area)	30	65	80	80 [d]	37	20	69	50
Ownership (per cent of total forest area) [e]								
5. State	14	31	50	5	11	5	15	23
6. Communal	22	22	14	65	33	50 [f]	15 [g]	23
7. Private	64	42	35	29	54	43	65 [h]	52
Silviculture, etc. (per cent of total forest area)								
8. High forest [i]	41	91		92	50	72	80	
9. Coppice with standards [i]	29	2		8	28	0	19	
10. Coppice [i]	25	5			16	28	1	
11. Under sustained-yield management	39	67	64	71	79	42	22	
Growing stock								
12. 1,000,000 cu. cm. [j]	805	625	253	200	46	10.1	15	1,954
13. Volume per ha.	75	101	92	237	70	124	61	90
Net growth per annum								
14. Cubic meters	32,425	25,000	5,410	3,300	2,260	170	647	69,212
15. Cu. m. per ha.	3.0	3.8	2.0	3.9	4.0	2.9	2.6	3.2

[a] Based on FAO, *World Forest Resources*, Rome, 1955.

[b] Totals do not include 77,000 hectares in the Saar; 20,000 hectares in Berlin; and 4,000 hectares in Liechtenstein.

[c] Includes 100,000 inaccessible hectares.

[d] Excludes both 100,000 inaccessible hectares and 5,000 unexploited hectares.

[e] Does not include forests owned by institutions, which amount to 330,000 hectares in West Germany, 6,000 hectares in the rest of Western Europe.

[f] Excludes 23,000 hectares of bark-coppice.

[g] Includes provincial and polder corporation forests.

[h] Excludes inaccessible and unexploited forests.

[i] Does not include certain open areas (e.g., clear-cut areas, firebreaks), which amount to 567,000 hectares or 5 per cent of the total forest area in France, 180,000 hectares in the rest of Western Europe.

at present, for industry. In ancient and medieval times Europeans were content to harvest what was available in the forests, and floristic changes were largely unintentional. Since the rise of industry, however, they have deliberately transformed their forests, seeking a higher proportion of more useful species and types. The direction and degree of success of these efforts have varied from country to country and from century to century, as will be pointed out below.

Western Europe falls within three great forest regions. One is the western extension of the North European plain, including the northwestern two fifths of France, the Low Countries, and northwestern Germany from the Rhineland and Westphalia to Mecklenburg. In this fertile belt forests today cover less than a tenth of the land. Equally divided between broadleaf and coniferous types, they provide the population of the area with only 0.13 hectare of forest land per capita. The second zone is the central-European coniferous belt, which includes Switzerland, southeastern France north of Provence and as far west as the Rhone, and all of Germany southeast of a line joining Frankfurt and Berlin. In this area between 25 and 40 per cent of the land is forested, three fourths of it in conifers, and there are about 0.3 hectare of forest per person. The third area includes the remainder of southern France, where, as in the rest of southern Europe, broadleaf forests prevail, although only Provence has a strictly Mediterranean forest flora. Southern France is between 25 and 30 per cent forested.

Western Europe as a whole is not too poorly forested—22 per cent as compared with 28 per cent for all of Europe and 29.5 per cent for the world—but because it is very densely populated the forest area per capita is only 0.17 hectare compared with 0.34 hectare for all Europe and 3.5 hectares for North America. The small amount of forest land per capita and the great demand for wood in this highly industrialized area are the major reasons why western Europe is a timber-deficit area. The wonder is that the countries of western Europe meet as much of their timber needs as they do from domestic stocks.

That western Europe can supply itself so well is largely the result of the remarkable development of scientific forestry. Relative scarcity of wood has long compelled the Europeans to manage their forests carefully and to use their forest crops more intensively than do any other people in the world. Thanks to the application of advanced silvicultural techniques, France, Germany, Switzerland, and the Low Countries together achieve an average annual net growth of 3.2 cubic meters of wood per forest hectare, as compared with 2.0 cubic meters for Europe as a whole and 0.4 for the world. Many large forests in Germany, France, and Switzerland produce between 5 and 8 cubic meters per hectare each year, and in due time west-European foresters hope to bring the entire region's average yield up to this high level.

France

In no western European country have forests suffered more than in France, yet nowhere do future timber prospects seem better assured. This is fortunate because the forest industry in France is intimately integrated with the whole economy, particularly with agriculture. The forest situation to a considerable degree is an indicator of national health.

EXTENT. One measure of the significance of forests in France is the large per capita forested area, 0.3 hectare, double the figure for Germany and higher than in any other western European country save Luxembourg. Yet there is no excessive concentration on forests to the detriment of agriculture and grazing. On the contrary, France's 11,407,000 hectares of forests comprise only 20.7 per cent of her area, a smaller proportion than in Germany or Switzerland.

Like the rest of western Europe, France was much more heavily wooded at the time of the Roman Empire, and even in the Middle Ages, than it is today. Before the arrival of the Gauls, three millennia ago, probably only Champagne was free of forests, and two thirds of Caesar's Gaul was wooded. But clearing for settlement commenced earlier and went on more rapidly than elsewhere north of the Alps; by 1300 the forests covered only 13 million hectares. After that demands for fuel and industry became so great, and forest management so poor, that by the beginning of the French Revolution the wooded area had shrunk to about eight million hectares. The excesses of the Revolution reduced it still further, and not until the middle of the nineteenth century was the tide turned by afforestation. Since then the forest acreage has grown as indicated in Table 13–II.

TABLE 13–II

FRANCE: LAND IN FORESTS, 1790-1953

(In Million Hectares)

Year	Area	Year	Area
1790	8.0	1929	10.7
1863	9.3	1938	10.8
1892	9.5	1944	10.4
1913	9.9	1948	11.1
1920	10.3	1953	11.4

Source: "La forêt française," *Études et conjoncture*, 6 (1951), 68.

World War II damaged French forests much less than did World War I, largely because of the co-operation of German foresters. Overcutting, neglect, and war damage did somewhat reduce forest acreage, but postwar afforestation has more than made up this loss.

The distribution of the forests appears in Fig. 36 (p. 300). The Landes of the southwestern part of the country are 50 per cent wooded; also heavily forested are the mountains that ring France on the east, the southeast, and the southwest: the Vosges, Jura, Alps, and Pyrenees. At the other extreme, forests are almost completely absent from the north and Brittany, and are scarce in Normandy, Poitou, and Maine, the finest agricultural regions.

The largest single forests, however, frequently occur in areas that are not generally heavily wooded. Remnants of the ancient royal, seignorial, and ecclesiastical forests, for example, many of them of more than 5,000 hectares, are principally in the Departments of the Orne, Sarthe, Allier, Aisne, and Indre, which are less than 15 per cent wooded. By contrast, the densely forested regions are characterized by large numbers of very small woods.

Most French forests are in the lowlands. Although the mountains and other areas of rough relief are proportionately more wooded than the rest of the country (except for the Landes), nevertheless 60 per cent of the forests lie below 400 meters, 29 per cent between 400 and 1,000 meters, and only 11 per cent above 1,000 meters.

COMPOSITION. France is the only west-European country besides Belgium where man's alteration of the forests has not destroyed the primacy of the hardwoods. Nonconifers still occupy 70 per cent of the forest area, the principal broadleaf species being oak, followed by birch and hornbeam, and the main softwoods maritime pine (*Pinus pinaster*),[1] Scots pine (*Pinus sylvestris*), fir, and spruce (Table 13–III).

TABLE 13-III

FRANCE: PER CENT OF TOTAL FOREST AREA OCCUPIED BY PRINCIPAL SPECIES, 1912 AND 1948

Species	1912	1948	Species	1912	1948
Oak (all species)	31.5	35	Maritime pine	4.0	12
Beech	18.2	15	Scots pine	6.5	7
Hornbeam	11.0	8	Fir	7.1	6
Other broadleaf species	16.0	12	Spruce	2.7	3
			Larch	1.8	1
			Other conifers	1.2	1

Sources: (1912) T. S. Woolsey, *Studies in French Forestry* (New York, 1920), 40, Table 2; (1948) *La forêt française* (La documentation française illustrée, No. 24, Dec. 1948), 6.

The proportion of the forest occupied by broadleaf species two thousand years ago was even greater than it is now. Selective clearing for settlement and agriculture between the third and twelfth centuries affected principally these forests. Afforestation in the past century—maritime pine in the Landes, Scots pine in Champagne, other conifers in central France —has increased the proportion of conifers by half, as shown by the following figures for the per cent of conifers in the total forest area of France: 20 in 1879, 26 in 1912, 29 in 1929, 30 in 1953.[2] But the rage for fast-growing, profitable conifers which transformed Germany's forests a century ago hardly touched France, and France today intends to keep its

[1] Clapham *et al.* (1952), Kelsey and Dayton (1942). For full references see pp. 301-302.
[2] Silvy-Leligois (1955):11.

hardwood forests. Nevertheless, the proportion of conifers will be increased, both to meet increasing demands for industrial wood and to help convert coppices to high forest.

Human activities have altered the composition of the forests throughout the country. Sessile and pedunculate oak (*Quercus petraea, Q. robur*), which once dominated most of central and northern France, are still the most important trees in central France and much of the east. Such forests as exist on the barren soils of the northwest are predominantly oak and beech, but maritime pine and Scots pine have been introduced in recent years, and Normandy has a good deal of fir. In addition to beech, which frequently accompanies sessile oak, the Paris basin has considerable chestnut and hornbeam, both introduced species. Large numbers of poplars, favored because fast-growing, have been planted along rivers and roads. The once grassy plains of Champagne are dotted with clumps of Scots and Austrian pine (*Pinus nigra* ssp. *nigra*), introduced in the nineteenth century, and Scots pine has also reforested the impermeable soils of the Sologne district, south of the Loire.

To the east, the Ardennes and Argonne are covered with rather poor forests of oak, beech, and birch. As one approaches the Vosges, beech becomes the dominant hardwood; but in the Vosges, as in the Jura and the Alps, conifers dominate: silver fir, Scots pine, and spruce, with a belt of larch above them in the Alps, and montana (*Pinus mugo*) and cembra pine (*P. cembra*) still higher.

Southern France, particularly Provence, which is said to lack the *esprit forestier* of the north, is completely different. Mediterranean rather than west-European in both climate and soils, Provence has enormous areas of scrub and garrigue that remain unforested because landowners are apathetic or fear the constant and serious threat of fire. The species that do flourish are: pubescent oak (*Quercus pubescens*) and ilex, or holm oak (*Q. ilex*), in coppice, which provide firewood and charcoal and yield truffles around their roots; three species of juniper, one (*Oxycedrus*) providing an antiseptic oil used in soap; some eucalyptus; and cork oak (*Quercus suber*) in the Esterel, the Maures, the eastern Pyrenees, and to some extent in the Landes. In the foothills of the Pyrenees the oaks give way to beech above 120 to 150 meters, and the beech, in turn, to silver fir (*Abies alba*), the dominant Pyrenean species, which occupies the mountains between 750 and 1,200 meters, with montana pine above it to the tree line.

Along the coast between the Pyrenees and the Gironde are the Landes, a plain originally covered with maritime pine, but drastically deforested during the later Middle Ages. By the end of the eighteenth century sand dunes were moving landward at the rate of twenty to thirty miles a year, even endangering Bordeaux, but subsequently they were halted and pinned down by a barrier of maritime pine along the whole coast, after which plantings covering a million hectares were extended inland by private landowners.

In the Massif Central, long a derelict area forestally, mixed conifers (spruce, Scots pine, and silver fir) and beech are being planted.

FOREST MANAGEMENT AND SILVICULTURAL METHODS. Although felling regulations in the French forests date back to Charlemagne, and organized forestry in the royal woods to the thirteenth century, it was not until the nineteenth century that France developed forest policies that were both sound and effective. Until then, the history of forest administration was one of recurrent crises: a period of overcutting would lead to serious shortages of wood and this, in turn, to forest legislation so thorough and severe as to be unworkable; the forest laws would then be flaunted and another period of anarchy would ensue.

So seriously were the forests depleted—partly owing to the sale of offices and general corruption in the forestry service—that in 1669 Colbert, fearing that France would perish for lack of timber for her navy, promulgated a new and sweeping set of regulations and reformed the forestry service from top to bottom. Not content with merely preserving the remaining forests, Colbert made positive efforts to improve their quality and to build up new reserves. Nevertheless, a century later the forests were again declining in quality and quantity; and the woods were further diminished by the disturbances of the Revolution, the wiping out of feudal forest privileges and the widespread pillaging which followed, the transfer of almost a million hectares of ecclesiastical forest land to the state and to individuals, and the timber requirements of Napoleon's campaigns. In addition, deforestation on the steep slopes of Savoy and Dauphiné led to excessive erosion and devastating torrents and floods.

The havoc caused by the Alpine floods helped to bring home the need for reform. The French and Swiss foresters were the first in Europe to understand and evaluate the protective functions of forests and the first to establish principles for the protection of watersheds. They accomplished more than this. Under its first director, Bernard Lorentz, the National Forestry School at Nancy (founded 1824) developed a new and comprehensive Forest Code (1827), embodying the results of forestal research and many of the principles of silvicultural management that had been worked out in Germany over the previous half century. Of particular importance were techniques of natural regeneration designed to restore the French forests to silvicultural and economic health after centuries of misuse.

Throughout the Middle Ages, the proportion of coppice in the French forests had been increasing, to meet local demands for fuel wood, and by the Revolution most of the private and communal woods were coppice. Only the royal properties maintained much high forest. These were exploited by the "tire et aire" method, a section of the forest being felled annually, with a few standards left to ensure regeneration. As demands for timber—and for royal revenue—rose, the annual cut likewise increased, and many of the broadleaf forests of western and central France diminished in extent and in quality. In the sixteenth century Francis I had established sustained-yield cutting in the oak forests, decreed that one third of all the coppice wood in the royal forests should be left to grow into high forest, and ordered the Church authorities to reserve a quarter of their woods as high forest; but these ordinances were of little effect. Over-cutting continued, and high forest continued to degenerate into coppice. Only the conifer woods of the east, where "jardinage" was practiced (a proportion of the trees in a given area is cut and the young growth allowed to mature), remained in good condition.

Lorentz' introduction of natural regeneration has played a major role in the improvement of the French forests during the past century. The Forest Code of 1827 was extended, in part, to the communal forests, which had never before been under the supervision of the forestry service, and large-scale afforestations—in the Landes, in Champagne, and the east—in which the government assisted private owners, added 1.5 million hectares to France's forest lands between 1800 and 1914.

Although some private owners learned the new techniques, private forests remained immune from state control and supervision and on the whole were, and are, less well managed and far less productive than the state or communal forests. France still needs to convert much coppice into high forest. In 1953, 25 per cent of the nation's forests were in simple coppice and 29 per cent in coppice with standards; only 41 per cent were high forest, less than half the proportion in Germany and Switzerland.

OWNERSHIP. Most of France's forest problems, including the prevalence of coppice, are largely due to the facts that a higher proportion of her forest lands—64 per cent—is in private hands than in any other western European country save the Netherlands, and that private owners are subject neither to the forest code nor to supervision by state foresters. Furthermore, three fifths of the public forest land is communal, leaving only 14 per cent in state hands and under the direct and permanent control of the forest service.

Ownership varies considerably from region to region. Private forests comprise more than three fourths of the total in the west, the Paris Basin, the Massif Central, the Garonne valley, and the Landes, but less than half in the east, the Pyrenees, and the Alps. Communal forests exceed all others in the Vosges and the Pyrenees. State forests are more important than communal in the north and east, and in the western part of the Paris Basin, but nowhere in France do they account for more than 25 per cent of the forested area.

Forest sizes range rather evenly from small to large (Table 13–IV). But although most of the state forests and even the communal forests are fairly sizable, the private forests are almost incredibly fragmented. Of some million and a half owners, only about 6 per cent own more than 10 hectares. Their holdings were as follows in 1945: 63,724 persons owned between 10 and 50 hectares, 11,247 owned between 50 and 100 hectares, and 7,996 owned more than 100 hectares. Of this last group, only 710 had

more than 500 hectares. In 1912 only 79 private forests in France exceeded 1,000 hectares.

In sum, a very high proportion of France's forest area is privately
owned and not subject to government forestry control, save where the
forests serve a primarily protective function; and very small holdings predominate. These facts, together with the historic dominance of coppice,
largely account for the low yields and poor quality of the French forests.

TABLE 13–IV

FRANCE: PROPORTION OF FOREST AREA IN FORESTS OF VARIOUS SIZES, 1942

Forest Size (Hectares)	Per Cent of Total Area
Less than 1	0.2
1 to 4.9	2.7
5 to 9.9	6.2
10 to 19.9	14.2
20 to 39.9	17.9
40 to 49.9	4.3
50 to 99.9	13.9
100 to 199.9	11.4
200 to 499.9	13.0
Over 500	15.2

Source: "La forêt française," *Études et conjoncture,* 6 (1951), 71.

INCREMENT AND YIELD. France's growing stock is estimated as 805 million cubic meters, or only 75 cubic meters per hectare, as compared with
101 for West Germany and 237 for Switzerland. Despite the high proportion of coppice, which permits a gross annual increment of 4 per cent
of the growing stock (equal to that of Germany and twice that of Switzerland), France's net annual increment is only 32,425,000 cubic meters, or
3.0 cubic meters per hectare, well below the average yield for the rest
of western Europe save the Netherlands and Luxembourg.

Fellings were held below growth in the 1920's and 1930's, and although
there was some overcutting during and immediately after World War II—
in 1943, 32 million cubic meters were cut compared with a growth of 26
million cubic meters—since 1948 France has again maintained fellings
below net growth, thanks to ten million cubic meters of timber taken from
the French occupation zone of Germany and later thanks to salvage timber
that became available after forest fires in the Landes and the ravages of
the bark beetle in the Vosges. In 1948 the allowable cut was about 25.3
million cubic meters, of which two thirds came from state and state-
controlled forests; in 1953 the allowable cut [3] and actual fellings were 29.4
million cubic meters, the same as the net increment. Trees outside the
forest supplied 3.64 million cubic meters, or 14 per cent of the total yield.

In short, France maintains her growing stock intact, but gets less wood
from her forests than does Germany, although France has a larger forested
area.

[3] Total amount of roundwood which can be cut during a year in conformity with sustained-
yield practices, as prescribed by forest policy.

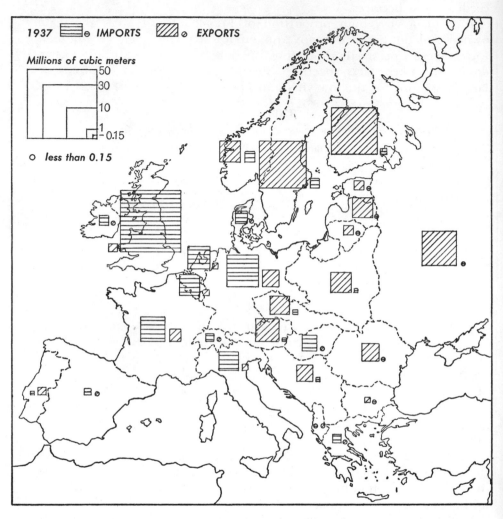

FIG. 32. Europe: imports and exports of forest products, 1937. Based on plate "Import and Export of Wood and Wood Products in Europe," Fig. 6 in *Weltforstatlas*, Hamburg, 1952; and FAO, *Yearbook of Forest Products Statistics, 1954*, Tables 40 and 41.

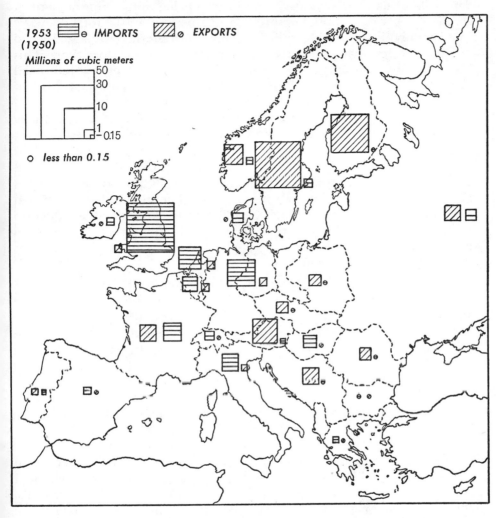

FIG. 33. Europe: imports and exports of forest products, 1953 (1950). Based on plate "Import and Export of Wood and Wood Products in Europe," Fig. 6 in *Weltforstatlas*, Hamburg, 1952; and FAO, *Yearbook of Forest Products Statistics, 1954*, Tables 40 and 41.

CONSUMPTION AND FOREIGN TRADE. France's wood supplies are as deficient in quality as they are in quantity. Owing to the large amount of coppice, 57 per cent of the forest fellings (61 per cent of the total domestic wood supply) is fuel wood, while elsewhere in western Europe fuel wood accounts for less than half the total—in Germany only 23 per cent. This leaves France with only 11,150,000 cubic meters of domestic industrial wood, 31 per cent more than in the 1930's but only about one third of the combined East and West German production.

France exports 500,000 cubic meters of saw logs and veneer logs, chiefly to Belgium-Luxembourg and secondarily to Switzerland, the Netherlands, and Italy. But she imports more pit props (from Germany and Sweden) than she exports (to French North Africa and the United Kingdom), and also imports more than 200,000 cubic meters of pulpwood, mainly from Finland. Altogether France's 1953 imports of forest products exceeded her exports by 410,000 cubic meters, but that is a considerable reduction from the 1,370,000 cubic meters of 1952 and still more from the 3,970,000 cubic meters annual average of 1935-38; it amounts to only 2.4 per cent of her total net consumption.

FOREST PRODUCTS AND INDUSTRIES. Not including the million and a half private owners who work on their own properties part-time, there were in France in 1948, 113,500 individuals engaged full-time in forest exploitation, 61,700 as loggers and 51,800 in sawmills. In view of the amount of production, these are high employment figures, but they are more than matched by the number of sawmills, which from 6,000 in 1914 rose to 15,000 in 1939 and to 20,000 in 1951. The majority of these mills are small: 62 per cent employ 5 men or less; 28 per cent engage between 6 and 20, and 10 per cent more than 20, with only 36 mills in the whole country employing more than 100 men. Production per mill is correspondingly low; only 10 per cent are equipped with modern machinery capable of producing 13.0 cubic meters of sawn lumber in an eight-hour day, while three fifths of them are ancient models which yield an average of only 4 cubic meters daily. The excessive number of mills, their antiquated machinery, the high degree of competition among them, and their location far from areas of consumption make transportation of wood to the factories difficult and expensive, and add significantly to the cost of forest products.

Almost two thirds of the industrial wood cut in France, 7.5 million cubic meters in 1953, is used in saw logs and veneer logs. Pit props consume almost one fifth (2.0 million cubic meters), but are less and less needed; and pulpwood takes one sixth (1.7 million cubic meters). France used 900,000 cubic meters of her saw logs to make box boards, 870,000 cubic meters for sleepers, and 147,000 cubic meters for plywood.

Nonwood forest products in 1953 included 4,500 tons of bark for tanning, a small amount of cork from cork oak, and 670,000 hectoliters of resin from the maritime pines in the Landes, the last being only two thirds of the prewar production, owing to recent disastrous fires. Most of the resin is refined to yield turpentine and colophane, of which France accounts for more than 10 per cent of the world's production.

FORESTRY ORGANIZATION. The state forests and, to some extent, the communal forests are administered by the Service des Eaux et Forêts, technically a part of the Ministry of Agriculture but actually an autonomous organization with its own headquarters in Paris. The name and many of the traditions of the forestry service date from the Middle Ages, but its present structure and duties originated in 1824, when it was reorganized, and 1827, when the Forest Code was promulgated. It is no longer responsible for inland waterways save mountain streams, but protects game and leases hunting licenses in the state forests.

The country is divided into forestry "conservations," or districts, each covering up to 100,000 forest hectares, and each under a "conservateur," with an "ingénieur" in charge of each of the larger state forests within the districts. These officers are recruited from the Forestry School at Nancy. Each forest also has a technical officer, trained at Les Barres near Montardis, and a corps of forest rangers, each responsible for perhaps 1,000 forest hectares. The rangers are recruited locally, often from the same families generation after generation; even in the higher branches of the forestry service the occupation is semihereditary. It is difficult, but not impossible, to move from a lower to a higher branch of the service.

The ingénieur must administer not only the state forest but also the communal forests in his area, for which he decides rates and locations of fellings. The local parish councils, however, determine the actual disposition of the communal forests—e.g., whether they are to be treated as coppice or high forest—and up-to-date forestry policies are adopted very slowly, if at all. Furthermore, even in the state-owned areas the forestry service has less power than in most other countries. Thus the timber is sold standing at auction, and is cut and hauled out of the woods by the private purchaser. Subsidiary jobs, such as draining and road-making in the forests, are also let out to local contractors, a system which promotes neither efficiency nor economy.

The École Nationale des Eaux et Forêts at Nancy remains world famous for its two-year training course, in which some 35 students from France, the overseas territories, and at times from other countries study all branches of forestry. The school arboretum at nearby Amance, however, is inferior to the great 300-hectare arboretum at Les Barres, which is supposed to contain practically all species capable of living in a temperate climate. In addition to the arboretum and the technical forestry school, Les Barres has the principal forest research station in France: it carries on experimental grafting, hybridization, ecological and environmental studies, and the development and perfecting of forestry machinery and equipment.

FUTURE PLANS AND PROSPECTS. With her communal forests only partly under state direction and private forests almost entirely free from control,

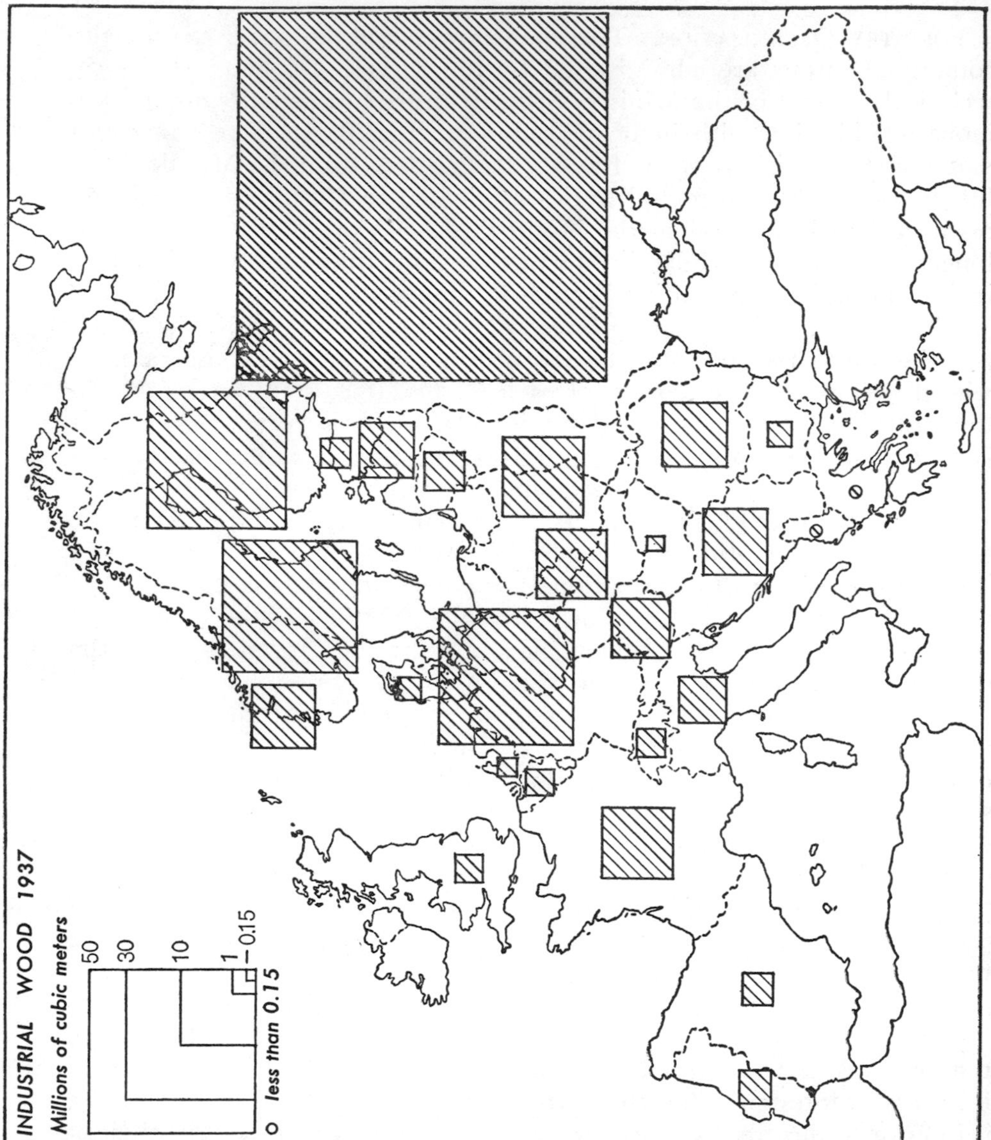

INDUSTRIAL WOOD 1937

Millions of cubic meters

50
30
10
1
0.15

O less than 0.15

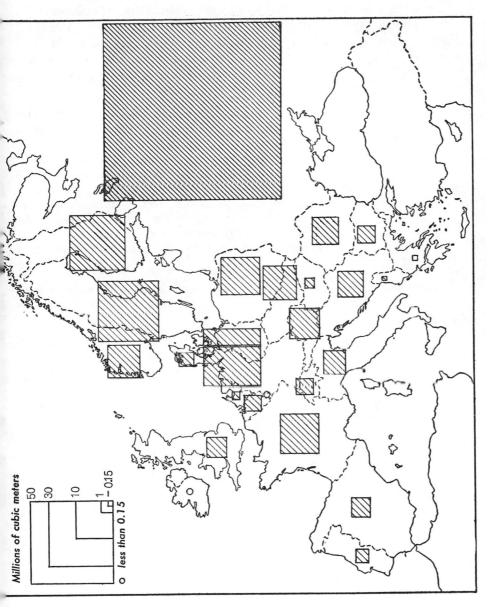

Fig. 35. Europe: production of industrial wood, 1953. (1950). Based on plate "Wood Production and Wood Products in Europe," Fig. 1 in *Weltforstatlas*, Hamburg, 1952; and on FAO, *Yearbook of Forest Products Statistics, 1954*, Table 1.

France has not been able to profit as much as she should from her well-run forestry service and advanced silvicultural techniques. Together with wartime shortages, postwar import costs, and the increasing need for industrial wood, this led in 1946 to the establishment of a National Forestry Fund (raised by a tax on timber sales, at first 6 per cent, now 3 per cent) designed to improve and expand French forests by means of the following measures:

1. The conversion to high forest of 800,000 hectares of communal and privately owned coppice within a generation, through the introduction of conifers which will yield pulpwood.
2. The enrichment and reconstitution within 30 years of 700,000 hectares of impoverished, mistreated, and burned-over forest land, especially in the Vosges, the Landes, and Provence.
3. The eventual afforestation of 6,000,000 hectares of partially or completely unproductive land, particularly in the Alps, the Vosges, the Pyrenees, the Massif Central, and Provence, where large areas are being abandoned by agriculture. In the first 30 years 400,000 hectares are to be afforested.

The total area to be treated in the next 30 years in these three programs, together with another 100,000 hectares to be planted with poplars, is 2,000,000 hectares, which implies an annual rate of 70,000 hectares. Between 1947 and 1952, 107,200 hectares actually were afforested, and another 100,000 should be planted by 1957.

4. The purchase of tractors, bulldozers, and other machinery for the forestry service, so that it can undertake its own forest improvements.
5. Overhauling the obsolete communications and transportation network in the state forests, especially by constructing metalled roads to reduce transport costs and enable fire-fighting equipment to reach endangered areas rapidly. By the end of 1951 more than 1,000 kilometers of new roads had been built.
6. The encouragement of planting in private forests, by (a) reducing inheritance taxes, (b) providing loans to enable one of several heirs to compensate co-heirs and thus maintain the woodlands undivided, (c) encouraging the integration of small parcels of woodland by the formation of forestry co-operatives, and (d) exempting newly forested land from all taxation for thirty years. Private forest owners can receive assistance in the form of cash subsidies (half the cost of planting), supplies of seed and young plants from state nurseries, fifty-year loans at low rates of interest, or share-cropping with the state, the forestry service assuming all risks; the last method is preferred by the great majority.

Through these measures France hopes to increase timber production about 48 per cent, and in the process: (1) to eliminate all timber imports within 25 to 40 years; (2) to export about two million cubic meters of roundwood annually by 1975, mainly in the form of pit props; (3) substantially to increase domestic timber sales from state forests within the next generation; (4) in anticipation of future growth, to raise the annual rate of felling in state forests almost immediately; (5) to increase domestic supplies of wood pulp after 1958; (6) to modernize industries using timber and its waste products, notably alcohol, tar, sugar, varnishes, and veneers, and to eliminate imports of timber waste; and, finally, (7) to establish a new agricultural-pastoral-silvicultural equilibrium, in which forests will not only supply timber, but enrich the soil, stabilize stream flow, protect watersheds, and perhaps even ameliorate the climate.

Germany

EXTENT. Despite defeat in two world wars, excessive felling in the inter-war period, and reparations and reconstruction requirements which necessitated considerable clear-cutting after 1945, Germany remains one of the best-forested countries of western Europe. Almost three million hectares of forest land were lost to Poland and Czechoslovakia, but there remain 6,732,000 hectares of forest in West Germany (1953) and 2,749,000 hectares in East Germany (1949), respectively 28.1 and 25.6 per cent of the total area. This provides West Germany with 0.14 hectares of forest per capita and East Germany with 0.16, about half the figure for France, but yielding almost as much timber per capita.

While Germany is now one-quarter forested, at the time of Tacitus less than a quarter of the land was free of woods. As the population has grown, the forests have retreated, and forest land per capita has declined to a small fraction of what it once was, as the following figures showing hectares of forest land per capita make clear: 36 in A.D. 500, 8 in 800, 2 in 1346, 0.28 in 1878, 0.19 in 1935,[4] 0.15 in 1953. The proportion of forest land in the total area, however, has been stable for several generations. Seven per cent of the German forests were clear-cut immediately after World War II to supply fuel to destitute German cities and reparations to the French and British. A forest survey of 1948 showed that 15.7 per cent of the forest area of Niedersachsen was bare, and 450,000 hectares (6.7 per cent) in all West Germany, but by 1952 only 143,000 clear-felled hectares remained, or 2.1 per cent of the total. West Germany planted 14,000 hectares of forest in 1947-52 and planned to add 20,000 hectares more by 1957, while East Germany in 1949 intended to afforest between 1951 and 1955 no less than 320,000 hectares, more than 10 per cent of her existing stand.

The distribution of the German forests appears on Fig. 36. The best-wooded areas are those which rugged relief and poor soils render unsuitable for agriculture: the steep Alpine slopes below timber line, the sandstone plateaus and hills of the central upland, the poor sandy soils of Brandenburg. The proportion of land in forests generally increases from north to south. Much of the entire northern coast is devoid of trees, while in southern Germany only the Rhineland is less than 30 per cent wooded.

4 Ebner (1940):90.

COMPOSITION. German forest composition has undergone many changes. The primitive oak-hardwood association which covered most of Germany, except for spruce and fir at high altitudes and pine on the sandy soils of the north, has given way to a predominantly softwood forest. In the last fifty years the trend has reversed once more, but, even so, 65 per cent of the West German and 80 per cent of the East German forests are coniferous. The great bulk of the coniferous forests are spruce and Scots pine, but silver fir and larch are also important, and there are small quantities of Douglas fir (*Pseudotsuga taxifolia*), white pine (*Pinus strobus*), and other pines. The broadleaf forests are 90 per cent beech and white oak (*Quercus alba*); the minor deciduous species are hornbeam, alder, maple, birch, ash, poplar, and red oak (*Quercus borealis*), the last becoming increasingly popular.

Two developments have caused the transition from deciduous to coniferous. The first was the centuries-long process of clearing and settling. The best agricultural soils were almost invariably occupied by the broadleaf species, which suffered most as settlement progressed. Mixed forests also became more and more coniferous as the broadleaf trees were browsed by livestock and culled for lumber. Oak was particularly in demand for houses and for ship timbers to be exported. Overcut mixed forests were usually replanted to less exacting conifers.

The second was the development early in the nineteenth century of a strong economic preference for conifers, because they grow faster and straighter than hardwoods. Spruce was particularly prized, and pure stands were planted all over Germany. Clear-cutting was widely practiced, making the natural regeneration of hardwoods like beech more difficult and less likely. The extent to which these changes altered the composition of the German forests may be seen in the shifting composition of the age groups (Table 13–V). Forests formerly oak are now mainly beech and pine, those that were beech are now spruce and pine, and those that were fir have become spruce.

TABLE 13–V

GERMANY: COMPOSITION OF HIGH FOREST BY PRINCIPAL SPECIES AND AGE CLASSES, 1927

(In Thousand Hectares)

Dominant Species	Dates of Origin						
	Before 1807	1807-26	1827-46	1847-66	1867-86	1887-1906	1907-26
Oak	69	61	79	99	119	140	84
Beech	161	253	305	281	239	218	181
Pine	145	232	471	802	1,033	1,225	1,328
Spruce	66	116	237	411	596	753	811
Fir	22	28	35	40	48	54	60
TOTAL	463	690	1,127	1,633	2,035	2,390	2,464

Source: Franz Heske, *German Forestry* (New Haven, 1938), 58, Table 5.

There are marked regional differences in species distribution. Conifers completely dominate not only East Germany but also the eastern parts of West Germany, while the forests of Brunswick are more than half deciduous, and those of Hesse and Oldenburg almost half. The forests of Prussia and Mecklenburg are overwhelmingly pine, while spruce occupies 64 per cent of Saxony's forest area and 49 per cent of Thuringia's. The western forests are far more varied than those of the east, north, and center, but oak in Westphalia and what used to be the Rhine Province and beech in Hesse and Brunswick are frequently dominant, as is fir in parts of Baden and Württemberg.

FOREST MANAGEMENT AND SILVICULTURAL METHODS. German foresters are primarily responsible for the origin and development of the principles of modern forestry, and the roots of German forest regulation lie far in the past. Fearing timber famines, many German states and cities between the thirteenth and the sixteenth centuries laid down strict rules prohibiting overcutting. The systematic development of forestry did not come, however, until the havoc and destruction of the Thirty Years' War and the decades of unrestricted cutting and grazing that followed had reduced German forests to the verge of ruin. German rulers then strengthened laws against destructive clearing, organized the felling and hauling of timber, regulated wood-using industries and commerce, forbade unnecessary waste of wood and injurious forest uses, such as goat-grazing and potash-burning, and in many areas insisted that reforestation accompany exploitation. In order to ensure permanent dependable local supplies of timber, German communities adopted several types of sustained-yield management, notably the theory of the so-called ideal, or normal, forest, which would always produce an equal annual increment.

The scientific bases of silviculture were developed during the early nineteenth century by G. L. Hartig in Prussia and Heinrich Cotta in Saxony. They and their students surveyed the state and most of the large communal and private forests and systematically organized them on a sustained-yield basis. This involved new techniques both of cutting and of regeneration—including special attention to methods of thinning and care of immature growing stock. Cotta's periodic area-allotment method of cutting was a great advance on earlier more rigid systems; owing to its adoption, many German forests today are systematically arranged by area according to age classes. Volume-allotment methods and normal-growing-stock methods were also developed. As for regeneration, Hartig's shelter-wood system, first applied to high forests of beech, spread to nearly all species, replacing unregulated selection cutting and seed-tree cuttings. This form of natural reproduction was supplanted, however, owing to its failure in the northern pine region, by clear-cutting with artificial regeneration, which became the rule in most German forests after about 1840. A great many types of artificial regeneration were developed in the latter part of the nineteenth century. At the same time, the growing demand for industrial wood stimulated the planting of profitable timber species, mainly conifers, and pure stands of spruce and pine, as already indicated, replaced broadleaf and mixed stands.

Both clear-cutting and pure, even-aged stands were condemned at the time by experienced silviculturalists, notably Carl Gayer, whose warnings have since been borne out by declining yields in the second and third rotations and by the disasters (windfall, insect damage, fire, podsolization) that have befallen many of the monocultural softwood stands. Since 1918 Germany has swung back toward natural regeneration, selection felling, mixed forests, and a preference for hardwoods—a combination that has come to be known as the "Dauerwald." At the same time, spokesmen for a "back to nature" movement, particularly prominent during the Nazi regime, insisted that forests be treated as national heritages rather than cellulose factories, and emphasized aesthetic and recreational values. In essence, the Dauerwald ideal is to remove individual trees in a manner which will affect the forest as a whole as little as possible. This principle has been extended by law all over Germany, even in the northern lowlands, where it hardly applies. There remain many areas, however, like the summit of the Harz uplands, where spruce monoculture has continued for a century without any evidence of deterioration.

Regular high forest is the only silvicultural form of importance in Germany. Coppice, with or without standards, covers less than 7 per cent of the forest area of West Germany and still less in East Germany. Only in Oldenburg does coppice account for as much as 10 per cent of the total.

OWNERSHIP. In West Germany, as Table 13–I shows, the state owns less than one third of the forested area, but in East Germany postwar confiscations of large private holdings have raised the proportion of state forests from 33.6 to 50 per cent of the total. Private wood lots smaller than 10 hectares cover almost 1,700,000 hectares in both Germanies, or 42 per cent of all private holdings, and are most numerous in the southwest and in East Germany, where estates larger than 100 hectares no longer exist. Between 1946 and 1950 the East German state took 827,000 hectares (29 per cent of all the forest land) from the big estates and turned over 581,000 hectares to communities and peasants in the form of one- and two-hectare parcels.

As in France, small forests in Germany are managed less efficiently than are the larger holdings, and produce less timber. But the German forest services have more power to enforce their silvicultural policies than do the French. In West Germany, extraction and regeneration in the private as well as the public forests are under strict state supervision, either by the Länder, or by the Bundesministerium für Ernährung, Landwirtschaft, und Forsten. The East German forests are all managed by the Central Administration (since 1949 the Department for Agriculture and Forestry). State, communal, and private holdings in an area are exploited as a single forest unit. Owners of small wood lots are encouraged to form forestry co-operatives, and in practice their boundary lines are ignored in the interests of more efficient, large-scale forest management.

INCREMENT AND YIELD. Growth in both West and East German forests has suffered seriously as a result of the two world wars. After centuries of careful management, the pressures of the Nazi regime forced first state and then private forests in the 1930's to supply wood at rates ranging from 134 to 150 per cent of growth. This excessive felling substantially diminished annual growth and impaired the age composition of the forests. Apart from the loss of eastern territory, the total growing stock was reduced 210 million cubic meters, or 16 per cent, by excessive fellings between 1934 and 1946, and net growth per hectare declined 12 per cent. Allied occupation and reconstruction needs between 1946 and 1950 cost the growing stock another 141 million, or 16.5 per cent of what was left. A recent FAO report [5] estimates net growth per hectare (including bark) at 3.8 cubic meters in West Germany and 2.0 cubic meters in East Germany. Growing stock is 625 million cubic meters in West Germany (1953) and 253 million cubic meters in East Germany (1949)—a total of 878 million cubic meters as compared with 1,140 million cubic meters for the same area in 1934.

Fellings exceeded net growth by 23 per cent in West Germany in 1951-52 and by far more in East Germany. Yet the total net yield was only 36 million cubic meters, as compared with 62 million cubic meters during World War II and about 40 million cubic meters before 1933. West Germany has succeeded in reducing fellings steadily since the end of reparations, especially since economic recovery has enabled her to import more lumber and pulp; from a postwar high of 37.6 million cubic meters in 1947 fellings dropped to 22.4 million in 1952-53. Not until 1954, however, when the allowable cut was set at 20.5 million cubic meters, could West Germany, for the first time in eighteen years, look forward to living within her forest income. Matters are still far different in East Germany; although extensive afforestation is planned, the allowable cut is still about twice the net growth, though little more than half the fellings in 1946-48.

CONSUMPTION AND FOREIGN TRADE. Except during the Nazi period, Germany has traditionally been able to supply its timber requirements with little help from foreign sources. Net imports dropped from 20 per cent of Germany's total consumption of industrial wood in 1935-38 to 4 per cent in 1950, partly because consumption was lower, partly because Germany increased her exports of finished wood products after the end of the war. In terms of total industrial wood, net annual imports into Germany fluctuated as follows (in million cubic meters): 12.0 in 1924-29, 4.8 in 1930-34, 8.6 in 1935-38, and 1.3 in 1950. But this trend toward self-sufficiency may have been short-lived, to judge from postwar trends shown by Table 13–VI. Most of the imports have been in the form

---

[5] United Nations. FAO. *World Forest Resources* (1955).

of pulpwood from Scandinavia and Austria, softwood logs and sawn timber from Czechoslovakia and Yugoslavia, and hardwood and veneer logs from Poland, Rumania, and France; finished or semifinished products are re-exported. East Germany imports little if any timber, but her exports dropped from a high of 1,210,000 cubic meters in 1947 to 840,000 in 1950.

TABLE 13–VI

West Germany: Foreign Trade in Industrial Wood and Fuel Wood, 1946-1950

(In Thousand Cubic Meters)

Year	Imports	Exports
1946	20	2490
1947	690	6590
1948	1360	7320
1949	2540	4340
1950	3820	1780
1951	4900	1300
1952	7750	540
1953	7620	750

Sources: FAO, *European Timber Statistics 1913-1950*, Table T 43, 44; FAO, *Yearbook of Forest Products Statistics, 1953, 1954*, Tables 42, 43.

Only 22 and 25 per cent of the wood felled in West and East Germany, respectively, is fuel wood, leaving a higher proportion for industry than in any other west-European country save Belgium. Almost three quarters of the industrial wood felled in West Germany goes for saw logs, veneer logs, and sleepers, while pit props are relatively more important in East Germany. In 1953 West Germany devoted 484,000 cubic meters to the manufacture of plywood and also produced a small amount of bark for tanning—9,000 tons.

Germany's pulp and paper industry was particularly hard-hit by the partition, for most of the prewar supply of raw materials came from, and more than half of the prewar capacity was located in, the eastern occupation zone and the area lost to Poland. Most of the West German plants, however, were little damaged by the war and its aftermath, and high demands for paper products have spurred the industry to rapid recovery. The industry has a capacity of over two million metric tons per year, and its 378 plants employed 61,800 people in 1952, most of them in enterprises of more than 100 persons. West Germany exports some finished paper products, processed paper, and paperboard, but depends heavily upon foreign sources for wood pulp, waste, and newsprint. Imports of pulp and its products, which used to come from eastern Europe and now come from Finland and Canada, rose from 5,000 metric tons in 1947 to 149,000 tons in 1948, 249,000 tons in 1951, and 557,000 tons in 1953, one third of West Germany's total consumption in the last year. Before the war Germany had a net annual export of 300,000 metric tons of pulp equivalent; today West Germany imports 473,000 tons net and by 1960 will need at least 600,000 tons, or about a million cubic meters roundwood equivalent. This is the largest single deficit in Western Europe's timber situation.

FORESTRY RESEARCH AND EDUCATION. World War II and the subsequent partition crippled forestry education and research in Germany. They have been reorganized in West Germany on a far less centralized basis than before the war; the role of the "Länder" is more important than that of the Federal government.

Education and research are closely allied in the universities of Freiburg-im-Breisgau, Munich, and Göttingen, which offer four-year forestry courses. Each of these universities carries on a wide variety of forestal research in eight or ten separate fields: at Freiburg, for example, the Institute of Forest Management and Economics is attempting to improve farm wood-lot productivity, and the Institute of Forest Policy is setting up timber balances for the Federal domain; at Göttingen the Institute of Applied Silviculture studies the transformation of pure even-aged high forest into mixed uneven-aged stands; at Munich the Institute of Silviculture is concerned with forest sociology. Hesse, Württemberg, and North Rhine-Westphalia, which lack forestry schools, have Länder experiment stations (at Giessen, Stuttgart, Tübingen, Bonn, and Lintorf) directly responsible to the forest administration. Like the university institutes, the Länder experiment stations concentrate on regional problems of site appraisal, silviculture, and forest management.

Federal research is concentrated at the Federal Institute of Forest and Wood Economy, established in 1947 at Reinbek. The Reinbek Institute is allied with the University of Hamburg, which offers the four-year Federal forestry course formerly given for the German Reich at Eberswalde. Research at Reinbek specializes in world forestry problems, ecological studies of domestic and exotic species, the afforestation of wasteland, forest genetics and plant breeding, and the improvement of timber extraction and transport. At Hannoversch-Münden another federal research agency, the Institute of Applied Mycology and Wood Protection, studies forest diseases and tests protection measures in conjunction with the Federal Biological Institute of Agriculture and Forest Economy at Brunswick. Wood-preservation studies are carried on at the Berlin-Dahlem Materials Testing Laboratory, and other important forest-products researches at Hannoversch-Münden, Munich, Reinbek, Dortmund, Hannover, Karlsruhe, and Stuttgart. Two private bodies—the Institute of Logging at Reinbek (transferred from Eberswalde) and the Scientific Institute of the German Poplar Association at Brühl—complete the long roster of research and educational organizations in West Germany.

In East Germany, forestry research and education are both concentrated at Eberswalde, the major prewar forestry school, and at Tharandt. Forestry courses are of one- and two-years' duration.

Switzerland

EXTENT AND COMPOSITION. Although forest industries are a significant part of Swiss economy, and Switzerland is often thought of as a well-forested country because much of it is too rugged or inaccessible for agriculture, the forested area is only 23.6 per cent of the total. Furthermore, 100,000 of the 950,000 forested hectares are inaccessible, and Switzerland's available forest area per capita is only 0.18 hectare, little more than half the figure for France. Only 50,000 hectares are in hardwood forest, but an additional 350,000 hectares are covered by mixed broadleaf and coniferous forest; in all, 20 per cent of Switzerland's forest area is in deciduous stands. In the past, hardwoods, especially oak, were much more prominent.

The forests of Switzerland are unevenly distributed as between the Jura, the Swiss Plateau, and the Alps. The Jura, with 31 per cent of the nation's forest area, is about 37 per cent forested, with pure stands now giving way to more stable and productive mixed stands of beech, fir, and spruce. The Alps contain 44 per cent of Switzerland's forests, but are only 17 per cent forested, almost exclusively with softwoods—spruce and fir at lower levels, larch and cembra, montana, and Scots pine above. The remaining forests (25 per cent) are found in the Swiss Plateau, which although it contains most of the population and agricultural land, is 22 per cent forested. Hardwoods, particularly oak, were formerly dominant on the deep soils of this well-watered upland. Long maintained as coppice, many of these stands were converted into high forest during the second half of the nineteenth century by the introduction of softwoods, particularly spruce and Scots pine. Today the forests are reverting to mixed stands, in which such hardwoods as oak, beech, and hornbeam occupy an important place beside the softwoods.

OWNERSHIP. The proportion of the Swiss forests that are publicly owned is larger than that of any other west-European country. Only 40,000 hectares, however, are owned by the state, and only in the cantons of Schaffhausen, Fribourg, and Neuchâtel does the state's proportion of the forest area exceed 10 per cent. The cantons possess 550,000 hectares, or 65 per cent of the total, and more than 90 per cent of the forests in the Alpine cantons of Uri, Obwalden, Glarus, Grisons, and Valais. However, in Lucerne and Appenzell Ausser-Rhoden three fourths of the forests, and in Geneva (the least wooded of all the cantons) 93 per cent, are privately owned.

FOREST MANAGEMENT AND SILVICULTURAL METHODS. Until the end of the nineteenth century the Swiss forests were generally subjected to clear-cutting and artificial regeneration, which produced regular and homogeneous even-aged high forests. But the ecological studies of Ammon, Boilly, and other foresters demonstrated the advantages of a more natural silviculture, and mixed, uneven-aged stands have become the ideal.

Largely a process of selection management, conversion is very slow, however, and only about 15 per cent of the Swiss woods, mostly fir-spruce-beech mixtures, are true selection-type forests. Not only is regeneration easier in these forests than in homogeneous, even-aged stands, but windfall and snowbreak are less frequent and less damaging, erosion is stemmed, and floods are less severe. The species in about three fourths of the Swiss woods have been selected primarily for protective purposes and for long-range preservation, and only secondarily for economic yield.

Some of the cantons recognized the significant protective functions of forests early in the millennium, but not until the eighteenth and nineteenth centuries, when the exploitation of mountain forests to provide wood for the metal industry caused a disastrous increase in destructive torrents, was any general distinction made between economic and protection forests. A law of 1902 placed all forests, private, cantonal, and other, under the surveillance of the federal forest police, who enforce strict rules respecting cutting and clearing. All forests were classified as protection or nonprotection, and, by 1904, 71 per cent of Switzerland's forests were in the first category, in which all cutting was carried on under the direct supervision of forestry officials. By 1950, 71 per cent of the forests were under sustained-yield management.

INCREMENT, YIELD, AND FOREIGN TRADE. Thanks to good management, the Swiss forests are highly productive; the annual increment in 1952 was 3,400,000 cubic meters, or 3.9 cubic meters per hectare. In the past, domestic supplies have never been adequate, but Switzerland today has almost enough to satisfy her needs. In 1953 she had to import 890,000 cubic meters of wood products, 19 per cent of her total consumption (compared with 23 per cent in 1935-38), most of it from France (fuel wood, saw logs, veneer logs), Austria (coniferous sawn wood), and Canada (newsprint).

Excessive fellings were necessary during World War II, but no permanent damage to the growing stock resulted, and fellings at present exceed net growth by only 9 per cent. Between 1947 and 1952, 10,000 additional hectares of forest, 1.2 per cent of the total, were made accessible, and another 10,000 hectares should be opened up by 1957. In addition, 1,300 hectares were afforested in 1947-52, and 1,500 more should be planted by 1957. Switzerland should soon be able to keep fellings at or below the level of growth.

CONSUMPTION AND FOREST INDUSTRIES. A rather high proportion of the wood felled in the Swiss forests, 40 per cent in 1953, was used as fuel wood, more than half of it commercially. Saw logs and veneer logs accounted for 68 per cent of the 2,350,000 cubic meters of the industrial wood felled. Switzerland's veneer and cellulose industries are especially advanced and require increasing amounts of domestic and imported lumber. Furthermore, Switzerland also produces about one million tons a year of bark for tanning.

Belgium

EXTENT AND COMPOSITION. Although Belgium is densely populated and the pressure for land is considerable, 600,000 hectares, or about a fifth of the area, are forested. This provides 0.07 forest hectares per capita—considerably less wood than Belgium needs. Nevertheless, the domestic forests play an important role in the national economy.

Little remains of the oak forest that covered most of Belgium before the Middle Ages, and conifers today cover 37 per cent of the total forest area. Except for a few estate and national forests, trees occupy only poor, thin, and infertile soils, those which cannot be used for agriculture. Flanders is only 3 per cent wooded but Scots-pine coppices have dotted the plains and acid heaths of the northeast, especially the sandy Campine, ever since the species was introduced in the sixteenth century. The main afforestation of the Campine, however, occurred in the latter part of the nineteenth century. Corsican pine and *Pinus nigra* are replacing Scots pine today. On the sandy loams of the central Belgian plateau, particularly in the great state forest of Soignes, oak and beech high forests are still dominant, though beech does not regenerate naturally in this region. Coppice of beech, oak, and hornbeam is gradually giving way to coniferous high forest, much of it spruce. Southern Belgium, the rugged Ardennes, is the most heavily forested part of the country, with the province of Luxembourg 41 per cent wooded. The three southern provinces, Luxembourg, Namur, and Liége, contain 70 per cent of Belgium's forests. Beech high forest, together with oak and birch, is extensive between 200 and 500 meters, with spruce, Douglas fir, and larch on higher and more exposed sites.

FOREST MANAGEMENT. Because Belgium was long divided among various foreign powers, no common or enduring forest policy has marked its history. The replacement of high forest by coppice with standards in the late seventeenth century was a French policy, and the Belgian coppices provided abundant fuel wood, charcoal, and tanbark. In the late nineteenth century, after decades of depletion and deforestation, Belgium adopted the German practice of conversion to coniferous high forest in order to meet demands for industrial wood, especially pit props. Today half the total forested area is in high forest, a quarter in coppice with standards, and 16 per cent in simple coppice. The conversion of coppice into high forest is continuing.

OWNERSHIP. Slightly over half the Belgian forest area is in private hands, and the communes own three quarters of the remainder. The state, which possesses little more than a tenth of the forest land, supervises the communal forests, but has no control over private holdings beyond administering a mild law of 1931 prohibiting excessive fellings. However, private, communal, and state forests are so thoroughly intermingled that most private owners can and do take advantage of the advice and example of the state forest service, and almost four fifths of Belgium's forests are under sustained-yield management.

INCREMENT AND CONSUMPTION. Belgium's forests were not seriously overcut during World War II. About 15,000 hectares were severely damaged, but state-aided replacement has already made up most of the loss. The net growth in 1950 was 2,260,000 cubic meters, or 4.0 cubic meters per hectare, the highest average increment in western Europe. Fellings, of which trees outside the forests, especially along roadsides, yielded 12 per cent, were slightly below net growth.

Belgium's net imports of wood and wood products declined from an average of 3.5 million cubic meters in 1935-38 to 3.1 million in 1950 and 1.9 million in 1953, 42 per cent of her net consumption in the latter year.

Fuel wood takes only 13 per cent of the total fellings, a smaller percentage than anywhere else in western Europe. Almost half the domestic industrial wood, 1,000,000 cubic meters, goes into pit props, some of which are exported to the Netherlands; slightly less (995,000 cubic meters) into saw logs and veneer logs. The main imports are sawn wood, saw and veneer logs, and wood pulp. In recent years increasing proportions both of the domestic wood supplies and of the imports from the Belgian Congo have gone into the manufacture of paper and veneer.

FORESTRY ORGANIZATION AND FUTURE PROSPECTS. The Administration des Eaux et Forêts de Belgique controls all forestry affairs save roadside plantings, which are carried out by the department of bridges and roads. Headquarters of the forest service are in Brussels, and the state forest research station is nearby at Groenendal, in the forest of Soignes. In addition to supplying seed to the state and to private owners, the research station concentrates on silvicultural problems involving soil science and genetics, and maintains more than 2,000 experimental plots and arboreta all over Belgium.

Other kinds of forest research—forest pathology, entomology, seed testing and extraction, and wood technology—are carried on at the Agronomical Institute at Gembloux. Education for the higher state forest posts and for the colonial service is provided at the universities of Ghent, Gembloux, and Louvain, while communal foresters are recruited by the forest service, which gives its own courses of instruction.

Belgium should have no difficulty maintaining the volume of her growing stock, so long as she is able to import sufficient timber supplies. To meet increasing industrial demands, she plans to convert more of her forests to fast-growing softwoods and to plant considerable poplar. Some 3,200 hectares were afforested in 1947-52, and 2,400 hectares more should be planted by 1957.

Luxembourg

EXTENT AND COMPOSITION. The smallest country of western Europe, Luxembourg is also the best forested, with 81,000 hectares, or 31.4 per cent of her land, occupied by forests, amounting to 0.3 hectares per person. The forests of Luxembourg are similar in character and composition to those of Belgium, with which they are combined for purposes of foreign trade. Broadleaf species, especially beech and oak, cover four fifths of the total forest area, but the proportion of softwoods is increasing both through colonization and by afforestation.

Luxembourg's forests are fairly well distributed throughout the Grand Duchy, but those of the cooler, higher, thinner-soiled Ardennes in the north differ from the woods of the Bon Pays in the south. The high plateaus and steep slopes of the Ardennes are heavily wooded, particularly in the west and center, where forests occupy more than half the land surface. Oaks predominate on these acid soils, followed by birch, spruce, and Scots pine; beech is less common; willows share the highest plateaus with heath grass; and alders line the streams in the valleys. The Bon Pays has a slightly smaller proportion of woodland but many sizable individual forests, especially near Luxembourg City; oak and beech dominate the older stands, and conifers, especially fir and larch, the younger forests.

Although relatively rich in forest resources, Luxembourg has nothing like the amount of forest land she had as recently as 1811, when three quarters of the country was wooded. Indeed, at that time Luxembourg, then under French rule, was called the Département des Forêts. The prime factors in reducing the forests have been the burning of charcoal for the iron industry and the clearing of land for cultivation. Both world wars hastened the rate of depletion.

FOREST MANAGEMENT AND OWNERSHIP. High forest accounts for 72 per cent of Luxembourg's forests, bark coppice for the remainder. More than half of the high forest is public property, most of it communal, although a few thousand hectares are owned by the state. Most of the communal forests are under sustained-yield management.

INCREMENT AND CONSUMPTION. Despite Luxembourg's considerable forest area, the yield per hectare is low, and fellings in 1952 exceeded net growth by 16 per cent. About two fifths of the 180,000 cubic meters cut is used as fuel; the piles of fuel wood stacked outside the houses in most Luxembourg villages are characteristic of the landscape. Half of the industrial wood is consumed in local woodworking industries, while most of the remainder becomes pit props. Luxembourg's coppices yielded 365 tons of bark for tanning in 1952.

FORESTRY ORGANIZATION AND FUTURE PROSPECTS. Luxembourg's public forests are managed by the Administration des Eaux et Forêts, which also regulates hunting and fishing. State protection dates from 1914-18, when

Luxembourgers became alarmed by the rapid depletion of their forest resources. The forest service has established nurseries and plantations throughout the Grand Duchy. Within the last fifteen years it has raised the proportion of conifers, largely in Scots-pine plantations, from 10 to 20 per cent of the total forest area. Natural regeneration, afforestation, and a recent reduction in the domestic consumption of wood would seem to assure to Luxembourg adequate forest reserves for the future.

The Netherlands

EXTENT AND COMPOSITION. The most densely populated country in Europe, the Netherlands is also the least forested, with only 7.6 per cent of its land in forests, or 0.02 hectare per person. The importance of the Netherlands' forests, however, transcends their areal extent and their productive value, for they serve many protective and noneconomic functions.

Heavily wooded at the time of the Roman Empire, the Netherlands was almost completely deforested by the sixteenth century; the 250,000 hectares of forest now in existence have all been planted since that time. Before World War II the state forestry service afforested about 1,400 hectares annually, but during the period 1947–52 the annual rate was about 900 hectares, only slightly more than were lost to other uses during the same period. By 1957 an additional 5,000 hectares should be afforested.

Afforestation began as early as the fifteenth century, at first largely for hunting and recreation on the estates, but after the mid-nineteenth century principally to provide pit props for mines. The earlier artificial woods, like the primitive forests of the Netherlands, were mainly deciduous or mixed, but in the nineteenth century the trend shifted to conifers, and today 69 per cent of the forest cover is coniferous. However, Dutch foresters favor converting much of the existing softwood forest back to hardwood, in order to combat increasing acidity, pests, and timber deterioration. Red oak and other broadleaf species are now strip sown under the conifers. And everywhere Scots pine, at present the dominant species, is being replaced by, or mixed with, other conifers and broadleaf trees.

The proportion of conifers is highest in the heavily wooded eastern provinces. Scots pine is found all along the coast and on the islands, where it has been planted to reclaim heathland and to help fix sand dunes, but Japanese larch (*Larix leptolepis*) and Douglas fir, together with red oak and beech, are replacing it in the heath lands. *Pinus nigra* and other shade-bearing conifers are currently favored for coastal dune reclamation and erosion control, and the shelterbelts behind the dunes consist of alders in front of a mixture of hardwoods. The most important broadleaf species in the Dutch forests are beech and ash, with a scattering of oak, maple, and elm, and of birch, which grows spontaneously on the heaths. Small copses of poplar, particularly numerous near Eindhoven in South Brabant, are important for the paper industry and the manufacture of wooden shoes.

Outside the forests, willows are planted extensively along most of the rivers, the twigs being used for basketry and for matting to protect dikes. Avenues of poplar in Brabant and Limburg, and of oak and beech elsewhere, line the roads and dikes; shelterbelts of poplar (*Populus canadensis* var. *marilandica, P. robusta, P. canadensis* var. *serotina*), together with ash, sycamore (*Acer pseudoplatanus*), and alder protect farms on newly reclaimed polders.

Four fifths of the wooded area is high forest, the remainder coppice.

OWNERSHIP AND FOREST MANAGEMENT. Although 65 per cent of the Netherlands' forest area is in private hands, with the remainder equally divided between state and communal (chiefly municipal) ownership, much of the private forest land belongs to provincial and polder corporations. All forests are under state supervision, and since 1939 no fellings have been permitted without a special license from the state forest service.

Only 22 per cent of the Dutch forests are under sustained-yield management, but most of the rest are young plantations, for which working plans are prepared as they mature. Advice from the state forest service is free but not compulsory.

INCREMENT, YIELD, AND FOREIGN TRADE. The Netherlands forests were hard hit during World War II. Cutting was excessive throughout the occupation; the flooding of polders and the bombing of homes and industries created demands for wood which have not yet been satisfied. As the Dutch economy has gained ground, an increasing proportion of the rising lumber needs have been met from imports. Wood and wood products cost the nation 278 million guilders in 1949 and 472 million in 1954. Of industrial wood consumed, domestic forests supplied 12 per cent in 1935-38, but only 7 per cent in 1950; thus, despite the heavy increase in total use, local woods were less heavily tapped.

The allowable cut is 7 per cent less than the annual increment of 650,000 cubic meters and in 1953 actual fellings slightly exceeded the allowable cut. Trees outside the forests account for 25 per cent of the total yield.

CONSUMPTION AND FOREST INDUSTRIES. Less than one third of the Netherlands fellings becomes fuel wood, and the fraction is smaller every year. Most of the industrial wood is used for construction; wood-pulp and paperboard industries depend more on imports than on domestic production; most sleepers and pit props are imported. A large plywood factory at Eindhoven uses mainly veneer logs from West Africa and Surinam.

FORESTRY ORGANIZATION. Overexploitation of coniferous plantations for pit props led to the founding of the Society for Heath Reclamation (Heidemaatschappij) at Arnhem in 1880. This, and the establishment of the Netherlands State Forestry Service in 1899, marked the beginnings of modern forest policy in the Netherlands. Laws passed during World War I and the Forestry Act of 1922 prohibit the destruction of scenic woods and avenues of trees, compel corporations to manage forests properly, authorize state acquisition of private forests by eminent domain, and make private owners responsible for loss by fire. A Scenery Act of 1928 grants tax reductions and other benefits to owners of forests of scenic or historic value, provided they agree to conserve them properly. A separate public body, the Forestry Board (Bosschap), was established in 1954.

Silvicultural research is carried on at the Forestry Institute of the University of Agriculture and the Forest Experiment Station at Wageningen. The Institute provides a two-year forestry course for future chiefs of the state forestry districts, graduating about twenty students annually. Other forestry personnel is recruited mainly from graduates of the School of Forestry and Land Development conducted by the Heidemaatschappij.

Conclusion

The countries of western Europe are determined to maintain the high standards in forest management for which they have so long been noted. Most of them intend to retain at least one quarter of their land surface in forest cover, and to produce high yields of good-quality wood. To achieve these goals, they are committed to long-term programs of afforestation and short-term policies of self-denial in order to increase growing stocks above prewar levels.

This means that for the immediate future, at least, western Europe will have to meet an increasing proportion of her wood and wood-products demands from imports. Per capita consumption of industrial wood is considerably below prewar levels (0.48 cubic meter in 1950 as compared with 0.60 cubic meter per annum in 1935-38, including the United Kingdom), but owing to population increases total wood consumption has not dropped so much. Domestic production has declined almost as much as consumption, partly because of the loss of forest acreage and partly because most countries are trying to compensate for previous overcutting by maintaining fellings below increments. Thus in Germany and France combined, the forests yielded 72.0 million cubic meters of roundwood per annum in 1935-38 but only 64.6 million cubic meters in 1950, and the supply prospects for 1955-60 are only 54.0 million cubic meters per annum.

While the domestic supply will continue to decline for the next decade or so, postwar recovery and new demands for industrial wood—especially pulp products—will inevitably require greater consumption. In 1950 western Europe consumed 65.9 million cubic meters of industrial roundwood; the FAO has estimated consumption for 1960 at 75.5 million cubic meters,[6] an increase of 15 per cent. Sawn-timber requirements will

[6] United Nations. FAO. *European Timber Prospects* (1953): Table XI/141, p. 109.

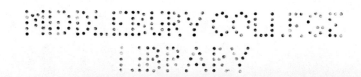

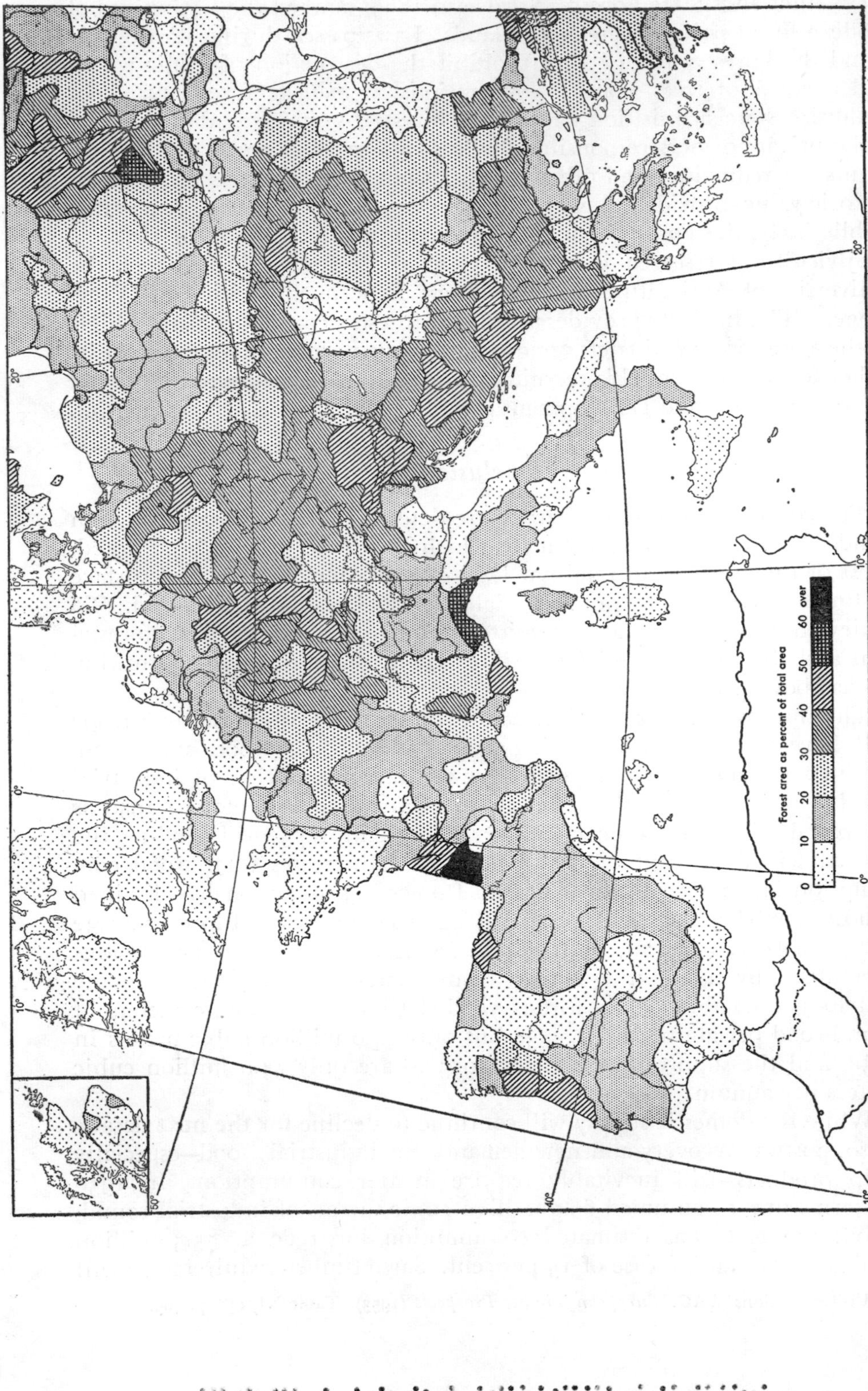

Fig. 26. Western, central, and southern Europe: distribution of forest areas. Based on plate "General View on the Percentage of Forests"

not be appreciably greater, but the consumption of pulp and pulp products will be 30 to 50 per cent higher than in 1950.

Gross imports into western Europe (excluding East Germany) are at present four times as heavy as exports, and net imports amount to 14,300,000 cubic meters, or 22 per cent of the total consumption. This is quite a decline from prewar imports, when industrial-wood products imports alone amounted to 24,100,000 cubic meters (1935-38 average). But by 1960 western Europe's import requirements are expected to approach prewar levels, largely owing to greater demands for pulp products, particularly in West Germany.

Whether western Europe can attain a greater measure of self-sufficiency in the more remote future will depend principally upon her success in increasing her growing stock and upon the development of demands—and perhaps substitutes—for wood products as yet unknown.

SELECTED REFERENCES

ANDERSON, M. L. 1949. "Some observations on Belgian forestry," *Empire Forestry Rev.*, **28**: 117-130.

CHAMPION, H. G. 1950. "Forest notes from Holland," *Empire Forestry Rev.*, **29**:20-27.

CLAPHAM, A. R., *et al.* 1952. *Flora of the British Isles.* Cambridge University Press, London.

DICKINSON, R. E. 1953. *Germany: a general and regional geography.* E. P. Dutton & Co., Inc., New York.

EBNER, ADALBERT. 1940. *German forests: treasures of a nation.* German Library of Information, New York.

FERNOW, B. E. 1913. *A brief history of forestry in Europe, the United States, and other countries.* 3d rev. ed. American Forestry Association, Washington, D.C.

"La forêt française," 1951. *Études et conjoncture* (Economie française), 6:66-87.

France. Secrétariat Général du Gouvernement. 1948. La forêt française. *La documentation française illustreé, No. 24.* Paris.

———. 1955. La forêt française, première partie: la forêt en France et les Territoires d'Outre-Mer. *La documentation française, No. 2071.*

German Federal Republic. 1954. *Statistisches Jahrbuch für die Bundesrepublik Deutschland, 1954.* Bonn.

———. Federal Ministry for the Marshall Plan. 1953. *Report of the German Federal Republic on the continuation of the American Economic Aid (MSA).* Jan.–Mar., Apr.–Jun. 1953.

———. 1953. *Recovery under the Marshall Plan, 1948-1952.* Bonn.

"Germany," 1950. *Unasylva*, 4:92.

HESKE, FRANZ. 1938. *German forestry.* Yale University Press, New Haven.

KELSEY, H. P., and DAYTON, W. A. 1942. *Standardized plant names.* 2d ed. J. Horace McFarland Co., Harrisburg, Pa.

LEOPOLD, ALDO. 1936. "Deer and Dauerwald in Germany: I. History," *Jour. Forestry*, **34**: 366-375.

NAGEL, J. L. 1946. "Conditions forestières du Canton de Neuchâtel," *Bull. Soc. Neuchâteloise de Géographie*, **52**:77-98.

Netherlands. Ministry of Economic Affairs. 1955. *The Netherlands 1945-1955: "a decade of decision."* The Hague.

———. State Forest Service and Ministry of Agriculture, Fisheries and Food. 1955. The work of the Netherlands State Forest Service. *Publ. No. E 113.* The Hague.

NETTL, J. P. 1951. *The Eastern Zone and Soviet policy in Germany, 1945-50.* Oxford University Press, London.

REED, J. L. 1954. *The forests of France.* Faber & Faber, London.

SCHELTEMA, IR. T. W. I. 1944. "Holland's man-made forests," *Amer. Forests*, **50**:540-542.

SILVY-LELIGOIS, M. P. 1955. "Structure et composition des forêts françaises." (In La forêt française, *La documentation française, No. 2071*:11).

Société Suisse des Forestiers. 1914. *La Suisse forestière.* Librairie Payot, Lausanne.

Spurr, S. H. 1953. "Post-war forestry in Western Europe: Part II—Germany, Switzerland, and France," *Jour. Forestry*, 51:415-421.

Tulippe, O. 1942. "L'homme et la forêt tempérée en Belgique," *Bull. Soc. Roy. Belge de Géographie*, 66:157-259.

United Nations. Food and Agriculture Organization [FAO]. 1953. *European timber statistics, 1913-1950*. Geneva.

———. 1953. *European timber trends and prospects*. Geneva.

———. 1946. *Forestry and forest products: world situation 1937-1946*. Stockholm.

———. 1955. *World forest resources*. Rome.

———. 1954. *World pulp and paper resources and prospects*. New York.

———. 1952-54. *Yearbook of forest products statistics, 1952, 1953, 1954*. Rome.

United States. High Commissioner for Germany. 1953. *Annual Industries Report, 1952: Federal Republic of Germany and Western Sectors of Berlin*. (Part VIII, Miscellaneous Consumer Industries. Section I: Pulp, Paper, and Paper Board.) Bonn.

———. Office of Military Government for Germany. 1948. The German forest resources survey. *Special Report of the Military Governor, No. 40*.

Weck, J. and Kollmann, F. 1952. "Research in the Federal Republic of Germany," *Unasylva*, 6:125-130.

Woolsey, T. S., Jr. 1920. *Studies in French forestry*. John Wiley & Sons, Inc., New York.

14.   EAST-CENTRAL EUROPE*

Eileen M. Teclaff

The eight countries of East-Central Europe—Albania, Austria, Bulgaria, Czechoslovakia, Hungary, Poland, Rumania, and Yugoslavia—contain between them some 35.8 million hectares of forests, or approximately 29.2 per cent of their combined land area. Although this proportion is slightly higher than that for Europe as a whole (28.3 per cent) and the region is in general comparatively well wooded, the distribution of forest land among the several states is uneven.

Albania, Austria, and Yugoslavia have respectively 41.2, 37.8, and 36.8 per cent of their total land area in forests. At the other end of the scale come Hungary with 13.5 per cent and Poland with 24.1 per cent, although Poland ranks second in terms of total forest extent. Differences in amount of forested land per capita are also marked. Yugoslavia has 0.52 hectare, Bulgaria 0.44, and Austria 0.40. Poland has 0.27 hectare (roughly the same as France) and Hungary again comes at the bottom with 0.11 hectare.

TABLE 14–I

EAST-CENTRAL EUROPE: FOREST AREAS AND COMPOSITION, *ca.* 1950 [a]

Country	Year	Total Forest Area	Forests in Use	Conifers	Nonconifers	Mixed [b]
		Thousands of hectares				
Albania	1950	1,130	992	210	782	–
Austria	1951	3,156	3,139	2,476	473	–
Bulgaria	1947	3,700	2,964	394	2,570	–
Czechoslovakia	1948	4,023	3,893	2,120	927	936
Hungary	1950	1,253	1,253	80	1,173	–
Poland	1947-49	7,503	7,103	6,222	881	–
Rumania	1949	6,326	6,326	1,600	4,726	–
Yugoslavia	1953	8,745	7,345	1,461	5,884	–

[a] Source: FAO, *World Forest Resources*, Rome, 1955, pp. 60, 71, and 78.
[b] Except for Czechoslovakia, included as either conifers or nonconifers.

East-Central Europe belongs for the most part to the zone of mixed forests, except for outliers of steppe in the plains of Hungary, Rumania, and Bulgaria, a fringe of Mediterranean vegetation along the Adriatic

* For maps, see above, pp. 278, 279, 282, 283, and 300.

coast of Yugoslavia and Albania and on the southern borders of Bulgaria, and a sprinkling of Alpine flora in the higher Carpathians and on the Austrian Alps. Over the centuries the mixed forest belt has been cleared for agriculture, until today forests are confined mainly to poorer soils and mountain slopes. Another long-term result has been a reduction in the proportion of deciduous trees to conifers. Table 14–I shows the composition of the forests.

Forest Types

The mixed forests of East-Central Europe show a remarkable variety of species, largely a reflection of climatic influences—oceanic, continental, boreal, and Mediterranean.

Albania. The flora of this little country is especially rich. It includes representative species of both Mediterranean and Central European botanical regions and transitional forms. Oakwoods are the most important forests both economically and in the extent they cover. The principal species are *Quercus pubescens,*[1] *Q. cerris, Q. frainetto, Q. trojana,* and *Q. petraea,* with, in the south, *Q. macrolepis,* the vallonia oak, whose acorn cups are used for tanning. On damper sites the oaks are replaced by maples (*Acer campestre, A. obtusatum*), hornbeam (*Carpinus betulus*), lime (*Tilia platyphyllos*), elm, beech, and flowering ash, and above the oakwoods, at altitudes ranging from 3,000 to 6,000 feet, there are beech woods, often in pure stands. Along the rivers and in the lowland marshes oak, ash, and alder occur together with willows (*Salix alba, S. purpurea, S. elaeagnos*), poplars (*Populus alba, P. nigra*), plane (*Platanus orientalis*), and tamarisk (*Tamarix parviflora*). A thorny evergreen scrub which contains such typical species as *Quercus ilex, Pistacia lentiscus, Erica arborea,* and *Arbutus unedo* is widespread along the coast.

Yugoslavia. Like Albania, Yugoslavia has several native oaks, of which the most important is *Quercus robur.* Beech is widespread at somewhat lower altitudes than in Albania and is often mixed with silver fir, Scots pine, and spruce. There are a number of native conifers—Aleppo pine, Austrian pine, Scots pine, silver fir, Norway spruce, larch, stone pine, Macedonian pine, white-barked pine, and mountain pine. More than 50 per cent of the conifers are found in Slovenia alone, whereas in certain provinces, notably in Serbia and Macedonia, less than 10 per cent of the area is in coniferous forest.

Bulgaria. Here the hardwood forests consist mainly of mixed stands of oak, elm, maple, linden, hornbeam, and beech, and of pure stands of beech on the slopes of the Stara Planina and of oak in a small area of the east and southeast. The conifer forests, concentrated mainly in the southwest, have a considerable wealth of species, including *Pinus heldreichii* var. *leucodermis, P. peuce, P. mugo, P. silvestris, P. nigra,* and *Abies*

---

[1] Source for botanical nomenclature: Rehder (1940). See below, p. 316.

borissii-regis. Some of the more inaccessible of these coniferous forests are in virgin stands.

Rumania. The mountainous areas of Rumania show much the same sequence of species altitudinally as those of Yugoslavia and Bulgaria, grading upward from oak through beech to fir, spruce, and larch. The plains, as in Hungary, contain little forest, mostly oak (*Quercus petraea, Q. cerris, Q. frainetto*), hornbeam, linden, and elm, with willow, ash, alder, and poplar along the rivers.

Czechoslovakia. Here "a number of circumstances have combined to produce a natural vegetation of extreme interest and variety . . . the flora of Eastern and Western Europe, of the great plain of the north and of the Mediterranean, meet in this part of the continent." [2] Some of the vast beech woods of the Carpathians have been lost to Czechoslovakia through boundary changes, but stands of pure beech occur in western Czecho-slovakia in the Erz Gebirge and the Lausitz Gebirge. A considerable wealth of spruce, much of it in pure stands, is found in Bohemia and Moravia-Silesia. Below the spruce are mixed broadleaf forests of oak, maple, ash, and elm; above it, beech and fir (*Abies alba*), and near the upper limit of tree growth, mountain ash, dwarf birch, wild cherry, and stunted beech. Imported species of great economic importance are Norway spruce and Scots pine, and since World War II poplar, which yields quick returns, has been planted in large quantities.

Austria. The forests here are similar in composition to those of Bohemia and Slovenia. Of the hardwoods, beech and oak are the prin-cipal species, the latter sometimes occurring in pure stands in Lower Austria. Conifers, occupying about 60 per cent of the total forested land at the end of World War I, have increased in proportionate area to about 66 per cent. The dominant species is spruce, but fir and black pine are also important.

Poland is exceptional in East-Central Europe in that it has by far the largest ratio of coniferous to nonconiferous forests. The best timbered areas are in the south in the Carpathians, where fir is the chief species, and in the former German lands of the west and north, where pine prevails on the sandy soils and spruce on the clays.

Forest History to 1945

The forests of East-Central Europe today have been reduced to only a small fraction of their former extent in historic time. Clearing for agri-culture has worked largely to the detriment of the broadleaf species, since these grew on the better soils, but all of the forests have suffered from the effects of war, exploitation for shipbuilding, pasturing of animals, mismanagement, and waste of one kind or another.

The forests of the south and southeast, in particular, were devastated by cutting for fuel and charcoal burning, by goat and sheep grazing, and,

2 Wanklyn (1954), 93.

in what is now Yugoslavia, by the demands of medieval Venetian ship-builders. Many of these malpractices have persisted to the present day. Grazing is still a problem, and until recently, in Bulgaria for example, forest fires have often been started to increase pasture land.

Measures of conservation, however, were undertaken at a very early period. In the twelfth century the city forest of Vienna was placed under management. An edict of 1237 prohibited clearings at Salzburg in the interest of the salt mines "so that the cut forest may grow up to wood again." In Bohemia legislation was enacted in the fourteenth century restricting the pasturing of animals in certain forests and the collection of wood there for fuel. In Poland a law of King Wladyslaw Jagiello of 1423 placed the yew under protection. The later Middle Ages were noted rather for unchecked clearing and exploitation, and much forest was destroyed also during the religious wars of the seventeenth century, especially in Bohemia and Moravia.

The late eighteenth century was a period of conservation in the Austro-Hungarian Empire. Undoubtedly the holding of large properties by the nobility and clergy was responsible for the preservation of much forest land, although the incentive to good management was frequently offset by heavy taxation. The Schwarzenberg family were noted for the excellent management of their forests.

The eighteenth century was also a period of considerable forest legislation, but the greatest advance came in 1852 with a Forest Code that effected a uniform administration for the forests of the entire Austro-Hungarian Empire and took into account the interest of the whole community in the forests and the relations between forestry and transport.

By 1878, when the former Turkish provinces of Bosnia and Herzegovina were added to the Empire, the major part of East-Central Europe was subject to a centralized forest administration, and even after the dissolution of the Empire in 1919 the forest policies of the succession states continued to be based in the main on the forest laws and traditions of the Danube monarchy. Such was the case in Czechoslovakia, where the Forest Code of 1852 was incorporated into the new laws of the Republic. Poland, however, divided until 1918 between Austria, Prussia, and Russia, was influenced for the most part by the German system of management, a system which was also practiced in Russia.

Despite the uniform administration, however, development in the Austro-Hungarian Empire was uneven. Fernow [3] distinguished seven regions after 1878: (1) the northwest (Bohemia, Moravia, and part of Silesia), the first settled and the longest under forest management; (2) the northeast (Galicia with the Carpathian mountains), either over-exploited or untouched; (3) the Danube lands, with the Vienna Woods and the forests associated with the saltworks, under some management since the Middle Ages; (4) the Alpine territory, much devastated and in

[3] Fernow (1913) 155-156.

need of reforestation; (5) the limestone coast lands of the Adriatic, with their inheritance of mismanagement; (6) Bosnia and Herzegovina, with rich, untouched forests; and (7) Hungary, with a great variety of special conditions.

Much good work was done in the latter part of the nineteenth century by the extension of proper management to backward areas, by forcible reforestation, and, notably, by recuperative measures in the Karst country of Dalmatia, but the effects of centuries of neglect could not be quickly obliterated.

After 1919 most of the East-Central European countries were faced with a scarcity of foreign exchange, which forced them to expand their exports, and timber was one of the most wanted and most readily available commodities. The result was heavy overcutting and a corresponding reduction in growing stock (see Table 14–II). In Austria overcutting since World War I is estimated to have amounted to 70 million cubic meters [4] and as a consequence it has proved impossible to replant and return to production more than 300,000 hectares or approximately 10 per cent of the potential forest area. Productive potential in Austria fell from 9.5 million cubic meters in 1936 to 7.7 million in 1949.

TABLE 14–II

EAST-CENTRAL EUROPE: ESTIMATED NET ANNUAL GROWTH (ACCESSIBLE FORESTS), 1913-1948 [a]

(In Millions of Cubic Meters)

Country	1913	1922	1927	1932	1937	1948
Bulgaria	3.50	3.20	3.40	3.60	3.80	4.00
Hungary	–	2.90	2.90	3.00	3.00	3.00
Poland	–	19.00	18.50	17.50	17.50	11.00
Czechoslovakia	–	16.00	15.00	14.00	13.50	10.40
Rumania	6.00	18.60	18.60	18.00	18.00	15.00
Yugoslavia	–	16.20	16.20	16.00	16.00	15.00
Austria	–	8.70	8.40	8.50	8.30	7.40
cf. *Sweden*	43.00	43.00	45.00	47.00	49.00	53.00

[a] Source: FAO, *European Timber Statistics 1913-50*, 1953, Table P1.

After 1918 walnut, once common in Albania, was so severely cut that in many areas it virtually disappeared. In Rumania and Yugoslavia operations were carried out by large logging companies on the basis of long-term concessions. These corporations left the selection forests exhausted or with too small a growing stock to permit new cuttings. In both Poland and Czechoslovakia the stands have become perceptibly younger as a result of overcutting in this period; the reduction in the proportion of age classes older than 80 years has meant a corresponding reduction in the

[4] FAO, Forestry Mission to Austria, 1949.

size of timber produced.[5] Excessive lumbering on the Danube watershed was responsible for the serious floods of the 1920's and 1930's along the northern and eastern tributaries of the Tisza.

The greatest damage, however, came during World War II. It is estimated, for example, that in Poland during the five years of German occupation two and a half to three times as much forest area was cut yearly as in prewar days. In *European Timber Trends and Prospects* (FAO, 1953) it is reported for East-Central Europe that: "Although there exists no reliable record of what happened during the war years . . . it is certain that vast areas of forest suffered heavy damage from excessive and destructive cutting, actual war devastation, and wholly inadequate reforestation."

Forest History Since 1945

The year 1945 marks a definite break in the pattern, with boundary changes involving considerable areas of forest land. Rumania lost 0.8 million hectares of forest to the U.S.S.R.; Czechoslovakia lost its easternmost and most densely forested parts of the country; Poland lost most of its eastern provinces to the U.S.S.R. and gained 2.5 million hectares of forests through the extension of its western boundary to the Oder River. This brought the total of forest land in Poland down to approximately 6.5 million hectares, a loss of nearly 30 per cent from the prewar figure of 8.9 million hectares.

It is therefore extremely difficult to compare pre- and postwar statistics. Moreover, none of the countries possesses a modern forest inventory (except Austria which has just completed one, of which the results had not been published at the time of this writing) and such postwar figures as do appear are often incomplete or estimates only and should be accepted with caution.

At the end of the war none of the eight countries regained its former independence. All, with the exception of Czechoslovakia, which succumbed later, and Austria,[6] became subject to more or less uniform systems of centralization and economic planning that were soon reflected in forestry legislation and practice, and virtually all forest land in these countries became state property (see Table 14–III).

In Rumania legislation passed in 1947 applied to all wooded areas of more than 0.25 hectare. All forests were to be placed under proper management and at least one graduate forester was to be employed for forests of more than 6,000 hectares. In 1948 a separate Ministry of Forestry was

[5] The distribution of age groups in Poland in 1950 was as follows [*Unasylva*, 1950, 4(4):186]:

Up to 20 years	24.7 per cent
20 " 40 "	22.6 " "
40 " 60 "	18.6 " "
60 " 80 "	13.4 " "
Above 80 "	13.3 " "
Not classified	7.4 " "

[6] For separate treatment of Austria see pp. 314-315.

created and the entire forest area divided into 28 regional units, similar to the U.S.S.R.'s timber trusts.

In Bulgaria a Ministry of Forests was set up in 1948, and here, also, regional directorates, 26 of them, were formed. In Czechoslovakia forestry and water supplies were linked together in legislation of 1953 which placed the country's water supplies and watershed management under the Ministry of Forests and Forest Industries.

TABLE 14–III

EAST-CENTRAL EUROPE: OWNERSHIP OF FOREST LAND [a]

Country	Year	Publicly Owned	Owned by Institutions	Privately Owned
		Thousands of hectares		
Albania	1950	1,130	–	–
Austria	1951	763	446	1,930 [b]
Bulgaria	1952	3,700	–	–
Czechoslovakia	1951	3,782	–	241
Hungary	1950	1,000	–	253
Poland	1947-49	6,598	7	898
Rumania	1949	4,266	–	2,060
Yugoslavia	1953	6,269	(............	2,126)
Europe		60,300	1,900	71,900

[a] Source: FAO, *World Forest Resources*, 1955, p. 70.
[b] Excludes forests owned by corporations.

Formal economic planning accompanied legislation and administrative organization. In January, 1950, Hungary announced a five-year plan, based on a U.S.S.R. model, as the first part of a long-term program aimed at making the country self-sufficient in forest products within 40 years. The plan provided for reforestation of cutover land and afforestation on poor soils, amounting to a total of 93,500 hectares. The Yugoslav plan for 1947-51 provided for the reforestation of 100,000 hectares of cutover and marginal land, and for the regular management of 3 million hectares of forest. Bulgaria has plans for the reforestation of 990,000 hectares over a period of 12 years, and Czechoslovakia has proposed to reforest 150,000 hectares within seven years.

It is difficult to estimate the progress or the results of these decidedly ambitious programs from the published statistics. Estimates of average annual growth per hectare, for example, a quantity not subject to wide fluctuations over short periods, differ considerably in the figures supplied by Czechoslovakia, Hungary, and Poland to the FAO in 1947, and those appearing in the Soviet journal *Lesnoe Khoziaistvo* in 1949.

It is perhaps permissible, however, to make some deductions of a negative character from other evidence. For instance, it has apparently been found necessary in some of the countries under review to release certain forest lands from state control and development. Thus in 1954 the Rumanian government handed back half a million acres of forest to local authorities in order to ease an acute shortage of timber for building needs. In October, 1953, the Albanian government announced a decree "aimed at facilitating the supply to the people of forest supplies such as firewood, charcoal, and timber." The decree included the following provisions:

1. Permission to cut and collect from the state forests free of charge dry or fresh wood and to make charcoal for fuel purposes, also to cut forage for stockbreeding.
2. Permission to peasants to cut wood for construction purposes, for their own personal use, or for resale.
3. Permission to small private merchants to cut and market wood.

Natural disasters must also be taken into account in any attempt at calculation based on published figures of afforestation. Prolonged droughts, notably in 1947 and 1950, killed unknown quantities of trees, both at the planting and the pole stage. The droughts also severely affected the high forests, as, for instance, in Bulgaria in the oak high forest where trees were reported to be dying from the top. There were many forest fires throughout the region, especially as a result of the droughts, and bark beetle infestation was an unwelcome accompaniment that reached epidemic proportions in Czechoslovakia. Insect infestation was also severe in Poland, and much of the timber supply of 1948-49 in that country came from sanitation cuttings.

TABLE 14–IV

EAST-CENTRAL EUROPE: AREAS OF ACCESSIBLE AND INACCESSIBLE FORESTS AND OF FORESTS IN USE, WITH A CLASSIFICATION PERCENTAGEWISE OF FORESTS IN USE, BY SILVICULTURAL SYSTEM [a]

Country	Year	Accessible	Inaccessible	Forests in Use	Silvicultural System			
					High Forest	Coppice with Standards	Coppice	Open
		Thousand hectares			*Per cent*			
Albania	1950	1130	–	992	50	(........ 50)		–
Austria	1951	2500 [b]	656 [c]	3139	90 [d]	1 [d]	3 [d]	6 [d]
Bulgaria	1947	3700 [e]	–	2964	41	(........ 59)		–
Czechoslovakia	1948	4023	–	3893	...	...	...	...
Hungary	1950	1253	–	1253	55	(........ 39)		6
Poland	1947-49	7503	–	7103	...	...	...	...
Rumania	1949	(6326)	–	6326	...	...	...	...
Yugoslavia	1953	8395	350	7345	64	–	36	–

[a] Source: FAO, *World Forest Resources*, 1955, pp. 60, 71, and 86.
[b] Accessible productive only.
[c] Includes accessible unproductive.
[d] Census, 1935.
[e] 1952.

Table 14–IV shows the areas of accessible and inaccessible forests and of forests in use, together with a classification percentagewise of forests in use, by silvicultural system.

Throughout most of the region methods of cutting vary with accessibility. Most often the forests are cut by the selection method, followed by natural regeneration, but the latter often fails and leads to coppice especially in hardwood forests, such as those of Bulgaria. Clear-cutting was extensively practiced in areas farther from established means of communication, but is now absolutely prohibited in Rumania and Bulgaria.

The figures for accessibility should probably be accepted with some reservations. Even when forest is classed as accessible, it does not necessarily follow that timber can be brought out easily, that roads are adequate, or that modern mechanized logging is employed. In the eastern part of Czechoslovakia, for example, in 1947 the rate of transportation was only one third of that planned, owing to the lack of snow in winter which made it impossible to transport timber to the sawmills in time.[7]

Forest Industries

Most of the countries of East-Central Europe suffered damage to their woodworking industries during World War II. In Yugoslavia it is estimated that more than 67 per cent of the industry, particularly the sawmills, was destroyed or damaged. Most of the 13 sawmills in operation in prewar Albania were destroyed, but, by 1948, 24 steam- and water-powered sawmills had replaced the original 13. In Poland the government took over 132 pulp and paper plants in 1945, but was able at the time to start only 5 of them to work again, although, by 1949, 92 of the 132 were in operation.

Table 14–V, showing figures for production of sawn timber, veneer, and pulp boards for Poland between 1945 and 1948, may be taken as an indication of the recuperation of the wood industries throughout the region in the postwar period.

TABLE 14–V

POLAND: PRODUCTION OF SAWN TIMBER, VENEER, AND PULP BOARDS, 1945-1948 [a]

(In Thousands of Cubic Meters)

	1945–46	1946–47	1947–48
Sawn timber	914	1,696	1,911
Veneer	216	663	1,344
Pulp boards	128	236	246

[a] Source: *Unasylva,* Oct.–Dec. 1950, p. 186.

Most of the countries planned an increase in production over prewar times, as illustrated in Table 14–VI, for Yugoslavia. Here, however, output failed to reach the levels envisaged. Thus production of plywood in 1951 was only 22,000 cubic meters and of paper and board in 1952 only 60,000 tons.

[7] *Unasylva,* 1948, 2(5):283.

TABLE 14–VI

YUGOSLAVIA: PLANNED INCREASE IN OUTPUT OF CERTAIN WOOD PRODUCTS BETWEEN
1939 (1946) AND 1951 [a]

	Unit	Production		Increase (Per Cent)
		Actual 1939	Planned 1951	
Plywood	Cubic meters	18,500	48,400	252
Furniture	Finished goods	10,494 [b]	41,000	391
Impregnated ties	Cubic meters	1,200 [b]	6,000	500
Paper	Tons	50,210	145,000	289

[a] Source: *Unasylva,* 1947, 1(3):47.
[b] 1946.

In Poland a redistribution of the pulp and paper industries is in progress. Before 1951 the bulk of the industry was centered in the southwest. Under a six-year plan (1951-57) it is to be shifted nearer to the centers of consumption and also nearer to the forests of the western territories. As part of the six-year plan wood industries are also to be built up in the northeast around Allenstein. A similar relocation of industry is slowly taking place in Yugoslavia. Before World War II the two plywood factories at Rijeka (Fiume) were strategically situated for the processing of okoumé logs imported from Africa. Now that domestic logs are being used, these factories are as much as 300 miles from the source of supply and the timber arrives in such poor condition that a great deal is wasted. It is probable that the factories at Rijeka will be dismantled and set up nearer a source of beech logs. Meanwhile a large and modern veneer-plywood-hardboard plant has been constructed near Sarajevo and is expected to add considerably to the production of the four existing plywood plants, which have obsolete and worn out equipment.

The organization of the woodworking industries and of the export trade in East-Central Europe shows the same centralized control as forestry itself. In Rumania this has meant an extremely close economic collaboration with the U.S.S.R. By an agreement signed in 1945 "Sovroms," or Rumanian-Soviet companies in which a Russian managing director decides the capacity and distribution of production, were established in all major branches of Rumanian industry. In 1954 the Sovromlemn of the woodworking industry owned 40 per cent of the total capacity of the Rumanian woodworking industry.

In Yugoslavia, on the other hand, following the break with the Cominform in 1948, there was a decentralization of industry. Many government powers were transferred to the ministries of industry of the six republics. In 1952 control by the regional ministries was in turn handed over to the factories and municipalities. In practice, however, the federal government still maintains control over the woodworking industries, indirectly by manipulation of currency and foreign exchange and directly by taxation.

Domestic Consumption and Foreign Trade

Very few figures are available for domestic consumption. The FAO lists only two of the East-Central European countries, Austria and Yugoslavia, in its table of consumption of forest products per capita (see Table 14–VII). Typical of East-Central Europe are the figures for consumption of industrial wood and processed wood—less than the European average—and fuel wood—greater than the European average.

TABLE 14–VII

EUROPE, AUSTRIA, YUGOSLAVIA: PER CAPITA CONSUMPTION OF FOREST PRODUCTS, AVERAGE OF 1949-1955 [a]

(In Kilograms per Capita)

	Roundwood			Sawn Wood	Plywood	Wood Pulp
	Total	Fuel Wood	Industrial Wood			
Europe	460	190	270	70	2.6	25
Austria	400	260	140	50	1.7	21
Yugoslavia	890	670	220	60	0.8	4

[a] Source: FAO, *Yearbook of Forest Products Statistics, 1954*, p. 116.

TABLE 14–VIII

EAST-CENTRAL EUROPE: TOTAL FELLINGS OF CONIFEROUS AND BROADLEAF WOOD, 1953 [a]

Country	Industrial Wood				Fuel Wood Including Wood for Charcoal	Total Fellings
	Saw Logs, Veneer Logs, and Logs for Sleepers	Pulpwood and Pit Props	Other Industrial Wood	Total Industrial Wood		
	Thousand cubic meters, solid volume of roundwood				*Thousand cubic meters*	
Austria	4,667	1,561	710	6,938	2,918	9,856
Bulgaria	1,980	100	200	2,280	4,500	6,780
Czechoslovakia	5,000	2,400	600	8,000	2,300	10,300
Hungary	400	250	50	700	800	1,500
Poland	4,700	4,800	1,100	10,600	2,000	12,600
Yugoslavia	3,488	794	513	4,795	15,000	19,795

[a] Source: FAO, *Yearbook of Forest Products Statistics, 1954*, p. 20.

There is no question that the over-all domestic requirement has increased in this region and in some countries far exceeds the supply. In Hungary the domestic timber requirement was estimated in 1950 at 6 to 7 million cubic meters as against an annual timber cut of approximately 1.2 million cubic meters. In Bulgaria there is evidence of a serious shortage of wood for construction and fuel.

Perhaps the most significant change has been in the export of hardwoods from East-Central Europe. Until World War II Poland, Czechoslovakia, Yugoslavia, and Rumania were the main hardwood exporters. Yugoslavia has almost regained the volume of its prewar exports, but the other three countries have fallen far behind, owing to a combination of factors: production capacity is less, areas in Czechoslovakia and Poland containing hardwood forests have been ceded to the U.S.S.R., domestic demands have increased, and there has been a trend toward the export of finished products rather than of rough timber. This last tendency is particularly evident in Yugoslavia, which is expanding its veneer and plywood industry, in Albania, which now exports parquet flooring and veneer, and in Poland, where an entirely new commodity—matches—has appeared on the export list since 1948 along with furniture, boxes, and veneer.

Austria Since World War II

The development of forestry and of forest products industries in Austria since World War II has differed considerably from that in the other countries of East-Central Europe. There was a similar history of depletion of forest resources and stagnation of forest industries during the war and early postwar years, but the damage in both cases was less severe.

In 1949 Austria was fortunate enough to be made the object of a comprehensive forest investigation by the Food and Agriculture Organization of the United Nations. The recommendations made by the FAO Forestry Mission affect the entire Austrian economy and include the following provisions: (1) an investment betwen 1949 and 1952 of approximately $80,000,000 for the improvement and modernization of Austria's forest resources and industries; (2) the preparation of a forest inventory; (3) the creation of a government-controlled finance corporation operating through four technical committees for forestry, sawmills, other woodworking industries, and pulp and paper; and (4) the expansion of research facilities, plus the establishment of a new research center.

The Mission further proposed the expenditure of some $2,000,000 per year for reforestation for a 16-year period from 1952 and the establishment of an Austrian Forestry Commission to be responsible for the rehabilitation of the forests.

It was estimated that adoption of the provisions outlined above would raise the annual output of primary and secondary forest products by 30 per cent, would increase annual exports of forest products by 60 per cent, and would go a long way toward closing the gap in Austria's balance of payments.

Many of these goals have now been reached. The forest inventory is complete. There was an export surplus for the first time in 1953 (see also Table 14–IX), and a considerable expansion has been achieved in the production capacity of the wood-pulp and paper industry.

TABLE 14–IX

AUSTRIA: QUANTITY AND VALUE OF EXPORTS, 1951-1953 [a]

(Quantity in Thousand Tons; Value in Million Schillings [b])

	1953		1952		1951	
	Quantity	Value	Quantity	Value	Quantity	Value
Total exports	5,212	13,190	4,484	10,803	3,843	9,635
Timber	1,903	2,532	1,621	2,118	1,443	1,630
Paper and paperboard	201	855	137	682	158	972
Forest products as percentage of total exports	40	26	39	26	42	27

[a] Source: FAO, *Timber Statistics for Europe,* 1954, **6**(4):16.
[b] 26 schillings = $1.00 (approximately).

In other ways progress has been less marked. Fuel-wood fellings are still too high. It has proved difficult to modernize the sawmill industry, which is centuries old and thus has problems not met with in younger industries. There are 6,000 of these mills, most of them small, owned by farmers, and operated only on a part time basis. In such a mountainous country there is need for a large number of small mills, but their present maximum efficiency falls short of the desired optimum by 50 to 55 per cent.

Future Prospects

According to the FAO (*European Timber Trends and Prospects,* 1953):

The forestry situation and outlook of the five wood-surplus countries of Eastern and Central Europe is highly alarming. Indeed, if the allowable cut has to be reduced substantially below annual growth in Northern Europe despite excellent forest management and rigorous observance of felling limits, it would be logical to assume that, in Central Europe, an even larger reduction of prospective cut below the estimated growth has become almost inevitable. In the past thirty years growth in these five countries is reported to have fallen by nearly 20 million cubic metres, or by 25 per cent, to its present level of 59 million cubic metres. Yet the traditional over-cutting seems to continue; in 1950, the total cut for the five countries was officially reported at 74.4 million cubic metres.

The survey goes on to express surprise that there has not been a drastic curtailment of forest production. However, three possible explanations have been adduced: (1) that official statistics, in the absence of modern forest inventories, may conceal hidden reserves; (2) soil and climate provide better conditions for forest production than in Northern Europe;

and (3) estimates of growth may indicate allowable cut rather than net growth.

The cautious hope is expressed that felling plans may be carried out without further damage to the forest resources in East-Central Europe and that even a slight upward revision in estimates may be envisaged. The average annual wood production expected from these five countries is just under 63 million cubic meters or 15½ million less than the 1935-38 average from their prewar territories. The output of sawn timber from the higher age classes is likely to decrease, but an increase may be expected in the production of small-diameter logs for the pulp industries.

SELECTED REFERENCES *

BETTS, R. R. 1950. *Central and south-eastern Europe.* Royal Institute of International Affairs, London.

CONRAD, G. J. 1952. *Die Wirtschaft Jugoslawiens.* Duncher and Humboldt, Berlin.

FERNOW, B. E. 1913. *A brief history of forestry in Europe, the United States, and other countries.* 3d rev. ed. Amer. For. Assoc., Washington, D.C.

FROMER, RUDOLF. 1951. *Leśnictwo w planie sześcioletnym.* Panštwowe Wydawnictwa Techniczne, Warsaw.

MARKERT, WERNER. 1954. "Jugoslawien." In *Osteuropa-Handbuch* (p. 253), Böhlau-Verlag, Köln.

MARKGRAF, FRITZ. 1949. "Eine neue Hohenstufenkarte der Vegetation Albaniens," *Ber. Geobotanische-forschungsinstitut Rubel in Zürich für das Jahr 1948*:109–119. Zürich.

MURRS, E. N. 1948. "Forest education in Poland," *Jour. Forestry,* **46**:679–682, and 903–907.

News from Behind the Iron Curtain. Published monthly by the National Committee for a Free Europe, New York.

PRONIN, D. 1952. "Forestry activities in Yugoslavia," *Jour. Forestry,* **50**:484.

REHDER, A. 1940. *Manual of cultivated trees and shrubs hardy in North America.* The Macmillan Co., New York.

SAVICH, B. R. 1952. "Yugoslavia's forest resources," *Foreign Commerce Weekly,* **46**(4):3–4.

SIMONSSON, AKE. 1952. "Plans for the Austrian sawmill industry," *Unasylva* **6**(2):70–72.

TURRILL, W. B. 1929. *The plant life of the Balkan peninsula.* Clarendon Press, Oxford.

United Nations. Food and Agriculture Organization. 1953. *European timber statistics 1913-1950.* Geneva.

———. 1953. *European timber trends and prospects.* Geneva.

———. 1947-. "News of the World" in *Unasylva.*

WANKLYN, H. G. 1954. *Czechoslovakia.* Frederick A. Praeger, Inc., New York.

ZON, RAPHAEL, and SPARHAWK, W. N. 1923. *Forest resources of the world,* vol. II. McGraw-Hill Book Co., Inc., New York.

* For maps and bibliographies see "Bibliographical Note," at end of text of the present volume.

15. THE MEDITERRANEAN REGION

Guglielmo Giordano

Our civilization was born on the shores of the Mediterranean, and countless artistic treasures still speak to us of the genius of the Greeks, Romans, Arabs, and other peoples who have lived and worked around this sea. One cannot say, however, that these people have passed on to us the treasure of forests. In flying over Italy and Greece, the traveler sees green countrysides, but also, alas, enormous barren tracts and mountains hollowed and ravaged by waters, where mere ribbons of forest survive. Over Israel, Egypt, and North Africa the impression is still more harrowing. From the south the desert seems on the point of submerging the few forests that still remain, and near the border of Egypt and Cyrenaica the two immensities of desert and sea actually meet. In Algeria and Morocco a verdant coastal strip extends up to the mountains, but one senses the danger of progressive denudation.

GENERAL CHARACTER OF THE MEDITERRANEAN FORESTS. The visitor to the Mediterranean forests is struck by certain common characteristics that give the region unity from the climatic, phytogeographic, social, and economic points of view. The exceptional value of the Mediterranean forests and their significance in the economy of the area account for much of the abuse to which they have been subjected. This study, therefore, will not be limited to phytogeographic questions. Nor will it consider parts of countries only, but will deal with each nation as a whole. Hence the forests of Corsica and of the French coast between Spain and Italy are not discussed here but rather in the chapter on Western Europe, since most of the forests of France are non-Mediterranean, as are also those of Yugoslavia and Albania. On the other hand, Portugal, which does not touch the Mediterranean Sea, but still feels its influence upon climate and vegetation, will be considered here. So will the Italian and Anatolian Alps, which do not have a Mediterranean climate, but belong to countries that have a silvo-pastoral economy of Mediterranean type.

The typical Mediterranean climate is one of mild, wet winters and hot, dry summers. The summer drought is a limiting factor of extreme biologic importance. It renders regeneration and reforestation difficult. Along with the intense insolation, it accounts for special forms of tree adaptation, such as the development of cork for the protection of the trunk, and of the tough coriaceous leaves of many species, particularly those of the sclerophyll forests (e.g., *Quercus ilex*,[1] *Q. suber*) and of the xerophytic maquis, or macchia, so distinctive of the region. The climate also stimulates in Mediterranean trees an exceptionally high production of seeds and secretions (gums, volatile oils, tannins), whereas wood formation tends to be slow.

The species that form the Mediterranean forests are not as numerous as those of the American or Asiatic forests of the temperate zone, but much more so than are those of the forests of central and northern Europe. At the end of the Tertiary period the Pyrenees and the Alps barred the way to many northern species which, impelled by increasing cold, would otherwise have spread farther south, and these species could not survive the successive Pleistocene glaciations. Subsequently, the same mountains interfered with the diffusion toward the north of representatives of the much more numerous species of the south.

In central and northern Europe, with their great plains, most of the forests may be regarded as capital, which, if suitably managed, could forever furnish a large quantity of wood. Around the Mediterranean the situation is entirely different. In these generally poor and in many places overpopulated mountainous regions, the forests represent an extremely complex utility. Although not large, wood production is indispensable to the people as a source of fuel and charcoal to meet their immediate needs and for the manufacture of certain materials for sale. The forest, however, is also used for other purposes. It yields such by-products as cork, tannin, gum, and oleoresin. It protects valuable pastures. There are many places where grass can grow only under the cover of the trees during the hot, dry summers. Countless flocks of goats and sheep and herds of pigs wander through the forest at all seasons. To increase or restore the grass for them, and to eradicate bushes, the herdsmen use fire. Indeed, most of the people do not care whether the forest is degraded or even disappears entirely after a few years, as long as this means new land for crops. The three traditional enemies of the Mediterranean forest—the allies of a hostile climate—are the axe, livestock, and fire.

Against these adversaries the Mediterranean forest has long opposed a valiant resistance, in which it has displayed remarkable powers of adaptation. Where the destructive forces are not *too* persistent, there is always hope that the forest may be saved. On the other hand, the creation of new forests upon bare soils is exceedingly difficult. Special techniques are necessary to utilize what little moisture may be available and to build up the soil with pioneer species.

Once the forests have disappeared, the slopes have no adequate defense: water runs off the surface without being slowed down and without penetrating into the soil. What little humus is not burned by the sun is soon washed off. As denudation reaches an advanced stage, with gullying and

[1] Sources for botanical nomenclature: Rehder (1940), Tchihatcheff (1860), Post (1932), Bonnet (1896), Jahandiez (1931-41), Holmboe (1914), Durand (1910), Halácsy (1900-4), Arcangeli (1882), Willkomm (1861-80), Merino (1905-9). For full references see pp. 351-352.

landslides, detritus from the mountains covers the cultivated plains with thick layers of alluvium. Mountain and plain alike are devastated, with dire economic, social, and political consequences.

How can such a problem be solved? An equilibrium must be established between the uses of the soil for forest and for other purposes. To protect and improve the existing forests, or to create others, is not enough. The crying need is for integrated programs of total reclamation involving enterprises cutting across the domains of hydraulic engineering, agricultural and pastoral economics, public works, and social welfare.

Almost all the Mediterranean countries produce less wood than they need. Effective general programs of reforestation and forest improvement should eventually reduce the shortage, but can be of little help for some time to come. For the near future, increased commercial cultivation of fast-growing poplars, eucalyptus, and pines should be of considerable benefit. Excellent results have already been obtained in many regions with these species, in some cases with increments of 15 to 50 cubic meters per hectare per year in comparison with an average of 2 to 5 for the Mediterranean forests in general.

THE MEDITERRANEAN FORESTS IN ANTIQUITY. In early times trees and forests figured largely in religious beliefs and ceremonies. The forbidden fruit of the Tree of Knowledge was responsible for man's expulsion from the Garden of Eden. In Greek and Roman cults many a grove was consecrated to deities, especially the goddesses of springs, and forests adjacent to springs came under rigorous protection. The function of forests in assuring the perennial flow of the springs and thereby contributing one of the elements of soil fertility was thus already recognized.

Although no ancient inventory of forests has come down to us, it is certain that all around the Mediterranean the forests were much more extensive two thousand years ago than they are now. Greek and Roman writers, Theophrastus, Varro, Vitruvius, and Pliny, give us some interesting observations about the vegetal world, the culture of trees, and the importance of forests. As the Roman Empire expanded, much land around the metropolitan and colonial towns and harbors and along the roads was cleared and put under cultivation. Agriculture was on the march, "with torch and axe." *"Quid est agricola?"* cried the sophist Secundus: *"Silvae adversarius!"* But with the barbarian invasions whole populations fled and large tracts reverted to forest. The unity of the Empire was lost, and each of the countries around the Mediterranean began a new life of its own, the influence of which upon forest evolution must be considered separately.

THE IBERIAN PENINSULA (SPAIN AND PORTUGAL)

In the Iberian peninsula several mountain chains (which in the Pyrenees and Sierra Nevada exceed 3,400 meters) overlook extensive high plateaus. The average altitude of Spain is about 600 meters. Northern Portugal is mountainous (Serra da Estrêla, 1,993 meters), but south of the Tagus the greater part of the country is gently sloping or flat.

Spain may be divided into three main climatic regions: (1) a rather humid north, with precipitation throughout almost the whole year, heavy snowfall, and numerous cloudy days; and two relatively drier regions: (2) central Iberia, with moderate precipitation and marked differences in temperature between winter and summer; and (3) Mediterranean Spain, with hot, dry summers and mild, dry winters (the desiccating effect of the nearby Sahara desert is reflected in the regression of the spontaneous forest of this region). Portugal, influenced by the Atlantic, has a smaller temperature range than Spain. Here the summer drought is shortened and softened by high humidity and rains predominate in autumn and winter. The Atlantic islands have non-Mediterranean climates: that of the Azores is distinctively mid-Atlantic; that of the Canaries and Madeira is subtropical.

Spain

Types of Forests. In the northern climatic region mesophytic forests prevail. Stands of pure fir (*Abies alba*) are found in several valleys. Elsewhere the fir is mixed with *Pinus silvestris* or beech (*Fagus silvatica*), while in the Asturias and Pyrenees the beech is found in pure stands. Pure forests of *Quercus robur* occur in Galicia, of *Q. petraea* in Catalonia, with a mixture of these two species in the Asturias. *Pinus mugo* occurs particularly in the eastern Pyrenees, together with *P. silvestris*, *P. nigra* var. *poiretiana*, birch (*Betula pendula*), and linden (lime) (*Tilia ulmifolia*). At lower levels, *Pinus pinaster*, chestnut (*Castanea sativa*), and certain oaks (*Quercus lusitanica*, *Q. ilex*, *Q. pyrenaica*) are important.

In the central Iberian region the mountain vegetation comprises forests of *Pinus silvestris*, either pure or mixed with *P. pinaster* and *P. nigra* var. *poiretiana*, and also beech forests, in some places mixed with *P. silvestris* or *Quercus petraea*. Other oaks are also found, notably *Quercus ilex*, *Q. lusitanica*, *Q. pyrenaica*, and *Q. suber* (cork oak), while in the extreme south of the region there is *Abies pinsapo*. In the forests of the mesetas oaks (*Q. ilex*, *Q. suber*, *Q. lusitanica*) and pines (*Pinus pinaster*, *P. pinea*, *P. halepensis*) predominate.

The Mediterranean region shares several species with the central Iberian region, e.g., *Pinus halepensis*, *P. pinea*, *P. pinaster*, *Quercus ilex*, and in places, *Q. suber*. The growths, however, are less dense owing to the dryness, and vast degraded areas are almost like deserts. Several forest plantings have been made on coastal dunes, and a palm forest in Elche is worthy of note.[2]

---

[2] Classified according to the forest zones of Mayr-Pavari, the Spanish forests would consist of: (a) a restricted area of Palmetum; (b) a large area of Lauretum where forests of *Pinus halepensis* and *P. pinea* are dominant, although at higher elevations *P. pinaster*, *Quercus ilex*, *Q. suber*, and *Q. lusitanica* are either mixed with or take the place of these pine forests; (c) small islands and irregular strips of Castanetum, with *Castanea sativa*, *Quercus* spp., *Pinus pinaster*, *P. nigra* var. *poiretiana*, and, at higher elevations, *Abies pinsapo*; (d) a large area of Fagetum,

THE FORESTS IN PAST AGES. At the beginning of the Christian era, Strabo wrote that a squirrel could have gone across Spain from north to south on the treetops. This is hardly the case today. The extreme heat and dryness that prevailed all over southern Europe around the year 1000 was detrimental to the forests. Incessant warfare between Arabs and Christians was unfavorable to forest conservation, and severe forest laws, decreed on several occasions in the name of the Catholic kings, failed to bring satisfactory results.

PRESENT STATE OF THE FORESTS. According to a recent official report to the European Forestry Commission (1953), the total area of Spain (50,300,000 hectares) may be subdivided thus:

	1,000 Hectares	Per Cent
Forested land	7,300	14.5
Cultivated land and meadows	24,400	48.5
Other land	18,600	37.0

About a third of the forests belong to the state and two thirds to private owners. Since the population of Spain is approximately 28,000,000, there is roughly a quarter of a hectare of forest land per capita.

The areas covered by forests in Spain are distributed thus (per cent of total forest area):

High forests: 64; softwoods, 35.8; hardwoods, 28.2.
Mixed forests (coppices under clear high forests): 13.9.
Coppices: 22.1.

The areas occupied by different species are as follows (per cent of total forest area):

Softwoods: 35.9; *Pinus halepensis*, 9.3; *P. pinaster*, 8.9; *P. silvestris*, 5.9; other pines, 10.7; *Abies* and *Juniperus*, 1.1.
Hardwoods: 64.1; *Quercus ilex*, 23.4; *Q. pyrenaica*, 6.4; *Q. suber*, 4.1; other oaks, 6.3; *Fagus* and *Castanea*, 18.3; other hardwoods, 5.6.

Existing conditions in the Spanish forests are not good in general. The forests have been exploited for centuries without thought of regeneration. Most of the high forests are rather thin and contain many different species, with an irregular distribution of the trees in terms both of spacing and of age. The Forest Administration, however, is now striving to introduce rational methods designed to assure the perpetuation of the forest and of its production and an easy regeneration by natural processes.

Oak coppices are on the decrease, whereas in the chestnut forests, because of the disease affecting this species, there is a trend toward converting the high forests into coppices. In general, the coppices are clear-

---

much of it mixed with *Pinus silvestris*, the firs *Abies pinsapo* and *A. alba*, *Pinus nigra* var. *poiretiana*, and the oaks *Q. petraea* and *Q. pyrenaica*; (e) a restricted area of Picetum, with *Abies alba*, *Pinus mugo* var. *rostrata*, and *P. silvestris*; (f) an Alpinetum, lacking real forests and represented only by bushes (see Gonzalez Vasquez, 1948).

felled; in the Pyrenees, however, a coppice selection system [3] is sometimes applied to beech coppices. Very often a coppice degrades into pasture with scattered bushy clumps. Where the demand for pasture is pressing, some coppices are given over exclusively to the feeding of stock and constitute veritable browse pastures.

In addition to the natural forests, the highly productive plantations of eucalyptus in the provinces of Huelva and Santander and of *Pinus insignis* in Guipúzcoa and Vizcaya are of substantial industrial importance. In Santander increments of eucalyptus of from 8 to 42 cubic meters per year have been recorded. The output is used primarily in the manufacture of paper.

FOREST PRODUCTION AND NEEDS. The Spanish forests do not suffice for Spanish needs. Some recent official statistics are shown in Table 15–I.

TABLE 15–I

SPAIN: AVERAGE ANNUAL FELLINGS IN SELECTED YEARS, 1946-1953

(In Thousand Cubic Meters)

	1946-47 1947-48	1951	1953
Industrial wood (total)	2,800	2,348	2,350
Softwood	2,000		
Hardwood	800		
Fuel wood (total)	5,250	5,430	2,200
High forests	2,590		
Coppices	1,610		
(Pastures with shrubs, matorral)	1,050		
TOTAL (INCLUDING MATORRAL)	8,050		
TOTAL (FORESTS ONLY)	7,000	7,778	4,550

The totals in the last row reflect an annual production per hectare of about one cubic meter or less, very low figures but nevertheless for 1946-51 in excess of the allowable annual cut of the Spanish forests.

The normal annual consumption of industrial saw timber was estimated (1953) at about 3,300,000 cubic meters and the annual deficit of the country at about 830,000 cubic meters. Nearly all of this must be made good by imports from foreign countries, since the overseas colonies contribute only modest quantities of hardwood and no softwood. Since 1948 the imports have been down to between 350,000 to 400,000 cubic meters owing to a reduction in consumption, but this state of affairs has had an adverse influence upon industrial activity in general.

The Spanish forests yield by-products of considerable value. Oleoresin production reached almost 44,000 tons per annum during the years 1946-47 and 1947-48, and two thirds of it was exported; cork exceeded 63,000 tons, three quarters of it exported. Alfa or esparto grass (*Stipa tenacis-*

[3] See below, p. 326, note 5.

sima), largely employed for paper making, reached 138,000 tons. Three hundred tons of licorice (*Glycyrrhiza glabra*) were exported. Chestnuts and the seeds of *Pinus pinea* are also of some value. Although we do not have figures concerning the use of private forests for pasture, figures for the state forests and the forests declared of public utility suggest the magnitude of such use. On 6,300,000 hectares of forests, pastures, and "uncultivated lands with shrubs" (a figure which represents only about a quarter of the total lands of this category in the republic) graze about 6,000,000 domestic animals or the equivalent of 10,500,000 sheep in eating capacity.

FORESTRY POLICIES. The government is trying to improve the existing forests and to develop commercial plantings, especially in the north and northwest, where ecologic and climatic influences are favorable and where important consuming industries are located (mines in the Asturias, paper making in the Basque provinces, pulp in Santander). In the central region of high plateaus it is seeking to establish the species and systems that seem most likely to assure the reforestation of such now uncultivated areas as are undeniably suited to forestry.

FOREST AND WOOD INDUSTRIES. There are some 4,200 sawmills in Spain, the majority of modest importance only and with little modern machinery. The most important provinces for sawn timber are: La Coruña, Pontevedra, Barcelona, Vizcaya, and Lugo. Paper mills (including those which work up raw materials other than wood) are 157 in number, mostly in the provinces of Barcelona, Valencia, Guipúzcoa, and Alicante.

The Spanish plywood industry originated in 1915 with a factory in Valencia. Today there are 23 plywood factories, three of which (in the provinces of Santander, Vizcaya, and Barcelona) are of some importance. The most extensively utilized raw material is okoumé (*Aucoumea* sp.), of which Spain possesses reserves in its colonial territory of Guinea.

Portugal

PRESENT STATE OF THE FORESTS. The total area of Portugal (8,906,000 hectares) is distributed as follows:

	1,000 Hectares	Per Cent
Forests	2,467	27.7
Cultivated lands and pastures	4,864	54.6
Nonproductive	1,575	17.7

Since the population is 8,200,000, there are approximately three tenths of a hectare of forest land per capita. State-owned forests cover only 88,000 hectares, 3.5 per cent of the total forest area. The areal distribution as between principal species is as follows (in percentages):

Softwoods: 50; *Pinus* spp., 47; others, 3.
Hardwoods: 50; *Quercus suber*, 28; other oaks with evergreen leaves, 15; other oaks with deciduous leaves, 4; *Castanea sativa* and others, 3.

In general, the forests of Portugal are in good condition, although exploitation during World War II and ravages from a hurricane in February, 1941, have undoubtedly reduced their value. The net annual growth is estimated at 4,800,000 cubic meters (almost 2 cubic meters per hectare per year), with a normal annual cut of 3,700,000 (softwoods, 66 per cent; hardwoods, 34); during the war, however, the cut amounted to 7,000,000 cubic meters per year.

Two species, *Pinus pinaster* and *Quercus suber* (cork oak), are of such outstanding importance that two research institutes are devoted especially to them. *Pinus pinaster* is found mostly north of the Tagus, where it constitutes the greater part of the forests. It occurs in even-aged stands along the sandy Atlantic coast and up to 700 or 800 meters on mountain slopes exposed to oceanic influences. The increment may amount to 3 or 4 cubic meters per hectare per year; regeneration is easy and reforestation by direct seeding succeeds well. The wood is used for saw timber, pit props, and box boards, and provides an important export.

The bark of *Quercus suber,* which is cut and used as cork, is a source of great wealth for Portugal, and, indeed, cork culture, with which is often associated the raising of pigs fed on the acorns, has been brought to its most advanced stage in this country. The cork oak is grown mainly southeast of the Tagus in the province of Alentejo.[4]

North of the Tagus there are good stands of *Quercus robur* in the northwestern part of the country, of *Castanea sativa* and *Quercus pyrenaica* in the northeast and east-center, and of *Q. lusitanica* in the central part. Eucalyptus and acacia are associated with the pines in many places. *Pinus pinea* occurs south of the Tagus, in the vicinity of Setúbal.

FOREST POLICIES. In 1938 a reforestation plan was adopted with comprehensive economic, hydraulic, and social objectives in view. It provided for the reforestation of 430,000 hectares and the improvement of 60,200 hectares of pasture, and has been carried out in part. Among other things, it seeks to secure better soil and water conservation, flood control, an increase in forest products, the reclamation and settlement of mountain areas, and a reduction of unemployment.

FOREST PRODUCTION AND NEEDS. Although present production of wood has gone below prewar figures, exports ordinarily tend to exceed imports. Besides wood, the pines give great quantities of oleoresin (60,000 tons per year). The annual cork production is said to average 165,000 tons. Most of the cork is worked into various finished products for export. Exports of forest products in 1950 represented 27 per cent of the value of all exports (cork, 17 per cent; oleoresin, 6 per cent; wood, 4 per cent).

Facilities for cutting, transporting, and working forest products are adequate. Although there are more than 200 sawmills in Portugal—most of them in or around the pine forests—the majority are very small. In-

4 See below, pp. 349-351.

deed, only 48 make use of more than five saws each (by provinces: Viana do Castelo, 12; Santarém, 8; Braga, 7; Leiria, 7; others, 4). Firewood from the pine forest of Leiria, on a state-owned tract of 11,000 hectares, is used in the glass manufacturing industry of Marinha Grande. Six veneer and plywood factories, four pulpmills, 92 paper mills (which also use other materials than wood pulp), and a fiberboard factory complete the inventory of Portugal's wood-using industries. Only three of the veneer and plywood factories (at Lisbon, Porto, and, most important, Vila Franca de Xira) employ more than 50, and only nine of the paper mills more than 100 workers apiece. The larger paper mills are in the provinces of Aveiro, Coimbra, Lisbon, Porto, Viseu, and, most important, Santarém.

ITALY

The Alps bound Italy on the north and northwest, with many summits of over 3,000 meters (Mt. Blanc, 4,807 meters). The Apennines (highest mountain group: Gran Sasso d'Italia, 2,914 meters) form the axis of the peninsula. Between them extends the intensively cultivated plain of the Po, the industrial core of the country. Plains are scarce in the peninsula, and in many places the Apennines dip directly into the sea. Sicily, mountainous in the north and northeast (where the volcano Mt. Etna reaches 3,069 meters), presents the aspect of a low plateau in the west and south. Sardinia is rugged, with almost no level land.

Near the coasts of the Italian peninsula the climate is typically Mediterranean with mild winters and long, dry, hot summers. In the Apennines the altitude diminishes the temperature and the duration and intensity of the dry season. The climate of the Po plain is continental, with cold winters, hot summers, and heavy precipitation in autumn and spring. In the Alps one passes to a cool temperate climate, with severe winters, mild summers, and heavy precipitation (rain and snow); even in summer the rains are abundant.

TYPES OF FORESTS. Three principal forest zones may be differentiated: (1) a zone of *sclerophyllous evergreen hardwood* species (Lauretum), where the Mediterranean type of climate prevails, from sea level to 800 meters; (2) above this, a zone of *deciduous hardwoods* (Castanetum, Fagetum) on the Apennines and the Alps reaching to 1,400 meters; and (3) a zone of *microthermic softwoods* (Picetum, Alpinetum) on the Alps above 1,400 meters.

1. In the lowest zone, that of *evergreen hardwoods* (Lauretum), the most typical forest association is the maquis, a true climax formation made up of sclerophyllous species (*Arbutus unedo, Erica* sp., *Phyllirea variabilis, Pistacia lentiscus, Quercus ilex, Myrtus communis*) and usually treated as coppice with a 12–18-year rotation. While its annual growth tends to be low (it reaches, however, 4 or 5 cubic meters per hectare per year), the maquis is of great economic importance as a source of charcoal. There are good *Pinus pinea* forests along some sandy coasts, notably in

the Tuscan Maremma and near Ravenna. These have been planted by direct seeding after clear-cutting. The edible seed is their most important product. Tapping for oleoresin is little practiced because the return is small. Inland, *Pinus halepensis* and *P. pinaster* are associated with *P. pinea*. These trees are sometimes exploited by clear-cutting, with reserves of seed trees. Cypresses are a characteristic element of the landscape of central Italy.

2. In the zone of *deciduous hardwoods* of the Apennines are (a) oak, (b) chestnut, and (c) beech forests.

(a) The oaks (*Quercus petraea, Q. pubescens, Q. cerris*), which occur both in high stands and coppices, are relics of great oak forests that covered vast areas in the Middle Ages and have since been greatly reduced through clearings, especially during wars. The main product of the coppices is still charcoal; that of the high forests, railway ties and, to a lesser degree, pasture for pigs.

(b) The high chestnut forests, almost entirely planted, are cultivated for the fruit which, in some valleys, is the essential food of the population during the winter. These forests are often in a poor state because of advanced age (more than 150-200 years), or lack of care, or chestnut blight, or other diseases. Chestnut coppices afford one of the richest forms of forest culture in Italy, yielding a whole series of products: after one or two years sticks for the support of flowers may be obtained from them; at three or four years, shoots which, split lengthwise, are used in basket making, as packing, and as binding for wooden casks; at eight to twelve years poles, piles, and vine and plum props; at 20 to 30 years telegraph poles, clapboards, house beams. The increment, very small in high forests with old chestnut trees, reaches 8 to 20 cubic meters per hectare per year in the coppices. The large area occupied by chestnut forests (one tenth of the total forest land) testifies to their great importance in the economy of the mountain populations and accounts for the recent founding of a center for chestnut studies in Florence.

(c) Above the chestnuts and oaks are beech forests (*Fagus silvatica*). Here the best high stands are even-aged and have been subjected to successive cuttings (shelterwood system) with a rotation of 100 to 130 years; they yield increments of 3 to 4 cubic meters per hectare per year; but there are also uneven-aged stands where good silvicultural methods have not been employed. The wood is used for ties, staves, oars, and laths, and the best logs for veneer. Beech coppices, which occupy vast areas, have rotations varying from 20 to 30 years. They are often found near the upper tree line, and, where overpastured, break up in time into isolated bushy clumps. As these offer no protection to the soil, it is soon eroded and carried off by rains. The increment here is less than 1 cubic meter per hectare per year.[5]

[5] One method designed to maintain an area as pasture after cutting is known as the coppice selection system. Instead of all the shoots being cut at the end of the rotation, the rotation is divided into three periods and each time only the stalks that have reached a given thick-

In the same middle zone of the Apennines there are also softwoods. *Abies alba* is maintained in the famous forest of Vallombrosa in even-aged high stands with a rotation of 100 years and artificial regeneration by planting. Elsewhere in Tuscany, as well as in the Abruzzi and Calabria, *A. alba* forms high stands that are cut more or less selectively. The increment varies between 3 and 5 cubic meters per hectare per year. In the Abruzzi *Pinus nigra* and on the high Sila plateau in southern Italy beautiful stands of *Pinus laricio* occur, more often in groups of different ages than in even-aged stands, with increments of from 2 to 3 cubic meters per hectare per year. All of these softwood forests were seriously damaged in World War II.

In the Alps there is a lower zone of chestnut forest (superbly cared for in certain provinces, such as Cuneo), and of coppices of oaks or other hardwoods (*Ostrya, Corylus*).

3. Above this lies the domain of the *microthermic softwoods* (Picetum and Alpinetum). Here *Pinus silvestris, Picea abies, Abies alba, Larix decidua,* and *Pinus cembra* succeed each other up to the tree line. The first four species are sometimes mixed with beech. Particularly worthy of note are the selection forests of spruce and fir of the Cadore valleys, still operated according to rules laid down in the Middle Ages by the Republic of Venice, and the even-aged spruce forests of the Trentino (100 to 140 years' rotation, annual increment 2 to 5 cubic meters per hectare), which are treated by clear-cutting in strips. As for the larch, the rotation of which varies between 100 and 150 years, the high forests are always even-aged and are exploited by clear-cutting, often with artificial regeneration. The best larch stands are in Piedmont, and although the annual increment is small (1 to 2 cubic meters per hectare) their wood is highly prized.

On the plain of the Po, although the genuine spontaneous hardwood forests (*Quercus robur, Ulmus, Fraxinus*) have almost completely disappeared, a considerable wood production is assured by the commercial planting of poplars and of coppices of alder (*Alnus glutinosa*) and *Robinia pseudoacacia*. The annual growth amounts to 6 to 10 cubic meters for the coppices and 10 to 25 for the poplars.

Sicily is very poor in forests, but pines, chestnuts, and oak and beech coppices are found in the mountains. In Sardinia there are high forests and coppices of *Quercus ilex* and other oaks, but the most extensive and interesting formation is the ancient forest of cork oak (*Quercus suber*).

THE FORESTS IN PAST AGES. The barbarian invasions of the third, fourth, and fifth centuries of our era caused the abandonment of large fertile areas which had been cultivated by the Romans, and a succession

---

ness are cut; thus upon each stump there are retained shoots of three ages and the soil is always covered. With beech coppice, the increment in the best situations reaches 8 cubic meters per hectare per year; the product is used as firewood and charcoal.

of forests again took possession of the land. The feudal lords, moreover, greatly valued their woodlands as hunting preserves. This favorable situation for the forests, however, was inevitably modified with the passage of centuries. The repeated division of the lands and the progressive restriction of the rights of the feudal lords, together with an increasing population, necessitated the replacement of woods by fields, and vast forests were sacrificed to agriculture, especially on the plains. Some forests on monastic lands, however, survived the encroachment, and certain existing forests (Camaldoli, Vallombrosa) are inseparably associated with the names of religious orders such as the Benedictines and Cistercians. It is entirely natural that among the cultured, patient monks, lovers of nature should have studied ways of preserving their woods and thus developed the germs of the science which, several centuries later, came to be known as silviculture.

In the *comuni,* or small urban centers that began to take shape about the eleventh century, the importance of forest production, as well as the defenses that forests afford against avalanches and landslides, was recognized in municipal ordinance. Even so, wars and other abuses brought enormous destruction, especially in the Apennines. With the development of petty principalities (fifteenth century) the rulers often sought to form forest domains, but could not refuse rights of use to the people. There was little or no "forestry conscience" at this time, and the inhabitants usually disregarded laws promulgated to preserve the forests. Among such laws, those of the Duchy of Aosta and of the Venetian Republic were noteworthy. The seafaring Venetians were particularly energetic in the defense and national exploitation of the oak and spruce forests of their territories, since these assured them timber for ships.

Increasing population, lack of adequate regulation, and the abolition of feudal rights in the Kingdom of Naples at the beginning of the nineteenth century, all contributed toward the further reduction of the forest area of Italy, and when the country was united as a Kingdom (1870) it faced an extremely serious forest situation.

PRESENT STATE OF THE FORESTS. The distribution of land use in the Italian Republic was as follows in 1953:

	Hectares	Per Cent
Forests (about one sixteenth not productive)	5,648,286	19
Cultivated lands and pastures	22,115,118	73
Other lands	2,341,503	8
Total	30,104,907	100

The state owns 2.5 per cent of the productive forests, communes and institutions own 33.5 per cent, and private owners 64 per cent. In terms of character of stands, the distribution is as follows (in percentages):

High forests: 39; softwoods, 19; hardwoods, 19; mixed, 1.
Coppice: 61; with standards, 21; simple, 40.

As to species: fir and spruce, 6 per cent; larch, 3 per cent; pines, 7 per cent; oaks, 31 per cent; chestnut, 23 per cent; beech, 22 per cent; others, 8 per cent.

Since Italy has a population of about 47 million inhabitants, the total forest area amounts to 0.12 hectares per capita and the high forest to only 0.046 hectare per capita, very low figures.

FOREST PRODUCTION AND NEEDS. In 1947 the volume of growing stock in productive and accessible forests was 299 million cubic meters, with an estimated annual growth of 11,600,000 cubic meters (2.1 per hectare), as against an annual cut of 13,400,000—which meant a net loss of capital. Of the production, 29 per cent (3,800,000 cubic meters) was commercial timber and the remainder fuel wood. In addition, roughly 800,000 cubic meters of wood for industry and 10,000,000 of fuel wood (four fifths of which is branches and wood waste consumed directly on farms) are produced annually on nonforest areas.

Beside wood, the forests supply several by-products: chestnuts (285,000 tons), acorns (100,000 tons), cork (13,800 tons), fodder (655,000 tons of dry grass), leaves, mushrooms, etc. This suggests the enormous contribution of the forests to the feeding of livestock.

Italian wood production is not sufficient to cover the domestic demand for industrial timber and pulp. Imports are about 4,000,000 cubic meters per annum in excess of exports (which comprise staves, furniture, plywood, and other finished products). This heavy deficit, which worries public authorities and industrial leaders alike, can be eliminated by concerted action only.

FOREST POLICIES. In the co-ordinated planning for soil conservation, flood control, and the social and economic improvement of mountain communities, careful study will have to be given not only to the reforestation of large tracts and the improvement of existing forests, but also to the improvement of pastures and of stock raising outside the forest. This is the spirit of the program of *Bonifica Integrale,* or "total reclamation," now supported by financial resources that are fairly large in comparison with the little that has been available hitherto. Another promising means of reducing the wood shortage, however, is the development of industrial planting. In the plain of the Po poplars have exceeded all hopes. Either in regular plantations or in rows along roads and canals, they have yielded very high annual increments (10 to 20 and sometimes 25 cubic meters per hectare). The short rotation (10 to 18 years) and the demand for the wood for plywood and matches favor this culture. In Apulia and in Sicily large areas are being reforested with eucalyptus, as a result of the inspiration furnished by its successful use for windbreaks near Rome and near Arborea in Sardinia, where eucalyptus coppices have yielded annual increments of 20 to 40 cubic meters per hectare.

On many steep slopes, with dry soil and sunny exposures, good results have been obtained by the construction of *gradoni,* or terraces, at uniform levels. These hold the rain so that it penetrates the soil, reduces erosion, and provides moisture for plants and seeds sown on the leveled surfaces.

FOREST AND WOOD INDUSTRIES. Most forest operations in Italy still have an artisan character: logs are felled by hand and transported by animals. In the Alps, however, some logging crews rely on wire skidding or aerial cableways for transport out of the forest. There are some 6,000 sawmills, most of them small, for there are no great forest areas capable of supporting large single establishments. The most important in the Alps are in the provinces of Trento, Bolzano, Belluno, Udine, Sondrio, Novara, and Bergamo, and in the Apennines in the province of Cosenza. The machinery is not always modern: in the oldest sawmills of the Alps the Venetian saw still prevails, a one-bladed gang saw operated by water power; in more modern establishments multiblade vertical gang saws and band saws are used. Because labor is abundant and cheap and facilities for transport are poor, the logs are often processed in the forest itself, as for example in the making of railway sleepers, half-squared timbers (called *uso Trieste*), and staves. Few dry kilns for seasoning sawn timber are used. In general, the price of sawn softwood timber is regulated by the price of imports from Austria.

Wood charcoal is made in charcoal pits in the forest, although metal ovens were used to some extent during the war. There is no true wood distillation industry. Woodworking is better developed than sawmilling, and its products are appreciated, particularly furniture, which furnishes fine exports.

There are 210 paper mills, most of them in northern Italy; they utilize native chemical pulp, native mechanical pulp, and imported chemical pulp. About 35,000 workmen in all are employed in pulp and cellulose industries.

The plywood industry, 90 per cent of which is based upon poplars, has made enormous strides; there were only three factories in 1918 as compared with more than 100 today, employing 8,000 workmen and producing 150,000 cubic meters of plywood a year. This meets the domestic demand and also provides for a modest export. The industry is centered on the plain of the Po, particularly around Turin and Milan.

A chemical industry of great value uses chestnut wood in the manufacture of extracts for tanning purposes; there are 38 factories, with an annual productive capacity of 170,000 tons of extract, enough for both domestic needs and a good export trade.

There are three fiberboard factories, in Bolzano (its product is patented as "Masonite"), in Faè ("Faesite"), and in Capua ("Castex"). The plant in Capua uses chestnut wood from which tannin has been extracted. There are also a few factories producing chipboards ("Nevopan," "Fibrisol," "Celsa") and wood-wool panels ("Populit").

Other important wood products are: matches, which are mostly exported; packing materials, used in large quantities in the transport of fruits and vegetables of all kinds; and casks and staves, in demand by Spain, France, North Africa, and Greece.

Woodworking or wood-using crafts have developed such artistic products as the carved woods of the Val Gardena, the wood marquetries and mosaics of Sorrento, and the ancient wooden carved and painted *objets d'art* of Florence.

Although several impregnation establishments provide for the preservation of ties and poles, comparable protection of lumber and of timbers used in building has not yet become general.

GREECE

Greece is essentially a rugged, mountainous country with a few small plains. The northern part and the inland mountains are exposed to continental influences, with very cold winters. Elsewhere the climate is characteristically Mediterranean, with mild winters, rainless summers, and intense insolation. The mountains account for marked local climatic differences. Precipitation is much more abundant in the west than in the east.

TYPES OF FORESTS
1. Mediterranean Forests
    a) Evergreen-oak-madroña association. Oaks (*Quercus coccifera, Q. ilex*) and strawberry madroña (*Arbutus unedo* and *A. andrachne*), with *Pistacia lentiscus, Phyllirea media, Olea europaea,* and others as secondary species. Although the term "maquis" is often applied to it, this type of vegetation is not bushy and open, like the true maquis, but resembles a dense low forest with evergreen leaves. It occurs in Epirus, Crete, the eastern Peloponnesus, and the peninsula of Chalcidice, and in some places forms an undergrowth in the softwoods zone above 900 meters.
    b) Pine association (*Pinus halepensis* and *P. brutia*). These forests are widely distributed in southern Greece, Euboea, the Chalcidice, the Sporades and Dodecanese Islands, and especially in Rhodes, where *P. brutia* predominates.
    c) Cypress association (*Cupressus sempervirens*). Sparsely distributed on the continent, although common in Crete, Melos, and Rhodes.

2. Deciduous Hardwood Forests
    a) Deciduous oak associations (*Quercus macrolepis, Q. pubescens, Q. frainetto, Q. cerris, Q. petraea*), with other hardwoods (*Carpinus, Fraxinus, Tilia, Acer,* etc.) as secondary species. These forests are almost invariably exploited as coppices. Widely distributed, they are of great economic value to the country.
    b) Chestnut association. On the more humid slopes of the mountains of central and eastern Greece; maintained both as high forests (cultivated for their fruits) and as coppices.
    c) Association of *Cotinus coggygria, Pistacia terebinthus, Cornus* sp., *Prunus* sp., *Cercis siliquastrum, Fraxinus ornus, Acer monspessu-*

lanum, Carpinus orientalis, and sometimes *Quercus* spp. This occurs in the northern mountains and is often a degraded form of forest.

3. Mountain Softwood Forests
    a) Fir association (*Abies cephalonica* and hybrids of *A. cephalonica* and *A. alba*), in the Pindus and mountains of the Peloponnesus and of Euboea.
    b) Pine associations (*Pinus nigra* var. *caramanica,* and *P. heldreichii* var. *leucodermis*), in the Peloponnesus and Epirus, sometimes with *Quercus conferta* or an understory of *Erica* sp.

4. Humid Beech Forests (*Fagus silvatica, Fagus orientalis,* and hybrids), in the central and northern mountains; generally pure high forests.

5. Softwood Forests of the Central European type (*Pinus silvestris, Picea abies, Pinus peuce*), near the Bulgarian border, north of Kavalla.

THE FORESTS IN PAST AGES. In ancient times Greece was much better wooded than it is today. Since the climate is on the whole favorable to forest vegetation, the regression would appear to have been caused primarily by the destructive action of man: fires, irrational cutting, and overgrazing. Long centuries of human occupation, invasions, wars, foreign domination, and paucity of wealth and natural resources have all combined to impoverish the forest to a terrible degree. World War II brought considerable damage to more than 25 per cent of the forests.

PRESENT STATE OF THE FORESTS. Of a total land area of 13,020,000 hectares, forests cover today 1,957,980 hectares (15 per cent), of which, however, only 500,000 hectares (4 per cent) are productive and accessible. Cultivated lands amount to 77 per cent and other lands to 8 per cent of the total area. Greece's population of 7,780,000 has only 0.06 hectare of productive and accessible forest land per capita.

Of the total forested area, softwoods account for about a third, *Pinus halepensis, Abies cephalonica,* and *Pinus nigra* var. *caramanica* being the major species. About half of the hardwood area is covered by deciduous oaks and the other half by evergreens, beech, and chestnut. High forests, usually worked by a selection system, comprise only 43 per cent of the whole area; the remaining 57 per cent is divided about equally between simple coppice and coppice with standards.

Of the forests 63 per cent belong to the state, 22 per cent to private owners, and 15 per cent to communes or are collectively owned.

The total growing stock is estimated at 44 million cubic meters in productive and accessible forests, with an annual growth of 950,000 cubic meters. The annual cut amounts to 1,144,000 cubic meters, which exceeds the allowable cut.

FOREST PRODUCTION, NEEDS, AND POLICIES. The wood production of the country for the years 1951 and 1952 is estimated at an annual total of about 3,900,000 cubic meters, only about 197,000 cubic meters (2 per cent) of which was for commercial use. Part of the fuel wood and charcoal produced is, of course, derived from forests not qualified as "productive" and from trees outside the forests (poplars, fruit trees, olive trees, etc.). The current decline in the production and consumption of charcoal is probably due largely to the substitution of liquid fuels.

If the production of fuel wood meets domestic needs, this is not true of industrial wood, of which the country must import annually the equivalent of about 640,000 cubic meters of roundwood against a negligible export of high-grade furniture woods (walnut, boxwood). Other forest products, however, help the balance of trade: the oleoresin of *Pinus halepensis,* of which in some years more than 20,000 metric tons have been exported, and the acorn cups of *Quercus macrolepis,* used in tanning skins, of which 17,000 metric tons are produced annually and in great part exported.

The forest policy of the country is to protect, restore, and improve the existing forests, to reforest steep and denuded mountain slopes, and so to improve the pastures that they may be grazed upon without destroying the soil.

FOREST AND WOOD INDUSTRIES. Few modern methods are employed in forest operations in Greece. In many places even roads are lacking. Postwar reconstruction efforts have aimed at opening up forests heretofore inaccessible, notably by building roads and installing cableways.

Five large government-operated sawmills at the most important state forests were destroyed during the war but have recently been rebuilt. Besides these and one other, there are about 1,000 privately owned sawmills, 45 of which are fairly important.

Eighteen paper factories, in Athens, Patras, Salonica, and Aighion, make use exclusively of imported pulp. There are no chemical pulp mills, or plywood or fiberboard factories.

THE LEVANT

The term "forest" as used with reference to the Levant has a broader meaning than that usually associated with it. It does not necessarily imply a tight stand that almost completely covers the soil, but may refer to stands of small trees, coppice, or even scattered bushes, which, in spite of their meager quality, afford the only possible economic land use. These vegetal associations sometimes represent the local climax, but in most cases are only regressive forms caused by the destructive action of man.

Turkey

TYPES OF FORESTS. The major relief features of Turkey are the plateau of central Anatolia and the Pontic and Tauric ranges that bound the plateau on the north and south, respectively. Within this broad framework and including European Turkey, six principal regions may be distinguished.

1. The *Black Sea region,* a strip 50 to 200 kilometers wide, comprises the northern slopes of the Pontic Range and a very narrow coastal plain. Here the climate is mild and rather humid; the precipitation is abundant toward the Black Sea, but diminishes rapidly inland. The low density of population and steep relief help explain the presence of rather extensive forests, to the east of Giresun of a humid type, consisting of beech (*Fagus orientalis*), fir (*Abies nordmanniana*), and spruce (*Picea orientalis*), and to the west of that town, consisting chiefly of beech and fir, in places mixed with chestnut. At lower altitudes and in European Turkey oaks predominate (*Quercus cerris, Q. pubescens, Q. petraea, Q. frainetto,* etc.). Toward the interior the climate becomes more continental and the forests merge into those of dryer types, composed of pines (*Pinus nigra* var. *caramanica*), deciduous oaks, and junipers.

2. In the low-lying *Marmora Sea region,* which surrounds that sea on both the Asiatic and European sides, the climate is of the Mediterranean type. Once extensive forests have been greatly reduced to provide croplands for a rather dense population. They are composed of *Fagus orientalis* and *Quercus* spp., either as high forests or coppices; *Pinus brutia* also occurs in places.

3. The climate of the rugged *Aegean region* is influenced by the Mediterranean even at considerable distances inland. Ancient civilizations, followed by centuries of farming, have stripped the forests from the best sites; a few scattered relics of maquis, however, may still be found, while in the mountains and other isolated localities there are beautiful stands of dry forest, with oaks (especially *Quercus macrolepis,* renowned for the tanning material provided by its acorn cups), chestnut, and pines (*Pinus brutia, P. pinea*), and juniper at higher levels.

4. The *Mediterranean region,* along the southern slope of the Taurus Mountains of Anatolia toward the sea, has a typically Mediterranean climate. The woodlands here grade from maquis to high forests of evergreen or deciduous oaks, and of pines (*Pinus brutia, P. nigra* var. *caramanica*), and, higher up, of *Cedrus libani* and *Abies cilicica.*

5. The vast plateau of *central Anatolia,* some 800 to 1,000 meters high, is very cold in winter, very hot and dry in summer. Overgrazing and other human activities have destroyed much of the native vegetation, and only in a few places in the mountains do we find shreds of oak and pine forest.

6. *Eastern and southeastern Anatolia,* which extends from the meeting of the Taurus and Pontic chains to the border with Iran and the U.S.S.R., presents a complex of high mountains (Mt. Ararat, 5,166 meters), with a markedly continental climate, characterized by pronounced temperature ranges and very cold winters. The vegetation, owing largely, no doubt, to man's destructiveness, has in most places been reduced to that of a steppe. The few existing forests are composed essentially of oaks.

THE FORESTS IN PAST AGES. In former times Turkey was better forested than it is today. Before the battle of Ankara (1402) Tamerlane hid his elephants in an oak forest in the neighborhood of the capital, a region now treeless. Anatolia appears to have been fairly well wooded up to the end of the seventeenth century. In the Middle Ages, ships called at Black Sea harbors for rich and varied cargoes of wood. Many of the older houses are made of wood in towns and villages whose environs today are entirely without trees.

PRESENT STATE OF THE FORESTS. With a population of 20,935,000 in 1951 and a total area of 77,698,000 hectares, Turkey had 12,000,000 hectares, or about 16 per cent of the total, in forests. Agricultural land accounted for 58 per cent and arid and uncultivated lands for 26 per cent. If, however, one considers the productive and accessible forests only, the figures are (in thousands of hectares): softwoods, 1,800; hardwoods, 1,000; mixed, 200; total, 3,000. This is 4 per cent of the total land area, and in relation to the population represents 0.15 hectare per capita. According to other statistics (OEEC), of a forest total of 10,500,000 hectares (14 per cent of the land area), productive and accessible forests cover hardly 1,000,000 hectares (10 per cent of the forest total) and coppices 2,500,000 hectares (about 23 per cent), while 7,000,000 hectares (67 per cent) have been totally degraded or reduced to brushwood.

The forests belong to the state, although the inhabitants enjoy considerable rights of use.

FOREST PRODUCTION AND NEEDS. The volume of growing stock is estimated at 159 million cubic meters and the annual increment, or allowable cut, at about 3,300,000 cubic meters, of which 600,000 are of industrial wood and 2,700,000 of fuel wood. This is greatly exceeded by the annual cut, in which one must include not only normal cutting, but also that designed to salvage wood from burned forests, as well as uncontrolled and abusive cutting. In addition to officially authorized cutting for 1948-49, which averaged 760,000 cubic meters for industrial wood and 5,127,000 cubic meters for firewood, it has been estimated that 3,650,000 cubic meters of industrial wood and 11,730,000 cubic meters of fuel wood were abusively cut, giving a total consumption of:

	Cubic Meters	Per Cent of Growth
Industrial wood	4,410,000	735
Fuel wood	16,857,000	624
Total	21,267,000	645

This excessive exploitation is augmented by fires caused by the clearing of forest land for crops and by intensive and continued grazing (in 1945 more that 53 million head of stock of all kinds were counted in Turkey). There is danger that all the exploitable forests of the country will be destroyed in 25 to 30 years. It would mean not only the loss of all wood production, but further denudation and erosion, the disappearance of surface moisture, the lowering of the ground-water level, and climatic changes, all of which would have catastrophic economic and social consequences.

Imports are small in relation to consumption; in 1951 they were 350,000 cubic meters of roundwood (31 per cent of which were pit props; 34 per cent, sawn wood).

FOREST POLICIES. The government is striving to solve the problem of overexploitation. This calls for the adoption of proper techniques in the forest domain and for other measures of a more general nature. Many people have been moved to regions where an extension of irrigation would assure a sufficient agricultural production; some of the comprehensive rights to forest products enjoyed by villagers have been modified, other fuels have been substituted for firewood, and materials obtained from the reutilization of waste have replaced industrial wood. The well-organized Forest Service is actively engaged both in reforestation and in the protection and improvement of existing forests.

FOREST AND WOOD INDUSTRIES. Most of the cutting is done abusively by the people, who use archaic methods. Controlled cuttings are made directly by the Forest Service, which the government makes responsible for: (a) felling, done by hand; (b) transport, by floating from a few forests of the Black Sea and Mediterranean regions, by narrow-gauge railway and cableway in all the more important forests, and by animal in most other cases (the last method, though inefficient, was introduced in order to give economic aid to the farmers); and (c) sawmilling, done by hand, except at seven mechanical sawmills (the most important is at Ayancik in the Black Sea sector).

Because of the difficulties of cutting and transport, the prices of the forest products regularly exploited by the Forest Service tend to be very high—often higher than prices for the produce of abusive cutting. Thus, notwithstanding the small quantities offered, the Forest Service's products are often not sold.

Oak and pines are the most desired species for construction wood. In large cities imported softwoods are utilized to some degree. Millwork is not highly developed, although there are a number of small shops with skilled workers. For pit props the consumption is about two fifths from local beech and three fifths from imported wood. Beech and pine are utilized for ties.

A modern paper factory in Izmit on the Sea of Marmora uses annually about 65,000 cubic meters of indigenous woods for chemical pulp and about 25,000 cubic meters of imported woods for mechanical pulp. Were it not for excessive costs, domestic production could meet the entire domestic demand.

The only flourishing wood-using industry is that of plywood, with four factories in Istanbul and another in Zonguldak. Using indigenous beech, elm, alder, and the renowned walnut tree, it satisfies all domestic needs and also provides a small export.

Among forest by-products, the tanning material produced by the acorn cups of *Quercus macrolepis* is important; 58,000 tons are produced annually (export, 41,000 tons).

Cyprus

PRESENT STATE AND TYPES OF FORESTS. Cyprus is dominated by two mountain chains (the southern one reaches 1,900 meters) separated by a cultivated plain. The climate is typically Mediterranean, with dry, hot summers and rainy winters. The island was entirely wooded in ancient times, but fires, cutting, and excessive pasturing have reduced the forest area to 171,000 hectares, or 18.5 per cent of the total area of 925,000 hectares. There are 137,000 hectares (15 per cent) in productive and accessible forests, which means 0.28 hectare per capita for a population of 484,000.

The forests are confined to the mountains. Softwoods predominate on the dry slopes, notably *Pinus brutia*, *P. nigra* var. *caramanica*, with a few *Cedrus brevifolia*, *Cupressus sempervirens*, *Juniperus foetidissima*. In some places there is also a lower zone of hardwoods (*Quercus alnifolia* and *Arbutus andrachne*) and patches of maquis. In the valleys the hardwoods *Platanus orientalis* and *Alnus orientalis* are found. The high forests are worked on the selection system.

The forests are of considerable importance in relation to soil protection and a suitable water regime. In the local economy they yield products needed by a large population and serve as an attraction to tourists.

PRODUCTION AND FOREST POLICY. The annual production of about 35,000 cubic meters of roundwood (two thirds of it fuel wood) is inadequate, and Cyprus imports more than twice as much wood (75,000 cubic meters) as it produces. The need for fuel is great and always increasing. Attempts are now being made not only to substitute coal, petroleum, and electricity for firewood, but also to augment the wood supply for the villages by increasing the productivity of the existing forests and by creating new forests. To this end good results have been obtained near sea level with eucalyptus and acacias.

In recent years, the government has been vigilant in protecting the forests against fires, excessive pasturing, and abusive cuttings, and has compensated those whose rights of use it has abolished. Along with the introduction of a good road system in the woodlands and the employment of local inhabitants upon forest operations, these measures have done much to improve the condition of the forests and to raise the standard of living.

Syria and Lebanon

In the region that comprises these countries two mountain ranges parallel the Mediterranean Sea—on the west the Lebanon, which reaches 3,000 meters, and on the east the somewhat lower Anti-Lebanon. The former slopes off steeply seaward, whereas the latter descends gently eastward toward the Syrian Desert and the plains of the Euphrates. At the extreme south rises the isolated volcanic massif of Jebel Druze. The climate of the coastal strip is typically Mediterranean, with winter rains (snow on the mountains) and a relatively limited range of temperature. Conditions are more severe on the mountains, and beyond them to the east become subdesertic, with six dry months and high maximum temperatures.

PAST AND PRESENT STATE OF THE FORESTS—TYPES OF FORESTS. The forests of Syria and Lebanon have much in common, owing to the fact that most of them are on the mountains that the two countries share. But, while Lebanon is almost entirely mountainous, Syria extends over a large area of desert and of cultivated plains along the Euphrates; hence forests occupy, proportionally, a much larger part of the former than they do of the latter.

The present-day forests are but small relics of what were once far more extensive woodlands. In the Lebanon especially, Phoenicians, Egyptians, Chaldeans, and Jews all cut large quantities of lumber for their fleets and temples. That these forests still existed in the reign of Hadrian (A.D. 117-138) is evident from inscriptions stating that pines, cedars, firs, and cypresses were reserved for the Emperor.

In Syria forests cover 280,000 hectares of a total area of 18,268,000 hectares (more than 4,500,000 of which are desert or semidesert). This amounts to 1.5 per cent of the total area, and 0.09 hectare per capita for a population of 3,220,000. Most of the forest land is impoverished by pasturage, however, and only 50,000 hectares are in good condition.

In Lebanon the forests cover 74,000 (7.4 per cent) of a total area of one million hectares, or 0.06 hectare per capita for a population of 1,260,000. The distribution of species is as follows: *Quercus* sp., 43,000 hectares (58 per cent); *Pinus pinea*, 12,000 (16 per cent); *Juniperus* sp., 11,000 hectares (15 per cent); *Pinus halepensis, Cupressus*, etc., 5,000 hectares (7 per cent); *Abies* and *Cedrus*, 3000 hectares (4 per cent).

In regions such as Syria and Lebanon, where the forests have been reduced to scattered islands surrounded by tracts on which man has destroyed nearly all the rest of the vegetation, it is not easy to recognize phytogeographic zones. We may, however, distinguish a higher zone of pure softwoods from a lower zone of hardwoods more or less mixed with softwoods. In the higher zone, extensive only in Lebanon, *Abies cilicica, Juniperus excelsa,* and *Cedrus libani* are found in certain places at altitudes exceeding 1,200 meters. The Cilician fir predominates in northern Lebanon in almost pure stands or mixed with cedars. It reaches a large size (more than two meters in diameter and 30 meters in height) and may be regenerated rather easily where grazing has not become too much of a curse. The Cedar of Lebanon, so highly esteemed in antiquity, today occupies a very small area and one where regeneration is poor because of the pastures or because the trees, as much as 4 meters in diameter, are too old. *Juniperus excelsa,* the species that grows in the highest altitudes (1,800-2,000 meters), is generally found in pure stands.

The lower zone, confined almost wholly to mountainous slopes, consists of some maquis and of oaks (especially *Quercus coccifera,* with *Q. cerris, Q. macrolepis, Q. libani*), pines (*Pinus halepensis, P. brutia*), plane trees (*Platanus orientalis*), and alder (*Alnus orientalis*), either in pure stands or, more often, mixed. In some places other species (*Acer, Arbutus, Cercis, Amygdalus, Juglans,* etc.) are represented by single trees. In the great desert plains of the east the only arborescent plants are *Pistacia* spp. Oaks are found (*Q. coccifera* especially) on the Jebel Druze. Man and animals have brought the stands of the lower zone to a deplorable condition in most places.

Artificial reforestations with *Pinus pinea* begun near Beirut eighty or ninety years ago have been highly productive, both of edible seeds and of wood. Mention should also be made of the cultivation of olive trees, fruit trees (almond, apricot, etc.), and poplar, of which last there are certain indigenous types: a male clone of the white poplar (*section Leuce*) called "roomi," a female clone of *Populus nigra* called "hamoni," and another black poplar called "farsi." The roomi and the hamoni are cultivated either along irrigation ditches or in multiple rows or in industrial plantations; their wood is appreciated for carpentry, structural purposes, matches, and plywood. *Populus euphratica* Oliv. grows in natural stands along the rivers, while in Lebanon foreign poplars have been introduced, notably from North America.

In Syria and Lebanon together about 72 per cent of the total wooded area is state property, 23 per cent is in private forests, and 5 per cent is in communal forests and forests held by religious organizations. In Lebanon nearly two thirds belong to the state, one sixth to communes, and one sixth to private owners.

FOREST PRODUCTION AND NEEDS. Since the forests are almost never cut according to systematic principles, the annual cut greatly exceeds the increment. The gravest danger, however, is from livestock, especially goats, which exceed one million in number and feed largely on coppices and young stands.

This lamentable situation, together with a low rate of forest growth is responsible for the small production of wood. Syria fells only about 750,000 and Lebanon about 49,000 cubic meters of roundwood annually. Consequently Syria has to import about 190,000 cubic meters of wood per year and Lebanon about 105,000, of which approximately one sixth is fuel wood.

It will not be easy to restore and increase the forest capital of these countries. Adequate protection of the forests would demand close surveillance and also greatly interfere with the pastoral economy that provides the only livelihood for the people in many localities. In addition to protecting existing forests and creating new forest stands, range land must be improved if a proper balance between the various types of land use is to be reached.

WOOD INDUSTRIES. The wood-using industries of Syria and Lebanon are very poorly developed. There are no forest sawmills. Logs are transported on the backs of animals to the towns. There are a few plywood and match factories in Lebanon. Increased production, following the development of eucalyptus, poplar, and pine plantations outside the forests, might help the general industrial growth of the two countries. It is estimated that not less than 150,000 cubic meters of poplar wood is consumed annually, of which two thirds is used for industrial purposes and the remainder as fuel wood.

Israel

The territory of the State of Israel, with an area of 2,059,000 hectares and 1,260,000 inhabitants, corresponds roughly to that of Palestine—i.e., the country between the Mediterranean Sea and the deep rift valley of the Jordan, Dead Sea, and Wadi Araba. Mountain chains, of which the loftiest summit is less than 1,000 meters high, run north and south, falling off gently toward the Mediterranean but steeply on the east into the rift valley, where the Dead Sea lies at 394 meters below sea level. The Desert of Negev to the south gives Israel an opening on the Red Sea.

The western slope of the country has a Mediterranean type of climate, with mild, relatively rainy winters, and hot, dry summers. In the east and south the weather is often very hot; the precipitation is so small that the climate is that of a semidesert and, in places, of a desert.

TYPES AND PRESENT STATE OF THE FORESTS. Along the Mediterranean coast there are fragments of forests of *Pinus halepensis, Quercus calliprinos, Q. ithaburensis* Decne., *Ceratonia siliqua,* and of maquis, all in general very degraded. There are no forests in the semidesert—only a few scattered trees (*Pistacia atlantica* and *Zizyphus lotus*). In the desert trees are limited to the wadis (*Acacia* sp.) and oases (*Tamarix* sp., *Phoenix dactylifera, Hyphaene thebaica*).

The wooded area of Israel is 50,000 hectares, about 5,000 hectares of which are accessible and productive. This is one quarter of one per cent of the area of the country (2,059,000 hectares), or 0.008 hectare per capita for a population of 1,260,000. Except for commercial plantations, there are almost no genuine forest stands that produce wood commercially, but merely vegetal associations in which the trees are very far apart, small, and badly formed, and only rarely provide any wood whatsoever. This is due mainly to the baneful influence of man, whose fires and whose animals have desolated the plains and the mountains alike.

FOREST POLICIES. The need for wood greatly exceeds the local supply. Production in 1937 was only 20,000 cubic meters, while 500,000 cubic meters were imported, a heavy load upon the national economy. The authorities are determined to enlarge the forested area in order to promote soil protection, humus formation, moisture retention, and wood production. A comprehensive program of reforestation and of windbreak development associated with agriculture has been considered. For the reforestation of the mountains, the results of certain successful trials suggest a more extensive future use of *Pinus halepensis, Pinus brutia, Pinus pinea,* and *Cupressus.* For the windbreaks as well as for the reforestation of stabilized dunes eucalyptus will mainly be planted, although acacias and pines will also be used on the dunes. Poplars and eucalyptus should give good results in the marshes. Most of the population is fairly well educated and comes from Europe; its attitude toward trees gives hope for the future.

WOOD INDUSTRIES. At present there is no forest industry, nor a real millwork industry, but the outlook is promising. A fiberboard factory and a chemical pulp mill have recently been opened, but they rely upon imported raw material.

NORTHERN AFRICA

Egypt

Of the total area of Egypt, 100,025,000 hectares, by far the greater part is desert. The Nile Valley and the Delta (3,520,000 hectares), however, support a dense, primarily agricultural population. The climate is that of a desert, very little influenced by the Mediterranean; the rainfall is extremely light and irregular. Although woods were not totally lacking in ancient times, no spontaneous forests exist today and the woody vegetation is restricted to the palm trees (*Phoenix dactylifera*) of the irrigated areas and oases and to a few arborescent or bushy elements in the desert and semidesert flora (*Acacia, Tamarix, Balanites, Zizyphus,* etc.). Hence wood production is almost nil (a few thousand cubic meters of firewood) and the country is obliged to import about 1,500,000 cubic meters of wood a year to provide for the needs of a population of 20,440,000. Although past attempts at reforestation have not been very successful, limited wood resources might be developed, in the form of windbreaks and rows of trees along the canals, by planting *Casuarina* sp., *Eucalyptus* sp., and *Pinus* sp., and by the fixation of sands and the reforestation of saline lands of the Delta with *Casuarina* and *Tamarix.*

Libya

Since they differ greatly, the two main regions of Libya, namely, Cyrenaica and Tripolitania, will be described separately.

CYRENAICA. The high plateau of Cyrenaica attains an altitude of nearly 900 meters and is bounded on the north by a narrow coastal plain. Barren plains spread out to the south. On the plateau the climate is of the Mediterranean type, with a precipitation, brought by the northwest wind, which increases with altitude. The Arab name of the plateau, Jebel el Akhdar, or Green Mountain, is justified by an arborescent vegetal association which, although degraded, represents the only true forest formation between Lebanon and Tunisia. It is a relic of forests that must have been far more extensive in pre-Christian centuries, as witnessed by petrified stumps well out in the desert and also by the testimony of several Roman historians.

The present area of this forest is estimated at 155,000 hectares and its character is varied. In some places it consists of a maquis of evergreen hardwoods (*Pistacia lentiscus, Arbutus pavarii* Pampan., *Rhus oxyacantha, Quercus coccifera*); elsewhere, softwood species are found in addition to or in the place of the hardwoods, notably *Pinus halepensis, Cupressus sempervirens,* and *Juniperus phoenicea.* Trees of the two last species may reach considerable dimensions. Arab needs for pasture and crop land, together with the effects of wars, have been the chief factors in the reduction of the flora, both in area and density.

Outside of the Jebel, the spontaneous vegetation is limited to species characteristic of steppes and deserts: *Pistacia atlantica, Tamarix articulata, Rhus* sp., *Zizyphus lotus, Acacia* sp.

During the Italian occupation, reforestation was carried out with pines and eucalyptus and the spontaneous forests were improved, but the war destroyed most of the results. Though both environmental conditions and the hostility of the nomads create grave difficulties, restoration and reforestation are not impossible and may well provide means in the future for meeting the domestic demand not only for firewood and charcoal (which formerly supplied a small export) but also for some wood for industry.

TRIPOLITANIA. Separated from Cyrenaica by the Syrtis Desert, Tripolitania consists of a coastal strip of dunes and sandy plains, with dry plateaus and desert plains in the interior. The climate is hot; the rainfall, irregular and occurring mostly in winter, is restricted chiefly to the coastal strip and the northern extremity of the plateaus. There is no spontaneous forest in Tripolitania and no evidence of its presence in antiquity. Spontaneous vegetation is limited to isolated specimens of *Pistacia atlantica, Acacia tortilis, Rhus,* and *Zizyphus* in the wadi beds, and to sparse traces of Mediterranean vegetation at a few spots on the plateaus.

LIBYA: FOREST POLICIES AND PRODUCTION. In connection with agricultural colonization, the Italians undertook far-reaching forestry work in Libya, involving the fixation of dunes and creation of windbreaks with acacias and eucalyptus and also reforestation with pine, cypress, and eucalyptus. They counted upon these plantations, rather than upon the poor spontaneous vegetation, to meet the demand for wood, which, before

World War II, for the whole of Libya was estimated at 90,000 cubic meters per annum (a quarter of which was for industrial wood).

Tripolitania possesses 19,000 hectares of forest land, of which 8,000 hectares, being in plantations, are productive. Cyrenaica's productive forests amount to 15,000 hectares. Thus the productive wooded area in the whole of Libya is about 23,000 hectares, which constitutes about 0.15 per cent of the country's 15 million hectares outside of the desert, and provides a population of 1,120,000 with 0.02 hectare per capita.

At the present time there are no wood industries in the whole country except on the high plateau of Cyrenaica where a little charcoal is made.

Tunisia, Algeria, and Morocco

Barbary, comprising Tunisia, Algeria, and Morocco, forms a well-defined geographical unit—a mountainous island, as it were—between the Sahara and the Mediterranean. From both the morphological and the floral points of view it is more European than African. The relief is dominated by the Atlas, a system of folded mountains, which become lower from Morocco (where 4,000-meter summits are found) eastward to Algeria (2,000 meters) and Tunisia (1,000 meters). There are two main chains. The southern one (Grand Atlas, Saharan Atlas) runs continuously along the edge of the desert. The northern (Middle Atlas, Tell Atlas) roughly parallels the sea, but without real continuity. It consists of a series of folded and disconnected ridges and summits. Between the two, high plateaus are found in Algeria and Morocco.

The climate is of the Mediterranean type, characterized by two main seasons: a cold and rainy one during the autumn and winter, and a hot and dry one during most of the spring and all of the summer. Atlantic influences moderate the extremes of temperature throughout the region and in Morocco control the precipitation (in Algeria and Tunisia, however, it is affected to a greater degree by the Mediterranean). In general, the precipitation increases both with altitude and from south to north. It is extremely irregular from year to year. Snow, which covers the Grand Atlas during the winter, falls in lesser quantity in Algeria and almost not at all in Tunisia.

It is not easy to answer the question whether the climate of Barbary has become more severe during historic times. Some authorities think this is the case, basing their opinion upon the recession of certain species. Although these could have been destroyed by man, the recession itself may well have modified the climate in the sense of rendering it more sensitive to the drying effects of the Sahara.[6]

[6] On this question we may quote the following statement by P. Boudy, a leading authority on the North African environment:

"En résumé, à la lumière de faits incontestables, tels que l'évolution climatique durant la période préhistorique et le processus de dessèchement du Sahara, force est de reconnaître que le problème du climat de la Berberie depuis la période historique, a été mal posé, parce que trop élargi dans l'espace et trop rétréci dans le temps. Si on l'envisage sans idées préconçues,

FOREST TYPES. The flora of Barbary has many affinities with that of Mediterranean Europe but is extremely xerothermic and includes certain ancient elements that no longer exist in Europe. The present vegetation may be grouped in zones corresponding to the Saharan, arid, semiarid, subhumid, and humid climatic zones. In Morocco there is also a high-mountain zone.

The *Saharan zone,* which borders the desert and is important only in Morocco, contains some extremely scattered wooded areas of *Acacia* sp., *Balanites,* and *Maerua* (elements entirely African), *Rhus* sp., and in the beds of the wadis, *Nerium, Tamarix,* and *Zizyphus.*

The *arid zone* occupies a vast area extending from eastern Morocco across the high plateaus of Algeria and over a good part of Tunisia. Here there are no dense forests, but only open stands (80 trees per hectare) of *Argania sideroxylon* Roem. & Schult., which in certain localities is associated with or replaced by *Acacia tortilis, Pistacia atlantica,* or *Zizyphus.* In the colder areas trees disappear, giving place to alfa (*Stipa tenacissima*) and artemisia steppe.

The *semiarid zone,* widely distributed, occupies plains and other areas not included in the mountains or in the two preceding zones. The forests here are of some importance; among the softwoods are *Pinus halepensis, Callitris quadrivalvis, Juniperus phoenicea,* and *Juniperus thurifera;* among the hardwoods, *Quercus suber, Q. ilex,* and *Olea.* The very irregular high forests of *P. halepensis,* a first-class colonizer, are mostly worked on the selection system by single trees or by groups, because of fire; their volume does not exceed 120 cubic meters per hectare. The stands of *Callitris,* or sandarac tree, even more irregular because of human influences, are almost always in the form of dense coppices. *Quercus suber,* the cork oak, appears in this zone, but is not at its best (its natural regeneration is often inadequate). The more resistant *Quercus ilex,* which does better, appears in light stands.

The *subhumid zone* occupies the lower mountain slopes; the typical forests are of *Quercus ilex, Q. suber,* and *Quercus faginea* (zéen oak) together with maquis (*Pistacia lentiscus, Erica* sp., and *Cistus* sp.) The cork oak here regenerates easily and resists the shock of cork-removal and even of fire without serious damage. The stands are denser than those of the semiarid zone; in old high forests of 120 to 150 years of age, however, one finds only 75 to 100 trees to the hectare, containing 70 to 100 cubic meters. However, a considerable volume also occurs in the undergrowth. The stands of *Q. ilex* are essentially the same as those of the humid zone (see below). *Quercus faginea* prospers only in moist places, whence it expels other species, especially *Q. suber.* It reproduces itself abundantly

---

on en arrive à penser qu'en présence de certains phénomènes, tels que le refoulement vers le Nord d'espèces végétales, comme le chêne-liège et le chêne-zéen, il est difficile d'affirmer qu'aucune modification ne s'est produite en Berberie à cet égard, durant les quatre millénaires que constituent jusqu'à nos jours la période historique." (P. Boudy. *Economie forestière nordafricaine.* Larose, Paris, 1950.)

by seeding and is a tolerant species; generally found in high forests with uneven-aged stands, it has a growing stock of 220 to 250 cubic meters per hectare.

The *humid zone,* where the higher rainfall promotes a relatively luxuriant forest growth not unlike that of Mediterranean Europe, is found on the mountains of Algeria, the Rif (Spanish Morocco), and the Middle Atlas, but is lacking on the Grand Atlas. *Quercus suber, Q. ilex, Q. faginea, Q. castaneaefolia,* and *Q. pyrenaica* are found here, and among the softwoods, *Cedrus atlantica, Abies numidica, Abies pinsapo,* and *Pinus pinaster.* Here the cork oak is at its best. Its density and volume in the high forests exceed those of the subhumid zone, and it is also found in overmature coppices. *Q. ilex* may form dense high forests with 500 to 600 trees per hectare; these are 100 to 200 years old and the volume is from 200 to 350 cubic meters per hectare. The cedar is the most valuable domestic species for the production of timber, but the capricious fashion in which it regenerates itself poses great problems. The constitution of these high forests of cedar is very irregular, since there are few middle-aged trees. In the 100 to 150 year-old groups the standing volume reaches 300 to 350 cubic meters per hectare and the annual increment may exceed 2.5 cubic meters per hectare. *Pinus pinaster,* which reaches 1,000 meters in only a few localities in Europe, here grows on mountains even above 2,000 meters.

In the *high-mountain zone* (Grand and Middle Atlas) there are forests of *Cedrus, Pinus pinaster,* and especially of *Juniperus thurifera.* Although it serves a useful purpose in holding the soil at high altitudes, the juniper is unfortunately in a state of regression, owing to human causes.

THE FORESTS IN PAST AGES. Latin writers have left us few documents about the forests of North Africa, but it is known that, during the later period of the Empire, Rome received wood, particularly cedar, from this region. The towns of the North African coast were founded close to forests, but the increase in population during the early Christian era led to extensive clearing. After the Arab conquest of the seventh and eighth centuries and especially with the invasions of Hilalian nomads from the Hejaz in the eleventh century, Tunisia and Algeria were devastated. Morocco, defended by the Almohades, suffered somewhat less, although there, too, the forests were largely destroyed to supply the cities (Fez, Marrakesh, Meknès, etc.) with firewood and tanning materials. After the French occupation, exploitation was carried on along somewhat different lines in each country. In Tunisia, after a period (1883-92) during which overmature and decaying cork oaks were used for tannin, the large-scale exploitation of cork was begun, and oak wood (especially *Q. faginea*) was utilized for railroad ties and other industrial purposes. Unregulated cutting in Algeria during the years 1838-70 was followed by a period of exploitation of tannin and cork. In Morocco, where cutting by the local population had always been destructive, efforts at restoration

TABLE 15–II

TUNISIA, ALGERIA, AND MOROCCO: FOREST AREAS IN RELATION TO POPULATION AND TOTAL AREA, *ca.* 1950

Country	Estimated Population (1950)	Land Area		Forest Area				
		Total (Political)	Less Desert	Total	Per Cent of Land Area (Less desert)	Productive and Accessible		
						Area	Hectares per Capita	Per Cent of Land Area (Less desert)
	In thousands	*Thousands of hectares*				*Thousands of hectares*		
Tunisia	3,470	15,583	7,000	900	12.9	(900)	(0.26)	(12.9)
Algeria	8,750	220,486	26,265	3,070	11.7	1,635	0.19	6
French Morocco	8,410	39,080	27,000	3,520	13.0	2,450	0.29	9
Spanish Morocco with Tangier	1,190	2,095	2,000	400	20.0	(380)	(0.32)	(19)

( ) Estimated.

began to show good results during the years 1914-39. In all three countries, however, World War II brought a marked increase in intensive cutting for fuel wood, pit props, industrial wood, etc. In sum, man's action
has been and still is very harmful to the Barbary forests.

PRESENT STATE OF THE FORESTS. Data for the forest areas of North
Africa are presented in Table 15–II. The relative areas occupied by
different species are as follows, in percentages of the total forest area.

> Softwoods: 36 (*Pinus halepensis*, 15; *Callitris quadrivalvis*, 11; *Juniperus*
> sp., 7; *Cedrus* and others, 2).
> Hardwoods: 64 (*Quercus ilex*, 26; *Q. suber*, 11; species characteristic of
> maquis, 16; *Argania sideroxylon*, 9; others, 2).

In the productive forests the ratios are: softwoods, 31 per cent; hardwoods, 63; mixed, 6.

In Tunisia all lands subject to forestry control are the inalienable property of the state. Nevertheless some forest areas are leased to private
owners and to religious foundations. In Algeria 77 per cent of the forests
belong to the state, 6 per cent to the communes, and 15 per cent to private
owners. In Morocco all forests belong to the state in principle, but in
practice 16 per cent of the total forest lands are operated as private
properties.

Well organized, the forestry administrations have accomplished a great
deal toward the development, conservation, and improvement of the
forests. The latter, however, are everywhere subject to various rights of
use by the people, which interfere with measures designed to protect the
soil and restore the stands.

FOREST POLICIES. While most of the rivers of Morocco and Tunisia are
nontorrential, with basins well protected by forest cover, in Algeria many
streams have dangerous floods owing to their steeply sloping watersheds,
where vast clearings have caused bad soil erosion. Here corrective works
are being carried on actively, especially by the "banquette" system (the
equivalent of Italian *gradoni*). Little is being done in the way of reforestation. The major effort is directed toward the planting of fruit trees (figs,
almonds, etc.), which contribute much to the stability and well-being of
the population.

A number of reforestation projects, however, have been carried out
with good results in connection with the fixation of dunes near Mogador
in Morocco, and near Bizerte, Tabarka, and Cape Bon in Tunisia. Some
commercial plantations of eucalyptus and acacias have been established
north of Mamora (Morocco), where they cover 7,000 hectares, and also
elsewhere.

FOREST PRODUCTION AND NEEDS. The forests of Barbary were severely
exploited during World War II and today the annual cut exceeds the
annual increment, which is very low (for Algeria and Morocco, 0.5 cubic

meter per hectare). Table 15–III shows recent fellings and imports. The imports consist mostly of softwoods for millwork, packing, and box making. Exports are negligible from all countries but Algeria, and, even there, are very low (*ca.* 50,000 cubic meters per annum). The only strictly wood products exported are the burls of the sandarac tree (*Callitris quadrivalvis*) and brier (*Erica*) stumps for the manufacturing of pipes. Certain by-products, especially cork and tannin, are also profitable. Cork production exceeds 50,000 tons per year. The cambium layer of *Quercus suber* (as well as the barks of *Q. ilex* and of *Pinus halepensis*) is rich in tannin; widely used locally, it is also exported to some extent. Likewise rich in tannin is the wood of the tizra, or *Rhus pentaphylla*, which, although merely a bush, serves very well for soil protection.

TABLE 15–III

TUNISIA, ALGERIA, FRENCH MOROCCO:
FELLINGS, 1951; IMPORTS OF FOREST PRODUCTS, 1951-1952

Country	Fellings in 1951		Average Annual Imports 1951-52 (Thousand cubic meters)
	Thousand Cubic Meters	Cubic Meters per Hectare of Productive and Accessible Forest	
Tunisia	23	0.026	150
Algeria	778	0.48	570
French Morocco	830	0.34	270

In the past all of these materials have been dangerously overexploited. Now the tendency is to regulate their exploitation and at the same time to help meet the demands with industrial plantings (e.g., Australian acacias and *Coulteria tinctoria* H. B. & K.).

Sandarac, a kind of resin, is obtained by tapping the sandarac tree (*Callitris quadrivalvis*); although not produced in any great quantity, it is used in the varnish industry. Gum arabic, collected in the Sahara only, is a spontaneous secretion of several acacias that grow there and in tropical Africa.

Besides the fodder produced by the forests (grass and acorns), which feeds enormous herds of livestock, *Argania sideroxylon* plays an important role in the indigenous economy of southwest Morocco; its fruits give oil, its leaves a browse pasture, and its wood a highly prized charcoal. Although the alfa grass (*Stipa tenacissima*) of the high Algerian plateau is not strictly a forest product, it supplies a chemical pulp and paper mill in Algiers, and is exported in considerable quantities for the manufacture of paper.

FOREST AND WOOD INDUSTRIES. Although forest operations were somewhat modernized during World War II, antiquated methods both of

European and of indigenous origin persist, such as the fashioning by hand of ties and planks and the making of charcoal in clay stacks. There are no large mechanized sawmills, and the existing sawmills are of minor importance. Thus in Morocco there are ten, only one of which has a productive capacity exceeding 30,000 cubic meters per year. In the ports, however, a few small sawmills work with imported wood. There are few plants for the further processing of timber. Where this is done to meet local needs it is simply a question of handicraft work, which may be truly artistic, as shown in the carved wood of windows, doors, etc., of the Moroccan houses.

Barbary is a great consumer of packing material for use in the export of fruits and vegetables; but although a few well organized box-making factories (especially in Algeria) utilize local *Pinus halepensis,* most of the raw material is imported.

Match factories in Morocco use eucalyptus from the Rharb plantations, and in Algeria they use *Pinus halepensis.* A factory for the manufacture of wood for pencils has been installed near Meknès (Morocco) and uses cedar. An important chemical pulp factory, planned at Sidi Yahya du Rharb (Morocco), will make use of eucalyptus; another, working with alfa, is already in operation in Algiers. A plywood factory, which, however, makes use exclusively of imported okoumé, has been established recently in Casablanca.

APPENDIX

Cork

The finding of various household objects made of cork in the *nuraghe* (prehistoric buildings) of Sardinia and of bottle corks in the excavations of Pompeii shows that this substance was used by Mediterranean people in ancient times. Portugal exported cork to northern Europe in the fifteenth century, but it was not until the end of the seventeenth that bottle corks came into use in Spain and France. This led to the birth of the modern cork industry about 1760 with the establishment of the Spanish *taponerias* or cork factories, and by the nineteenth century many countries were buying the raw material, for a wide variety of purposes. Today not only bottle corks, but also linoleum, insulating materials, hats, soles for shoes, safety belts, floats, tips for cigarettes, and many other products are manufactured from cork.

To produce cork, the bark of *Quercus suber* is stripped periodically (without damage to the tree) at intervals of from 9 to 18 years. The first harvest yields a coarse cork, called "male" cork, and the later harvests a finer product called harvest or "female" cork.

No other species has been found that yields a cork like that of *Quercus suber.* Although the barks of certain hybrids of *Quercus cerris* in Turkey and Syria, of *Quercus variabilis* and *Quercus mongolica* of the Far East, of *Acer suberosum* Dum. and *Phellodendron amurense* of northeastern China, of *Ulmus carpinifolia* (which seems to have been utilized in Russia), and of *Kielmeyera coriacea*

Mart. in the Amazon Basin (Brazil) are somewhat similar, it is generally acknowledged that there is no substitute for the true cork. Since cork production is restricted to a rather narrow climatic zone, several countries have attempted to acclimatize the tree—notably the United States in California, and Russia in Crimea—but without sufficient success to endanger the cork-oak industry of the Mediterranean. In short, cork is a forest product of which the output is limited to the western Mediterranean, and, strictly speaking, to Portugal, Spain, France, Italy, Tunisia, Algeria, and Morocco.

In Portugal, the cork oak covers an area of 750,000 hectares and yields an annual crop of 165,000 tons. It is found in pure stands, or in association with *Q. ilex, Q. robur, Q. coccifera,* or *Pinus pinea.* The most productive region is the Alentejo, in the central part of the country south of the Tagus. The trees are found not only in genuine forests but also in *montados,* the remains of old forests. These *montados* are comparable to orchards; in them pigs graze upon herbs and acorns, and cereals are periodically cultivated. Plowing and the cleaning away of bushes here expose the soil to erosion, exhaust its fertility, and render its regeneration difficult. The Cork Institute (Estaçao de Experimentoçao Florestal do Sobreiro) is carrying on a useful educational program in this respect.

In Spain the area occupied by the cork oak (unfortunately diminishing) is about 300,000 hectares (40,000 hectares in Spanish Morocco), with a production of 77,000 tons (2,000 in Spanish Morocco). *Quercus suber* grows both in pure stands (Andalusia, Estramadura, and Catalonia) and to a small extent mixed with other oaks (*Q. lusitanica, Q. pyrenaica, Q. robur, Q. canariensis*) or *Olea europaea.* The most productive region is in the southwest (provinces of Cadiz, Seville, Huelva, Badajoz). In Spanish Morocco, the cork oak is found on the Rif and near Ceuta in open stands mixed with other oaks and sometimes with *Cedrus.*

In France the typical *Quercus suber* is found along the Mediterranean (Departments of Corsica, Eastern Pyrenees, Var) whereas *Quercus occidentalis* Gray, which differs very little from the typical species, is found in the Atlantic sector (Departments of the Landes and of Lot-et-Garonne). In Corsica *Quercus suber* occurs in open pure stands, and also mixed with *Q. ilex* or *Pinus pinaster,* and in the maquis. In Var, where fires are frequent, it is mixed with *Pinus pinaster* or with other oaks. In the Pyrenees it occurs mixed with *Q. ilex* and in the maquis as well as in pure planted stands on the sites of old vineyards that have been destroyed by disease. In the Landes *Quercus occidentalis* Gray is associated with *Arbutus unedo* (strawberry tree or madroña) and *Erica* sp., or with *Pinus pinaster;* this last association predominates in the Department of Lot-et-Garonne. Everywhere in the Atlantic sector, the cork oak is in regression. The total area occupied by the cork oaks in France (Corsica included) is about 50,000 hectares, with an annual production of 9,200 tons.

In Italy the area of cork oak is 50,000 hectares of pure stands and 39,000 hectares mixed in coppices with other oaks. About 20,000 tons of female cork and 15,000 of male cork are produced annually. The richest regions are Sardinia, with two thirds of the cork-oak forests; Tuscany; and Sicily. Where the trees occur in pure stands their regeneration and culture are far from satisfactory. They are the remains of great forest resources destroyed during the last century in the quest for tannin, wood for charcoal, and ashes for potash. Much of the Italian cork is of such fine texture that it can be cut into "cork paper," i.e., extremely thin sheets used, for example, to tip cigarettes.

In North Africa the cork oak occupies vast areas. From Bizerte to Algiers it grows between the northern slopes of the mountains and the coast. In Tunisia it covers 140,000 hectares, on 90,000 of which the stands are almost pure; on the remainder it is mixed with *Q. faginea* and *Pinus,* which reduces the actual area of the cork oak to 115,000 hectares; the annual production is 4,000 tons.

In Algeria the area covered by cork oak is estimated at 440,000 hectares, with a production of 35,000 tons. Here the cork trees form high forests with a good regeneration, especially where the *Q. suber* is in competition with *Q. faginea* (zéen oak).

In French Morocco, cork oak occupies 327,000 hectares and yields annually 4,000 tons of female cork and 10,000 of male cork. Here there are some remarkable stands, the best known of which is that of the Mamora near Rabat. The stands are often pure, but regeneration, especially in the semiarid zone, is often difficult.

TABLE 15–IV

MEDITERRANEAN COUNTRIES: CORK, AREAS AND PRODUCTION, *ca.* 1952

Country	Area Occupied by Cork Oak (Thousand hectares)	Production of Cork	
		Thousand Tons	Per Cent
Portugal	750	165	48.3
Spain	300	77	22.6
France	50	9	2.6
Italy	89	35	10.3
Tunisia	115	4	1.2
Algeria	440	35	10.3
French Morocco	327	14	4.1
Spanish Morocco	40	2	0.6
TOTAL	2,111	341	100.0

SELECTED REFERENCES

ARCANGELI, GIOVANNI. 1882. *Compendio della flora Italiana.* E. Loescher, Turin.

BARO, F. 1926. Bosquejo geográfico forestal de la Peninsula Iberica. *Actes du Ier Congrès International de Sylviculture,* vol. II, pp. 70-126. Institut International d'Agriculture, Rome.

BONNET, E., and BARRATTE, G. 1896. *Catalogue raisonné des plantes vasculaires de la Tunisie.* Imprimerie Nationale, Paris.

BORGES, J. FERREIRA. 1926. Monographie sur les forêts du Portugal. *Actes du Ier Congrès International de Sylviculture,* vol. II, pp. 57-69. Institut International d'Agriculture, Rome.

BOUDY, P. 1948. *Economie forestière nord-africaine.* 2 vols. Larose, Paris.

CARULLO, F. 1940. "I rimboschimenti della Tripolitania," *Rivista Forestale Italiana,* 2.

DURAND, E., and BARRATTE, G. *Florae Libycae prodromus.* Imprimerie Romet, Geneva.

FUNICIELLO, L. 1939. "Il problema forestale in Tripolitania," *Rivista Forestale Italiana,* 1.

GEORGOPULOS, A. 1950. *Die Forsteinrichtung in Griechenland: Rückblick und Ausblick.* Thessalonika.

GONZALES VASQUEZ, E. 1948. *Silvicultura.* Ciudad Universitaria, Madrid.

HALÁCSY, E. DE. 1900-1904. *Conspectus florae Graecae.* 3 vols. G. Engelman, Leipzig.

HESKE, F. 1951. "Die Waldwirtschaft in der Türkei," *Zeit. f. Weltforstwirt.,* 14:161-170.

HOLMBOE, JENS. 1914. "Studies on the vegetation of Cyprus," *Bergens Mus. Skrifter,* 1(2):1-344.

Italy. Istituto Centrale di Statistica. 1952. *Statistica forestale, 1950-51.* Rome.

JAHANDIEZ, E., and MAIRE, R. 1931-1941. *Catalogue des plantes du Maroc.* 4 vols. Imprimerie Minerva, Algiers.

LEONE, G. 1926. Il problema forestale della Tripolitania. *Actes du Ier Congrès International de Sylviculture,* vol. V, pp. 611-626. Institut International d'Agriculture, Rome.

MANZONI, G. 1940. "Flora forestale spontanea della Cirenaica ed esperimentazione specie esotiche," *Rivista Forestale Italiana,* 2.

MAUGINI, A. 1926. Aspetti del problema forestale nelle Colonie Libiche. *Actes du Ier Congrès International de Sylviculture,* vol. V, pp. 649-656. Institut International d'Agriculture, Rome.

MERINO, R. P. B. 1905-1909. *Flora descriptiva é illustrada de Galicia.* Tipografia Galaica, Santiago.

PHILIPPIS, A. DE. 1951. "Reboisement et recherche forestière dans l'Etat d'Israël," *Schweiz. Zeit. f. Forstw.,* 102:97-107.

POST, G. E. 1932. *Flora of Syria, Palestine, and Sinai.* (2d ed. rev. by J. E. Dinsmore). American Press, Beirut.

REHDER, ALFRED. 1940. *Manual of cultivated trees and shrubs hardy in North America.* The Macmillan Co., New York.

ROLLEY, J. 1948. "Forest conditions in Syria and Lebanon," *Unasylva,* 2:77-80.

SACCARDY, L. 1950. "Notions générales sur la lutte contre les erosions du sol en Algérie," *Terres et Eaux,* 9:51-61.

TCHIHATCHEFF, P. DE. 1860. *Asie Mineure, description physique, statistique et archéologique de cette contrée.* Imprimerie de J. Claye, Paris.

TERLIZZI, L. 1927. I boschi della Cirenaica. *Actes du Ier Congrès International de Sylviculture,* vol. V, pp. 627-648. Institut International d'Agriculture, Rome.

TSCHERMAK, L. 1951. "Pflanzengeographische Grundlagen der Forstwirtschaft in der Türkei," *Zeit. f. Weltforstwirt.,* 14:171-176.

United Nations. Food and Agriculture Organization. Division of Forestry and Forest Products. 1952. "Forestry in the Middle East," *Unasylva,* Sept., 104-123.

WILLKOMM, M., and LANGE, J. 1861-1880. *Prodromus florae Hispanicae.* 3 vols. E. Schweizerbart, Stuttgart.

16.   TROPICAL AFRICA

André M. A. Aubréville

There are two great types of African forest, just as there are two Africas: wet and dry. Wet Africa is largely covered by wet forests, the rain forests, which are sometimes also given the incorrect but convenient and rather widely used name of "equatorial forests." [1] These wet forests are by far the most important from the economic point of view. Dry Africa, outside of its deserts, is or has been covered by dry forests over considerable areas. These may be subdivided into many climatic, edaphic, and regional types. The variety of forest landscapes in arid and semiarid Africa is astonishing and contrasts with the uniformity of the wet forests, which cover all kinds of soils—whatever their nature—with a thick mantle. This chapter deals with the forests, both wet and dry, of the whole of Africa between the Sahara on the north and the Karoo plateau on the south.

The Rain Forests of the Atlantic Watershed
(Guinea-Equatorial Rain Forests)

GEOGRAPHICAL DISTRIBUTION. The rain forests of western and central Africa cover an immense tract, stretching across from Sierra Leone to Kenya and the high plateaus of Uganda. These vast "Guinea-Equatorial rain forests" may be divided into three chief masses: (1) the Guinea Forest, (2) the Nigerian Forest, and (3) the Equatorial Forest.

1. The *Guinea Forest* borders the Guinea Coast from Sierra Leone eastward to the plains of the Black Volta River in the Gold Coast, covering a small part of Sierra Leone and of French Guinea, almost the whole of Liberia, and most of the Ivory Coast and the Gold Coast. Its length is some 800 miles. It begins within a few yards of the sea shore and stretches in places more than 400 kilometers into the interior, only occasionally interrupted by soil-determined savannas. On the north it terminates abruptly at the beginning of the savannas and wooded savannas of the interior. Here the forest margin is sharply defined but extremely intricate, like lace work; in certain sectors it is hard to say whether there is more forest than savanna, or vice versa. Furthermore, outside the main forest mass but in a fairly wide marginal area within the zone of wooded savannas, the rivers and streams are bordered by gallery forests which vary in width

---

[1] See note on nomenclature, pp. 383-384, below.

from a few dozen to several hundred meters. Narrow extensions of the rain forest into the neighboring drier country, these gallery forests are composed chiefly of the same species as those found in the main forest mass.

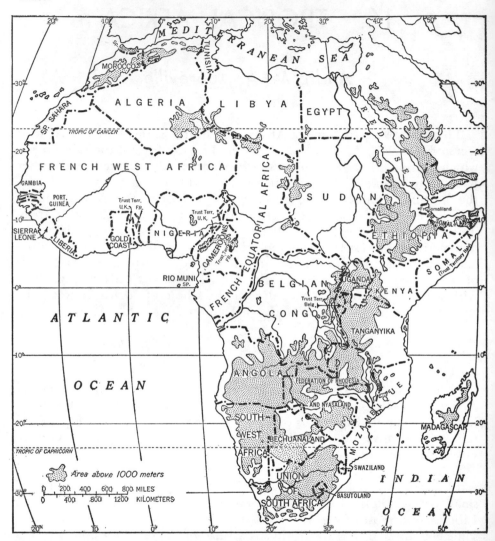

FIG. 37. Africa: general location map.

2. The *Nigerian Forest* is separated from the Guinea Forest by a wide gap that extends from the plains of the Black Volta in the Gold Coast to the Dahomey-Nigerian frontier. Here, in the coastal region of the Gold Coast, Togoland, and Dahomey, the forest gives place to wooded savannas, groves of *Elaeis guineensis* [2] (the oil palm), and cropland. This break is

[2] Sources for botanical nomenclature: Hutchinson (1927-36), Dalziel (1937), Gardner (1936). For full references see p. 384.

due in part to the relatively low rainfall characteristic of this coastal region, and in part to the presence since remote times of a dense, agricultural population, which has completely replaced the former forests with cultivated crops and palm groves. Only in the mountainous interior can rain forests still be found, and even these are broken by numerous coffee and cacao plantations.

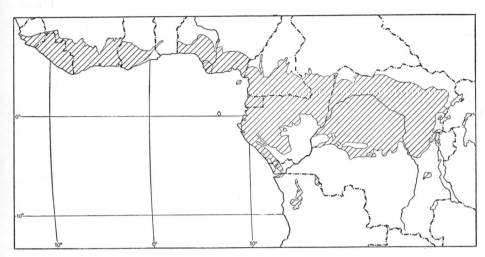

FIG. 38. Equatorial Africa: distribution of the Guinea-Equatorial rain forests (crosshatched).

The Nigerian Forest begins practically at the Dahomey-Nigerian frontier and extends over the whole of the Nigerian lowland on both sides of the Niger delta. In the mountains approaching the French Cameroons the forest narrows, its width hardly exceeding 120 kilometers.

The Guinea and Nigerian forest masses are nourished by the moisture-laden monsoon that blows over the warm waters of the Gulf of Guinea.

3. The great *Equatorial Forest* stretches for more than 2,400 kilometers from the Cameroons eastward into the interior of the continent. In the coastal regions it benefits from the periodic rains of the Atlantic monsoon, but it owes its extension into the heart of the continent to the equatorial rains which prevail in this part of Africa.

The Equatorial Forest covers southern Cameroons, Spanish Guinea, most of French Gabon, Middle Congo, Ubangi-Shari, and the whole central Congo basin in the Belgian Congo. Along the meridian of Léopoldville, however, the southern savannas advance to a point just short of the equator, reducing the width of the Equatorial Forest to little more than 320 kilometers, and dividing it essentially into a western section, which may be called the Cameroons-Gabon Forest, and an eastern section, the Congo Forest proper.

The northern margin of the Equatorial Forest is exceedingly tortuous and broken. On the west it extends roughly as far north as latitude 4° N., but farther east reaches its limit at about the third parallel. The eastern margin of the forest lies at mid-slope on the highlands bordering the great African rift valley, in which lie Lakes Albert, Edward, Kivu, and Tanganyika. High-mountain forests cover the crests of these ranges and in places adjoin the upper edge of the Congo Forest, but generally a strip of grassland, probably of human creation, intervenes between them.

East of the rift valley, on the high plateau of Uganda, isolated forests are found within a region of wooded savannas at altitudes above 1,000 meters. Resembling the Equatorial Forest both in general aspect and in species, they appear to have been united with it in ancient times. Indeed, it seems probable that much of the Uganda plateau (with the exception of the dry northern part) was formerly covered by the Equatorial Forest, which may well have reached the shores of Lake Victoria and the lower slopes of the Kenya highlands, giving way only northeast of Lake Victoria to special high-mountain formations.

The southern margin of the Equatorial Forest, like the northern, is extremely irregular. In the Belgian Congo it lies between the third and fourth parallels, but west of the Congo River, as we have seen, it retreats before the savannas as far as the equator itself. Farther west there are long southward salients, one of which follows the Mayumbé mountains almost to the Congo. South of that river, important outliers of the Equatorial Forest form a discontinuous band in northern Angola, paralleling the coast nearly to the twelfth parallel of south latitude.

South of Cape Lopez, in the Gabon, the Equatorial Forest seldom reaches the coast. Between the sea and the continuous forest mass of the interior there is a littoral zone of savannas, which broadens from north to south and is about 50 kilometers wide near Pointe Noire, in the French Middle Congo. Although these savannas are in part man-made, the relative lack of rainfall along this coast suggests that this area was never occupied by the true Equatorial Rain Forest, but rather by formations of bush or scrub, of which vestiges remain.

THE FOREST ZONE: PRIMARY AND SECONDARY FORESTS. The "forest zone" of the Guinea-Equatorial forests comprises: (1) virgin or primary forests, largely uninhabited and untouched by man; (2) secondary forests, including cleared forest patches which are cultivated on a short-term rotation and therefore have the aspect of brush; (3) permanently cultivated areas from which the forest has been cleared.

The term "secondary forest" is used for all types of forest and brush that grow up on the sites of forests cleared by the indigenous inhabitants. These people practice the well-known system of shifting cultivation on burnt-over clearings. They cut down the trees in the dry season, set fire to the fellings, and spread the ashes over the ground; then, without "cultivating" it in the strict sense, they set slips or seeds of food crops directly into the soil: manioc, banana, maize, yam, taro, and the like. Considerable areas within the forests have been cleared in order to provide these food crops with sunlight.

After two or three harvests in a site thus prepared, the soil is exhausted or else has been invaded by forest growths, and the cultivator moves on to clear other patches in the vicinity. Once abandoned, the ground is soon covered with a thicket of creepers, roots, seedlings, and vigorous herbaceous plants, all constituting a "secondary brush." Exposed to the full sunlight, this usually grows extremely fast, and within a year becomes a dense growth several meters high.

This brush is composed of species that differ from those of the forest that was cleared; usually they are small trees with soft wood and rapid growth. In a few years they develop into a jungle from 9 to 18 or more meters high, beneath which seedlings of species belonging to the former forest begin to spring up. Highly distinctive, these secondary forests are composed of common and widely distributed species that are sometimes found in pure stands, such as those of the parasol tree (*Musanga smithii*).

After a period of time, the farmers return to cultivate their former crop patches. These periods of abandonment vary from three to fifteen years, with an average of ten, depending on the density of the population and the fertility of the soil. When he returns to cultivate a former plot, the farmer has to clear a young brush only, which is easier to fell than the great trees of the primary forest.

The secondary brush growths are, in fact, forest fallow land. Today they cover enormous areas, and in some regions there is no primary forest left, except on marshy soils bordering the streams or in inaccessible mountains. The primary forests have commonly disappeared along the roads, for such lands are occupied as soon as the roads are opened. As a result, one can drive today for hours and days in an automobile across the forest zone without passing through a single true primary forest. Turn off the road, however, and go through the brush, perhaps for only a few hundred meters, and you will often enter virgin timber.

When the agriculturalists do not return at regular intervals—as might occur, for example, when a whole population leaves an area to settle elsewhere—the secondary forest may ultimately revert to primary forest, but this can happen only where seed trees of the latter have been left. Reconstitution of the primary forest is slow, moreover, for there are many intermediate stages between a recent secondary forest, with distinct physiognomic and floristic characteristics, and the virgin forest. What appears to be virgin forest may often, in fact, be a very old secondary forest. The appearance is the same: dense and entirely closed stands, some huge trees, enormous woody lianas, and bare or almost bare soil. One can, however, nearly always recognize a formerly cleared forest by studying its floristic composition. If most of the trees are of types that normally belong to the secondary formations, one can be certain that the forest is not truly virgin. Clusters of oil palms (*Elaeis guineensis*) are a sure sign of former human occupation, for the oil palm, a sun-loving species, is incapable of natural regeneration in the understory of the primary forest.

TABLE 16-I

TROPICAL AFRICA: LAND AND FOREST AREAS, 1950

Country	Land Area	Forest Area[a]		Wet Forests		Dry Forests		Reserved Forests		
		Total	Per Cent of Land Area	Zone	Forests	Zone	Forests	Total	Wet Forests	Dry Forests
	1,000,000 hectares			*1,000,000 hectares*						
French Guinea	25.00			1.00	0.25			0.54	0.20	0.34
Sierra Leone	7.25	0.26	35.9	0.50	0.26			0.24	0.24	
Liberia	9.52	5.52	58.0	9.44	5.52	0.08		2.77	2.00	0.77
Ivory Coast	30.96			14.00	7.00	16.96	11.05	1.82	1.50	0.32
Gold Coast	23.79	15.13	63.2	7.87	4.09	15.91	2.06	0.11	0.005	0.105
French Togoland	5.65	2.24	39.7	0.20	0.18					
Nigeria	96.58	33.08	34.2	15.56	4.10	80.10	28.99	7.33	2.20	5.13
French Cameroons	43.20	25.10	58.1	15.93	13.10	27.27	12.00	0.94	0.50	0.44
Spanish Guinea	2.50			2.50	2.00					
Gabon	27.50			20.00	15.00			0.02	0.02	
French Middle Congo	40.00			20.00	10.00			0.05	0.05	
Ubangi Shari	63.40			1.20	0.60			0.07	0.05	0.02
Belgian Congo	234.39			106.00	75.00	168.00	10.00			
Ruanda Urundi	2.45	0.31	12.7	0.30	0.19		0.12	0.19	0.19	
Cabinda	125.58	0.23	0.018	0.40	0.23					
Angola		31.90	25.3	2.00	1.90		30.00			
Uganda	20.79				0.65			1.64	0.65	0.98
Kenya	56.91	1.43	25.2		1.43[b]			1.43[b]	1.43[b]	
Tanganyika	88.76	42.31	47.7		1.58[c]		40.56	2.17[c]	0.81[c]	1.36

[a] For more recent figures see United Nations Food and Agriculture Organization, *World Forest Resources*, 1955, Rome.
[b] Includes 0.05 mangrove.
[c] Includes 0.08 mangrove.

AREAL EXTENT. This intermingling of lands left in forest and those used for agriculture in the forested zone, together with the lack of reliable maps, makes it difficult to estimate the extent of the actual forested areas. The crude figures by political divisions in Table 16–I suggest relative orders of magnitude. Here the data in columns 2 and 3 refer to the entire forest zone. Table 16–II shows that, of the total area of the Guinea-Equatorial forest zone (218,000,000 hectares), perhaps 139,000,000 hectares, or about 60 per cent, are in actual forest; the remainder are given over to indigenous agriculture of the type described above.

TABLE 16–II

GUINEA-EQUATORIAL RAIN FORESTS: APPROXIMATE AREAS IN MILLION HECTARES, 1950

	Forest Zone		Forests	
Guinea Forest [a]	33		17	
Nigerian Forest [b]	16		4	
Equatorial Forest	169		118	
Cameroons-Congo [c] ...		(63)		(43)
Central Congo [d]		(105)		(74)
Eastern mountains [e] ..		(1)		(1)
	218		139	

[a] Includes wet-forest areas (see Table 16–I) in French Guinea, Sierra Leone, Liberia, Ivory Coast, and Gold Coast.
[b] Includes wet-forest areas in French Togoland and Nigeria.
[c] Includes wet-forest areas in French Cameroons, Spanish Guinea, Gabon, French Middle Congo, Ubangi-Shari, Mayumbé (Belgian Congo), Cabinda, and Angola.
[d] Includes wet-forest areas in Belgian Congo, exclusive of Mayumbé and Ituri-Kivu.
[e] Includes wet-forest areas in Ituri-Kivu (Belgian Congo) and Ruanda-Urundi.

Only when forest reconnaissances have been carried out district by district will more accurate figures become available. Such prospecting is now in progress, and in some regions, notably the British colonies of Nigeria and the Gold Coast, is fairly well advanced. From Table 16–I it may be determined that only about 26 per cent of the forest zone in Nigeria and about 52 per cent in the Gold Coast are actually forested. In the less densely populated regions, such as Gabon and French Middle Congo, the corresponding ratios are, of course, higher.

ECOLOGICAL CHARACTERISTICS. The Guinea-Equatorial forests are aptly called "rain forests," for they lie in the zone of heavy precipitation that extends along the coast of the Gulf of Guinea and into the interior of equatorial Africa. The forest borders receive a minimum annual rainfall of 1,200 millimeters, but most of the forest zone receives more than 1,500 millimeters, and often more than 2,000 millimeters falls in the maritime regions of Liberia, the Ivory Coast, the Niger delta, and the Bas-Cameroun, and in the heart of the Congo Basin. But the finest forests are not necessarily those having the heaviest rainfall: magnificent stands are found where the mean annual rainfall is between 1,400 and 1,500 millimeters. A more significant limiting factor than the total annual rainfall is the length of the dry season.

The Guinea-Equatorial forest mass is, in fact, subject to three different rainfall regimes: the equatorial regime proper, marked by regular rainfall throughout the year, with minima about the time of the solstices, maxima about the time of the equinoxes, and no really dry month; the subequatorial regime, comprising two rainy seasons and two short dry seasons; and the "tropical" regime characterized by one long rainy season and one long dry season. All these regimes have one common characteristic: almost nowhere does the dry season, if there be one, last longer than three months. (Here a dry month is defined as one having a precipitation of less than 30 millimeters, since the forest vegetation shows clear signs of drought when less than 30 millimeters of rain fall during a month.)

Along the margins of the forest, notably in the southern part of its Mayumbé salient, the dry season may last four months; but such lack of rain is partially compensated by a permanent high humidity, frequent fogs in the dry season itself, and an often clouded sky, all of which reduce the saturation deficit.

The climate of the greater part of the Guinea-Equatorial forests is remarkably constant from the point of view of the regularity of rains, temperature, water-vapor pressure, and saturation deficit. The saturation deficit, an extremely important ecological factor, remains low (2 to 4 millimeters) all the year round, because the water-vapor pressure remains high (around 20 millimeters) and the temperature is not excessive and varies but little (24°-27° C). On the northern margins of the forests, however, the saturation deficit may reach 10 millimeters or more between the months of December and February, when a dry northeast wind, the *harmattan,* blows from the Sahara. Rain forest can survive where the mean monthly deficit does not exceed 9 millimeters during more than two consecutive months, but, where extreme dryness caused by the wind from the desert lasts longer than this, the rain forest gives way to dry forest formations.

Where the biological equilibrium between the forest and its environment—especially the length of the dry season and the saturation deficit—deviates from normal without, however, deviating so far that the rain forest can no longer survive, the floristic composition of the forest is modified. Thus, on the northern borders of the Guinea-Equatorial forests, the true rain forest is replaced by a subtype designated "deciduous forest" by the foresters of West Africa. In the dry season, when the true rain forest retains its foliage, the trees of the "deciduous forests" lose some of their leaves. Since the undergrowth remains evergreen, and the defoliation of the big trees of the high forest is neither complete nor simultaneous, these forests never present anything like the winter aspect of the deciduous forests of temperate lands. At a given time some trees (or even branches on an individual tree) may be completely leafless, while neighboring trees (or branches) may retain their old leaves, and still others may already be putting on new leaves.

Although the period of defoliation is usually brief, lasting hardly more than two to four weeks, this adaptation to the short dry season causes profound changes in the composition of the stands, so that the most characteristic species of the "deciduous forests" are quite different from those of the true rain forests. Among the more abundant of the former are samba or obeche (*Triplochiton scleroxylon*), limbo or afara (*Terminalia superba*), a number of big Sterculiaceae, bété (*Monsonia altissima*), and iroko (*Chlorophora excelsa*). The species especially characteristic of the rain forests, however, include azobé (*Lophira procera*), niangon (*Tarrietia utilis*), and avodiré (*Turraeanthus africana*).

Another important consequence of such climatic modifications may be increased instability of the deciduous forest, which can more easily be burned in the dry season, and is more slowly reconstituted after clearing or fire. This instability is even greater where there are unfavorable edaphic conditions—highly permeable sandy soils, for example, or shallow soils underlain by ferruginous hardpan.

PHYSIOGNOMIC CHARACTERISTICS. The rain forest is very dense, with a tightly closed canopy. Three stories may be distinguished. The upper story is discontinuous, composed of a relatively few gigantic and usually isolated trees with mighty crowns rising 40 to 45 meters above the ground. At a height of about 25 to 30 meters a continuous middle story of crowns pressed one against another gives the forest, as seen from an airplane, a characteristically undulating and unbroken appearance and hides the trunks from view. The lowest story is made up of small trees and bushes whose crowns fill almost all of the remaining space.

Not much light penetrates to the undergrowth through the higher levels of foliage, and the sun's rays seldom reach the ground. Nor can one, from the ground, see the crowns of the biggest trees, hidden as they are by those of the lower stories. Indeed, because of the dimness in the undergrowth and the clutter of small trees and lianas, one cannot see even the trunks of the largest trees, except from close at hand. Hardly ever does the rain forest offer those beautiful vistas of great columns that are presented by some of the mature forests of temperate lands. The ground, however, is bare, or garnished with a few sporadic herbaceous plants. It is easy enough to walk through the forest, but creepers frequently hinder rapid progress. The humidity is high, but the air seems fresh by contrast with that of sun-baked clearings unprotected by the forest screen. The secondary forests, on the other hand, are difficult to penetrate because of the density of the stems, which are often spiny, and the great quantity of lianas and herbaceous plants.

Lianas of all kinds also abound in the primary rain forest: filiform lianas, stretched like strings; huge woody lianas that curl around the tree trunks; ropelike lianas that hang to the ground from branches. Some of the lianas ramify out into the sunshine in the crowns of larger trees, joining the upper stems and branches one to another, and making the forest canopy yet more dense. Epiphytes are equally abundant, gripping tree trunks and branches. Palms are infrequent except for those of the genus *Raphia,* which grow in stands in marshy bottoms, and thorny creeping rattan palms. The latter proliferate on the banks of streams and climb to the highest tree tops with the help of leaves provided with hooks along their rachises.

In the mountains and in humid ravines there are sometimes clumps of beautiful arborescent ferns. Here and there one finds the strangler fig. Springing from seed lodged in the crook of treetop branches, it grows into a small epiphytic bush; its roots reach the ground by spiraling down around the trunk and then grow into powerful tentacles that anastomose and stifle the supporting tree. After the latter's death, the fig may live on independently as a large tree. Some trees are cauliflorous: first their flowers and then their fruits—some of which may be huge—are produced directly from the tree trunk itself.

The crowns of the trees seldom have any one characteristic shape. Some are wide and strongly sculptured; others, where compressed by neighboring crowns, may be ovoid and astonishingly narrow. Yet more remarkable are the tabular crowns composed of the verticils of horizontal branches (e.g., of *Terminalia superba* and *T. ivorensis*). Other crowns—notably Mimosaceae—spread out like parasols.

Many tree trunks are remarkably free of branches to great heights. Standing almost perfectly upright, they look like narrow cylinders and give the impression, when they are seen from a distance, that they are inordinately tall and thin, although their actual diameters may be large. Indeed, some trees, free of branches up to a great height, have cylindrical trunks that seem technologically perfect (*Entandrophragma utile, Mimusops heckelii, Terminalia superba*). Others have trunks of irregular cross section or are fluted at the base. Trees with really large diameters (i.e., more than 2 or 3 meters) are exceptional. Eighty centimeters at the larger end of the utilizable portion of the trunk is about the average diameter of the timber trees now being exploited.

The most remarkable physiognomic characteristic of many of the great trees of these forests is the buttress structure at their bases. Usually triangular, these buttresses serve as firm anchors for very tall trees that are otherwise attached to the soil by shallow root systems only. The buttresses rise several meters above the surface and sometimes stretch out 10 meters or more along the ground in the shape of winding flattened roots. Some of them are spectacular indeed. Their presence and in some cases their form characterize different species. Some species have no buttresses, but merely trunks thickened at the base, as in temperate-forest trees. The degree to which the buttresses are developed in individual trees depends on the depth of the soil. Sometimes parts of them are raised completely off the ground to form true aerial roots that let one see clear under the tree (*Tarrietia utilis,* many *Xylopia, Musanga smithii,* etc.). Other trees, yet more curious, are upheld by systems of adventitious curving and ramifying roots (which may be as thick as a man's arm), in such a way that each tree appears perched upon a network of intertwined roots. Among trees of this type are the mangroves (genus *Rhizophora*), found in marshy soil, and trees of genus *Uapaca,* which grow in dry soil.

Buttresses and aerial roots naturally make felling difficult. Cutting is commonly done above the buttress, and the woodsmen build a platform around the tree on which to work.

All types of bark are represented in the tropical rain forest: smooth, thin, thick, fissured, gnarled, prone to come off in sheets, and so forth. Some barks are conspicuously colored yellow or even bright red (*Distemonanthus benthamianus,* some of the *Copaifera* and *Xylopia*). The fragrance of certain barks is equally distinctive: the cedar smell of mahogany, *Guarea, Lovoa;* the garlic smell of *Scorodophloeus zenkeri.* Latex, appearing in a gashed bark, and dripping gum likewise give valuable clues to the forester, who can thereby recognize certain tree families (Moraceae, Sapotaceae, Apocynaceae, etc., with latex; Guttiferae and Hypericaceae, with dripping gum).

EDAPHIC TYPES. Where the ground is marshy, the rain forest takes on a special appearance and distinctive composition. Only a few tree species can adapt themselves to the special conditions of this environment, and the stands tend to be composed either of a single species or of a small number of species. In structure, the marsh forest is limited to a single story of timber trees of medium height and a ground cover of large herbaceous marsh plants. Some species of these stands have commercial value, as, for example, bahia or abura (*Mitragyna ciliata* Aubrev. & Pellegr., *M. stipulosa*) which yields a soft, homogeneous, fine-grained wood. The forest on the main floodplain of the Congo and along the banks of its chief tributaries contains a notable species, *Copaifera demeusei,* the most important source of copal in Africa. The marshy bottoms are also often occupied by palm thickets, composed of species of the genus *Raphia.*

At high altitudes the rain forest also changes its character. Toward 1,800 meters above sea level differences in appearance and floristic composition tend to be marked, and by 2,000 meters the change is usually complete. The trees in the high-mountain rain forest are not so tall as those at low and intermediate levels. They are more squat, their crowns are often vigorously developed, and their branches are bearded with heavy lichens. In some places the undergrowth is dense, in others, open, and elsewhere it is invaded by large herbaceous plants.

Another edaphic type is that of the forests on white sands near the coast. The stands here are lower and are composed primarily of certain specialized species. Along the seashore itself, in front of the real forest, there is often an arborescent fringe, forming an almost impenetrable bush of which the sides facing the ocean look as if they had been neatly trimmed off by the sea breeze. Local species such as *Manilkara lacera* and *Chrysobalanus ellipticus* predominate.

BIOLOGICAL CHARACTERISTICS. In the true rain forest the foliage is always green and never leafless. Even so, there is a vegetative rhythm in harmony with the climatic rhythm; there are periods when new leaves appear and periods when old leaves fall. Certain trees, such as azobé (*Lophira procera*) and okoumé (*Aucoumea klaineana*), at certain times of year present entirely red crowns—not the colored autumnal foliage of temperate countries, but the first appearance of the new foliation.

The rain-forest foliage is extremely varied in size, ranging from tiny leaflets to large and broad leaves. Frequently leaves or leaflets are acuminate—that is, the stalk is prolonged in a little tongue or ligule, from which the water drips after rain.

Efflorescence takes place to some extent all through the year, but there is a peak of flowering at the beginning of the dry season. Some species, however, flower in the middle of the rainy season and others during the dry season. Where there are two dry and two rainy seasons, certain species bloom twice during the year. Although the climate is remarkably constant in these countries, there are years of abundant and years of but indifferent fructification, and in some years certain trees do not bear fruit at all. The flowers seldom are of striking color: nearly always they form small greenish-white or yellowish-white blossoms hidden in the crowns, although there are exceptions, such as the Gabon tulip tree (*Spathodea campanulata*) with its great red flowers.

The forest trees generally grow much more slowly in diameter and in height than one might expect in view of the warm, humid climate. This is because the crowns, pressed too closely against one another, receive insufficient light, for growth is vigorous only where the crown is fully exposed to sunshine. Furthermore, total insolation is markedly reduced by frequently overcast skies. This high degree of cloudiness combined with a considerable humidity diminishes the amount of solar radiation received by the vegetation.

Natural regeneration of the tree species is, in general, subject to great hazards. Insects or fungi destroy many fruits and seeds on the ground. Arboreal animals eat the fleshy fruits in the crowns. Many seeds are oleaginous, become rancid, and hence quickly lose their ability to germinate. The seedlings of sun-loving species quickly perish in an undergrowth that is too sombre for them. Such species can regenerate only on open ground, in accidental or artificial clearings. The shade-loving seedlings that survive in the undergrowth also have difficulty in growing, for the struggle for light—which means for life—is severe in the forest. Constricted by their neighbors in the air and on the ground, the seedlings sprout slowly, and only when their shoots can disengage themselves from the grip of the surrounding vegetation does their growth become vigorous.

Seeds are disseminated by widely varied means. Many fruit kernels are scattered by animals. Elephants aid in the dissemination of ozouga (*Saccoglottis gabonensis*) and makoré (*Mimusops heckelii*). The fleshy seed-filled berries of certain species of the Moraceae family are eaten by birds; in this way the iroko (*Chlorophora excelsa*) has been dispersed over a considerable area in Africa. It is the same with the parasol palm. Many large trees have winged or tufted fruits or seeds, which the wind carries afar. All of these fruits are, in general, of sun-loving species, which do not regenerate except on open ground. The fruits of shade-loving species which regenerate easily in the undergrowth tend to be heavy and to fall at the foot of the mother tree. A true primary forest is chiefly composed of shade-loving species with such heavy seeds. The most notable example is ditschipi (*Macrolobium dewevrei*), which constitutes almost pure-stand forests over considerable areas in the Congo.

Owing to the humid atmosphere the rain forests cannot be set on fire. The trees, shrubs, and creepers found in them, however, are sensitive to fire. When the natives first cut down the forest in preparing land for cultivation they sometimes leave a few large trees standing—either trees with hard wood that are difficult to fell, or else trees with a light high foliage that does not interfere with the food crops planted underneath. When cultivators set fire to the fellings, the bases of the trees left standing may be reached by the flames and the bark calcined. These slight wounds may be enough to kill the trees within a few months. Even a creeping fire, confined to the ground cover of dead leaves, may kill off those trees and shrubs whose feet it merely touches.

BOTANICAL COMPOSITION. The rain forest is heterogenous, composed of a complex mixture of species. One hectare may contain 50 to 90 species of trees and large shrubs, exclusive of creepers and herbaceous plants. The composition varies greatly from place to place. A forest of some thousands of hectares may include 200 or 300 species of trees and large shrubs, and a complete inventory of a whole territory would add up to several hundred more. No such inventory has yet been made, and botanists are always finding new species and even new genera. This floristic complexity is the chief reason why the African rain forest has not as yet been much exploited. Neither commercially nor technically is it possible to offer on the market, simultaneously, hundreds of kinds of wood of which the qualities, and consequently the uses, are not only very different but also in most cases still imperfectly known.

This complexity of floristic composition, combined with the difficulty of viewing the tree crowns, makes identification of forest trees an arduous problem for a forester afoot. Luckily, most of the natives who live in the forest are skilled in recognizing the different species, each of which nearly always has its own name in each dialect. Thanks to good native prospectors and to botanical glossaries of vernacular terms with the corresponding scientific ones, Europeans can now undertake forest prospecting and inventories without undue difficulty.

DENDROLOGICAL CHARACTERISTICS. From a practical point of view, the rain forest is less complex than would appear from the long list of species that grow in it. Obviously these species are not all of equal importance in the "tree population." Only a few are represented by relatively large quantities of trees—not more than about 5 per cent of the total. Indeed, in terms of frequency of occurrence, one or two species may usually be considered dominant and only about a half dozen others as relatively abundant. A dozen species at most, which constitute one half or in some places three quarters of the entire "tree population," are what give a particular aspect to each forest. From the practical point of view, these are by far the most interesting species, since they alone can produce large volumes of timber. The recognition of these few dozen characteristic species is generally all that is needed to define a type of forest; hence the forests are fairly easy to describe.

The majority of the species are unevenly distributed. Abundant in one place, a particular species may be wholly absent a short distance away, then reappear in scattered form, then, farther off, again dominate the stand, only to disappear elsewhere, and so on. Trees of the same species are often grouped abundantly in belts, outside of which they are either scattered or wholly lacking. Over very large areas a species that is abundant in particular localities is usually represented by a relatively smaller total quantity of trees than one that is always found scattered. Such variations in frequency of occurrence greatly complicate the problem of exploitation where it is limited to a small number of species, as is the general practice today.

Another factor making for complexity and difficulty is the localization of each species within what are often small and scattered but distinctive geographical areas. This means that the lumberman operating in a particular district may actually find only a few of the species previously reported as present in the general region of his operations. Knowledge of the floristic nature of these districts is therefore important not only from the scientific but from the practical point of view.

The accompanying sketch maps show extensive tracts comprising various species—mahoganies, for example; but it should not be assumed that such species are abundant throughout the Guinea-Equatorial forests. The boundaries do not embrace vast homogeneous regions, but, rather, numerous small, isolated areas, some of which are fairly far apart. This fragmentation contrasts remarkably with the homogeneity both of the rain forest and of the environment as a whole.

DENSITY OF MERCHANTABLE TREES. The density of merchantable trees —that is to say, the number per unit of area—is generally low for any considerable tract of forest land; and such low densities apply, unfortunately, to the most valuable varieties of African trees. Thus the density

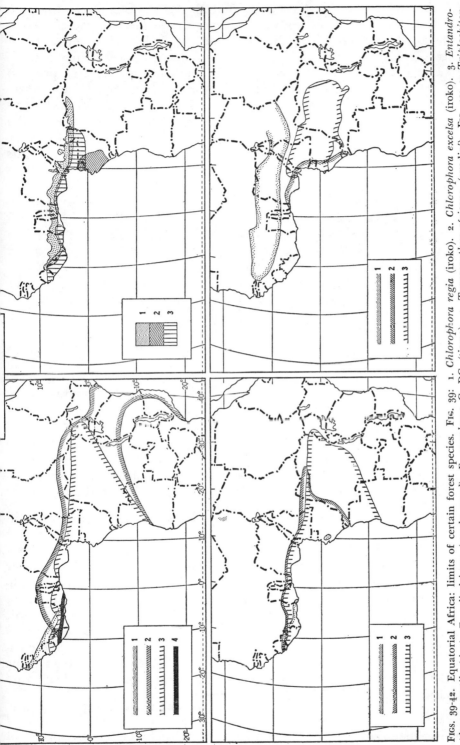

FIGS. 39-42. Equatorial Africa: limits of certain forest species. FIG. 39: 1. *Chlorophora regia* (iroko). 2. *Chlorophora excelsa* (iroko). 3. *Entandrophragma utile* (sipo). E. *cylindricum* (sapele wood), E. *angolense* C. DC. (tiama). 4. *Turraeanthus africana* (avodiré). FIG. 40: 1. *Triplochiton scleroxylon* (samba). 2. *Aucoumea klaineana* (okoumé). 3. *Lophira procera* (azobé). FIG. 41: 1. *Tarrietia utilis* (niangon). 2. *Terminalia superba* (limbo). 3. *Khaya ivorensis, K. anthotheca* (African mahogany). FIG. 42: 1. *Butyrospermum parkii* (karité). 2. *Gossweilerodendron balsamiferum* (agba, white tola). 3. *Guibourtia demeusei* (Harms) Léonard (copalier du Congo).

of the merchantable *Khaya* mahoganies in the Ivory Coast forests has been calculated as of the order of one tree per 10 hectares (a merchantable mahogany tree is one with a diameter, measured above the buttresses, of at least 80 centimeters). Among the many logging concerns in this territory, only one has reported one merchantable mahogany tree per two hectares, and areas that yield one such tree per five hectares are exceptional. All the other mahoganies (i.e., those of the genus *Entandrophragma,* sapelle or sipo) have equally low merchantable densities, of the order of one tree per 8 or 10 hectares. Niangon, a more social species, may reach a density of three or four trees per hectare, but, unhappily, its habitat is restricted. Similarly, avodiré, of which there are in some places as many as four or five trees per hectare, would be commercially important, were it not also restricted to a small area. In the colony of Gabon, okoumé is considered abundant; there are, indeed, small pure stands with 25 trees per hectare to fell, but the density for the whole forest area falls to two merchantable trees per 3 hectares. Some species, such as samba (or obeche), afara (or limbo), and ekki (or azobé) are more abundant.

Under good conditions, and in particular when a sawmill complements the cutting of the timber, an average of two, three, or even four trees can be felled per hectare. Since the general costs of forest operations, and especially the costs of the preparatory operations are roughly the same per hectare whatever may be the density of merchantable trees, it follows that the smaller the number of trees cut per hectare the higher must be the cost per ton of wood. Hence forest exploitation, where restricted to a few choice varieties, as is usual in the African forest, is inevitably costly. These high costs, moreover, necessitate detailed prospecting and planning. The forest operator cannot go forward blindly into the forest; he must direct his access roads toward the places where the trees to be felled are most numerous. These considerations go far toward explaining why the exploitation of the African rain forests differs essentially from that of the forests of temperate lands.

VOLUME OF COMMERCIAL TIMBER. The forest operator is interested in the volume of commercial timber that he can cut advantageously, and the number of merchantable trees disclosed by prospecting gives him a clue to this. Although the volume differs with individual trees, for different regions an average merchantable volume per tree may be established by species. Avodiré, for example, normally yields only about 4 cubic meters per tree, whereas makoré averages close to 30. Including all species, the average volume of wood per hectare in these rain forests may be estimated at 300 cubic meters, of which about 100 might be used commercially. Current yields, however, are hardly more than 10 to 15 cubic meters per hectare, and 30 cubic meters under the most favorable circumstances.

COMMERCIAL SPECIES. The early fame of the African forest was based on its "mahoganies." This commercial term includes certain species of the genera *Khaya* and *Entandrophragma,* large, fine forest trees, that grow either in groups or singly.

There are two species of mahogany of the genus *Khaya* (*K. ivorensis* and *K. anthotheca*) and four of the genus *Entandrophragma.* Two of the latter (*E. utile* and *E. cylindricum*) make beautiful cabinet woods; the other two (*E. angolense* C. DC. and *E. candollei*) are suitable for carpentry work. Besides these mahoganies, certain other red timbers are exported, some of them more beautiful than the mahoganies themselves— for example, makoré (*Mimusops heckelii*), which often has a moiréed appearance, and bossé (*Guarea cedrata*). Makoré, the most magnificent tree in the Guinea Forest, yields on the average 30 cubic meters of export timber, and a few giant specimens provide more than 80 cubic meters. Bossé, a smaller tree, has a fine-grained, cedar-scented, pale rose wood. *Khaya* and *Entandrophragma* mahoganies and bossé occur throughout the Guinea-Equatorial forests, but makoré is found only in the Guinea Forest.

Among other cabinet woods in common use, several deserve mention. Avodiré (*Turraeanthus africana*), a tree of average height, is found in commercial quantities only in a few small and scattered localities in the Guinea Forest. Its white and fairly soft wood is often beautifully moiréed and is much sought after for cabinet work; when not so figured, the wood is used for general carpentry. Iroko (*Chlorophora excelsa*) is one of the best-known species and yields one of the best woods of the whole African forest (a related species, *C. regia,* occurs only in the western part of the Guinea Forest). A very big tree, widely scattered through the forest but most frequent in old secondary bush, iroko produces a timber of high value, often employed for the same purposes as Asiatic teak and hence, formerly, though improperly, called "African teak." The wood is a pale brown or dark brown, which usually deepens with exposure to light.

Various species of the genus *Guibourtia* provide rose woods more or less deeply veined with red; small quantities of these are sold. Ebony is exported from the Cameroons and Equatorial Africa in small billets.

The veneer industry uses a number of African species. Easily the most in demand is okoumé (*Aucoumea klaineana*), found exclusively in Gabon and Spanish Guinea. It provides the largest tonnage of all timber exported from the West African Coast. Its pale pink wood can be peeled, dried, and easily applied. The timber is transported in rafts on the Gabon estuary to Libreville, and also down the Ogooué, the chief river of the Gabon territory, to Port Gentil. Since the supply is beginning to diminish and okoumé must now be cut far from the coast, other woods have been sought to take its place. Hence the veneer and the saw-timber industries are also using limbo or afara (*Terminalia superba*).

The limbo tree, tall, straight, and cylindrical, is often abundant in old secondary forests, for like the okoumé, it regenerates chiefly on the cleared land of abandoned crop sites. Its soft, pale yellow wood is also used for cabinet work. The heartwood is often veined with black, or is wholly brown-black in color, which either depreciates its value or makes it acceptable for cabinet work, according to the taste of the purchaser. The Belgian Congo and French Middle Congo are the great exporters of limbo, but the species is found in nearly all parts of the African rain forest.

Samba or obeche (*Triplochiton scleroxylon*), which has a soft white wood, is also used in the veneer industry, as well as for crates and boxes. The tree is tall, but the trunk, unhappily, is often misshapen. It is abundant in certain deciduous stands along the northern margins of the Guinea-Equatorial forests. For some years samba has been exported in large quantities from Nigeria, the Gold Coast, the Ivory Coast, and the Cameroons, but none is left in French Equatorial Africa.

Among other soft-wooded species sometimes used in the manufacture of veneers, the following may be mentioned: agba or white tola (*Gossweilerodendron balsamiferum*), which occurs in small stands from the forest of Mayumbé to southern Nigeria; bahia or abura (*Mitragyne ciliata* Aubrév. & Pellegr.), a tree of average height, with a soft gray wood useful for many purposes, found in pure stands in certain marshy forests; and illomba (*Pycnanthus kombo*), a small or medium-sized tree of the secondary forests, with a soft wood sometimes used as a substitute for okoumé. Equally suitable but less well known are certain leguminous trees—as yet not well identified—with pale pink wood similar in color to okoumé. In Gabon these are known under the name of andoung. Ozigo (*Dacryodes buettneri* [Engl.] Lam), with a medium-hard pink wood, is also suited to the same uses. So is olon (*Fagara heitzii* Aubrév. & Pellegr.), with a magnificent straw-yellow wood that is generally moiréed; very soft, it would be splendidly adapted for veneers, and even for cabinet work, were it more common. It seems limited to Gabon and the Lower Cameroons.

Other timber woods in regular commercial use are as follows:

Niangon (*Tarrietia utilis*), a tree of the second order of size, is fairly plentiful in places but occurs only in highly localized spots. The wood, although like mahogany in color, cannot be used in cabinet making because it contains a resin. It is, however, admirable for construction or carpentry work, perhaps all the more so because of its slight shrinkage and excellent behavior under humid conditions. Niangon is chiefly exported from the Ivory Coast.

Dibétou (*Lovoa trichilioides* Harms), a tall tree distributed throughout the African rain forests, belongs to the same family as the mahoganies (Meliaceae) and yields a medium-hard, walnut-colored wood that can be used for cabinet work.

Framiré or idigbo (*Terminalia ivorensis*), of the Guinea Forest, is an average-sized tree of old secondary stands. Its medium-hard, pale yellow wood is excellent for carpentry.

Bété (*Mansonia altissima*), likewise of the Guinea Forest and exported chiefly from the Gold Coast, is also well considered.

Movingui (*Distemonanthus benthamianus*) is a tall tree, striking because of its entirely red trunk. It is distributed throughout the African rain forests. Although its wood, medium hard and a beautiful yellow, is useful for many purposes, it is exported in small quantities only.

Several species of *Afzelia* from southern Nigeria and the Cameroons yield a medium-hard wood known as doussié, which has the same value and uses as iroko. At present little known, it is one of the best timbers of the African coast.

The primary forests contain many species with durable, resistant woods, which, up to the present, have found limited uses and, consequently, limited markets because of their hardness. The commonest, from the Ivory Coast to the Cameroons, is azobé (*Lophira procera*), a large tree which in some places in the Cameroons accounts for 20 per cent of the stands of full-grown trees. Its dark chocolate-colored wood is used for pit props, underwater and other heavy construction work, floors and stairways subject to heavy traffic, and the like. It is today exported in large quantities from the Cameroons. Kusia trees are giants of the wet forests, locally abundant in places; their hard wood is a beautiful yellow. Other hard-wooded trees, less well-known on the market, are douka and moabi in the Cameroons and southern Nigeria; denya (or oken), exported chiefly from the Gold Coast; tali, which provided the ordeal poison of old-time Africa; and niové, whose new-cut wood is orange colored.

Altogether, some forty species are exported to some degree, although only fifteen of these are subject to any considerable regular demand. All of them, however, constitute but a small part of the Guinea-Equatorial forests. They are listed below, with the commercial names commonly in use in the British and French-controlled territories. It should be added that the African rain forests are the natural habitat of a number of species of value because of their fruit, such as *Cola nitida,* which produces cola nuts, and several coffee trees.

PRINCIPAL COMMERCIAL SPECIES

MAHOGANIES AND SIMILAR WOODS

Khaya ivorensis, K. anthoteca	African Mahogany, Acajou
Entandrophragma utile	Sipo, Assié, Utile
Entandrophragma cylindricum	Sapele Wood, Aboudikro, Sapelli
Entandrophragma angolense C. DC.	Tiama, Gedunohor, Edinam
Entandrophragma candollei	Kosipo, Omu
Mimusops heckelii	Baku, Makoré
Guarea cedrata	Scented Guarea, Bossé

OTHER CABINET WOODS

Turraeanthus africana	Avodiré
Guibourtia pellegriniana Léonard, *G. demeusei* (Harms) Léonard, *G. tessmannii* (Harms) Léonard	Bubinga
Chlorophora excelsa, C. regia	Iroko
Millettia laurentii Willdem.	Wengé
Diospyros spp.	Ebony, Ebène

SOFT-WOODED TREES FOR VENEERS

Aucoumea klaineana	Okoumé
Terminilia superba	Limbo, Limba, Afrar, Ofram
Triplochiton scleroxylon	Samba, Obeche, Ayous, Wawa
Gossweilerodendron balsamiferum	Agba, Tola blanc, White Tola
Mitragyne ciliata, M. stipulosa	Bahia, Abura, Subaha
Pycnanthus kombo	Ilomba, Pycnanthus
Monopetalanthus heitzii	Andoung
Dacryodes buettneri	Ozigo
Fagara heitzii	Olon tendre
Poga oleosa	Ovoga, Poga

MEDIUM-HARD GENERAL TIMBER

Tarrietia utilis	Niangon, Cola Mahogany
Lovoa trichilioides	African Walnut, Dibétou
Terminalia ivorensis	Idigbo, Emeri, Framiré
Mansonia altissima	Mansonia, Bété
Distemonanthus benthamianus	Movingui, Ayan, Dahoma, Bonsandua
Afzelia pachyloba Harms	Ape, Doussié
Piptadenia africana	Ekhimi, Dabéma
Piptadenia leucocarpa Harms	Ossimiale

VERY HARD GENERAL TIMBER

Lophira procera	Ekki, Azobé
Sarcocephalus badi, S. trillesii, S. diderrichii	Bilinga, Badi, Opepe, Kusia
Mimusops africana Lecompte	Douka
Mimusops djave	Moabi
Cistanthera papaverifera	Kotibé, Otutu, Danta
Cylicodiscus gabunensis	Denya, Oken
Erythrophleum guineense	Tali
Staudtia gabonensis Warb.	Niové

ECONOMIC VALUE, PRODUCTION. The Guinea-Equatorial rain forests are the only African forests important in the world wood-products trade. Because of their vast extent, they constitute one of the largest timber reserves in the world. The rest of Africa, with its open forests and wooded savannas, has almost no surplus for export and the dry parts of Africa can hardly meet their own needs for wood. The dry forests in general consist of trees that are small indeed, compared with those in the rain forests, and are obviously not capable of producing great quantities of timber.

The forest map of Africa shows that the valuable forests are concentrated in certain great continuous masses, outside of which are few forests of real commercial value. Parts of the west coast and the Congo basin have a proportion of land under timber approaching 100 per cent, but elsewhere the proportion is extremely low. This low level, however, has not been evident up to now because the continent is still largely occupied by economically backward populations, whose per capita consumption of wood is small.

What do the African rain forests contain in the way of present and future wood resources? Table 16–III shows that exports of wood products for all the territories between the Ivory Coast and Angola amounted in 1950 to 1,037,000 metric tons of logs and 141,000 cubic meters of lumber and veneers, or the equivalent of about 1,230,000 metric tons of logs. These figures are impressive and bear witness to the progress achieved in the exploitation of the African forest, which was *terra incognita* no more than fifty years ago. But viewed in the light of the 139 million hectares of forest that are still untouched within a forest zone of some 220 million hectares, this production is small; and similarly, the forty-odd species currently exported are but a small proportion of the hundreds that constitute this forest. This enormous disproportion calls for an explanation.

TABLE 16–III

WESTERN AFRICA: EXPORTS OF LOGS, LUMBER, AND VENEER, 1947, 1950

	Logs		Lumber		Veneer	
	1947	1950	1947	1950	1947	1950
	1,000 metric tons		*1,000 cubic meters*			
Ivory Coast	48.7	107.0				
Gold Coast	150.0	235.0	14.5	58.2		
Nigeria	54.0	208.0	16.9	15.5	1.3	8.0
French Cameroons	36.3	67.2	24.7	9.9		
Spanish Guinea	62.8	72.7				
Gabon	125.9	226.2	8.0	6.4	5.9	7.0
French Middle Congo	6.2	19.7	5.6	3.9		1.0
Belgian Congo	67.0	76.0	38.6	27.6		1.0
Angola-Cabinda	16.0	25.0		2.2		
TOTAL	566.9	1,036.8	108.4	123.7	7.2	17.0

Considerable difficulties lie in the way of an adequate exploitation of the African forest. Africa in general, and especially that part of it covered by great forests, has a low population density. Local wood consumption is therefore small in relation to the forest resources—the more so because the warm climate does not oblige man to use large amounts of wood for shelter or heating. Furthermore, the continent has been opened up to economic development only recently, following European penetration. Ports, roads, railways, and other public utilities are few, industrialization is rudimentary and demands but little local wood. The European population amounts only to a few thousand persons in each territory and needs little wood for its own use in house construction and for furniture.

The markets for African woods are, therefore, almost wholly in Europe, South Africa, and America. Unhappily, however, the African forests do not include many of the conifers which furnish the great essential raw materials in the world trade in forest products. The African rain forests consist chiefly of hard and very hard woods, and the purposes for which these are needed are normally met by the production of the deciduous forests of the temperate countries themselves. The commercial demand, therefore, is almost wholly for particularly beautiful cabinet woods, for a few woods having special qualities suited to special purposes, and for woods for veneers. The development of the veneer industry has opened a fairly large market for certain species of soft-timbered trees, such as okoumé. But all of these demands are so limited that most of the forest species remain unused.

If African woods could be offered in great quantity at prices lower than those of equivalent woods of the temperate forests, the African forests would be exploited far more extensively. The fact is, however, that the prices are usually a little higher than those of the domestic products of the temperate countries. This is because African woods are burdened with freight charges that sometimes represent half of the total cost. Forest operations are also costly. How could it be otherwise in a heterogeneous forest where the operator takes out only a small number of trees and a small volume of timber per unit of area, and this after incurring high preliminary costs? The operator himself must prospect the forest and build his own roads. He must pay high wages to European top employees, and use costly motorized equipment. The cost of the standing timber is very low, and native labor is relatively inexpensive (though inefficient), but these factors hardly compensate for the difficulties.

The high prices of African woods in Europe and America account for the restriction of the demand to a few species of special value. But forest operations limited to such species leave the greater part of the trees untouched, and consequently raise production costs. Total African resources vastly exceed the demands of the European and American importers, but, except for certain woods with special uses, little use is made of them. The commercial and technical problem is to find outlets for African woods whose qualities, preparation, and uses are virtually unknown.

These woods might find an easier market as finished or semifinished products after processing in African mills than when offered as logs. The useful yield of logs is not more than about 50 per cent, and transportation consequently involves costly freight charges for waste. Since the end of World War II, therefore, important sawmill and veneer industries have been set up in Africa and use many woods not suited for export and also woods of the less well-known species. They will promote more efficient forest operations and lower production costs.

THE FUTURE OF THE AFRICAN RAIN FOREST. The rain forest today constitutes an unquestionably important timber reserve. Although it has barely been scratched by forest operations, clearings for agriculture may make the future maintenance of this reserve difficult. Throughout Africa population and agricultural acreage are growing, and deforestation is increasing with the search for new forest territories for the extension of industrial export crops like coffee, cocoa, oil palms, bananas, and pineapples.

Forest exploitation in general promotes deforestation of all sorts. When roads are built through a forest under exploitation, natives plant food crops all along them, and eventually the forest is replaced by crops and secondary brush. Hence the forest margin retreats from the sawmill, which may find difficulty in keeping itself supplied with wood. Stabilization of native agriculture in the forest regions would tend to promote the conservation of the forests, but such stabilization could come about only through a revolution in the native system of farming. The traditional practice of shifting cultivation on burnt-over land is still generally followed by the native populations. Hence there is a grave risk that the forests will disappear, to be replaced by valueless secondary brush or by savanna. Concerned with this threat, the African forest services are establishing permanent public forest reservations, managed with a view to continuous wood production. Table 16–I shows the areas of the forest reservations set up in certain territories. It is to be feared, however, that the rate at which this work can be carried out—for lack of personnel or for other reasons—is less than the speed of clearing. The danger, pressing where the population is dense, is less so where it is sparse, as in certain parts of Gabon and of the Belgian Congo.

The total area of the forest reservations in tropical Africa amounts to some 20 million hectares, including both rain forest and dry forest. For the rain forest alone, the area is some 10 million hectares. This is small in relation to the 139 million hectares of virgin forest. Unless it is increased greatly in the next ten to twenty years—before the whole of the forest zone is transformed into secondary brush—the forest resources of Africa will have become negligible.

A few governments, notably those of the Ivory Coast, the Gold Coast, and Nigeria, are particularly alive to the danger, and are striving vigorously to set up forest reservations. Equally serious efforts, however, are needed elsewhere.

Rain Forests of the Watershed of the Indian Ocean

Eastern Africa is much drier, as a whole, than western Africa and hence lacks great compact masses of dense evergreen or semi-evergreen forest like those found on the continent's Atlantic watershed. The dense forests of eastern Africa are concentrated in small patches along the coast where the rainfall is heaviest, and on the upper slopes of the higher mountains that intercept the trade winds.

In eastern Africa a series of mountain chains trending generally north–south succeed one another from Ethiopia to the cliffs of the Drakensberg in the Union of South Africa. On their eastern slopes and escarpments, exposed to the wet winds of the Indian Ocean, mountain forests grow—or used to grow before their destruction—above the cloud ceiling. Where the mountains are isolated, as are the great volcanos, Kenya, Kilimanjaro, and Meru, forests encircle bare or glacier-clad summits. The highest mountain forests differ both in appearance and composition from the forests of somewhat lower levels, which more closely resemble the rain forests of West Africa. On the coast, the dense forest is less lofty than the Guinea-Equatorial rain forest and very different in composition. It often is composed of species characteristic of the African dry forest. All in all, the dense forests of eastern Africa, both highland and lowland, rain forest and dry coastal, do not add up to any great area. The total is roughly 3,550,000 hectares, distributed as follows:

Kenya	1,400,000	hectares
Tanganyika	1,500,000	"
Mozambique	600,000	"
Nyasaland	50,000	"

Although most of the forests of Abyssinia lie in the Nile watershed, their geographical position and floristic affinities make it appropriate to consider them here along with the forests of the Indian Ocean watershed. Their area may well amount to 6 million hectares. The rain forests of Uganda also belong to the Nile basin, although their floristic affinity is definitely with the equatorial Congo region. They have an area of some 654,000 hectares.

The high-mountain forest formations present divergent types. At the lower levels, they resemble low-altitude rain forests with many species common to both. Between 1,800 and 2,000 meters there is a total change in floristic composition. New species appear, a few in almost pure stands; the large trees with tall, straight trunks so characteristic of the lowlands disappear, and the number of species diminishes.

One of the Lauraceae, *Ocotea usambarensis,* is characteristic of the East African rain forest. On the drier slopes, the forest comprises mixed localized species with deciduous leaves, such as *Brachylaena hutchinsii.* Coniferous forests at a higher elevation include a large tree, *Juniperus procera,* and various species of *Podocarpus,* generally mixed with broadleaf species. The juniper is of a dryish type and usually occurs at an altitude of 2,100 to 2,700 meters; its underbrush in some places is dense, composed of evergreen shrubs and herbaceous plants; the trees are festooned with moss and lichens; creepers and ferns are abundant. These stands of African juniper stretch from Eritrea and Abyssinia as far as Mount Rungwe, north of Lake Nyasa. Farther south, in Nyasaland, at elevations between 1,800 and 2,000 meters, pure stands of another conifer, *Widdringtonia whytei* (Mlanje cedar), cover a small area of 2,000 hectares.

Above these mountain forests, dense, pure bamboo forests of the species *Arundinaria alpina* are sometimes found. The trees, which grow 20 meters tall, may cover a zone on a mountain side several hundred meters in depth. In the mountains of Kenya some 200,000 hectares are in bamboo and some 800,000 hectares in coniferous forest.

From Abyssinia to Tanganyika an open prairie forest of *Brayera anthelmintica* occurs in places at altitudes of between 2,600 and 3,000 meters. It is from 10 to 12 meters high and without underbrush, the soil being covered with a continuous herbaceous vegetation, rich in Umbelliferae.

Many other types of scrub and bush with sclerophyllous leaves are found on relatively dry slopes. Above the high-mountain and bamboo forests, arborescent shrub formations rich in Ericaceae flourish up to and above 3,500 meters. They constitute a bush, here dense, there open, which in some places grows to a height of 18 meters and is remarkable for its great tree heaths. The shrubs are extremely branchy, with small, generally coriaceous leaves and ericoid, myrtoid, or cuppressoid limbs. The soil is often covered with a thick bed of moss, a sponge swollen by the rains. On the highest equatorial mountains, at altitudes between 3,000 meters and the upper limit of all forest vegetation, extraordinary clusters of giant *Senecio* and *Lobelia* may often be seen, towering over thick swards of *Achemilla,* amid continual cold fogs.

Mangroves cover considerable tracts in East Africa: in Kenya, 33,000 hectares; and in Tanganyika, 84,000 hectares.

ECOLOGICAL CHARACTERISTICS. The forests of the coastal zone from Kenya to Mozambique fall within a climatic region having an annual rainfall that ranges generally from 750 to 1,200 millimeters but exceeds 1,400 millimeters on the coast. There is either no dry season or a very short one: at most there may be three dry months with less than 30 millimeters of rain each. The full rainy season is also confined to three or four months. In the vicinity of Beira in Mozambique, however, it may last as long as six months. The water-vapor pressure is medium or high, with a small annual range; the saturation deficit is also small and varies little throughout the year.

Farther south, on the coast of Natal, the annual rainfall is of the order of 1,000 to 1,200 millimeters, the rains are well distributed through the year, there is no truly dry month, the season of heavy rains lasts from six to seven months, and the saturation deficit is slight, with little annual range. These humid conditions explain why, in spite of a mean annual temperature of but 20° C., a forest of equatorial type here crosses the Tropic of Capricorn and reaches as far south as the thirtieth parallel.

The mountain forests also have mild temperatures, dry seasons of less than three months, and rainy seasons of highly variable duration. Precipitation depends on the altitude and position of the site in relation to the prevailing winds. Certain mountain slopes clothed with rain forests receive more than two meters of rain a year; others, equally covered with forest, but of a dry type, receive less than one meter. The differences may be large even between two places close to one another.

ECONOMIC VALUE. Because of their small extent and because most of them are situated on high mountains, the rain forests of eastern Africa provide little wood for export overseas.

Kenya exports pencil slats of African pencil cedar (*Juniperus procera*). The log equivalent in 1950 of the wood exported was some 36,400 cubic meters out of a total log production of about 210,000 cubic meters (some 101,500 cubic meters of podo, 46,500 of cedar, 22,000 of cypress and pine from plantations, and 40,000 of broadleaf species), the whole sawn in local mills.

In 1950 Tanganyika exported about 24,000 cubic meters of logs out of a total log production of about 168,000 cubic meters. Eighty per cent of the exports consisted of *Podocarpus;* a little iroko and other timbers cut in the dry open forests were also exported.

Exports from Mozambique are of the order of 80,000 tons of lumber, which goes, chiefly in the form of railroad ties, to the neighboring countries of southern Africa.

The forests of Uganda, which belong floristically with the Guinea-Equatorial rain forests, produce some 20,000 tons of lumber, of which some 3,000 tons are exported to Europe via the railroad that runs 800 miles from the shores of Lake Victoria to the port of Mombasa on the Indian Ocean.

PRINCIPAL COMMERCIAL SPECIES

Dalbergia melanoxylon	African Blackwood
Khaya nyasica Stapf ex E. G. Baker	African Mahogany
Juniperus procera	African Pencil Cedar, Cedar
Ocotea usambarensis	East African Camphorwood, Camphor
Chlorophora excelsa	Mvule, Iroko
Olea chrysophylla	Olive
Podocarpus spp.	Podo

The Dry Forests

The tree and bush flora of the dry forests of Africa, although floristically heterogeneous, is much less complex than the flora of the rain forests. Many genera but few species are common to the floras of dry and of wet Africa, and the two floras are biologically different. Many genera are found exclusively in dry Africa.

Between the true rain forest and the thorn-bush steppes that border the deserts, divers types of dry forests succeed one another with such continuous transitions that it is often puzzling to know how to classify a specific forest landscape. Thus there is no sharp cleavage between dry open forest and savanna forest. Similarly, between dry open forest and dry dense forest there are numerous intermediate types. The floristic composition of the open forest and the dense forest may be largely the same if the open forest has been derived from a former dense forest by clearing, fire, or both. Elsewhere there may be an intricate mixture of different formations, soil and relief determining the presence of one or another. Thus, in certain regions with gently undulating relief, clumps of dry open forest may cover the relatively high, tabular, uneroded areas, while the slopes are covered with sparsely wooded or unwooded savanna and seem denuded, and the valley floors themselves exhibit dense gallery forests. In relatively humid areas cleared by cultivators, the invasion of earlier formations—wooded savannas, for example—by secondary thorny growths may produce mixtures.

Indeed, the vegetation complexes of dry Africa today differ considerably from those that developed there primitively under the sole influence of the natural environment. Man's intervention, by clearing and above all by fire, has upset the former biological equilibria.

Nearly all dry Africa burns during the dry season; few parcels of soil are exempt from the fires that sweep through the savannas and dry open forests, attack the edges of the dry dense forests, and make them retreat year after year. Some of the thornlands escape from the periodic fires, either because the grassy vegetation is discontinuous or thin, or, more important, because there is generally no agriculture in these arid regions and therefore little reason for starting fires; the fires that do occur are accidental.

The brush fires burn for the most part in the herbaceous vegetation. Fanned by the parching winds of the dry season, they pass rapidly over the soil, leaving it littered with ashes and carbonized fragments, but they seldom destroy the trees. Indeed, if the trees and bushes could not resist these short-lived fires they would have disappeared entirely long ago, for brush fires have been ravaging dry Africa for centuries. The persistence of the forest vegetation, despite the annual fires, is due to the protection afforded by thick and often corklike barks which are bad heat conductors, and to the ability of the woody species to regenerate by stump shoots and suckers. But the brush fires each year destroy the new woody growths not yet sufficiently protected by thick bark—namely, seedlings, shoots, and, when the flames rise to the crowns, branchlets that have been formed during the year. Under these conditions the trees often take defective shapes, with twisted, ill-formed trunks, and undeveloped, skeletal crowns. Such a degraded forest tends to open up and give place to savanna. The disastrous effect of the periodic brush fires is easily demonstrated where parcels of wooded savanna are protected against fire for a number of years. The forest cover slowly re-forms and then closes completely, killing the herbaceous plants beneath its shade. Unhappily, however, it is very difficult to control the brush fires. The custom of burning the savannas is deeply rooted in the native tradition, and surveillance of these vast areas is practically impossible except in a few special places.

Dry Africa, therefore, appears condemned to the degradation of its forests and their conversion into savannas, although the forest services in the dry regions are striving to reserve the finest stands and protect them against fire and all other damage.

THE DRY DENSE FORESTS. Dry dense forests, some deciduous, others evergreen, occupy only minor areas. Western Africa has been almost entirely stripped of them, although a few small tracts still remain, for example, in the Casamance basin, in French Guinea, and in Ubangi-Shari. In Kenya, Tanganyika, and Mozambique forests of this kind occur along the coasts where the rainfall is heaviest. On the high plateaus of southern Africa there are large masses of dry dense forest of three different types: (1) forests rich in certain species of the leguminous genera, *Brachystegia* and *Isoberlinia;* (2) dense sclerophyllous forests in the southern

Belgian Congo (here called *Mabwati*), northeastern Angola, and north-western Northern Rhodesia; and (3) low evergreen forests, composed chiefly of one of the Leguminosae, *Cryptosepalum pseudotaxus* E. G. Baker, a small tree with the shape and general appearance of a yew, which forms dark green masses known locally as "Livunda Forest."

THE DRY OPEN FORESTS. Because of their large extent, the dry open forests, which have succeeded the dry dense forests of former times, deserve somewhat fuller description. In southern Africa they cover large areas in Angola, Belgian Katanga, Tanganyika, the two Rhodesias, Nyasaland, Mozambique, and Bechuanaland. Here they are found chiefly on the high plateaus at altitudes of over 1,000 meters (the valleys are occupied by more xerophytic formations). They grow in a zone where the mean annual rainfall is between 650 and 1,300 millimeters and the dry season lasts from five to seven months.

Brachystegia and Isoberlinia Forests (Miombo Woodland). The most important of the dry open forests, these are characterized by the marked predominance of a few leguminous species, chiefly *Brachystegia* and *Isoberlinia*, with *Baikiea, Cryptosepalum,* and *Burkea* locally important, and less frequently Euphorbiaceae (*Uapaca*) and Dipterocarpaceae (*Monotes, Marquesia*). The finest stands average 15 to 18 meters in height, with, per hectare, some 60 to 120 trees of more than 30 centimeters in diameter. The cover is light. The grown trees sometimes keep their leaves during a large part of the dry season. The undergrowth is open, with partially deciduous leaves, though where brush fires burn every year there is no undergrowth but only a short savanna grass, the annual burning of which does not seriously damage the stands.

Although some twenty to thirty different species are found per hectare, from one to five of these, usually of the genera *Brachystegia* or *Isoberlinia,* are predominant. Many subtypes of this forest could be distinguished, depending on the presence of one or another of the two dominant species.

The forests characterized by the dominance of the leguminous *Baikiea plurijuga* Harms (Rhodesian Teak Forest, or Umgusu Forest) grow exclusively on the Kalahari sand formation in western Northern Rhodesia and northwestern Southern Rhodesia. Where not subjected to brush fires, they are dense, with a thick arborescent undergrowth; but otherwise they are open.

THE DRY OPEN FORESTS OF WESTERN AFRICA. In western Africa, on both sides of the equator, there are dry open forests comparable with those of southern Africa, but less extensive, much further degraded by fire, and much poorer in number of species. Two species of *Isoberlinia* and one of *Uapaca* account for the finest open forests in this part of Africa. The grown *Isoberlinia* stands average 15 meters in height and in some places have an understory, from 5 to 8 meters high, of clumps of *Uapaca* with semipersistent leaves. There is practically no undergrowth, and the soil is covered with a thin savanna grass. Other open forests, also composed chiefly of leguminous trees, might be grouped in many geographical and floristic subtypes. As in southern Africa, the dry season usually lasts five to six months. The annual rainfall is above 1,000 millimeters, the finest forests receiving from 1,300 to 1,500 millimeters.

THE WOODED SAVANNAS. The most extensive forest formations of dry western Africa, the wooded savannas, form low, open forests that differ greatly in appearance from the stands of well-grown trees of the dry open forests. The degree of coverage of trees and bushes and the height and thickness of the grasses are variable, so that many types of forest landscape may be distinguished. As in the open forests, certain species of trees or bushes are often clearly dominant.

In the semiarid parts of southern Africa almost pure stands of mopane (one of the Leguminosae: *Colophospermum mopane* [Kirk ex Bth.] Léonard) occupy considerable areas, usually in the depressions. Some of these stands are large and continuous, and others form narrow galleries along watercourses and around pools. On deep alluvial soils the trees may reach a height of 18 meters and form dense stands, but more often they are widely dispersed in the high-grass savanna and are mixed with acacias. Such mopane-wooded savannas are extensive in the valleys of the Limpopo and the Zambesi. They occur in regions of low annual rainfall (450 to 700 millimeters), where the dry season lasts six to seven months and the full rainy season does not in general exceed four months.

Two other types of savanna deserve mention: (*a*) savannas dotted with great termite mounds on which thickets of bushes, small trees, and lianas have established themselves (these are common in Uganda and Tanganyika); and (*b*) savannas that carry fine open stands of tall palms and are usually found on poorly drained plains. In Africa the palms are generally of the genus *Borassus;* in Madagascar, though of similar appearance, they are of the genus *Medemia.*

BUSH AND SCRUB. These formations of low, generally dense, and in some places almost impenetrable forest are frequent in East Africa, especially in central Tanganyika. Here they appear as thickets from 2 to 6 meters high, usually dense but sometimes open, composed of bushes and small trees that tend to be spiny, twisted, and exceedingly branchy, and that have deciduous leaves. A few taller trees, irregularly spaced, may dominate these thickets, and the ground may be covered with a herbaceous carpet of Acanthaceae. Lianas are common. In central Tanganyika, where this bush covers about 1,500,000 hectares, the annual rainfall averages 650 to 750 millimeters, with a six- to seven-month dry season and a rainy season of three to four months.

THORNLANDS. Where the climate is somewhat drier, forest formations do not altogether disappear, but consist mostly of thorny trees and shrubs, among which many species of acacia are represented. Some of these are fine trees that may reach 12 to 15 meters in height, with crowns typically outspread in parasols and a delicate foliage that casts little shade. In certain places these trees are spaced fairly far apart and form open forests on grassy steppe land. Elsewhere, the thorny shrubs draw close together in dense or even impenetrable thickets. More frequently, however, the formation is of savanna or of thorny steppe type. The drier the climate becomes, the more open become the thorny steppes, and, as true desert is approached, the shrub stands become extremely scattered.

THE ECONOMIC VALUE OF THE DRY FORESTS. Only occasionally in the finest open forests and in the gallery forests can trunks of suitable shape and quality for export be found. The dry forests are cut almost exclusively to meet local needs, and their wood supply is important wherever a large quantity of fuel wood is needed, as, for example, for locomotives or for the stationary engines that supply power for small local industries. All saw wood produced is usually consumed locally, but in Mozambique there is a fairly large export of railroad ties to the neighboring provinces of the Union of South Africa.

To appraise the usefulness of these forests other factors besides wood production must also be taken into account. Certain trees are important in the lives of the native populations because of their fruit: the karité (*Butyrospermum parkii*) of West Africa, for example, has a fruit with an oily kernel which provides the chief source of fat for the population (the surplus is exported either as kernels, or in the form of a firm, fatty substance known as "karité butter"). Other trees and shrubs are valued for their kapok (the *Bombax*), their gum (Senegal acacia), or their copal (copal trees of the coastal forests and bush). Certain regions covered by wooded savannas or savannas with thorny clumps are essentially pastoral, and their trees and bushes provide important forage for herds in the dry season.

Perhaps the most important function of these dry forests, which have only a limited direct economic value, is to preserve the environment of dry Africa from a deterioration that would aggravate the effects of the severe climate. Indifferent producers of wood, the forests conserve and improve the soils—at least they do so where they are dense enough to play a protective role. When they disappear, they give place to savannas or steppes; and, after the annual fires have passed over these in the dry season, the soil lies bare and blackened, exposed to the intense heat of the day, to desiccation and wind erosion, and to water erosion by the violent rains of the wet season.

PRINCIPAL COMMERCIAL SPECIES OF LOCAL USE

SOUTH AND EAST AFRICA

Pterocarpus angolensis	Muninga, Mukua, Umbila
Baikiea plurijuga	Umgusu, Rhodesian Teak
Afzelia quanzensis, Erythrophleum guineense, Guibourtia	
coleosperma (Bth.) Léonard	African Mahogany, Mahogany Bean
Khaya nyasica	Mukusi

Khaya senegalensis	Caicedrat
Pterocarpus erinaceus Lam.	Vene
Afzelia africana	Lingué
Daniellia oliveri	Sandan

The Forests of Madagascar

In Madagascar, there are two principal types of forest, the Eastern and the Western.

1. The Eastern Forest, an evergreen rain forest of extraordinary floristic richness, forms a band extending along the whole eastern coast of the island for a distance of some 1,500 kilometers. At one time it stretched continuously from the coast to the eastern edge of the high plateaus that occupy the middle of the island, but today it has been cut into many separate blocks, except in the north, where its maximum width is between 115 and 130 kilometers.

2. The Western Forest, wholly different in composition and separated from the Eastern by the grass-covered central plateaus, is a dense forest of the dry type, with leaves that fall during the long dry season. Today it is no more than a series of isolated tracts, some large, some small.

There is also in southern Madagascar a dense thorny scrub, remarkable because of its big euphorbias and its multitude of extraordinary octopus-like trees of the Didieraceae family, with bottle- or spindle-shaped trunks. The climate of Madagascar, like the forests, shows a sharp contrast between east and west. The Eastern Forest, which has virtually no dry season, receives 2 to 3 meters of annual rainfall. The Western Forest has a dry season of five to seven months, with summer rains varying between 750 and 1,800 millimeters.

Madagascar's forests are cut chiefly to meet local needs. For export they do not provide more than a few hundred cubic meters annually of such luxury products as rosewoods (*Dalbergia* spp.) and ebony (*Diospyros* spp.). These are exported from Najunga on the west coast and from Tamatave on the east coast.

Today the Madagascan forests occupy an area that may be estimated roughly at not more than 6 million hectares. Formerly, the island was entirely forested, but the trees have now mostly disappeared, the victims of clearings and of fire. The Western Forest in particular is insecure. Where destroyed by clearing followed by fire, it either regenerates or is replaced directly by savanna, without the transitional stage of secondary brush characteristic of the African rain forests and of the Eastern Forest of the island.

A Note on Nomenclature

The African forests are still imperfectly known as regards their species, kinds of timber, and territorial distribution. Nor is the terminology relating to them well established. Each author has his own system of nomenclature, and confusion arises because the same words are often employed with different meanings: "savanna" and "steppe," for example, represent exclusively herbaceous formations for some authors, but for others stand for mixed formations of grasses and trees. It is important in a general survey of this kind to define clearly the terms designating the forest formations.

The terminology used in the present chapter for the most important forest formations is *physiognomic* and *ecological;* within each main division, the subtypes are designated geographically and botanically, often by names in local use. Every author prefers the terminology with which he is familiar, and can justify his preferences by good arguments. But his views are not often shared by others. Hence, while I have used my own nomenclature, I have taken care to define every term to enable the reader to compare it with terms used elsewhere. In designating types of forest, I have felt it preferable to employ terms already established, where these exist, for in the long run the names consecrated by usage will prevail rather than those not so consecrated, however logical may be the arguments in favor of the latter. Accepted terms are already established for the principal types of forest in Africa, since for several decades forest services have been developing in this continent and evolving nomenclatures. I have been guided by their usages in establishing my own terminology.

SOURCES FOR BOTANICAL NOMENCLATURE

DALZIEL, J. M. 1937. *The useful plants of West Tropical Africa.* Crown Agents for the Colonies, London.

GARDNER, H. M. 1936. *Trees and shrubs of Kenya Colony.* The Government Printer, Nairobi.

HUTCHINSON, JOHN, and DALZIEL, J. M. 1927-1936. *Flora of West Tropical Africa.* 2 vols. Crown Agents for the Colonies, London.

17. SOUTH AFRICA

Robert S. Adamson

CLIMATE—FORESTED AREA—SAVANNA AND TRUE FOREST. The Union of South Africa is, for the greater part of its area, a land marked by a strongly seasonal climate, with alternating wet and dry seasons, and also a land where the amount of rainfall is both variable and unreliable. Such conditions are adverse to the development of forest, and it is therefore not surprising that a large proportion of the country is naturally treeless and that forests of any kind are a small percentage of the total vegetation cover.

In statistical tables it is often stated that 3 per cent of the total area is forest land, but this figure is obtained by taking "forest" in a very wide sense and includes much that is actually covered by scrub or open savanna. True high forest is confined to small areas where there is a continuous supply of moisture and no prolonged dry season. At the present time true forest actually occupies about 600,000 hectares, or only about 0.5 per cent of a total area of 122,248,000 hectares, and is confined to parts of the coastal belt on the south and east coasts and to sheltered areas on seaward mountain slopes

While there is no evidence that within recent times there has ever been an extensive forest over the country, there is no doubt that the existing forest patches are but a small fraction of what existed prior to the occupation of the country. Ruthless exploitation and destruction by fire have taken a serious toll. As early as the close of the seventeenth century the government at the Cape had become alarmed by the rapid diminution in timber supplies and passed a law requiring, under penalty, that any felling must be accompanied by tree planting.

In South Africa tree vegetation is divisible into two classes, open savanna and true high forest. The former is by far the more extensive, covering much of the northern Transvaal and Natal and extending westward to the neighborhood of Kimberley and southward to the eastern Cape. Over most of this area the trees are deciduous hardwoods, generally of small size and of little value for timber. The majority belong to the Leguminosae. This savanna type of vegetation, a southward extension of that occupying large tracts in Central Africa, needs no elaboration here.

THE TRUE FOREST. True high forest in South Africa is of the evergreen hardwood type. It has been variously classified as Subtropical Forest, Temperate Rain Forest, and Laurel Forest. Though limited in total extent, the forests are by no means uniform, either in composition or in structure. All are marked by the lack of any clear dominance of species. The canopy is made up of a number of species of similar size and usually of uniform leaf form. Such features make the separation of the different kinds of forest somewhat difficult. Various schemes have been proposed, but no one seems wholly satisfactory. In general, three main types of forests may be distinguished, which are separated from one another by their relations to climate and by various elements of composition and structure. They are:

   a) *South-Coast and Montane Forests.* These forests are in sites with no pronounced dry season, no frost, and no great extremes of temperature.
   b) *Forests of the Southeastern Coastal Belt.* These exist in a warmer climate than do those of the first type, and one with a more distinct seasonal rainfall. They occupy sheltered slopes at lower altitudes than do the first group.
   c) *Forests of the Natal Coastal Strip.* These have a definite subtropical climate, with relatively high rainfall and no distinct dry season.

South-Coast and Montane Forests. The greatest extent of forest of this kind occurs in the coastal belt, between George on the west and Humansdorp on the east, with its center near Knysna. This is a region of uniformly distributed rainfall. Westward, forest patches occur in mountain ravines as far as the Cape Peninsula, and, to a very limited extent, northward on the west coast. Eastward and northward, patches are found on south- or east-facing mountain slopes of the eastern Cape Province and of the Drakensberg in Natal and the Transvaal.

These forests are evergreen, with a rather uniform leaf type. The leaves are small (about 3 by 1 inches) and almost without exception polished on the upper surface. Simple leaves predominate. The canopy is in two strata, but the upper one is discontinuous. This gives the forest a characteristically irregular outline when seen from without. The trees of the upper stratum may attain 100 to 150 feet in height. The main, or lower, stratum is about 50 to 80 feet high.

The actual composition varies considerably from place to place. The upper stratum is made up of *Podocarpus* [1] (4 species) and *Olea laurifolia,* for the most part, though many other species may be represented in it. There is a large variety of trees in the main canopy, among which *Ocotea bullata* (stinkwood), *Apodytes dimidiata* (white pear), and *Curtisia faginea* (assegai) are among the most important.

The double story of trees results in much reduction in light, and shrubs are confined to shade-tolerating species. Climbers, though not numerous in species, are of frequent occurrence. Epiphytes of small size are also frequent. The ground vegetation is shade-tolerant and largely composed of ferns.

---

[1] Sources for botanical nomenclature: Adamson and Salter (1950), Marloth (1913-15). For complete reference, see below, p. 390.

In the Knysna region the forests cover a plateau traversed by deep ravines. On the upper and steeper slopes, with good drainage, is the so-called "dry" forest, while the "wet" forest is found in the valleys. Between the distinct extremes of these two there are all stages of transition. In the "dry" forest *Podocarpus latifolia, P. falcata* R. Br., and *Olea laurifolia* are the prominent trees in the upper stratum, with a great variety in the main canopy. Below is a shrub layer in which *Trichocladus crinitus* is the most abundant species, especially under medium moisture conditions. Shrubs become much less abundant both in the drier sites and in the markedly moister ones. Ferns, together with shade-tolerating monocotyledons such as *Moraea iridioides* and *Schoenoxiphium* spp., cover the ground.

In the "wet" forest there is often less differentiation into tree strata. *Podocarpus* is wanting in the wettest parts. The most important trees are roi els (*Cunonia capensis*) and wit els (*Platylophus trifoliatus*). The shrub layer is absent or discontinuous, though locally *Plectranthus* spp. abound. In the wettest areas the tree fern *Hemitelia capensis* takes the place of the shrubs. The ground layer is mostly composed of ferns. Epiphytes, especially ferns, are often abundant.

The forests on the mountains west of the Knysna region are essentially similar, though the variety in species is less and the trees are smaller. On the eastern and northern mountains the forests show some differences both in species and in structure. The shrub layer is often wanting, but the ground layer is more varied and contains a number of hygrophilous species. Climbers are more abundant and more varied in species. Locally *Podocarpus henkelii* Stapf. forms almost pure stands, with no associated small trees or shrubs. In the wetter parts the tree fern *Cyathea dregei* is abundant and replaces *Hemitelia* of the south coast.

Widdringtonia Forests. Brief mention should also be made of the so-called forests of the Clanwilliam cedar (*Widdringtonia juniperoides*) on the Cedarberg Mountains about 100 miles north of Cape Town. Unique here in being pure stands, they are found in an area of a few square miles on a dissected plateau between 3,000 and 5,000 feet above sea level, and have been known since the earliest exploration of the country. *Widdringtonia juniperoides* forms groves or thickets rather than a true closed forest. Individual trees may attain a height of 50 to 60 feet and a diameter of 4 feet, though the majority are smaller. At the present time these *Widdringtonia* communities are a mere remnant of their one-time extent. Fire has been the chief agent in their destruction, and they are now almost wholly confined to rocky sites where burning is impeded. Some attempt has been made to extend the area by planting, but the trees are of slow growth. These communities almost certainly represent a stage in forest development which is prevented from further elaboration by the dryness of the climate.

Widdringtonia juniperoides is a local endemic species confined to this small area. Another local endemic species, *W. schwarzii*, forms open pure groves at about 3,000 feet elevation in mountain ravines a short distance inland from Knysna.

Forests of the Southeastern Coastal Belt. These forests occur at low altitudes in a climate characterized by summer rainfall and dry winters. They are for the most part confined to steep-sided river gorges and steep east- or south-facing slopes, where the effect of the dry season is somewhat mitigated. They form a rather varied group, with gradual transitions at higher altitudes to the first type, described above, and in the north to the Natal coastal type. In general features they are rather drier than the forests of the first group. The separation into strata is much less sharp, but there is the same absence of dominant species. The leaf form is much less uniform both in size and in texture. Leaves with a dull surface are frequent and compound leaves much more common. Deciduous or semideciduous trees are generally present and may account for an appreciable percentage of the canopy.

Among the more important trees mention may be made of *Podocarpus henkelii* Stapf., *Ptaeroxylon utile* (sneezewood), and *Xymalos monospora* (lemonwood). Shrubs are often very abundant, especially prominent being *Plumbago capensis* and *Tecomaria capensis*. Climbers, both woody and others, are often abundant. The ground layer is more varied and includes ferns, shade-loving grasses, Acanthaceae, and xeromorphic monocotyledons such as *Sansevieria*. In the drier parts, and especially near the coast, tree species of *Euphorbia*, especially *E. grandidens* Haw., may become abundant and, on very shallow soils, locally dominant.

In the northern part of the Cape Province and the southernmost part of Natal the Cape box (*Buxus macowani*) abounds and is even locally dominant on shallow limestone soils. Though a large shrub rather than a tree, it has a definite timber value.

Natal Coast Forests. These are found on the narrow low-lying coastal strip in Natal from the northern border southward to the neighborhood of Port Saint Johns. In all essentials of structure and composition these forests are a southward extension of the tropical forests of east-central Africa, and as such really belong to that section, but within the Union there is a progressive lessening in species variety and some simplification of structure. There are no dominant species, and great variety in leaf form, size, and texture exists. The canopy is usually bound together by a large number of climbers. Palms and large monocotyledons, such as *Strelitzia augusta*, are of frequent occurrence.

These forests have been much reduced in area by clearing for sugar plantations. Where adjacent to the plantations they tend to be further reduced owing to demands for fuel for the sugar mills. Forests which have been cut but not cleared rapidly become an impenetrable tangle of bushes bound together by climbers. Under such conditions the growth of tree seedlings is inhibited by competition and the reduction of light.

PRESENT ECONOMIC USES OF THE FORESTS. As mentioned earlier, the present extent of the forests of South Africa is much less than it once was. Ever since the arrival of settlers, exploitation of the forests has been under way, and burning, both accidental and deliberate, has also played a big part in their destruction, along with grazing and native cultivation.

The fact that much land which, without any doubt, at one time carried forest now has other and simpler types of vegetation is often quoted as showing that the forests are relics of past times when the climate was more favorable. While there is a considerable volume of evidence to show that the climate of the country as a whole is slowly tending to become drier, there is also evidence that forest regeneration can and does take place. The process, however, is a long one, occupying centuries, and under existing conditions is interrupted by the much more rapidly recurrent agencies of destruction. Further, areas of forest, especially in the west, often appear to be at or near the critical point for forest growth. If destroyed, regeneration can take place only under the most favorable conditions—along streams, for example. Eventually the forest might spread from these sites over the whole area, but in the meantime the less favored parts become occupied by less moisture-demanding types of vegetation.

Since the government, through its Forestry Department, took control of the indigenous forests in 1876, the unconsidered exploitation has been checked, though, owing to a variety of causes, economic and other, overfelling continued for many years. Apart from clearing, this overfelling, by opening the canopy, often admits a number of shrubs and climbers that form dense thickets in which tree regeneration is prevented for long periods. Since 1913, however, the Forestry Department has been pursuing a policy of conservation of what remains of the indigenous forests. Cutting has been much restricted and is aimed at an amount that is clearly not in excess of the annual increments. For example, the average annual production from the indigenous forests from 1913 to 1932 was 1,000,000 cubic feet, whereas in 1948-49 this was reduced to 226,000 cubic feet.

This direct conservation policy has been assisted to a small extent by certain experimental treatments, such as assisted regeneration of valuable species, and clearing of undergrowth. These have, however, been on a quite limited scale.

THE SUPPLY POSITION. While there can be no doubt that strict conservation is essential for the preservation of the small remaining amount of indigenous forest, the demand in the country for timber is steadily increasing. To meet the situation the Forestry Department has carried out a fairly extensive development of plantations. These plantations are almost wholly of exotic species, for the indigenous trees are slow growers and few are at all successful in the ordinary form of plantation. Further, they are hardwoods—even *Podocarpus* is hard and heavy as compared with most gymnosperms. The demand, however, is for softwoods, and therefore the plantations consist predominantly of softwoods. The most commonly planted species are *Pinus radiata, P. pinaster,* and *P.*

canariensis in the southwest, and *P. longifolia* Roxb., *P. patula* Schiede and Deppe, and *P. taeda* L. in Natal and the Transvaal. Hardwoods, especially species of *Eucalyptus,* are planted to a much lesser extent and are used especially for mine props, scaffold poles, etc.

In addition to strictly forest plantations, wattles (*Acacia mollissima* and others) are grown to a large extent in Natal and the eastern Transvaal, covering an area of some 500,000 acres, most of it privately owned. Wattles are grown primarily for their bark and bark extracts, which are used for tanning; the timber is used partly for mine props, partly as local fuel.

Excluding wattles, the forest plantations in 1948-49 yielded more than 28,000,000 cubic feet of timber, of which about two thirds was from government plantations. The total was about a third of the total consumption of the country: imports in 1950 exceeded 50,000,000 cubic feet. Since, however, many of the plantations were still immature, the yield has doubtless increased and should go further toward closing the gap between production and demand. In 1949-50 the government plantations yielded $2,415,000 (£930,000) in revenue. It may also be noted that the use of home-grown timber for pulp has commenced on a small scale.

PROGRAM, POLICY, AND RESEARCH. The area of plantations, especially of softwoods, is being steadily extended and the existing plantations are being maintained. The policy with regard to the indigenous forests at the moment is one of strict conservation. Financial considerations limit the development of any special schemes of management.

In the field of research long-term experiments are being carried out on the influence of plantations on water supplies in a region naturally almost treeless. This work is in progress at Jonkershoek near Stellenbosch in the winter-rainfall area and at Cathedral Peak in the Drakensberg in Natal in the summer-rainfall area. Research is also being undertaken on the growth requirements and timber qualities of a number of exotic trees. Problems of seasoning and utilization of various timbers are also being investigated.

SELECTED REFERENCES

ADAMSON, R. S. 1938. *The vegetation of South Africa.* British Empire Vegetation Committee, Royal Botanic Gardens, London.
———, and SALTER, T. M. 1950. *The flora of the Cape Peninsula.* Juta, Cape Town.
CRAIB, I. J. 1941. "South African wattle bark and wattle extract with special reference to the American market," *Jour. S. Afr. Forestry Ass.,* 6(71):71-88.
DE VILLIERS, P. C. 1951. Die ekonomiese onwikkeling van die bosbou-onderneming in Suid Afrika. Thesis (unpublished), University of Stellenbosch.
HUTCHINSON, J. 1946. *A botanist in southern Africa.* P. R. Gawthorn, London.
KING, N. L. 1941. "The exploitation of the indigenous forests of South Africa," *Jour. S. Afr. Forestry Ass.,* 6(26):26-48.
LAUGHTON, F. S. 1937. "The sylviculture of the indigenous forests of the Union of South Africa, with special reference to the forests of the Knysna region." *Union of S. Afr. Dept. Agri. and Forestry Sci. Bull. 157,* Forestry series, no. 7. Pretoria.
MARLOTH, R. 1913-1915. *The flora of South Africa.* Darter Bros., Capetown.

PHILLIPS, J. F. V. 1931. Forest-succession and ecology in the Knysna region. Union of S. Africa, Dept. of Agriculture, Div. of Botany. *Bot. Surv. S. Afr. Mem. 14.* The Government Printer, Pretoria.

Union of S. Africa. Dept. of Agriculture and Forestry. Annual Reports of the Department of Forestry. Pretoria.

18. THE UNION OF SOVIET SOCIALIST REPUBLICS

Raphael Zon

Area, Climate, and Vegetation

To understand the forest resources of the Union of Soviet Socialist Republics and their potentialities it is well to keep in mind a few essential facts regarding the physical and natural conditions of the country as a whole.

The U.S.S.R. occupies a major portion of northeastern Europe and of northern and central Asia. It extends in a direct line from west to east for more than 9,000 kilometers and from north to south for more than 4,500 kilometers. Its territory lies within those latitudes of the globe (40° N. to 70° N.) where land predominates over oceans, and it forms a huge land mass, which in its compactness has no equal anywhere in the world. It comprises about 22.3 million square kilometers, of which 5.1 million are in Europe and 17.2 million in Asia.[1]

Biogeographically, the U.S.S.R. lies in what is known as the holarctic realm, a region that includes the northern parts of the Old and New Worlds. Vegetationally the territory of the U.S.S.R. is divided from north to south into four broad zones, stretching practically without break from its western boundaries far across Europe and Asia: (1) tundra, (2) forest, (3) steppe, and (4) desert.

Since the character of the vegetation is primarily influenced by such factors of climate as temperature, precipitation, and wind, and only secondarily by soils, hydrography, and altitude, and to some extent by the interference of man, these vegetational zones reflect the climatic differences of this vast country. Nowhere is the relationship between climate and the character of the vegetation so marked as in the great east-European plain, which includes practically the whole of European Russia. This low-lying plain is an enormous expanse of land, extending from the Arctic Sea over 25 degrees of latitude (70° to 45°) and for nearly 2,500 kilometers in an east–west direction. It has no elevations high enough to affect the natural distribution of the vegetation. Mountains occur only on its rims: the Urals on its eastern borders and the Caucasus on the

[1] Dobrinin (1947):71-81. For complete references, see below, p. 419.

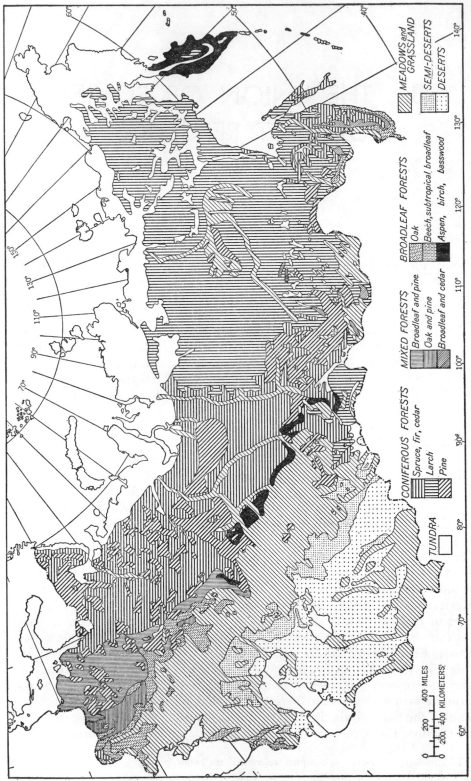

FIG. 43. U.S.S.R.: major forest regions. Based on map in Great Soviet Encyclopedia, Moscow, 1948.

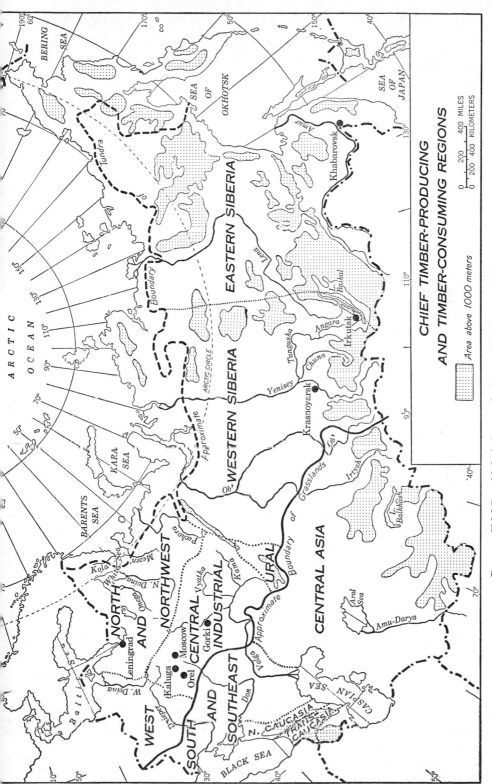

Fig. 44. U.S.S.R.: chief timber-producing and timber-consuming areas.

south. Thus, the distribution of the vegetation is a direct expression of the climate prevailing in the different parts of the plain.[2] East of the Urals and the Caspian Sea, while there is the same zonation of vegetation, it is broken up by the intrusion of mountain ranges such as the Altai, the Pamirs, the Tien Shan, and others.

The United States and Soviet Russia in many respects have similar physical, climatic, and vegetational characteristics, a geographic fact that has long been familiar. If you turn a map of either one at right angles to a map of the other, you will find a similar succession of climatic and vegetation zones. In the United States, if you start from the Atlantic Ocean and travel westward, you first encounter, after passing some marshy and swampy vegetation close to the shore, a zone of spruce (*Picea* spp.) and pine forests (*Pinus* spp.).[3] As you approach the Appalachian Mountains, you enter into a dense forest of oaks (*Quercus* spp.), maples (*Acer* spp.), birches (*Betula* spp.), and similar hardwoods. Farther west the hardwoods gradually thin out; grassland openings appear, and farther still begin the great treeless plains. At first the prairies are covered with tall grass, but as the climate becomes drier westward, the tall grass gives way to short grass, and the prairies to the Great Plains. These extend to the foothills of the Rockies, and between the Rockies and the Cascades and Sierras lie semideserts and deserts. The slopes and the tops of the mountains are covered with dense forests of pine, spruce, and fir (*Abies* spp.), and the forest becomes luxuriant on the western slopes, facing the Pacific Ocean.

In the U.S.S.R. the succession proceeds from north to south. Along the Arctic shoreline there is first a zone of swamp, known as tundra, where the ground is permanently frozen a few feet below the surface (permafrost). South of this lies a wide belt of spruce, fir, and pine—the taiga—and, south again, another forest belt of birch, oak, and maple. Yet farther south the forest gradually thins out and is succeeded by a flat grass country, the steppes, similar to our prairies. These become more arid as one proceeds, changing first into semideserts and then into true deserts, which reach to the foothills of mountains whose slopes and tops are covered with dense forests not unlike our forests of Douglas fir (*Pseudotsuga taxifolia*), spruce, and pine.

THE TUNDRA. In the U.S.S.R., the tundra extends along the entire Arctic coast from the Kola Peninsula to Bering Strait, and accounts for some 3.12 million square kilometers, or about 14 per cent of the entire continental territory. The more northerly parts of the tundra are a polar desert; but farther south mosses and lichens form a solid ground cover and forest trees appear, making a transition zone between the tundra and the forest.

Climatically the tundra is characterized by short and cold summers. The vegetative period, even in its southern part, is only 3½ months, and

---

[2] Heinrich (1943).

[3] Sources for botanical nomenclature regarding the U.S.S.R.: Komarov *et al.* (1939–), Köppen (1889).

the ground thaws out in summer to a depth of only about 150 to 200 centimeters. The total annual precipitation is about 400 millimeters in the west and as low as 150 millimeters in parts of Siberia (Yakutsk Arctic). Fifty to 60 per cent of it falls in summer and only 10 per cent in winter. The average temperature of the warmest month (July), even in the southern tundra, does not rise above 13°-14° C. Strong winds, as well as cloudiness, are frequent. The tundra, however, is not entirely without economic value. Mosses in summer and lichens in winter provide pasture for reindeer, which the thin snow cover does not prevent from grazing.

Within the last few decades the government has made strenuous efforts to push the cultivation of cereals, vegetables, grasses, and small fruit-bearing shrubs into the Arctic waste lands, and has apparently succeeded to some extent. Barley and some vegetables are now being grown there in the open.

The coast of the Arctic Sea is destined to play an important role in the development of the timber industry in northernmost European and Asiatic Russia, for a great industrial transformation has taken place in the U.S.S.R. within the Arctic Circle, with the mastery of the Northern Sea Route. This passage, dreamed of for centuries, has become a reality, and cargo ships now ply between Leningrad and the Vilkitski Straits without serious accidents.[4] As a result, the development of the Soviet Arctic has been remarkable. The population of this region has increased during the last ten or twenty years from practically nothing, save a few scattered nomads, to 3½ million people.[5] The town of Murmansk, for example, by the outbreak of World War II had attained a population of 150,000, and Igarka, on the lower Yenisei River, has grown in ten years to 25,000 and is now one of the world's largest timber centers.

THE FOREST ZONE. This is by far the largest of the vegetational zones, embracing within its boundaries 11.2 million square kilometers, or 50 per cent of the continental U.S.S.R. Not all of the forest zone, however, is solid forest. It includes, especially in western and northern European Russia and in western Siberia, vast swamps and low-lying, periodically inundated meadows, which in some areas cover from 40 to 70 per cent of the total surface. The northern part of the forest zone is considered the last remaining great reservoir of coniferous timber in the world, and is the center of one of the basic industries of the U.S.S.R.—that of timber.

Between the forests and the steppes there is a transitional subzone of forest alternating with steppeland, the *semisteppes* or *wooded steppes*.

THE STEPPE ZONE. The steppe, a region of fertile black soils (cher-nozem), is the bread basket of the U.S.S.R. Its total area is in the neigh-borhood of 3.5 million square kilometers, or about 16 per cent of the continental U.S.S.R. territory. The total annual precipitation ranges be-

---

[4] This may be accounted for in part by the fact that, according to Russian meteorologists, there has been a rise in the annual temperature in the Arctic during the last 20 years, making the Northern Sea Route safer for navigation.

[5] Hanson (1949):316-340.

tween 250 and 600 millimeters, increasing from east to west. Most of the precipitation falls in June and July. The summer, as a general rule, is hot, with strong desiccating southeasterly winds. The mean temperature for June is close to 24° C. Practically no virgin steppe is now left in European Russia or western Siberia; the steppe is nearly all in crops (chiefly wheat, corn, sugar beet, and sunflower).

THE DESERT ZONE. To the south of the steppes in southeastern European Russia there is a subzone of semideserts, which stretches thence in a more or less broad band to the foothills of the southwestern Altai and the borders of western China. The true deserts are found only in Central Asia, beginning at the eastern shore of the Caspian Sea and extending to the mountain ranges of the Tien Shan and the Dzungarian Altai. While the area of semidesert is estimated at only 0.9 million square kilometers, the true desert comprises some 2.1 million, of which about 0.7 million are moving sands. The semideserts and true deserts together account for about 13 per cent of the U.S.S.R. territory.[6]

The deserts present a serious problem. Aside from the fact that they constitute a huge land area which does not contribute food, timber, or other organic raw materials to the national economy, they are a constant threat to the richest agricultural lands in the U.S.S.R., in the Ukraine, central Russia, the Volga region, and northern Caucasia. Because of the exposure to the prevailing hot, dry, easterly and southeasterly winds that blow from the Kyzyl-Kum and Kara-Kum deserts, these farmlands are subject to periodic droughts, which have caused many calamitous famines in the past. In 1946 these regions suffered from a very severe drought, and in 1948 there were serious crop failures at many localities in the Volga basin. The Russians, therefore, are feverishly seeking reliable measures for resisting the droughts—such as the large-scale planting of shelter belts and forest barriers to temper the dry winds, the fixing of shifting sands by means of suitable vegetation, and the construction of irrigation works to bring millions of hectares of desert land into cultivation.

Only 70 per cent of the land area of the U.S.S.R. is thus sufficiently favored by climate and soils to grow productive plant crops. To bring even a small portion of the remaining 30 per cent into productivity would require extensive drainage systems in northeastern European Russia and western Siberia, large and costly irrigation works in Central Asia, and the enormous task of reclaiming millions of hectares of now barren wasteland by planting trees or seeding to grass.

Forest Wealth of the U.S.S.R. as a Whole

EXTENT AND CHARACTER OF THE FORESTS. There is no internationally accepted standard by which the forest areas of the different countries can

6 Shishkin (1947):182; Nestorov (1947):943.

be compared. Such comparison depends largely on the definition of what constitutes "forest lands." Some countries class an area as "forest land" only if it is permanently dedicated to timber growing and actually covered with forest growth of recognized economic value, although in different stages of maturity; others include land covered with arborescent vegetation of any description, including shrub. Most of the countries do not exclude from the category of "forest land" swamps, meadows, natural openings, large burns, or areas only sparsely covered with timber. Furthermore, the term "forest land" is often applied to all land that happens to be under the jurisdiction of a department of forestry, irrespective of its heterogeneous character. In the case of the U.S.S.R. there is a further complication—namely, that not all forests have been carefully surveyed or even explored. More than 410 million hectares have been covered by aerial surveys, but more than half of this area lies in Siberia, in the basins of the rivers Yenisei and Lena. In European Russia only the forests in the basins of the Mezen and the Pechora have been entirely covered by aerial surveys.

There is no private ownership of land in the U.S.S.R. The forests constitute a public domain known as the "National Forest Fund," administered by the Ministry of Forestry and Timber Industry. This ministry, created in 1947, has full responsibility for the surveying, mapping, exploiting, planting, protection, and general management of all the forests in the National Forest Fund. Revised estimates of the extent of the forests, their character, the amount of standing timber, and other related facts, are issued by the Ministry of Forestry.

The land area that comes within the jurisdiction of the Ministry amounts, roughly, to a grand total of some 1,068.6 million hectares,[7] subdivided thus:

Area covered with timber .... 628.3 million hectares, or 62 per cent.
Forest land of low productivity .... 440.3 million hectares, or 38 per cent.

[7] After World War II the productive forest area of the U.S.S.R. was increased by 16.1 million hectares, or about 2 per cent, through the addition of southern Sakhalin (formerly Japanese Karafuto), Karelia (eastern Finland), Latvia, Estonia, Lithuania, western Ukraine and western White Russia (formerly eastern Poland, Bessarabia, Bukovina, and Transcarpathian Ukraine).

Against these additions, however, must be placed the devastation of some 20 million hectares by the German invaders, when forest destruction in some places assumed a wholesale character, especially in the poorly forested Ukraine, in the Baltic republics, in the region south of Leningrad, and in all accessible forests of Orel, Tula, Smolensk, Kalinin, White Russia, and Karelia. In the southern semisteppe region, particularly between the Don and the Volga, 900,000 hectares of the forest plantations and 1,500 hectares of forest nurseries were put to the axe and torch. To combat the partisans, who were hiding in the forests, the Germans cut clean and burned lanes from 200 to 500 meters wide along all railroads and main thoroughfares. On the whole, therefore, the aggregate area of productive forests was not substantially changed in the U.S.S.R. after the war. The only probable advantage of the postwar period may be that some of the newly acquired forests are located in the westernmost part of European Russia. Because of their superior accessibility to water and rail transportation and proximity to industrial centers, these forests, when restored to their former productivity, should have a greater economic importance than similar forests in remote and inaccessible regions.

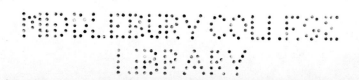

The "forest land of low productivity" is covered with slow-growing conifers, broken by vast swamps, meadows, burns, and other nonforested land, and therefore counts very little in timber production. Of the 628.3 million hectares covered with commercial timber, 145 million hectares (23 per cent) are in European Russia, and 483 million (77 per cent) in the Asiatic part of the country. The prevailing stands are conifers; they occupy about 492 million hectares or close to four fifths of the entire timber-covered area, and the broadleaf species (hardwoods) occupy the remainder (136 million hectares).[8] This ratio is even greater in European Russia, where conifers occupy about 88 per cent and hardwoods 12 per cent of the forest. Russia is thus a relatively poor hardwoods country.

By species, the timber-covered area is divided about as follows (in million hectares):

Conifers			Broadleaf Species		
	Larch	270		Birch	65
	Pine	100		Aspen	50
	Spruce	75		Oak	4.6
	Kedr (Cedar; Cembra Pine)	32		Beech	1.7
	Fir	15		Maple	1.7
		492		Basswood	1.5
				All others	11.5
					136.0

GRAND TOTAL 628

The principal commercial forest trees of the U.S.S.R. are pine, spruce, larch, birch, aspen, oak, and beech. Pine and spruce forests occur principally in northern European Russia. Larch predominates in Siberia, where, too, are found extensive birch and aspen forests. Other broadleaf species are located chiefly in the northeastern parts of the forest zone, in Siberia, and especially in the Far East of Siberia. Oak occurs largely in the central forest zone, where the forests merge into the steppe, in western European Russia (the Ukraine and White Russia), and in the south (Transcaucasia and Crimea). Beech is found in the Caucasus, the Crimea, and southwestern European Russia.

The FAO report on the 1953 World Forest Inventory credits the U.S.S.R. with 743 million hectares of timber-covered land, divided between 318 and 425 million hectares, respectively, of inaccessible forests and of accessible, economically exploitable forests. Of the latter only 350 million hectares are now in actual use.[9] These figures do not differ essentially from a Russian estimate of 1938 which placed the area of productive, accessible forests in the U.S.S.R. at 484 million hectares—137 million in European and 347 million in Asiatic Russia.[10] The distinction between the total forest area and the area of productive, accessible forests available for immediate exploitation should be constantly borne in mind in interpreting forest-area statistics.

[8] Koldanov (1951):1-18.
[9] United Nations. FAO (1955):60.
[10] *Bol'shaia* (1938):667.

On the basis of the area alone, if we accept the figure of one billion hectares (in round figures) as representing the total forest-land area of the U.S.S.R., and about four billion as that of the world, Russia may have some justification in claiming about a quarter of all the world's forests. Viewed, however, in the light of the total amount of standing timber, stand per hectare, geographic distribution of the forests, quality of the timber, annual yield per hectare, and large amounts of inaccessible, over-mature, and mature timber, the picture is less impressive. Still, the importance of the U.S.S.R. forests as the largest remaining source of coniferous timber in the world should not be minimized.

VOLUME OF TIMBER. The total amount of standing timber, according to the official U.S.S.R. statistics of the year 1951, is about 58.7 billion cubic meters, of which coniferous timber forms 85 per cent. Although, in the absence of extensive and accurate timber inventories, these figures can be regarded as rough approximations only,[11] if we accept the total forest area as around 628 million hectares (or 743 million, according to the FAO report), 58.7 billion cubic meters as the amount of standing timber in the entire forest area does not seem unreasonable.[12] Whether this be the total, or only 30,[13] 40, or 45 billion [14] cubic meters, as claimed by some on equally insufficient evidence, the quantity in any case is very large—larger than that of any other country (and indeed of several combined countries) still in the possession of large areas of coniferous forest.

The average annual growth is estimated at only 1 cubic meter per hectare. This is very low when compared with the annual growth of 5 to 6 cubic meters per hectare in Denmark, 3 to 4 cubic meters in prewar Germany, and 2.2 cubic meters in the United States. Yet, because of the vastness of the forest area, the total annual growth amounts to about 750 million cubic meters.[15] Since the annual cut is at present only around 400 to 450 million cubic meters, it would be theoretically possible for the U.S.S.R. almost to double its present timber output and still remain on a permanent self-sustaining basis, provided, of course, that the cuttings could be spread out sufficiently evenly over the entire territory.

QUALITY OF TIMBER. Growing for the most part in a harsh northern climate not favorable to plant growth, the forest trees of the U.S.S.R. are in general slow to develop, reaching at maturity (150-200 years) only 60 to 80 centimeters in diameter at breast height. The forest conditions are especially poor in the Asiatic part of the U.S.S.R. While the forest area

11 All present available statistics regarding area, stand, cut, and growth of the forests of the U.S.S.R. must be considered as approximations, open to all kinds of interpretations. Not until these forests are surveyed and administered on a more or less permanent basis will more reliable data become available.

12 The 1953 World Forest Inventory also gives 58.7 billion cubic meters as the volume of growing stock on all forests (50 billion for conifers, 8.7 billion for nonconifers) and gives 95 cubic meters as the amount of growing stock per hectare (FAO [1955]:88).

13 *International Yearbook* (1936).

14 Vasilev and Nevzorov (1948).

15 FAO (1955):92.

here is about three and a half times as large as that in the European U.S.S.R., the stand of timber is only a quarter again as large, and only in the Far East do some of the forests equal those of the European U.S.S.R. in quality. On the whole, moreover, the forests of the European U.S.S.R. are better and more accessible than those of either interior Siberia or the Far East. The wood of the slow-growing trees of the north is generally of a high technical quality; thus, the fine-grained wood of Russian spruce makes an exceptionally good pulpwood. However, the proportion of high-grade structural timber obtained from a given volume of trees is low compared with that obtained from the forests of western Europe. Nearly half of the timber cut in the U.S.S.R. is for fuel wood, whereas in western Europe structural timber constitutes 80 per cent and cordwood only 20 per cent of the volume cut. This difference may be partly due to the shorter height and poorer form of the trees and partly to less efficient utilization methods, but it is also due in a large measure to the great demand that exists for firewood, since wood is still one of the principal fuels for domestic use and for many industries in the U.S.S.R.

ACCESSIBILITY. Although many of the U.S.S.R. forests are mature or overmature, they cannot be opened for exploitation in the near future. This means a great economic loss, at least temporarily. Of the estimated 58.7 billion cubic meters of standing timber, only about 30 billion are available for exploitation, either immediately or in the near future. At present, only about 1 per cent of the total timber stand is being cut each year, a very low cut. This 1 per cent, however, is obtained, not from the entire timber-covered area, but from the most accessible forests, which, therefore, are being cut in excess, while, at the same time, overmature timber on millions of hectares in inaccessible localities remains unused, deteriorates, and rots on the stump. Furthermore, forest fires, often set by natives to improve hunting or wild berry crops, rage unchecked in the remote regions, and insects and diseases exact an enormous toll. Thus, it becomes evident that vastness of area alone is far from being a sufficient basis for appraising realistically the forest wealth and potentialities of the U.S.S.R.

UNEVEN DISTRIBUTION OF THE FORESTS. The most serious handicap with which the U.S.S.R. is confronted in realizing to the full the possibilities of her great forest expanse is the uneven geographic distribution of the forests, coupled with an inadequate system of water and rail transportation. While the thinly settled and industrially undeveloped northern and eastern parts of European Russia have a great surplus of timber, the densely settled and industrially developed central and southern regions either completely lack forests or have a great deficiency of them. Asiatic Russia, where 77 per cent of all the forests of the country are located, has only 19 per cent of the population. In European Russia, it is just the reverse. With 81 per cent of the population, European Russia has only 23 per cent of the forests.

This necessitates bringing timber from constantly longer distances from the north and east to the densely populated industrial centers. In 1913 the average distance from which structural timber and firewood were brought by rail from the north was 415 kilometers; in 1932 it was 680, and, in 1938, 1060 kilometers, a very long railroad haul for logs. The rivers which transect the northern wooded regions—the Onega, Northern Dvina, Mezen, Pechora—flow north and seem to have been created as if by natural design to float timber down to the Arctic for export abroad, while the timber destined for domestic consumption in the south has had to be carried for the most part by rail, a costly means of transport for roundwood. Only the Volga and to some extent the Dnieper, originating in wooded regions and flowing southward, offer the cheaper water transportation.

Forest Situation by Regions [16]

As regards natural transportation outlets and utilization possibilities, the forests of the U.S.S.R. lend themselves to a division into ten timber regions, of which the approximate boundaries are shown on Figure 44.[17] These, in turn, fall into two groups: mainly timber-producing regions and mainly timber-consuming regions.

TIMBER-PRODUCING REGIONS

NORTH EUROPEAN RUSSIA. This region includes the Karelian Soviet Republic and the provinces of Leningrad, Murmansk, Archangel, Vologda, Olonets, and Novgorod. It has an area of productive, accessible forests, largely pine and spruce, estimated before the war at some 60 million hectares, or more than 57 per cent of the total land area. The stand of mature timber is more than 5 billion cubic meters. The region is traversed by the rivers Pechora, Northern Dvina, Mezen, Onega, Kola, and others, which empty into the Arctic Sea or White Sea. In the past, enormous quantities of Russian timber products flowed through its ports to western Europe, but, as a result of a radical change in the timber-export policy of the U.S.S.R. during the last fifteen years, the importance of these ports as centers of export has been greatly diminished. Previously, the

16 See Zon and Sparhawk (1923):1:285-321, 476-487.

17 The figures presented in this section for the areas of the productive, accessible forests add up to about 490 million hectares, a quantity which approximates roughly that given by the FAO in 1953 (425 million hectares) as the area of the accessible forests in the U.S.S.R. and is almost identical with the area of the same category of forests (484 million hectares) given by the Russian foresters in 1938. The figures also tally closely when the forest areas are considered separately for the European and Asiatic parts of the country. Thus, for European Russia the estimated area of productive and accessible forests is 137 million hectares, as against a total by individual regions of about 145 million (the difference being due, probably, to some overlapping of boundaries); for Asiatic Russia the corresponding figures are 347 and 345 million, respectively. The total growing stock of close to 40 billion cubic meters for the several regions is the amount of standing timber in the productive, accessible forests only, and not that of the entire forest-covered land.

timber industry of the northern region had been geared for the greatest possible exports abroad at the expense of the domestic needs. The present policy is to curtail exports abroad to a minimum, and to increase the timber output but divert it into the interior of the country to feed the mills and factories of the industrialized, timber-hungry central and southern provinces.

WEST EUROPEAN RUSSIA. This region, which includes the Soviet republics of White Russia, Estonia, Latvia, and Lithuania, is credited with 12 million hectares of forest and with a total stand of timber estimated at 446 million cubic meters. The forests, owing to overcutting and war devastation, are depleted and cannot soon produce large quantities of timber, whether for wood-using industries within the region or for shipment out of it. Next to food production, however, timber is still the most important industry. Geographically the region is favorably located as regards markets and transportation facilities. It has ready access both to the industrial centers of Russia and to the countries to the west. Besides being served by the water systems of the Western Dvina and the Dnieper, it is traversed by a dense network of railroads. The west European region, therefore, should continue to be an important center of wood-using industries and to grow in importance in this respect as its forests are brought to their full productive capacity.

CENTRAL INDUSTRIAL OR INTERIOR REGION. This is a large region, and industrially the most important. The greatest home market for forest products, it includes not only such industrial centers as Moscow, Kaluga, Orel, and Tula, but also the densely forested districts of the upper and central Volga valley, such as Kalenin (Tver), Yaroslav, Kostroma, Kirov (Vyatka), and Gorki (Nizhni-Novgorod). It occupies an intermediate position between the mainly timber-producing and the mainly timber-consuming parts of Russia. Located in the center of European Russia, with a large number of streams and railroads radiating from it in all directions, the region has long been the principal industrial area, in which about one third of all the wood-processing plants in the U.S.S.R. have been concentrated. Probably about a quarter of all logs transported by water and railroads in the U.S.S.R. are brought to this region. The region comprises 23 million hectares of productive forests, located for the most part in the upper and central Volga valley, and has an estimated total volume of standing timber of 1.7 billion cubic meters.

THE URAL REGION.[18] This region, with 38 million hectares of productive forests and a stand of nearly 11 billion cubic meters of commercial timber, occupies a unique position among the timber regions of the country. The Urals are the center of a great metallurgical industry and during and since World War II have experienced a remarkable general industrial growth. The forests ensure an ample permanent supply of timber, both

[18] Klevtsov (1951):32-34.

for the existing industries and for further expansion, since the present timber output represents only half of the productive capacity of the forests. Large rivers, especially the Kama and certain of its tributaries, and a well-developed network of railroads provide facilities for transporting great quantities of timber to the lower Volga region, the South, and the Southeast.

NORTH CAUCASIA. This region lies on the north side of the Caucasus Mountains, roughly between the Black and Azov Seas on the west and the Caspian Sea on the east. Only the foothills and slopes of the mountains are timbered, the rest of north Caucasia being for the most part a flat steppe country, containing some of the richest agricultural land in the U.S.S.R. (the Kuban), densely populated and needing large quantities of forest products. Yet the forests of north Caucasia are undeveloped and supply timber in quantities far below their potential capacity. Aside from their commercial possibilities, however, they have a high watershed-protection value. Some 2.7 million hectares are wooded. Overmature, mature, and nearly mature stands occupy 682,000 hectares, comprising close to 203 million cubic meters. Although this represents less than 0.5 per cent of the entire stand of timber of the U.S.S.R., both because of its strategic hydrographic position in regulating stream flow and as a source of raw materials for rapidly growing industries on the surrounding treeless plains, its importance is out of proportion to its size.

Altitudinally, three forest zones are recognized: oak forests in the foothills at an elevation from 300 to 700 meters; beech forests at elevations from 700 to 1,500 meters; and fir forests at elevations from 1,200 to 2,200 meters. Hornbeam, ash, maple, elm, birch, aspen, and alder occur as admixtures. The north Caucasian forests are highly productive. Stands of the Caucasian fir (*Abies nordmanniana*), for instance, attain volumes of 1,000 cubic meters and more per hectare, while beech stands run to 400 cubic meters and more per hectare. Individual fir and spruce (*Picea orientalis*) trees attain, respectively, heights of 57 and 62 meters, diameters of 185 and 190 centimeters, and ages of 700 and 400 years. The annual cut of 2.5 million cubic meters amounts to only 30 per cent of the annual growth. The backwardness implied by this is due partly to the lack of systematic forest management, aggravated by the harm done to the forests in the war, partly to difficult logging terrain, and partly to the need for large-scale mechanization of all forest operations.

WESTERN SIBERIA. Siberia is divided by Lake Baikal into two almost equal parts, western and eastern. Western Siberia is credited with some 30 million hectares of productive forests, with a total stand of merchantable timber of about 3.5 billion and a possible annual cut of 16 million cubic meters.

In addition to the usual larch and fir, a forest tree typical of the Siberian forests is the Siberian "cedar." [19] This is not a true cedar ("kedr" in Rus-

[19] Tikhomirov (1949).

sian) but a five-needle pine (*Pinus cembra*), similar to the white pines of eastern and western North America. The wood is of high quality, suitable especially for pencils but also for veneer, furniture making, packing boxes, lumber, structural timber, and other industrial uses. There are close to 7 million hectares of exploitable cedar forests in Siberia, mostly in the provinces of Tomsk (2,400,000 hectares), Krasnoyarsk (1,220,000), and Irkutsk (1,150,000). Most of the cedar (87 per cent) is mature or over-mature and offers opportunities for the development of large operations. Recently, fairly extensive logging has been started in the cedar forests of the Tomsk province, and also in the Altai and to the south of Krasnoyarsk. Long before cedar was cut for logs, the "cedar nuts" (similar to the piñon nuts of the southwestern United States) were extensively used throughout Russia and formed a substantial source of income for the local population. One hectare of cedar forests may yield from 16 to 18 kilograms of nuts during an average seed year, and there are thus possibilities for developing a large nut industry.

EASTERN SIBERIA. Eastern Siberia has an area of productive forests of some 281 million hectares. Its total stand of merchantable timber is estimated at about 19 billion and the potential cut at 37 million cubic meters.

Here, the "Far East" (the Maritime Territory and the Khabarovsk region),[20] because of its vast resources and especially because of its variety of species, is destined to become one of the great future centers of hardwood raw materials. The exploitable broadleaf forests of the Far East constitute 24 per cent of all such forests in the U.S.S.R. and rate very high among the hardwood forests of the countries of the Pacific Ocean. Birch, maple, basswood, aspen, walnut (*Juglans* spp.), oak, elm (*Ulmus* spp.), ash (*Fraxinus* spp.), and such valuable species as the Amur cork tree (*Phellodendron amurense* Rupr.), used exclusively as a substitute for imported cork, and dimorphant *Acer pictum*, which produces a veneer of a most exquisite design—such are the species that form the hardwood forests of the Far East. There are at least twelve recognized species of birch, seven of maple (of which two, *Acer mandschuricum* and *Acer mono*, attain large sizes), two of basswood (*Tilia amurensis* and *Tilia mandschurica*), and several of aspen, the most important being the fragrant aspen (*Populus suaveolens*). The reserves of walnut (*Juglans mandschurica*) are not great. The Mongolian oak (*Quercus mongolica*) is the most widely distributed broadleaf tree. Some 80 per cent of the oak stands are found in the valley of the Ussuri River and on the coast of the Japan Sea, and the remainder along the middle course of the Amur River. There are several species of elm, but only two (*Ulmus propinqua* and *Ulmus laciniata*) are of commercial importance. One of the most valuable hardwood species is the Manchurian ash (*Fraxinus mandschurica* Rupr.), most of it found along the Ussuri River and on the coast of the Japan Sea.

[20] Zimek (1949).

Because of this great conglomeration of species, the Far East holds promise of becoming the center of many industries depending on hardwoods. First is the veneer industry, for which there is a rich selection of species; then, shipbuilding, furniture and vehicle manufacturing, tannin extraction, and chemical industries based on hardwood distillation. All this, however, is still in the future; at present only the conifers are being cut for lumber. The hardwoods, which form 30 per cent and more in the admixture, either remain uncut or are cut for firewood only. Although there are many streams suitable for floating loose logs, they cannot be used for hardwood logs, except birch, because the sinkage is too great. Although hardwood logs can be rafted when made up together with pine logs, the problem of transport will not be really solved until railroads and highways are developed, and this will take a long time.

THE TIMBER-CONSUMING REGIONS

SOUTH EUROPEAN RUSSIA. This region, which includes the Ukraine, Moldavia, the Crimea, and the lower Volga basin, has a forest area of about 9 million hectares, a total timber stand of 572 million cubic meters, and an annual cut of some 25 million cubic meters. The lower Volga basin is the least populated part of southeastern European Russia. Its small forest area of one million hectares supplies 60 per cent of the timber needs of the population; but the only large demand is for basswood staves. Its geographic position, however, at the crossroads between the Ukraine, the Caucasus, and Central Asia, makes it an important transit and distribution center for the great mass of logs that are floated down from the upper and central Volga regions. The Ukraine, on the other hand, has a very dense population, a highly developed agriculture, and a large mining industry. Without large forests of its own, it depends for 40 per cent of its wood needs on imports from outside.

TRANSCAUCASIA. This region includes the Soviet republics of Georgia, Azerbaijan, and Armenia. It has a considerable area of forests, amounting to 3.6 million hectares, but they are located in the foothills and mountains of the Lesser and Greater Caucasus ranges and are difficult of access, almost uninhabited, and a veritable forest jungle. Since the annual increment in the Transcaucasian forests is not less than 7.5 million cubic meters and the total volume of standing timber is close to 400 million cubic meters, it might seem that the timber needs of the region could easily be covered by exploitation of the region's own forests. Owing, however, to the undeveloped state of the timber industry, about 300,000 cubic meters of timber are actually imported each year to Baku from the lower Volga region. Most of it remains in the Baku area.

The present annual cut in Transcaucasia must be in excess of one million cubic meters of structural timber alone. The many small, primitive sawmills are now being replaced by large, well-equipped ones. A widespread wood-using industry is the manufacture of hand-hewn beech and oak staves, the former for vegetable-oil containers, the latter for wine barrels. The first sawn-staves factory was erected during the war. A large pulp and paper plant has recently been put into operation, but wood-distillation plants, for which there would be an abundant supply of raw material, do not as yet exist.

A great timber industry could undoubtedly be developed in Trans-caucasia. Among other needs are powerful logging machinery, and the construction of branch railroads linking the region to the main lines, of logging roads traversable by trucks, and of wooden sluices for carrying the logs down to the valleys.

THE CENTRAL-ASIATIC REGION. This includes the Kazakh, Uzbek, Kirghiz, Tadzhik, and Turkmen autonomous federated republics. Formerly known for the most part as Russian Turkestan, it is the driest part of the U.S.S.R. The land is largely steppe, which farther south becomes desert. The total forest area is 30.3 million hectares, but the extent of actually productive forest land is much smaller. Whatever forests there are occur mostly on the slopes of the Altai, Pamir, and Tien Shan mountains. They are almost inaccessible and for this reason are being cut very little, not more than 2 million cubic meters a year; yet the potential cut is several times that amount and could meet all local timber needs. Wood-using industries are practically nonexistent. Agriculture depends on irrigation, and for this reason the forests have a high hydrological value. Timber is imported from Siberia and from the Volga regions by way of the Caspian Sea.

Kirghizia, like her sister republics of Central Asia, is of no importance from a timber standpoint. The Kirghiz forests, however, are of national economic value to the whole U.S.S.R. because of the unique concentration in southern Kirghizia of a large number of fruit- and nut-bearing trees that grow wild here: [21] apples, pears, cherries, pistachios, and especially walnuts. From 50 to 75 per cent of all the wild-grown fruits and nuts gathered throughout the territory of the U.S.S.R. come from this region. The walnuts of southern Kirghizia are claimed to be of superior quality. In their content of oil (75 per cent) and albumen they surpass not only the French and Spanish walnuts but those grown in the other Central-Asiatic republics. Nowhere in the Soviet Union, and probably in the entire world, are there so many extensive pure walnut forests as on the slopes of the Fergana and Chatkal mountain ranges of southern Kirghizia. As compared with only 150 hectares in Uzbekistan, 250 in Turkmenia, 600 in Kazakhstan, and 28,000 in Tadzhikistan, some 50,000 hectares in southern Kirghizia are covered with continuous pure walnut forests. The government considers southern Kirghizia the richest source from which to collect seed of the wild-growing fruit and nut trees for propagation purposes in its reforestation work in other parts of the country.

[21] Grushetskii (1951).

Administrative Categories of Forests

NATIONAL AND LOCAL FORESTS. The forests of the U.S.S.R. are divided
by an administrative decree into several categories. One important division is between National Forests, which serve the broad economic and
social needs of the country as a whole, and Local Forests, which serve the
needs of limited localities or communities. The latter include such forests
as are allotted for the exclusive use of the collective farms (over 40 million hectares). The management of these farm wood lots is in the hands
of the farmers, with only slight supervision and advice from local representatives of the Federal Forest Administration. Like farm wood lots
all over the world, they are in too many cases overcut, overgrazed, poorly
protected against fire, and in general poorly cared for. This category also
includes forests allotted for the support of local wood-using industries and
for supplying villages with firewood and other timber products in every-
day use. The creation of the category of Local Forests was prompted by
the need of relieving the Federal Forest Administration from making
numerous individual small timber sales, and by a desire to give the rural
population a certain degree of proprietary interest and autonomy in the
handling of forests that it has always regarded as its own. These forests
as a general rule are not of high quality and yield mostly cordwood. The
timber cut in them does not figure materially in the timber production of
the country and is therefore not generally included in computations of
the national timber output. The Local Forests were first segregated as a
special category in 1923. In 1939 their area amounted to 112 million
hectares, but it has been growing and is now probably not less than 130
million hectares.

We have seen (p. 399 above) that, of the total forest area of the U.S.S.R.
(estimated at 1,068 million hectares), some 628 million hectares are in productive forests. Deducting the 130 million hectares of Local Forests
from this, we obtain about 500 million hectares as the approximate productive area within the National Forests.

RESERVES AND SANCTUARIES. Since 1943 the forests of the U.S.S.R. have
been officially divided into three large groups. Group I includes forest
preserves, animal sanctuaries, forests surrounding health resorts, forests on
blowing soils, forest zones around industrial plants and cities, and shelterbelts. In 1950 these forests comprised a total area of 27,200,000 hectares
and 3.3 billion cubic meters of standing timber, or about 5.5 per cent of
the total amount in the country. Cuttings in the forests of this group are
confined to thinnings, stand improvements, sanitary cuttings, and removal
of overmature and dying trees. Clear-cutting of any kind is strictly forbidden.

PROTECTION FORESTS. Group II includes chiefly forests having a water
shed protection value. They are located principally in the central and
western regions of European Russia, cover some 85,400,000 hectares, and

have a volume of standing timber estimated at 2.9 billion cubic meters, or 5 per cent of the total volume for the country. Except for strips of forests about 7 kilometers wide along the shores of the Volga and its right tributaries, in which no cuttings of any kind are allowed (this prohibition has lately been extended to some other rivers), light commercial cuttings are permitted in the forests of this group.

COMMERCIAL FORESTS. Group III includes all other forests. They are the commercial forests of the country, open for economic exploitation, and are found principally in the northern part of European Russia and in Siberia, embracing about 950 million hectares and comprising some 52.5 billion cubic meters or 89.5 per cent of the entire timber stand. In these forests all forms of cutting, including concentrated clear-cuttings, are allowed, the sole provision being that the cutover areas must be regenerated, naturally or artificially, within a specified short time. The volume of cutting is not limited by the annual growth, but is determined by the economic and industrial needs of the country.

The Timber Industry

In spite of the great forest wealth of the U.S.S.R. and the herculean efforts on the part of the government to foster its development, the timber industry is still yielding only 80 per cent of the country's timber needs. There are frequent timber shortages of one kind or another, and the industry is in a state of chronic crisis. Several factors contribute to this state of affairs.

GROWING DOMESTIC DEMAND FOR FOREST PRODUCTS. The industrialization of the country is making increasingly greater domestic demands upon the products of the forest, and an additional heavy demand is for materials needed in reconstructing the 21¼ million houses destroyed during the war. The timber industry is making strides but is not keeping pace with the more rapidly growing needs.[22]

The rate of growth of the industry may be judged from the available figures of timber consumption. In the 1920's the annual consumption of timber of all kinds was around 200 million cubic meters (including about 11.5 million exported abroad); in the early 1940's it rose to over 300 mil-

[22] Forest experts disagree as to how much wood is produced annually in the Soviet Union, and even the Russians themselves are very vague about it. Published estimates vary from 269 to 660 million cubic meters. The FAO *Yearbook* (1954), Table 1, p. 20, places the total production in 1953 at 400 million cubic meters, of which 170 were fuel wood (including charcoal) and 230 industrial wood. The 1953 World Forest Inventory estimates the annual timber cut (average 1950-52) for forests *in use* at only 330 million cubic meters, of which 190 million were industrial wood and 140 million fuel wood. (FAO [1955]:100-101.) The estimate of 330 million would seem too conservative and evidently covers large-scale logging operations only. After 1945 the industry began to grow very rapidly, and if it has continued to grow at the same rate during the last few years the annual timber output now cannot be much less than 400 million cubic meters; even 450 million would not be out of line, and this exclusive of cuttings in the Local Forests and those allocated to the oil and mining industries—agencies independent of the Ministry of Forestry.

lion, and at present it is estimated to be close to 400 million, of which very little is exported. Paper consumption, which before the war was 293,000 tons a year, has now been increased to about 360,000 tons; although the pulp and paper industry has been growing lately at the rate of about 18 per cent a year, paper consumption is still only half that of England and one fourteenth that of the United States.

The Eastward Shift of the Timber Industry. In the past most of the sawmills, cellulose and paper plants, and other wood-using industries were located in the southern, western, and interior industrial regions of European Russia. Because of the uneven geographic distribution of the forests in the U.S.S.R., these regions, especially the southern and western, were not well endowed with forests to begin with, and, as a result of prolonged overcutting, what forests there are in them have been nearing exhaustion for many years. Hence, to keep the industries going it has become necessary to bring logs from constantly increasing distances, mostly by rail and partly by water—a very uneconomical operation. Moreover, most of the plants themselves have become obsolete and inefficient.

The need of moving the centers of the wood-using industries from this region to northeastern European Russia, the Urals, and Siberia was already recognized in the 1920's and the war hastened the shift itself. Many of the plants were destroyed by the enemy and will not be restored; others were picked up bodily and hurriedly transferred to the east before the advancing armies.

During the last two decades the efforts of the government have been directed toward tapping the resources of the hitherto poorly developed territories. This has meant building new railroads and connecting the large rivers with canals to transport enormous stocks of mature timber from the north and east to the timber-deficient south. One of the first steps was to connect the Arctic and White Sea ports with Leningrad by rail and canal, and Leningrad with the Volga and Moscow by means of the Volga-Moscow Canal. Three new branch railroads, totaling 2,300 kilometers, were completed in the far north during 1937-42. These run from east to west over a difficult terrain and frozen tundra, connecting up with the main railroads running south from Archangel and Murmansk. The output of the sawmills in Archangel, which in the past was shipped almost entirely abroad, could now be diverted for domestic use in southern and central European Russia. Therefore, timber exports from the ports of Leningrad, Archangel, and Murmansk have become greatly reduced, and the character of the exports is also changing. At the same time, large new inland lumber-processing centers have come into existence, mostly at the intersection of rail lines and rivers; the most notable example is Kotlas, where the North Pechora railroad crosses the Northern Dvina River. Construction in the near future of an additional 3,600 kilometers of railroads through the forested regions of northern European Russia is projected, and a comparable increase for Siberia. At the same time, energetic measures are being taken to improve the water-transportation facilities, which play a very important role, since each year some 61 million cubic meters of timber are floated down the waterways of the U.S.S.R. The extent of these waterways is now 220,000 kilometers, and extensive river-improvement work is going on continuously to increase it.

In addition to the new railroads and river improvements, several deep canals connecting the main rivers are being dug. Some of these have already been completed, others now under construction are due for completion in the next few years, and still others are only in the blueprint stage. Thus, a great network of canals and railroads will ultimately enable all parts of central and southern European Russia—the Ukraine, the Donets coal region, north Caucasia, and Transcaucasia—to receive the needed supplies of lumber, mining timber, and pulp wood from Karelia and the upper reaches of the Kama, Volga, and Viatka rivers. Within the last twelve years several large cellulose-paper mills, sawmills, and wood chemical plants have been put into operation near the city of Gorki on the Volga, and also on the Kama.

A new industry has recently come into existence in the north: the manufacture of prefabricated houses and standardized constructional parts. The pressure for the construction of new dwellings in the U.S.S.R. is enormous, to restore the one third of the dwelling area of Soviet cities that was destroyed by the invading armies and to provide new dwellings for the growing population. Rapid erection of houses for the people who lost their homes during the war, as well as for the new towns and cities springing up around industrial centers—especially the mining centers, where, as in Donbas, no timber is available nearby—is an urgent necessity. Prefabricated houses seem to be an answer to the building problem, and the vast forests of the north provide the chief raw material for the house-building plants. The Five-Year Plan for 1950-55 envisaged the need for the erection and repair of some 3,400,000 dwellings, and there are now more than sixty plants turning out prefabricated houses in the U.S.S.R., some of them producing as many as 7,000 houses per year.

Similar developments are taking place in the Urals and in Asiatic Russia, especially in the basins of the rivers Ob and Yenisei, which flow through the heart of the enormous Siberian forests. A great deal of logging is being done along the banks of the Siberian rivers. The logs, in huge rafts containing 30,000 cubic meters each, are towed south up the rivers to Krasnoyarsk, Novosibirsk, Barnaul, and other industrial centers, and, with the opening of the Northern Sea Route for normal transportation, the larger Siberian rivers, which all flow north, are now assuming an increasing importance for floating down logs toward the Arctic. Along the Arctic coast there have sprung up many sawmill centers. At Igarka, at the head of the estuary of the Yenisei, for instance, large sawmills have been built, rivaling those of Archangel. Igarka is accessible to seagoing vessels, and may eventually become an important port for timber exports to western Europe.

Great stress is laid on the building in the near future of twenty new pulp and paper plants. The pulp and paper industry before the war centered largely in the west and in the Karelian and Leningrad regions—important Soviet battlegrounds in World War II—and, consequently, was greatly crippled. The first large pulp and paper plant in the Far East was erected in 1942 at Komsomolsk on the Amur River. In western Siberia two paper mills were built before the war, one in 1936 at Barnaul on the Ob and another in 1937 at Krasnoyarsk on the Yenisei.

A forest area in eastern Siberia which will no doubt soon become an important center of the timber industry lies on the upper Lena and Angara rivers and their tributaries within the Lake Baikal watershed and not very far north of Irkutsk. It is a part of a much larger area that has been only partially surveyed. Before the war there were a few small factories and shops in this region. The wood consumed, including that used by the river boats and the settlers, amounted to less than 700,000 cubic meters a year. The average density of the population was less than one person per square kilometer. By 1952 the timber output from this area, which contains a total volume of about 550 million cubic meters, had reached several million cubic meters a year. Large sawmills and cellulose, veneer, and wood-distillation plants have been built on the Chuna near the village of Bratsk. Since this vast region is remote from the main wood-using centers of the country, and local needs, because of sparse population, are insignificant, the forest products must be shipped to the industrial centers of western Siberia. To this end, branch railroads are being built from the Trans-Siberian line east to the Lena. After these railroads have been completed, the structural timber will be sent to the poorly wooded regions of northern Siberia, Kazakhstan, and Central Asia, and pit props to the coal basins of Cheremkhovo and Karaganda.

Thus, the timber industry is beginning to take a strong foothold in Siberia in the face of many heavy odds and the necessity of enormous capital investments. Indeed, in the course of the next several years most of the centers of the timber industry of the whole U.S.S.R. will shift from the south, west, and northwest to northeastern European Russia, the Urals, and Siberia. This migration is in many respects analogous to that of the timber industry of the United States during the last half century. In 1899 the states east of the Rockies produced 66 per cent, the South 24 per cent, and the western states 10 per cent of the entire timber output of the country. A half century later the timber production of the eastern states had fallen to about a quarter, that of the South stood at about a quarter (after a sharp decline from 37 per cent in 1919), while that of the western states had risen to nearly half the United States total.[23] Although

[23] H. B. Steer. Lumber production in the United States, 1799-1946. U.S. Dept. of Agriculture, *Misc. Publ. No. 669*, Washington, D. C., 1948.

in both cases the problem has been largely one of transportation, the exhaustion of the forests in the older regions of timber exploitation has not been without its effects.

Many difficulties will still have to be overcome before the planned shift can be completed in the U.S.S.R., but it is unmistakably under way. At the beginning of 1953 some 1,720 large timber-producing enterprises had received definite allocations in the new regions of exploitable timber reserves, with a total possible annual cut of 300 million cubic meters over a period of 21 years. It was expected that by the end of 1955 more than seven tenths of the total annual cut would be concentrated in the north of European Russia, the Urals, Siberia, and the Far East.

EXCESSIVE CONSUMPTION OF FUEL WOOD. While the government is endeavoring to open new territories for forest exploitation in order to meet the growing domestic demand for wood and especially for structural timber, it is also seeking to obtain more useful wood from the trees that are already being cut. The amount of structural timber that has been obtained in the past averaged only about 50 per cent of the volume of the trees, but by better utilization this percentage has now been increased in many places to 65 and 70. The hardwoods, which used to contribute only a small amount of structural timber, are being drawn upon for a larger share of it, up to 10 per cent of the entire output. But, most of all, the government is seeking to reduce the consumption of fuel wood and to substitute other sources of fuel. Wood is still one of the most used fuels in the U.S.S.R. for industrial purposes and especially for heating, although its relative place is diminishing. In the 1920's, wood constituted 41 per cent of all fuel used, whereas today it amounts to only 12 per cent. Even so, the city of Moscow alone still consumes from 3 to 5 million cubic meters of fuel wood per year, and the movement of such an enormous quantity places a heavy burden on the railroads. To relieve them, the government is seeking to devise means of transporting fuel wood by water. It learned during the war that it is practicable to float small round timber and fuel wood in rafts, and a great deal of this material is now reaching the capital in this manner from the upper Volga by the way of the Volga-Moscow Canal. Even this, however, involves floating the fuel wood to Moscow over a distance of 600 to 900 kilometers from the forests of the provinces of Vologda, Leningrad, and Gorki.

To decrease the use of wood for generating power and for heating purposes, the mining of coal, oil shale, and peat is being greatly stepped up, as well as the use of natural gas. Thus, during the war (1943-45) a pipe line 843 kilometers long was laid to bring natural gas from Saratov to Moscow. The city of Leningrad obtains a gas supply from the large shale deposits that are comparatively near by in Estonia. Kiev, on the other hand, must pipe in gas from the Carpathian foothills, a distance of 300 kilometers. In 1950 most of the large cities in the Soviet Union were obtaining a total of 8.5 billion cubic meters of natural gas through pipe lines aggregating 3,000 kilometers in length. Peat has long been an important source of fuel in the U.S.S.R. and its output increased from 1.7 million tons in 1910 to 32 million tons in 1940, and 44 million tons in 1950—a 39 per cent increase over 1940. New mechanized methods of peat cutting, milling, dredging, and artificial drying have been introduced.

SHORTAGE OF LABOR. Shortage of labor, and especially of skilled labor, is plaguing the timber industry. The mechanization of logging operations is evidently being pushed faster than the workers can master the techniques. There are frequent official complaints from different regions to the effect that labor efficiency is not up to par: that out of more than 10,000 power saws only one third are being used; that out of 3,500 tractors only 500 are in actual operation, many of them either in repair shops or idle because of lack of co-ordination between the different operations. Inadequate housing facilities and other hardships coupled with life in remote undeveloped regions do not make work attractive in the woods, with the result that the timber industry has only half as many workers as it needs. According to the Ministry of Forestry, many thousands of qualified laborers are needed to operate power saws, tractors, and electric stations, to serve as trained loaders, and to perform other tasks calling for expertness and skill.

The difficulties and shortcomings that characterize the timber industry today are manifestations of the growing pains of an industry trying to shake off the backwardness of its long past and, on the ruins wrought by the war and in remote and undeveloped territories, to build a new structure capable of meeting the needs of a vast and expanding economy. The potentialities inherent in the enormous amount of available timber cannot, however, be fully realized until the pressing problems of transport and labor have been successfully solved.

THE U.S.S.R. AS A SOURCE OF TIMBER FOR WESTERN EUROPE. The normal timber needs of western Europe for more than a hundred years have by far exceeded domestic production. Western Europe has depended, therefore, to a large degree on imports from Russia and the other eastern and northern European countries to make up the deficit. Before World War II Russia occupied first place among the timber-exporting countries in the actual amount of wood exported, and was second only to the United States and Canada combined with regard to the value of the exported product. The chief importing countries were Great Britain, Germany, France, the Netherlands, and Belgium. More than half of the entire quantity of Russian timber exported consisted of raw or half-manufactured products.

From the early 1930's, however, as a result of a complete reversal in its timber-export policies, the U.S.S.R. began to withdraw from the field of foreign trade in timber. From 12.1 million cubic meters in 1935, timber exports sank to 5.3 million in 1938 and gradually decreased still further until they ceased altogether during the war. The U.S.S.R.'s present share in the timber importation of western Europe is insignificant, except in fulfillment of occasional special trade agreements with other countries for the exchange of wood for badly needed machinery or manufactured goods.

Before World War II Poland, Rumania, and Czechoslovakia also exported to the West large quantities of unprocessed timber products, such as round logs, poles, and pulpwood. These exports greatly exceeded the volume that the forests could normally produce, and, hence, the present policy in these countries, too, is to bring cutting into balance with the productive capacity of the forests and to limit exports to a small amount of processed or semiprocessed material. Moreover, whatever forest products there may be that are available for export from these countries are now sent to the U.S.S.R. and not to the West. Outside the Iron Curtain, Sweden has also come close to the limit of the export possibilities, Norway has never been a very large timber-exporting country, and Finland, as a result of the war, has lost its former position as a major exporter of timber.

With timber imports from the U.S.S.R. and these other European sources reduced to a mere trickle, western Europe has looked to Canada and the tropics. Canada, however, while capable of exporting large amounts of timber, finds its largest market close at home—in the United States—and Canada's policy is to export processed wood and paper products for the most part, rather than timber. The extensive tropical forests hold out promising possibilities that deserve serious consideration, but their development still lies in the future. In the meantime, the world needs coniferous timber as the most valuable and economical for construction purposes, and the U.S.S.R. with its vast and still largely undeveloped coniferous forests remains the principal potential source of such timber.

Hence, there seems little doubt that the U.S.S.R. will eventually again appear in the world market as a great timber-exporting country, but just when is hard to predict. As long as its timber industry is under pressure, both to repair the ravages of the war and to keep pace with the expanding needs of a rapid industrialization, the U.S.S.R. will have no timber for export abroad, except as there is necessity at times for exchanging wood for particular manufactured goods not produced at home. Only when the timber industry is developed to a point where it can meet all domestic needs, and the capacity of its sawmills and other wood-using plants is large enough to turn out an excess of wood products, will the U.S.S.R. become an important factor in the world timber trade. This will take a long time, possibly a decade or two of peaceful, uninterrupted development. In no case, however, is timber export likely to reach the peak attained in 1933, when it formed over 16 per cent of the total exports of the U.S.S.R. and 20 per cent of the entire world's timber exports. It must also be borne in mind that, with the state owning all the forests, and foreign trade also a state monopoly, timber-export policies may be dictated as much by international politics as by economic considerations.[24]

[24] Buchholz (1948).

Forest Policies, Education, and Research

THE CONSERVATION MOVEMENT. The dominant trend of the present economic policy of the U.S.S.R., stated in oversimplified form, is toward the fullest development of all of the natural resources of the country so that it may become entirely self-sufficient economically (an autarchy) in the shortest possible time. Among the natural resources, forests are considered basic to the whole national economy because, without a plentiful supply of wood, most other industries are hampered in their development. Next to agriculture, forestry therefore rates the highest priority as regards capital investments and procurement of machinery and equipment. Great stress is also laid on the influence of the forests on climate, and on their hydrological role in controlling the regime of streams, their prevention of wind and water erosion, and their effect on agriculture, soil, and health. This is evidenced by the setting aside of large areas of forests as screens around health resorts and industrial centers, by the designating of forests on critical watersheds and along the banks of the larger rivers as "protection forests," in which timber cutting is restricted, and by the extension of the forest area through large-scale planting operations. The strong "forest-consciousness" that prevails today in the U.S.S.R. is reminiscent of the conservation movement inspired in the United States during the first quarter of this century by Theodore Roosevelt and Gifford Pinchot.

"REMAKING NATURE." The conviction that forests and great expanses of water have an ameliorating influence on climate has culminated in the adoption of a policy that has become known as "remaking nature." The scope of this new conservation movement, and the gigantic efforts it will involve if it can be realized, entitle it to be classed among the world's great undertakings in this field.

At the end of 1948 a project was initiated for the erection, in the path of scorching southeast winds, of forest barriers extending for some 5,320 kilometers in length and covering an area of some 117,900 hectares. In addition, the plan included the planting of shelter belts around cultivated fields to a total area of 5,709,000 hectares, stabilizing some 322,000 hectares of shifting sands by afforestation and other means, and constructing more than 44,000 ponds and reservoirs. The entire plan, designed for completion in fifteen years, is now well under way.

Russian foresters have calculated that the climate of the steppe region, when all the forest planting in the steppes is completed, should become more humid; the absolute humidity during the growing season should be increased by about 20 per cent and the relative humidity by 25 per cent. At present, shelter belts around cultivated fields, as numerous Russian records indicate, increase the yield of crops between the belts by some 30 to 35 per cent. When the entire region is covered with shelter belts, the yields are expected to increase by from 50 to 70 per cent.

In 1950 the original plan was supplemented by government approval of four new projects—all to be completed in the course of seven years and each in scope and size equaling, if not exceeding, the original plan. The main features revolve mostly around the construction of dams, navigable canals, and large-scale irrigation works, with forestry as a supplementary activity. The four new projects called for the construction of navigable canals connecting (1) the Volga with the Don, (2) the Caspian Sea with the Aral Sea and Amu-Darya (or Oxus River of antiquity), and (3) the Dnieper with the Sea of Azov and Black Sea, and also for (4) the erection of two huge hydroelectric stations on the Volga (at Kuybyshev and Stalingrad). The Volga-Don canal was completed in 1952 and is now in operation, and the other projects are well under way. When completed, they are expected to give the country 22 billion kilowatt-hours of additional electric energy, create an irrigation and watering system for 28,000,000 hectares of arid land, and link together the White, Baltic, Caspian, Azov, and Black Seas, and Central Asia in one great transportation system. The timber industry, which depends to a large degree on water transport, will be one of the chief beneficiaries of this unified system.

FOREST EDUCATION AND RESEARCH. There are now in the U.S.S.R. twelve forest institutes of university grade devoted exclusively to the training of specialists in all branches of forest management and forest utilization.

Among the forest schools of higher learning the Leningrad Forest Institute should be mentioned first. The oldest in Europe, it has several departments which give instruction leading to specialized degrees, such as Silviculturist, Forest Engineer, or Forest Chemist, and it graduates each year about 1,000 students. The forest department of the Timiriazev Academy, in Moscow, is also an old institution, enjoying a high scientific standing. It has produced many recognized leaders in forestry. Newer forest schools are located at Archangel in north European Russia, at Kiev in the Ukraine, at Kazan on the Volga, at Sverdlovsk in the Urals, at Tomsk in western Siberia, at Krasnoyarsk in eastern Siberia, and at Khabarovsk in the Far East. These schools graduate between 2,500 and 3,000 foresters and forest technicians each year.

Besides the regular forest schools there are also fifteen special forest research institutions and scores of experimental stations and laboratories in all parts of the country. The course in the forest schools is from four to six years. Anyone between the ages of seventeen and thirty-five who has completed secondary education and passed entrance examinations is eligible for admission to these schools. Much emphasis is laid on the training of specialists in forest engineering and in various branches of the timber industry, and several thousand of them have now been absorbed by the industry. Outstanding among the institutions carrying on research in the field of the mechanization, organization, and economics of timber operations are the Central Scientific Research Institute of Mechanization and Energetics of the Timber Industry, the Siberian Scientific Institute of Forest Management and Forest Exploitation, and the Scientific Research Sectors of the Leningrad Forest Technological Academy. All forest research is conducted in close contact with the forest industries. Research seeks to anticipate the needs of the industry and to help overcome its technical difficulties. Many vocational intermediary schools are engaged in training lower forest personnel, and there is also an All-Union Correspondence School in Forestry.

SELECTED REFERENCES

Bol'shaia sovetskaia entsiklopediia (Great Soviet Encyclopedia). 1938. Unsigned article on Forests. Vol. XXXVI, p. 667. Moscow.

BUCHHOLZ, ERWIN. 1948. "Die Forst- und Holzwirtschaft der Sowjet-Union nach dem Kriege," *Zeit. f. Weltforstw.*, **12**:18-30. (English and French summaries.)

DOBRININ, B. 1947. In *Bol'shaia sovetskaia entsiklopediia.* Supplemental vol., pp. 71-81. Moscow.

GRUSHETSKII, I. I. 1951. "Lesnoe khoziaistvo Kirgizii" (Forestry of Kirghizia), *Lesnoe Khoziaistvo*, **4**(3):52-57.

HANSON, E. P. 1949. *New worlds emerging.* Duell, Sloan, & Pearce, Inc., New York.

International Yearbook of Forestry Statistics, 1933-35. 1936. International Institute of Agriculture, Rome.

KLEVTSOV, I. P. 1951. "O lesakh Urala" (On the forests of the Ural area), *Lesn. Khoz.*, **4**(2): 32-34.

KOMAROV, V. L., *et al.* 1939–. *Flora S.S.S.R.* (Flora of the U.S.S.R.). 15 vols. Leningrad Academy of Sciences, Leningrad.

KÖPPEN, F. T. 1889. *Geographische Verbreitung der Holzgewächse des europäischen Russlands und des Kaukasus.* 2 vols. Buchdrückerei der Kaiserlichen Akademie der Wissenschaften. St. Petersburg.

NESTOROV, B. 1947. Article on Forests in *Bol'shaia sovetskaia entsiklopediia.* Supplemental vol., p. 943.

SHISHKIN, B. 1947. Article on Vegetation in *Bol'shaia sovetskaia entsiklopediia.* Supplemental vol., p. 182.

TIKHOMIROV, B. A. 1949. "V kedrovikh lesakh neobkhodimo kompleksnoc khoziaistvo" (Need for comprehensive methods in the cedar forests), *Lesn. Khoz.*, **2**(2):36-39.

United Nations. Food and Agriculture Organization. 1954. *Yearbook of forest products statistics, 1954.* Rome.

————. 1955. *World forest resources.* Rome.

VASILEV, P., and NEVZOROV, N. 1948. *Forest management and the lumber industry in the U.S.S.R.* Moscow.

WALTER, HEINRICH. 1943. *Die Vegetation Osteuropas.* Rev. ed. P. Parey, Berlin.

ZIMEK, A. A. 1949. "Lesny resursy Dal'nego Vostoka" (Forest resources of the Far East), *Lesn. Khoz.*, **2**(1):58-62.

ZON, RAPHAEL, and SPARHAWK, W. N. 1923. *Forest resources of the world.* 2 vols. McGraw-Hill Book Co., Inc., New York.

19.   SOUTHWESTERN ASIA

H. F. Mooney

There must be few major inhabited quarters of the globe with a percentage of forest area lower than that of southwestern Asia. Certainly none has a smaller area of good-quality high forest (confined exclusively to the oak-beech woodlands of northern Iran). Since the end of the glacial epoch, great tracts of plateau country, which had been well watered and fertile during the moist, cool, pluvial periods of the Pleistocene, have reverted to desert. The forests have receded gradually and new growth has been limited largely to those regions where there is sufficient rainfall to support it. Furthermore, with the emergence of man from the hunting and fruit-gathering stages and his development into a pastoralist, the forests have also suffered the impact of his destructive hand and the ravages of his flocks. Thus, we are left with little forest vegetation in this region, and most of what remains has degraded to open scrub. In general, the only forests of importance or potential value are those of the mountain tracts of northern and northwestern Iran and northern Iraq, and even these are in an advanced state of deterioration. The few small woodlands of southern and eastern Iran can barely be dignified by the name of forest, and, as far as can be ascertained, the patches of forest reported to exist in the mountain ranges of southwestern Arabia are also badly depleted and little more than scrub.

Forest conservation and management are, as might be expected, in their infancy. Efforts to organize a regular forest administration in Iran were made between 1948 and 1950, but it is uncertain how far they have been successful. A good start has been made in Iraq and in Jordan, and the outlook in those countries is promising. In the Arabian peninsula nothing has so far been done.

Iran

LOCATION AND EXTENT OF THE FORESTS. The principal forests of Iran are found in two main regions: in a belt along the northern slopes of the Elburz chain toward the Caspian (broadly speaking, between Tabriz and Meshed) and in the Zagros Range. The former comprises the Caspian coastlands and the slopes of the Talish hills and of the Elburz, which culminates in Demavend (5,600 meters).

The Elburz chain, the greatest feature in northern Iran, is nearly 1,000 kilometers long from the Russian border in the northwest to Jajarm in the east, beyond which it merges into the mountains of northern Khurasan. The Zagros range, which runs for about eight hundred miles from the Turkish and Iraq frontiers in the northwest as far south as the vicinity of Shiraz, forms a large extent of rugged country, much of which lies between elevations of 2,500 and 4,000 meters, i.e., above the tree line.

Apart from these two extensive regions, there are scattered areas of forest in northern Khurasan, in the Tarbati Haidari subprovince south of Meshed, and again in the southeastern part of the country towards Baluchistan, but they are of minor importance and little is known about them. Central and eastern Iran consist largely of deserts and arid plains.

Iran has approximately 20 million hectares of forest of one sort or another, representing 12 per cent of the total area of the country. The forest area, together with 15 million hectares of pasture land, might be considered as not unreasonable for a country of this size, with a population of some 16 million—especially where climatic conditions are on the whole uncongenial to the growth of closed forest—and such a view would be justifiable, were all the existing forests properly protected and prudently managed. But this is far from the case.

CLIMATIC AND OTHER INFLUENCES. The greater part of the annual rainfall in Iran occurs between November and April; on the Caspian coast, in the Talish hills, and in Gilan nearly three quarters of the annual rainfall occurs between early September and late June. One third of the country, in the north and northwest, has a rainfall of more than 400 millimeters, and one half receives 200 millimeters or more. But the remaining half of Iran gets less than 200 millimeters of rain a year. The highest recorded precipitation is in the Caspian region and along the Iraq and Turkish frontiers, where it reaches 1,000 millimeters or even 1,500 millimeters in the mountains.

While rainfall is the most important factor in determining the distribution and character of the forests, several other influences, both edaphic and biotic, also play their part. Without going into details regarding the geology of Iran and the large variety of soil types found there, we may say that most of the soils—especially those of limestone and sandstone origin—are highly erodible. This is all too evident on the hot, dry southern slopes of the Elburz mountains and is most marked in localities where the rainfall is sufficient to cause destructive erosion without being sufficient in quantity or distributed adequately enough to permit vigorous vegetational growth. Characteristic badland scenery occurs on the higher and, more particularly, on the southern slopes of the Elburz; and much of the silting of the three main rivers flowing into the Caspian is due to soil lost high up on the mountains in the headwater areas. Farther down the valleys the vegetative growth is of such vigor that only actual clearing of the brushwood and tilling of steep slopes promote soil erosion.

Widespread browsing by free-ranging goats is another factor of considerable and, in some localities, of overwhelming importance. In the northern area it is estimated that there are four million sheep and goats, in addition to one million cattle; but these figures are not very reliable. Although the goat is the enemy of all vegetation and, above all, of forest regeneration, the danger is not so great in Iran, owing to the compara- tively low density of population, as it is in countries like Syria, Jordan, and Lebanon; but the menace is there just the same, and in the interest of the survival of the forest it should be controlled.

The forests, more particularly those of the north and northwest, suffer considerable damage from fire and shifting cultivation; and the gathering of brushwood as fuel for the towns and villages, besides the ill-organized charcoal industry in the northern mountains, is a destructive force to be reckoned with.

VEGETATIONAL ASSOCIATIONS AND PRINCIPAL SPECIES. Five regional types of forest may be distinguished in Iran. While theoretically these may be further subdivided into a number of lesser communities or plant associations, in the present stage of our knowledge such subdivision is not feasible. Not all areas classed as forest are forest in the usual sense of closed woods; many are of open, dry types, much degraded by general maltreatment. In fact, closed forest is found only near the Caspian, where rainfall and humidity are high.

The five main types of forest vegetation and the approximate area covered by each are as follows:

	Hectares
Oak-beech (*Quercus-Fagus*) forests of the Caspian region	3,600,000
Scrub-oak forests of the northwest	11,300,000
Pistacia forest	2,800,000
Forests of the mountainous limestone region of the northwest	1,300,000
Forests of the dry subtropical region of the south and southeast	500,000
	19,500,000

Oak-Beech Forests of the Caspian Region. By far the most valuable forests in Iran occur along the northern slopes of the Talish Hills and the Elburz mountains. They have been described very broadly as oak-beech forests, but might, in fact, be subdivided into a number of important communities on a regional basis. No attempt will be made here to give an ecological classification, owing to lack of detailed knowledge of the flora and other factors involved.

Of the forested area in this region—approximately 3,600,000 hectares— perhaps 1,500,000 hectares consist of dense forest carrying 150 cubic meters per hectare; some 1,200,000 hectares consist of forest of medium density, of 75 cubic meters per hectare; and some 900,000 hectares are of open forest. Hardwoods predominate, among which oak (mostly *Quercus castanaeifolia*),[1] beech (*Fagus orientalis* Lipsky), and hornbeam (*Carpinus betulus*) constitute the principal species of potential commercial value.

[1] For sources of botanical nomenclature see below, p. 440.

The oak, in particular, attains large proportions and is capable of producing logs of excellent size and quality. The beech tends to prevail between altitudes of 1,500 and 2,100 meters, and the oak, often in nearly pure stands, between 600 and 1,500 meters. Some of the stands of beech and oak are very fine, with girths up to 240 or 270 centimeters and clean boles up to 12 or even 15 meters. It is said that there are as many as forty different species of timber-producing trees in this region.

In Gilan and the west the principal species on the lowlands are *Quercus castanaeifolia*, ironwood (*Parrottia persica* C. A. Mey.), *Carpinus betulus*, the Siberian elm (*Zelkova carpinifolia* Dippel), *Ulmus* spp., *Fraxinus*, *Prunus divaricata*, *Populus alba*, with climbing and scrambling shrubs such as *Vitis* spp., *Rubus* spp., and ivy (*Hedera helix*). In marshy places alder is found.

The hill and lower montane zone has *Zelkova*, oak, and hornbeam as the dominants, with the date-plum (*Diospyros lotus*), *Gleditschia caspica* Desf., *Prunus divaricata*, *Acer laetum* C. A. Mey., *A. insigne* Boiss., *Albizzia julibrissin*, and the Caucasian wing-nut (*Pterocarya fraxinifolia* Spach). Box (*Buxus sempervirens*) occurs as a small tree, or more commonly as a shrubby undergrowth forming dense thickets together with *Crataegus* spp., *Ruscus hyrcanus* Woron., *Danaë racemosa*, and the medlar (*Mespilus germanica*); but the box has been heavily exploited, and large specimens are rare. *Rubus* spp., asclepiads, ivy, and *Smilax excelsa* festoon the trees. Alder (*Alnus*) and *Pterocarya* are common near streams.

The middle montane zone is dominated by the Oriental Beech-Oak-Hornbeam Association, in which are also found less commonly *Zelkova*, maples, and common ash (*Fraxinus excelsior*). The maple under optimum conditions (generally at the lower altitudes) rivals the oak in size. The yew (*Taxus baccata*) occurs sparingly in small groves.

In the upper montane zone at about 1,800 to 2,400 meters the Caspian type of forest disappears and gives way to *Quercus macranthera* Fisch. & Mey. and *Carpinus schuschaensis* H. Winkl., above which species of *Pyrus* and *Prunus* predominate.

Farther east, in Mazanderan, the Caspian forest—sometimes called the Hyrcanian forest—is fully developed and reaches its climax. The commonest trees are oaks (especially *Quercus castanaeifolia*), *Parrottia*, *Albizzia*, *Celtis australis*, *Acer laetum*, *A. insigne*, *Alnus subcordata*, *Diospyros lotus*, *Gleditschia*, box, hawthorns, *Prunus divaricata*, and *Pyrus* spp. In open places *Paliurus spina-christi* and the pomegranate (*Punica granatum*) are common. Conifers generally are very rare, though there are some yews, cypresses (*Cupressus* spp.), and junipers (*Juniperus* spp.). *Cupressus sempervirens* was doubtless once more widespread in the Caspian region, where it occurs mainly on calcareous soils on moderate slopes; but it has been ruthlessly and continuously cut, and now what little remains is kept in a degraded condition by fire and overgrazing. The closed montane forest extends up the northern slopes of the Elburz range to between 2,100 and 2,400 feet, where it gives way to shrubs and brushwood; and above the latter level the shrubs are replaced by thorn-cushion and herbaceous and subshrubby mat communities, in which one of the most prominent genera is *Astragalus*.

The walnut (*Juglans regia*) is widely cultivated in the Caspian region, and occurs naturally to a limited extent in sheltered valleys. Poplar (*Populus nigra*), though not a component of these forests, must be mentioned, as it is largely grown along streams—especially in Azerbaijan Province—and is highly valued and extensively used as poles for building and other purposes.

On the southern slopes of the Elburz chain there is no forest and trees are few, apart from the rare occurrence of a juniper (*Juniperus macrocarpa*) and of poplars and willows along some of the rivers. There are certain shrubs, such as *Pistacia mutica, Rhamnus pallasii, Lonicera nummularifolia, Berberis densiflora* Boiss. & Buhse, *Amygdalus spartioides,* and *Astragalus* spp., but even these are sparsely scattered and inconspicuous.

Scrub-Oak Forests of the Northwest. These forests cover a vast area throughout the length of the Zagros Range, extending as far south as Shiraz. There are considerable variations in climate in this little-known mountainous tract, and precise knowledge of its flora is lacking. The mountains, where they have not been completely denuded of vegetation, carry a very open crop of gnarled scrub oak (*Quercus infectoria* and *Q. aegylops*) in the extreme northwest along the Turkish and Iraqi frontiers, and *Q. persica* Jaub. & Spach farther south around Shiraz. In most of the valleys and on most of the slopes trees are limited to what remains of former forests. Hill forest, however, occurs in some abundance in the more inaccessible parts of the mountains, although only in the remotest valleys is closed forest found. Trees of timber dimensions are extremely rare. Nevertheless, although these forests may be of low economic value at present, they have an important part to play in soil conservation and flood control, and, if protected and properly managed, could be made productive and a useful source of agricultural timber, firewood, and charcoal. The following small trees and shrubs occur in varying proportions in these scrub-oak forests: *Celtis transcaucasia, Amygdalus spartioides* and *A. orientalis, Daphne acuminata, Lonicera nummularifolia, Crataegus azarolus, Acer canescens, Pistacia khinjuk, Rhamnus* sp., *Cotoneaster nummularia, Prunus microcarpa* var. *tortuosa, Prunus brachypetala* Walp. (rare at high altitudes); *Hedera helix* and *Rubus* spp. are found near streams. *Platanus orientalis* (chinar), occurs along rivers in the valleys; walnut trees, often of immense size, are grown near villages; while the Euphrates poplar (*Populus euphratica*), and less commonly the white poplar (*P. alba*) and *Elaeagnus hortensis* var. *angustifolius,* are grown in small plantations along streams near villages, although these could scarcely be classed as forests.

A large number of the plants of the plateau and mountain country are adapted to xerophytic conditions. They consist of (1) thorn-cushions of

Acantholimon spp., *Astragalus* spp., numerous labiates (many of which
are aromatic), *Artemisia* spp., and many kinds of thistles; and (2) geophytes, such as tulips (*Tulipa* spp.), onions (*Allium* spp.), fritillaries
(*Fritillaria* spp.), grape-hyacinth (*Muscari botryoides*), irises (*Iris* spp.),
crocuses (*Crocus* spp.), gladioli (*Gladiolus* spp.), and orchids—plants whose
root systems take the form of bulbs, corms, tubers, or rhizomes. These
geophytes comprise a large proportion of the Iranian flora. Many of them
flower in the spring, when they make a striking display on the higher
mountains.

Pistacia Forest. This consists of scattered patches of extremely open,
low, degraded woods in the region of low rainfall (100 to 150 millimeters)
of the central and southern parts of the country and on the eastern hills
along the Afghan border. It has few woody components (chiefly *Pistacia
mutica, Amygdalus* spp., and a *Berberis*) and is in very poor condition
and of little economic value; nor is there much prospect of improving it,
owing to the adverse climatic factors.

Forests of the Mountainous Limestone Region. These are situated in
the northeastern corner of the country in northern Khurasan. Here the
limestone hills are heavily eroded, very barren, and carry little vegetative
cover. There are some open woods of juniper, once fairly extensive, no
doubt, but now so much degraded and so badly damaged by fire and overgrazing that only euphemistically can they be described as forests.

Forests of the Subtropical Region. These lie in the south, along the
coast of the Persian Gulf, the Mekran coast, and the borders of Baluchistan, where the annual rainfall is about 125 millimeters or less, and where
very high summer temperatures prevail. The forest cover, such as it is
and where it has managed to survive, is found mainly in rocky ravines, and
consists chiefly of open, low thorn scrub with isolated small trees such as
Tamarix articulata, Acacia spp., *Prosopis spicigera, Zizyphus spina-christi*,
and *Ficus* sp. It is the degraded remains of a forest which, if afforded
adequate protection, would undoubtedly recover sufficiently to have a
considerable local value.

STATE OF DEVELOPMENT. Forestry in Iran is at present at an extremely
low level, owing to inadequate staff, poor pay, insufficient transport, and a
general lack of interest among influential circles in forest conservation and
development. The Forest Department, such as it is, can do little more
than act as a permit-issuing organization and observer of the activities of
contractors, with little hope of exercising effective control. The state of
the forest organization is reflected in the condition of the forests. The
government obtains a revenue of 20 million rials a year from its forest
estate, and spends four million rials on personnel and expenses, besides
one million on work, such as planting. The forests themselves are worth
a large amount. Their value in the north alone has been estimated
at 63 billion rials (about $400 million). To entrust state property like
this to the custody of a few forest guards on starvation wages is the

height of imprudence. The Forest Department cannot be blamed for its own condition or for that of the forests under its charge. Unless the government remedies the former, nothing can be done about the latter.

There is a forest law which provides for the protection of the forests against fire, grazing, and other dangers, but it is virtually a dead letter, and no steps are taken to extinguish fires, control grazing, or deal effectively with theft and other offences.

Recommendations for organizing forestry were included in the Seven-Year Plan for Iran in 1949, and more recent proposals were put forward by the Forestry Advisor, British Middle East Office. How far they are likely to be put into practice is problematical. There is immense scope for forest development in Iran and the greatest need for forest conservation, but unless immediate and drastic steps are taken, the remaining forests can scarcely be saved from destruction, which is proceeding at an ever increasing tempo. Their disappearance would inevitably result in accelerated soil erosion and a rapidly deteriorating water regime.

INDUSTRIES BASED ON THE FORESTS. From the commercial point of view oak ranks first on the score of both quality and volume. It is not much used locally, except as firewood, but fetches a high price as cask staves for export. The species used for the latter purpose is mainly, if not exclusively, *Quercus castanaeifolia*. Beech is in good demand locally for a variety of purposes—for doors, door and window frames, furniture, and general building construction. The bulk of the timber in the Tehran market is beech. Other species, such as ironwood, hornbeam, and alder have a limited local sale; poplar is in constant demand for roofing timber and brings a high price. Walnut is used to a small extent for furniture; but there is little or no grading and the wood, unfortunately, is mostly of inferior quality.

The annual consumption of charcoal in Tehran and other towns is immense. No estimate is attempted here, as local figures are unreliable and it would only be misleading to quote them. Charcoal burning, which is carried out by primitive methods and without any control or management, has been the greatest single factor in forest destruction during recent years. Following the fellings made to feed the charcoal kilns, the forest is kept in a state of continuous degradation by the unrestricted and incessant grazing of herds of free-ranging goats and sheep, and by fires.

Methods of exploitation are primitive: small locally made woodsman's axes are used for felling and logging, and stumps are cut high, with much waste. Beech baulks and sleepers are sometimes pit-sawn, but as often merely roughly axe-dressed. There is, or was a few years ago, a state-owned sawmill at Punishan on the Caspian, with a daily average output of 25 cubic meters.

Transport is by pack mules in the mountains to the nearest road, and thence by motor truck to the town or railhead.

Iraq

LOCATION AND EXTENT

The forests of Iraq are situated almost exclusively in the extreme north, in the region known as Kurdistan along the frontiers of Turkey and Iran. This is a wild, mountainous tract, underlain very largely by limestones and ranging in altitude from 600 to 3,000 meters, with some peaks rising to more than 3,600 meters. Here mountain forests cover an area of about 2,550,000 hectares. There are also narrow strips of riverain jungle along all the major rivers, such as the Euphrates, Tigris, Greater Zab, Lesser Zab, and Diyala, the area of which may be put at some 20,000 hectares. These natural forests, which represent a mere four per cent of the total land area of Iraq, are for the most part poorly stocked and in a terribly damaged condition.

CLIMATIC AND OTHER INFLUENCES

As in all other countries of this part of the world, rainfall is the dominant factor determining the presence or absence of forest. Over the greater part of Iraq the annual precipitation is less than 150 millimeters, and desert conditions are widespread. In the northern foothills, however, in the vicinity of Mosul, Arbil, and Kirkuk, the rainfall increases to around 700 millimeters; and the increase persists as one continues farther north until the precipitation reaches 1,500 millimeters in the high ranges of the northeast corner between Haji Omran and Penjwin on the Iranian boundary. This is a region of winter precipitation, the wet season being from November to April or even May. Snowfall can be heavy in the mountains and is a factor to be taken into account in afforestation work.

The soils of the mountain region—the only important area as regards forests—are almost exclusively calcareous, mainly derived from Cretaceous limestone, and very easily eroded. Fortunately the rocks weather readily. Hence the soils, although subject to erosion if denuded, have a capacity to recover fairly quickly if protected, more particularly if some vegetative cover exists. This is an important point and an encouraging one; for, if the policy of protection and afforestation now contemplated by the government of Iraq is carried out, there is little doubt that the forests can be rehabilitated over a wide area.

Denudation and erosion have been at work over the whole of the mountain region, and there are few localities where man and his goats have not reduced the forests to the merest scrub or to barren hillsides. Some flagrant examples of this are to be seen on the mountain slopes flanking the fertile Harar valley north of Arbil and on the hills around Sulaimaniya; but the worst erosion, fortunately rather limited in extent, seems to occur on the red marls of the Eocene Red Beds north of Mosul.

Shifting cultivation is undoubtedly the prime factor in forest destruction in Kurdistan. It has been widely practiced for centuries and still continues. Vine culture by primitive methods on unstable slopes is another vicious form of soil mining practiced in the northern mountains and is one of the most potent causes of erosion in recent times. Whole mountainsides have been rendered barren by it. And, while shifting cultivation and improvident vine culture denude the hills of their cover and expose the soil, fire and continuous grazing by goats and sheep keep the vegetation in a degraded condition, inhibit regeneration, and accelerate erosion.

Charcoal burning must be reckoned with as yet another important destructive factor: large areas of oak forest are laid waste every year to feed primitive kilns and little control is exercised over the contractors to whom concessions are granted.

VEGETATIONAL ASSOCIATIONS AND PRINCIPÁL SPECIES

The following is a simple classification of the Iraq forests. As already mentioned, they fall into two regional types: mountain forests, or *ghabat,* and riverain forests of the plains, known as *ahrash.* The former may be divided into three main ecological communities: (*a*) oak (*Quercus*) forest, (*b*) pine (*Pinus*) forest, and (*c*) mountain riverain forest.

OAK FOREST. This consists in the main of low oak scrub, very poorly stocked for the most part and badly degraded by shifting cultivation, overcutting, lopping, fires, and grazing. It seems fairly certain that these forests owe their depleted condition to shifting cultivation in the first instance, and that they have been kept in that state by other adverse factors. But, however that may be, the oak forests constitute the main type of vegetation over the whole of Kurdistan, covering a total area of about 2,550,000 hectares, of which nearly 1,800,000 have been classified as forest fit for reservation, albeit some of it is of extremely poor quality. Within the oak-forest community three distinct associations may be recognized mainly on the basis of altitudinal zonation.

Zone A (450 to 750 meters). *Quercus aegylops,* with *Pistacia khinjuk,* the former predominating. Other associates are *Celtis tournefortii,* some *Quercus infectoria, Ficus carica, Prunus microcarpa, Amygdalus spartioides, Anagyris foetida, Vitex pseudo-negundo,* and *Rhus coriaria,* the last-named mostly west of the Greater Zab. *Nerium oleander* forms thickets along wadi bottoms, but mostly outside the forest. This type occurs mostly in the foothills, and undoubtedly, in the not far distant past, extended some distance into the present steppe region on the low hills that project above the plain between Mosul, Arbil, and Kirkuk.

Zone B (750 to 1,200 meters). *Quercus aegylops* and *Q. infectoria,* with some subsidiary species, notably *Crataegus azarolus, Pyrus syriaca, Prunus microcarpa, Amygdalus orientalis, Rhamnus kurdica, Cercis siliquastrum* (mostly in valleys), an asclepiad climber *Periploca graeca* (in valleys), *Paliurus spina-christi* (in open valley bottoms), and *Rubus* spp. near streams. This constitutes the dominant type over the greater part of Kurdistan, but only in remote and inaccessible mountain valleys and ravines does it form a closed forest. Generally speaking, the formation is an open stunted scrub. It says much for the hardiness of these oaks that they have withstood the vicissitudes of nature and the depredations of man; given protection, they respond quickly and could once more clothe these mountains with a green mantle. *Quercus persica* Jaub. & Spach. is reported in the mountains near Penjwin and Halebja in Sulaimaniya Province along the Iranian frontier. It resembles *Quercus aegylops* var. *brantii.*

Zone C (1,200 to 1,800 meters). *Quercus infectoria,* with *Q. libani* rather locally distributed above 1,350 meters, *Pistacia mutica,* and *Acer cinerascens.* This type occurs mainly in the Mosul Province, as on the Garadagh and in the forests north of Sirsing, toward the Turkish border. In these localities closed forest of good density and moderate quantity occurs, with trees of all age classes. Specimens of *Quercus libani* on the Garadagh have boles up to but rarely exceeding 6 meters in length, and the average height of the trees does not usually exceed 15 meters. Forest of this type must have covered large areas at the higher altitudes in former times but has suffered severely from shifting cultivation. Like the trees in the Kurdish cemeteries its surviving relics seem to commemorate the dead.

Subsidiary species in this association are *Crataegus azarolus, Pyrus syriaca, Lonicera brachypetala,* ivy, and occasionally *Prunus brachypetala* Walp. at the higher altitudes and *Rubus* spp. in the open near streams.

Above 1,800 meters the oak forest thins out and soon disappears. The only indigenous woody species which appear to thrive at higher altitudes are *Daphne angustifolia, Prunus brachypetala* Walp., *Salix purpurea,* and *Betula alba* (a group of this more northerly species of birch has been discovered above the oak forest on Kani Rash on the Iranian frontier).

As in Iran, above the forest zone thorn-cushion and mat plants of the genera *Astragalus* and *Acantholimon* are prevalent. Geophytes are also characteristic of these mountains, and their flowers make a showing in the spring.

PINE FOREST. The Aleppo pine (*Pinus brutia*) is found in a few patches of limited extent in the mountains north of Mosul, where it appears to be confined to the marls of the Eocene Red Beds. The best known area is at Zawita, on the road between Dohuk and Sirsing. *Quercus aegylops* and *Juniperus oxycedrus* are almost invariably associated with the pine. The pine, oak, and juniper are all Mediterranean species. It is therefore significant that plants such as *Fumana arabicum, Argyrolobium crotalarioides, Sideritis kurdica* Bornm., and *Teucrium divaricatum*—other components of the Mediterranean flora—should also be found in this locality. The ground vegetation is generally sparse or lacking; but this may be attributable to goats.

These small outliers of the Aleppo pine are of special interest as they appear to represent the extreme easterly limit of the range of that species. A report of its occurrence in Iran seems very doubtful.

MOUNTAIN RIVERAIN FOREST. This is an interesting type of limited extent, in which the chief species are the chinar or Oriental plane (*Platanus orientalis*), ash (*Fraxinus rotundifolia* Mill.), and willows (mostly *Salix acmophylla*, with *S. purpurea* at the higher altitudes). The plane occurs along rivers in the mountains from 600 meters up to about 1,500 meters, although unfortunately most of the large plane trees have been felled and removed. *Crataegus azarolus* and *Celtis tournefortii* are fairly common throughout, and thickets of *Rubus* spp. are abundant. The walnut (*Juglans regia*) is found in cultivation near villages, but is not, on the whole, abundant.

RIVERAIN FOREST OF THE PLAINS. These forests consist for the most part of low, degraded, but often very dense jungle on the floodplains of the large rivers. They are heavily cut for fuel and brushwood and seldom exceed 20 feet in height. The main species are the Euphrates poplar (*Populus euphratica*), willow (most *Salix acmophylla*), and tamarisk (*Tamarix pentandra* var. *tigrensis* is the commonest species, but there are several others). *Zizyphus spina-christi* occurs, the shrubby liquorice plant (*Glycyrrhiza glabra*) is common, and the low, thorny undershrub *Prosopis stephaniana* is ubiquitous. South of Baghdad *Tamarix articulata* is fairly common.

Although not natural forest, the plantations of poplar deserve mention. They are a conspicuous feature of many villages (e.g., Shaqlawa) in the mountain valleys between 600 and 1,500 meters in the provinces of Mosul and Arbil. The species used is *Populus nigra* (var. *italica*), and reports have it that it was introduced from Iran. These small plantations, no more than narrow strips fringing the banks of streams, are extremely valuable, as the poles when eight years old command a high price as roofing timber.

STATE OF DEVELOPMENT

The forests of Iraq are in a neglected and dilapidated condition as a result of centuries of maltreatment. Steps, however, are now being taken to organize a forest service and to give forestry its proper place in the nation's land-use organization. The need for forest conservation is at last becoming better understood by those responsible for the government of the country. But it will take time to gain the support of the public, even of the educated minority; and it will be many years before the peasants are weaned from their destructive and wasteful practices and convinced that forest protection is in their own interest.

A start has, however, been made. A fully qualified forester has been employed since 1947, at first in an advisory capacity and more recently as Director in charge of the Forestry Division of the Department of Agriculture. The work of demarcating the northern forests has been taken up; some 50,000 hectares have so far been delimited with boundary marks and surveyed; and an aerial survey is contemplated. It is intended to set aside 1,800,000 hectares as reserved forest, representing 70 per cent of the mountain forest area, in order to build up reserves of small timber and fuel, and more especially to protect the mountain catchments of the Tigris and its important tributaries, the Greater and Lesser Zab and the Diyala, all of which rise in or are largely fed from this region. Several afforestation projects have already been undertaken, largely on an experimental scale to start with; but they will soon be expanded as suitable techniques are proved.

In the plains irrigated plantations will be established along the valleys of the principal rivers to the extent of 500,000 hectares; and it is planned to plant the equivalent of 100,000 hectares as farm wood lots, windbreaks, and shelter belts in the cultivated tracts. The ultimate aim is to acquire, at the end of fifty years, a forest estate of about 25,000 square kilometers, which will represent about 5.5 per cent of the total land area of Iraq, or something like 20 per cent of the inhabited portion of the country.

A forest policy has been prepared and a new law drafted to replace the obsolete and inadequate Turkish Forest Law of 1857. A law to control the free-ranging goat, similar to one that has already proved successful in Cyprus, is contemplated. The new Iraq Development Board is taking an interest in forest conservation, more particularly in the afforestation of the mountain catchments of the Greater Zab, Lesser Zab, and Diyala, on each of which a large storage dam has been projected.

Although forestry is still in its infancy in Iraq, efforts are being directed along sound lines. The task is not an easy one and progress will, no doubt, be slow at first; but there is reason to believe that a few more years will see forestry firmly established in this country.

RELATION TO OTHER TYPES OF LAND USE

That forests can play a vital part in the land-use policy of Iraq is indisputable; in fact their role in soil and water conservation is likely to be more important than in timber production. This is particularly true of the mountain forests of Kurdistan, where runoff is severe and erosion widespread. These regions are unlikely to produce large saw logs, though they can yield a useful supply of small agricultural timber, firewood, and charcoal. A protective covering of forest is, however, a vital necessity.

In the realm of farm forestry, too, there is much to be done, but, as we have seen, a start has been made, in connection with certain schemes for rural development, to introduce farm wood lots and windbreaks. Wind erosion and damage to crops by desiccating winds are prevalent, two evils that can be mitigated by establishing shelter belts along the fringes of the cultivated tracts and by employing windbreaks on the individual farms. It is proposed to undertake this type of work under the scheme for afforestation in the plains.

INDUSTRIES BASED ON THE FORESTS

At present there is nothing that could be described as a forest industry, apart, perhaps, from the charcoal business, which is carried out in a haphazard and ill-organized way. Efforts are now being made to control fellings so as to check overexploitation of the badly depleted forests; but there is still much waste in connection both with the fellings and the manufacture of the charcoal, which is burnt in a primitive type of kiln. The quantity of timber utilized in the manufacture of charcoal in 1949 was 80,000 cubic meters.

For 1949 the yield of round logs and squared timber was given as 820 cubic meters, of poles (mostly poplar) as 5,800 cubic meters, and of fuel (chiefly oak) as 8,000 cubic meters. Minor products are gums, resins, and oak galls. The 1949 output of gums and resins was given as 25 tons, valued at 3,600 dinars, and of oak galls as 65 tons, valued at 13,200 dinars. Such statistics, however, are unreliable.

Future development lies in two directions. The mountain forests, apart from their protective role, will be managed mainly for the production of small agricultural timber, firewood, and charcoal. It is also likely that the production of oak galls for tanning will be enlarged. The greatest scope for development, however, lies in the expansion of irrigated plantations on the plains. Quick-growing hard and softwoods will be planted here, and, in particular, species of eucalyptus and poplar. The yield of these plantations should make it possible to develop such industries as the manufacture of matches, plywood, hardwood and softwood boards, and possibly even of paper pulp.

The Arabian Peninsula

The Arabian Peninsula, which exceeds 460,000 square kilometers in area and is thus almost as large as the Indian subcontinent, has probably less forest than any other tract of similar size in the world, apart from Antarctica and the Sahara. This, of course, is due to the desert conditions which prevail over practically the whole region, most of which receives less than 100 millimeters of rainfall annually. Indeed, only on the highlands of the Hejaz, the Yemen, the Aden hinterland, and the Hadhramaut—the Arabia Felix of the ancients—is there an appreciable precipitation. Here the annual rainfall is 400 millimeters or more, increasing to 800 millimeters in the extreme southwest of the Yemen, where the influence of the southwest monsoon is felt.

It is only in this latter high-rainfall region, in the mountains of the Hejaz, and to a lesser extent in those of Qara and the Hadhramaut, that forest cover of any kind is to be found. The type of vegetation in these regions is for the most part a low thorn-scrub, much degraded over many centuries by cutting and incessant browsing by camels and goats. Here and there in the less accessible parts scattered small trees are occasionally met with, and along the western escarpment and in the mountains of the Hejaz one finds some closed forest. Broadly speaking, however, the area that can be classed as forest is very limited. Owing to the arid climate, the destructive hand of man, and the ravages of his flocks, it seems improbable that at any time since the beginning of the Christian era or for several centuries before it the forests have been more extensive than they are at present. The region within which the forests of western and southwestern Arabia do occur is extremely mountainous. The ranges of the Hejaz rise to 2,700 meters, while the tablelands of the Yemen have an average altitude of 2,400 meters, with peaks towering to more than 3,650 meters. Many mountains of the Hadhramaut in the western part of the Aden Protectorate reach 1,800 to 2,100 meters.

So little is known about the meager forests of the Hejaz, Yemen, and the Aden hinterland that an accurate description of their floristic composition and ecological status cannot be given. The following is a short list of the principal trees and more important shrub species known to occur in these regions.[2]

The Red Sea Coast. There is no forest in the whole of this tract, apart from the white mangrove (*Avicennia marina*), which occurs at Rabigh in the Hejaz and forms small woods in salt marshes and on islands on the coast from the neighborhood of Jidda southward, including Hanish and other islands. The mangrove formation is well developed on parts of the coast of 'Asir and particularly about Luheiya in Yemen. The red mangrove (*Rhizophora mucronata*) is also found along the coast in the region of Hodeida. Although not actually forming closed forests, *Acacia seyal*, *A. ehrenbergiana*, *A. orfota*, *A. arabica*, *Capparis decidua*, and *Tamarix gallica* occur in wadies, and the dum palm (*Hyphaene thebaica*), which reaches its northern limit near the Gulf of Suez, is a common tree of the lowlands. Henna (*Lawsonia inermis*), date palms, and tamarinds (*Tamarindus indicus*) are cultivated.

At the Lower Altitudes and up to 1,500 Meters. *Zizyphus spina-christi*, *Prosopis spicigera*, *Tamarix articulata*, *Salvadora persica*, *Acacia flava*, *A. edgeworthii* (along wadies in the Hadhramaut), *Adenium* sp., the euphorbia tree (*Euphorbia ammak* Schweinf.), myrrh (*Commiphora abyssinica* var. *simplicifolia*), balsam or "balm of Gilead" (*Commiphora opobalsamum*), the frankincense tree (*Boswellia carteri*), *Aloe sabaea*, the wild fig trees *Ficus salicifolia* and *F. populifolia*, *Erica arborea* (in the Hejaz), *Osyris abyssinica* Hochst., *Salix babylonica*, and the asclepiadaceous shrub *Calatropis procera*. *Juniperus phoenicia* occurs at 4,000 feet in the mountains of Midian in northwestern Saudi Arabia and *J. macrocarpa* in the mountains of Oman.

[2] This list is not based on personal knowledge of the region, but has been compiled from the writings of Hugh Scott, Wilfred Thesiger, and D. Van der Meulen, and other sources.

At Elevations of from 1,500 to 2,700 Meters. Acacia seyal, A. senegal, Juniperus spp., wild olive (*Olea chrysophylla*), *Nuxia dentata* Benth., *Traconanthus camphoratus,* and *Cotoneaster nummularia.*

The flora of the 'Asir and Yemen highlands is the richest in Arabia. Narrow bands of fringing forest follow the mountain rivers in their steep descent, forming a zone of tropical vegetation, especially in the hot valleys of the Yemen at about 1,200 meters where *Ficus salicifolia, F. populifolia,* leguminous trees, and *Trichilia emetica* (Meliaceae) form patches of forest. *Phoenix reclinata* Jacq. is found in dense thickets along streams between 600 and 1,500 meters. Acanthaceous shrubs and undershrubs of the genera *Barleria, Ruellia, Justicia,* and *Crossandra,* and the prickly-leaved *Acanthus racemosus* are conspicuous at about 1,800 meters, and a widespread African buddleia (*Buddleia polystachya*) with orange spikes of scented blossoms also occurs in the Yemen at about 2,100 meters.

Socotra. The majority of the islands around the coast of Arabia, except for Socotra, are treeless. The flora of Socotra resembles that of the Somali coast and has been much studied. Some 600 species of flowering plants and ferns have been recorded. Many of the trees are remarkable for their swollen, gouty trunks, such as *Dendrosicyos sokotrana* and *Adenium sokotranum.* In the valleys there are small woods of a local red-flowered frankincense tree (*Boswellia ameero*), and above 300 meters of the dragon's blood tree (*Dracaena serrulata* Baker). The latter, which also occurs along the south coast of the mainland of Arabia in the Hadhramaut, yields a ruby-colored resin, the "cinnabar" of Pliny, from which a varnish is made. A wild pomegranate (*Punica protopunica* Balf., f.) and wild oranges are also reported. *Buxus hildebrandtii,* the Socotra box, is locally abundant.

In none of the states comprising the Arabian Peninsula is there at the time of writing any forest administration, nor has any attempt been made to protect or rehabilitate the small areas of forest that do exist. While it is true that there is not much scope for genuine forestry in this largely desolate region, something could well be done in the direction of tree planting on farms in the more fertile parts of the west and southwest, where relatively humid conditions prevail.

No wood-using industries of much importance exist. Frankincense and myrrh, for which the region (more particularly the mountains of Dhufar, Qara, and the Hadhramaut) was famous in Biblical times, continue to be collected and exported, the annual quantity varying from about 200 to 400 tons.

Jordan

LOCATION AND EXTENT. The state of Jordan as at present constituted consists of (*a*) a portion of Palestine including the towns of Hebron, Bethlehem, old Jerusalem, Ramallah, Nablus, Jenin, and Jericho, to the west of the River Jordan; (*b*) a 95-kilometer strip east of the Jordan

Valley; (c) the escarpment bounding the valley and the Wadi Araba farther south, with the mountains above it, which rise to a maximum altitude of about 1,800 meters; (d) the eastern desert, which begins about 30 to 40 kilometers east of the escarpment and stretches away to the borders of Iraq, occupying more than half the country.

The forests, such as they are, are situated in regions (a) and (c). It is certain that the mountain range, which stretches from Ajlun to the head of the Gulf of Aqaba along the eastern flank of the Jordan Valley and Wadi Araba, was formerly well covered with oak (mainly *Quercus coccifera*) forest and with juniper (*Juniperus phoenicia*) on the escarpment south of Tafileh. A good part of this forest is known to have survived until about 1900 or even later, after which it suffered severely from the cutting of fuel to supply the Hejaz Railway. The forests in western Jordan (i.e., Arab Palestine) received some protection and care between 1920 and 1947 but were devastated during the internecine turmoil of 1947-48, and are now in a sadly damaged and depleted condition.

The forested and scrub-covered areas of Jordan have been estimated at 153,133 hectares, subdivided as follows:

	Hectares
Existing closed forest	70,333
Recently afforested	800
Open scrub	82,000
TOTAL	153,133

In addition, there are some 169,000 hectares of wasteland, most of it submarginal and unfit for permanent agriculture. It is hoped to add some of this to the existing reserves and to afforest it. Ultimately the area under permanent forest in Jordan may well amount to at least 260,000 hectares.

CLIMATIC AND OTHER INFLUENCES. Rainfall is the dominant factor; the area where natural forest can exist lies entirely within the region receiving an annual precipitation of at least 150, and, preferably, 200 millimeters. Over a very large tract in the eastern half of the country, which receives less than the necessary amount of rain, the vegetation is that of a steppe and in places even of a desert. Jordan, like the Mediterranean region as a whole, is an area of winter rainfall (November-April), and the flora—particularly in western Jordan—is also of a Mediterranean type. The annual rainfall in the Palestine hills is of the order of 500 to 600 millimeters; while the main range above the escarpment in eastern Jordan (formerly Transjordan) gets 800 millimeters around Salt and Ajlun in the north, but only about 400 millimeters farther south at Tafileh and Shaubek. East of the range the precipitation soon dwindles to less than 100 millimeters.

Extremely high temperatures are experienced in the Jordan Valley during the summer months; here tropical conditions prevail, and plants such as bananas, dates, and sugar cane can be grown. On the mountains of eastern Jordan the summer is mild and dry, and low temperatures are common during the winter. Snow is by no means rare during the period December-February, but only in exceptional years, such as 1949-50, does it lie on the ground for more than a day or two.

Since the rocks are predominantly Cretaceous limestones, the soils are highly calcareous. Sandstone and igneous rocks occur—mainly in the south—but have no influence on the forest vegetation.

VEGETATIONAL ASSOCIATIONS AND PRINCIPAL SPECIES. The following is an outline of the main forest types and their condition.

Oak Forest. The principal species is *Quercus coccifera,* which often constitutes as much as 75 per cent or even more of the crop. The following are its more important associates: *Pistacia terebinthus, Crataegus azarolus, Arbutus andrachne, Pyrus syriaca, Styrax officinalis, Prunus ursina, Rhamnus palaestina, R. alaternus, Olea europaea* var. *oleaster, Amygdalus communis, Rhus coriaria, Lonicera etrusca,* and occasionally in the north *Spartium junceum.* Where the stands are dense, as is sometimes the case, there is little or no undergrowth; but, where they are open, *Poterium spinosum* and *Phlomis viscosa* occur locally with *Echium* spp. and *Onosma* spp. *Quercus infectoria* is often present and sometimes forms an appreciable element in the Ajlun and Wadi Sham forests, especially on the escarpment between 760 and 1,100 meters, where the rainfall is about 600 to 800 millimeters. The parent rock underlying the forest of this type is always limestone. *Quercus aegylops* comes in toward the extreme north on top of the escarpment, as in the Juffain forest, where it occurs in pure but very open stands. The carob (*Ceratonia siliqua*) also occurs in this oak association in both eastern and western Jordan, but only sparingly and where frost is not severe.

This association, with its minor variants, is clearly a form of maquis vegetation. It probably covered all the mountains of Jordan to a greater or lesser degree until forty or fifty years ago; and, in spite of heavy browsing by camels and goats, small remnants of *Quercus coccifera* still survive at an altitude of 1,650 meters even as far as the vicinity of Shaubek, but with few associates except *Pistacia terebinthus* and *Crataegus.* In western Jordan (e.g., at Um el Rihan) *Pistacia lentiscus* and *P. atlantica* are more frequent associates, and *Spartium* increases in abundance.

Pine Forest. This community occurs in the north only, on limestone at 2,500 to 3,000 feet, where the rainfall is about 600 to 800 millimeters. It is confined to a rather limited area around Ajlun, where it is best seen at Dibbin. *Pinus halepensis* predominates, with a sparse lower story of *Quercus coccifera, Arbutus andrachne,* and less commonly *Pistacia terebinthus* and *Crataegus azarolus,* with *Cistus villosus* and *C. salvifolius* also common in the undergrowth and *Poterium spinosum* in the more open places. The pine regenerates abundantly.

Juniper Forest. Juniperus phoenicia forms a very open type of woodland south of Tafileh for some 30 to 50 kilometers—as far as and beyond

Shaubek.[3] On the steep westerly slopes of the escarpment above the Wadi Araba at 900 to 1,200 meters, where the rainfall is about 400 millimeters, it grows on sandstone. A few shrubby specimens of *Q. coccifera* and *Pistacia terebinthus* are its sole woody associates. The endemic shrub *Daphne linearifolia* is found in the forest of this type and extends with the juniper as far south as Petra. Two species of *Astragalus,* a *Phlomis,* and *Poterium spinosum* are the principal constituents of the ground flora, together with *Origanum* and other herbs, several of which are labiates.

Pistacia Forest. This community, represented very sparingly in the steppe region, was probably more widespread in former times. The dominant species is *Pistacia atlantica.* It occurs in the Wadi el-Butum along the bank of a dry watercourse, with a few associates such as *Retama raetam, Artemisia herba-alba,* and *Atriplex.* Elsewhere, it is found as far south as Petra in scattered collections of trees or as solitary individuals, with no woody associates and often with little perennial vegetation of any kind.

All the forests of Jordan are in a more or less degraded condition, owing to overcutting and overgrazing in the past, and also to shifting cultivation. Nevertheless, the forests of eastern Jordan are showing signs of recovery as a result of the protection that has been afforded them during the past six or seven years. Much of the oak forest of the Wadi Sham is very dense, and the pine forests of Dibbin are regenerating remarkably well. The forests of western Jordan are still suffering from the vicissitudes of the recent past and from the depredations of the many refugees who depend on them for fuel.

There are no natural forests in the Jordan Valley, but only thickets of *Tamarix jordanis, Populus euphratica, Salix* spp., oleander, *Vitex agnus-castus,* the shrubby *Conyza dioscoridis,* liquorice (*Glycyrrhiza glabra*), *Arundo donax,* and the ubiquitous undershrub *Prosopis stephaniana,* which in places form a dense jungle along the banks of the river. *Zizyphus lotus* and *Moringa aptera* occur occasionally, while *Salvadora persica* and *Calatropis procera* have been recorded.

STATE OF DEVELOPMENT. Forest management is still in its early stages in Jordan, but a start was made in 1947, with good results. Considerable areas have been successfully afforested in undertakings in which *gradoni* and contour strip planting have been much employed. The work of survey and demarcation is making rapid progress. As must be expected at this stage, there is a dearth of trained staff, but steps are being taken to make this good. The forest service, still only a section of the Department of Agriculture, is headed by a competent officer who took a course of practical training in Cyprus.

---

[3] In this same region, on the top of the escarpment at about 1,500 meters, the very remarkable occurrence of a few ancient, relict specimens of cypress (*Cupressus sempervirens*) suggests that this tree once had a much more southerly distribution in this region.

An adequate forest law exists and is efficiently enforced. A general program of forest policy has been drafted and, it is hoped, will soon be adopted by the government. A law on the lines of the Cyprus goat law to control free-range grazing has recently been passed. This is a delicate matter, and some years may elapse before it really becomes effective, as the way will have to be prepared for it by educating the peasantry—especially the shepherds—as to its necessity.

Forestry in Jordan is now at that stage where the principal work is conservation—the demarcation, survey, and protection of those natural forests that have survived the vicissitudes of at least three millennia of human activities. This work is proceeding apace, and afforestation has been initiated. When more trained men become available, progress will be more rapid.

Data regarding the production of certain items from the forests of Jordan follow:

	1951	1952	1953
Firewood (tons)	9,939	22,700	21,500
Charcoal (tons) [a]	2,213	4,107	4,372
Timber (cubic meters)	2,037	3,670	3,361
Wooden ploughs (number) [b]	4,165	8,591	5,240

[a] Mostly from private forests.
[b] Entirely from the state forests.

RELATION TO OTHER FORMS OF LAND USE. One of the most important aspects of forestry in Jordan is that of soil conservation. The easily erodible soils derived from the soft limestones have been terribly denuded and subjected to all sorts of abuse from the earliest times, for Jordan is known to have been populated since the Palaeolithic and has experienced several periods of prosperity, starting with one in the Bronze Age. Several flourishing colonies existed—e.g., Gerasa (Jerash) and Philadelphia (now Amman)—during the Hellenistic (*ca.* 320 B.C. to 68 B.C.) and Roman (64 B.C. to *ca.* A.D. 400) periods, when the population was probably greater—at any rate in eastern Jordan—than it is at present. Even the now-arid southern tract had at least a moderately dense population—witness the ancient town of Petra of the Sabataeans and the scores of abandoned reservoirs and cisterns along the fringe of the eastern desert.

The importance of soil conservation has been fully appreciated, and most of the current afforestation projects have this as their main objective. Soil erosion is a serious matter in Jordan. One of its chief causes is the shortage of fuel and the consequent clearing of brush soil cover to supply firewood and charcoal; even undershrubs like *Poterium spinosum* and *Ononis vaginalis* are scraped off the hills to meet this demand. In the vicinity of the refugee camps denudation has been greatly intensified. The provision of cheap oil-burning stoves would help solve this problem.

Pasture management is another problem of land use that the forest service must solve in collaboration with the other services, if the government is to succeed in controlling goat grazing. This is a major issue, and one that will call for perseverance and tact. Experiments are about to be initiated with a view to improving pastures in open forests and introducing some form of rotational grazing. Trees suitable for pollarding for forage or with edible fruits (e.g., *Prosopis juliflora*) are being introduced in order to encourage the stall feeding of stock.

INDUSTRIES BASED ON THE FORESTS. At present there are no forest industries in Jordan, nor is there much prospect of any being started in the near future. If the country can become self-sufficient in small building and agricultural timber, firewood, and charcoal, which should be possible, it will be doing about as much as can be expected. The value of the forests will lie, not so much in what they produce, as in the protection they afford to the soil and water supply and in the amenity they provide to the country at large.

SOURCES FOR BOTANICAL NOMENCLATURE

BLATTER, ETHELBERT. 1919-1921. "Flora Arabica," *Records of the Botanical Survey of India,* 8:1-365.

POST, G. E. 1932. *Flora of Syria, Palestine and Sinai.* 2 vols. (2d ed. revised by J. E. Dinsmore.) American Press, Beirut.

TCHIHATCHEFF, P. DE. 1860. *Asie Mineure, description physique, statistique et archéologique de cette contrée.* 2 vols. Imprimerie de J. Claye, Paris.

VIERHAPPER, FRITZ. 1907. *Beiträge zur Kenntnis der Flora Südarabiens.* Kaiserlich-Königliche Hof- und Staatsdruckerei, Vienna.

20.   PAKISTAN

S. A. Vahid

Area and General Distribution of Forests

The two parts of Pakistan, West and East, are characterized by distinct climatic, topographical, and soil conditions, and these differences find expression in the character and composition of the forests. The treeless areas of Sind and Baluchistan, with their extremely arid climate, are in marked contrast to the dense evergreen forests of Sylhet and the Chittagong Hill Tracts of East Pakistan. Human activity has also greatly influenced the existing distribution, stocking, and composition of the forests.

Figure 45 shows the distribution of forests in Pakistan. According to the inventory taken in 1953 by the Forestry Division of FAO the total forest area in 1948 was about 2,700,000 hectares (10,400 square miles), of which 2,300,000 hectares were accessible and 400,000 inaccessible, the total being approximately 2.8 per cent of the total land area of the country, making a ratio of about 0.04 hectare per capita. Figures for the states, especially the frontier states of the northwest, which also comprise large tracts of valuable coniferous forests, are unavailable, but it is estimated that their total forested area is about 3,000 square miles (770,000 hectares).

The percentage of forest area in the country is very low, and the actual position may be even worse than the statistics indicate, because in many cases (Baluchistan, for instance) areas classed as forests have hardly any trees, and some are totally unsuitable for forests.

The above figures compare very unfavorably with the corresponding data for other countries, except perhaps in the Middle East. They fall far short of the arbitrary minimum of about 20 per cent needed for the balanced economy of an agricultural country such as Pakistan.

The distribution of natural forests in Pakistan is primarily a function of climate. The present pattern, however, has been influenced by subsequent and secondary factors, the most potent being the spread of population and modern means of transport. The forests of Pakistan can be broadly divided into two categories, natural and plantation forests.

Natural forests are met with in the following areas:

a) The northern and northwestern uplands of West Pakistan. Area: about 1260 square miles.

b) The dry hill forests of Baluchistan and the tribal areas in the west. Area: about 1980 square miles.

c) The plains forests along river valleys in West Pakistan. Area: about 1680 square miles.

d) Dry scrub forests in the plains of the Punjab. Area: 313 square miles.

e) Evergreen and semi-evergreen forests on the eastern boundary of East Pakistan. Area: 2660 square miles.

f) Tidal forests in the Khulna, Barisal, and Chittagong districts of East Pakistan. Area: 1252 square miles.

g) Central high alluvial-plains forests of Dacca and Mymensingh districts of East Pakistan. Area: 670 square miles.

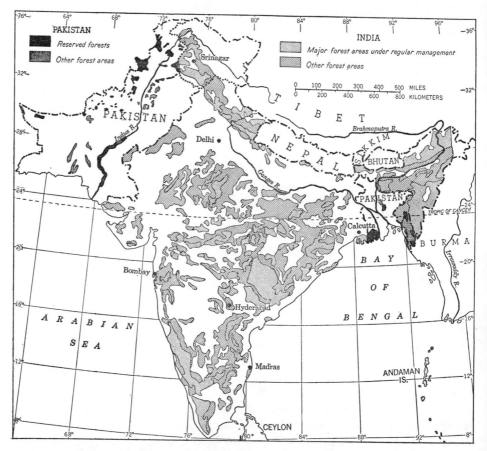

FIG. 45. India and Pakistan: forest areas.

The artificial or plantation forests are mostly confined to the Punjab in West Pakistan, though they are being created in increasing numbers in Sind and the North-West Frontier Province. These forests occur on thickly populated plains, chiefly along canals. Their present area is estimated as 200 square miles.

There is ample historical evidence to show that the sparse vegetation cover in West Pakistan is in large part the result of the incessant march through the ages of invading armies over the northwest of the subcontinent. Huns, Sakas, Aryans, Greeks, Pathans, Persians, and Moguls have all ravaged the region in turn. Alexander's armies are reported to have traversed this territory under cover of dense jungle. As late as the sixteenth century Babar in his famous "Memoirs" recorded luxuriant forest growth in Sind and the Punjab. Later, under British administration, the forests suffered heavily from destructive exploitation.

In East Pakistan, too, much deforestation has taken place. There has been considerable clearing for tea gardens in Sylhet and Chittagong and for agricultural use, owing to pressure of population, in the Sundarbans, Khulna, Bakarganj, Chittagong, Dacca, and Mymensingh districts. Even today squatters are a serious menace in the Dacca-Mymensingh forests and claim a sizable amount of forest land every year. The damage, however, has not been permanent, thanks to favorable tropical conditions of growth.

Forest Types

WEST PAKISTAN

Northern and Northwestern Hill Forests. These forests are found in the Rawalpindi District of the Punjab, the Hazara District of the North-West Frontier Province, and the hill states of Dir, Swat, Chitral, and Amb in the Malakand Agency, as well as in Kashmir. They occur from about 3,000 feet to about 10,000 feet above sea level and are mainly coniferous where deodar (*Cedrus deodara*),[1] kail (*Pinus excelsa*), spruce (*Picea morinda*), fir (*Abies* spp.), and, on hot southerly aspects at low altitudes, chir (*Pinus longifolia*) predominate. Precipitation, mostly in the form of snow, is highest in the eastern part of this belt (about 50 inches), but gradually decreases towards the west. Fir and spruce occupy the highest altitudes, while deodar and kail are found immediately below them. Common broadleaf associates of this forest type, depending upon altitude, aspect, and rainfall, are oak (*Quercus*), maple (*Acer*), willow (*Salix*), birch (*Betula*), horse chestnut (*Aesculus*), poplar (*Populus*), walnut (*Juglans*), juniper (*Juniperus*), and the usual rosaceous plants. Above 10,000 feet tree growth is replaced by alpine pasture covered in summer by multitudes of herbaceous flowering plants.

Submontane Siwalik Type. These forests extend up to an altitude of about 3,000 feet in the Gujrat, Jhelum, Rawalpindi, and Campbellpur Districts of the Punjab, and in the Hazara, Mardan, Peshawar, and Kohat Districts of the North-West Frontier Province, where the climate is dry and extreme in the cold and hot seasons. Chir is met with at the upper levels, but the typical forest formation is phulai (*Acacia modesta*), kao (*Olea cuspidata*), *Prosopis spicigera*, *Dodonaea viscosa*, *Zizyphus* spp., etc. Baib (*Ischaemum angustifolium*) and other rougher grasses are profuse.

[1] For sources of botanical nomenclature see below, p. 454.

Baluchistan Hill Forests. These forests occur from about 5,000 to 10,000 feet above sea level and are comparatively dry and in a somewhat moribund state at present. Chilgoza (*Pinus gerardiana*) and pencil juniper (*Juniperus macropoda*) are the two important species, but other hardy and drought-resisting species are also met with.

Riverine Forests. These are found along the big rivers of West Pakistan and are locally known as bela forests. They are generally confined to areas subject to annual inundations or seepage on either side of the rivers. Here occur species requiring good drainage, such as shisham (*Dalbergia sissoo*) and babul (*Acacia arabica*), and also those that can stand waterlogging, such as *Butea frondosa* and willows. The commonest species is babul, which occurs extensively except in northern localities subject to frost. Other associates are *Prosopis spicigera, Tamarix* spp., and *Populus euphratica.* This type is found in Sind and the Punjab.

The Rakhs. Rakhs are the scrub forests found all over the Punjab plains. Most of them occur away from human habitation and have not been destroyed so far because of their relative inaccessibility. They comprise typical xerophytic communities, with *Prosopis spicigera, Salvadora oleoides, Capparis* spp., *Acacia* spp., *Dodonaea viscosa,* and *Tamarix* spp. prevailing.

Irrigated Plantations. Plantations, pure or mixed, have been created by the Forest Department, mostly in the Punjab, but also in Sind and the North-West Frontier Province. The species generally grown are shisham (*Dalbergia sissoo*) and mulberry (*Morus alba*), though to a small extent babul, bakain (*Melia azedarach*), *Eucalyptus* spp., and *Prosopis* spp. have also been tried.

EAST PAKISTAN

There are five well-defined forest types in East Pakistan, together with certain minor vegetational communities.

Tropical Evergreen and Semi-Evergreen Forests. This is the most important type. It occurs in the vicinity of Cox's Bazar in the Chittagong District, and also in the Chittagong Hill Tracts and Sylhet. Uniform stands of evergreens are confined to depressions and valleys with an adequate water supply and comparatively humid conditions. On other sites the crop is semi-evergreen with a mixture of deciduous trees. The main species found are: chapalash (*Artocarpus chaplasha*), telsur (*Hopea odorata*), chemdul (*Tetrameles nudiflora*), narikol (*Sterculia alata*), and tali (*Palaquium polyanthum*). Trees of semi-evergreen type which have high commercial value are: garjan (*Dipterocarpus* spp.), semal (*Bombax malabaricum*), and koroi (*Albizzia procera*). Their height ranges from 80 feet to 200 feet. Garjan trees are particularly conspicuous on account of their size. There are subsidiary canopies of trees and other vegetation consisting of canes and bamboos, which form a dense undergrowth, sometimes too thick to penetrate without the aid of elephants.

In the Chittagong Hill Tracts large areas of semi-evergreen forest have been converted into beautiful stands of teak (*Tectona grandis*), the oldest plantation being more than 75 years old. Encouraged by the success of the operation, the technique of clear-cutting and regenerating the forest under the taungya system is being adopted on a large scale.

Tidal Forests. These are found near Cox's Bazar and in the Sundarbans. Important timber trees are: sundri (*Heritiera fomes*), passur (*Carapa moluccensis*), dhundul (*Carapa obovata*), gengwa (*Excoecaria agallocha*) and goran (*Ceriops roxburghiana*). Golpatta (*Nipa fruticana*), the well-known palm used for roofing, occurs along the banks. It has been noticed that the quality of the crop is inversely proportional to the salinity of the water.

Fresh-Water Low-Level Forests. Species such as hijal (*Barringtonia acutangula*), boran (*Crataeva religiosa*), and jarul (*Lagerstroemia* spp.) occur in low-level watery regions in East Bengal, especially in the southern parts of the Sylhet and Mymensingh Districts. These species regenerate well in some areas and can grow even under water.

Open Deciduous Forests. These occur in open and dry localities near Cox's Bazar and in the Chittagong Hills. The principal species are: koroi (*Albizzia procera*), pitali (*Trewia nudiflora*), bahera (*Terminalia belerica*), kanchan (*Bauhinia* spp.), and amlaki (*Phyllanthus emblica*). The forests are usually confined to exposed hilltops with scanty water supply, and are stunted in growth. The undergrowth is devoid of bamboos, which are a common feature of evergreen and semi-evergreen forests.

Sal Forests. Sal (*Shorea robusta*) occurs on the plains of the Dacca and Mymensingh Districts and on the high alluvium between the Brahmaputra and the Ganges. This type is perhaps a remnant of once virgin sal forests, subsequently overcut and depleted. The existing crop is mostly of coppice origin. Associates of sal are: bahera (*Terminalia belerica*), hargaza (*Dillenia pentagyna*), and koroi (*Albizzia procera*).

Minor Vegetational Communities. Many species of bamboos are found practically all over the evergreen and semi-evergreen forests of Chittagong and Sylhet and near Cox's Bazar. They predominate in the evergreen forests, particularly in areas where tree species are few, but in some places they also occur gregariously.

Another minor vegetational community occurs occasionally in East Pakistan, the savanna type, in which woody shrubs and bamboos or grasses and reeds such as *Imperata arundinacea* Cyril. and *Saccharum spontaneum* predominate. While the former occurs on the well-drained sites, the latter is invariably found in swampy localities. The savannas occur in patches and may be attributed to retrogression brought about by biotic and other factors.

Ownership

Except for relatively small areas in the North-West Frontier Province and East Pakistan, the forests of the country are mostly government-owned. Not all government forests, however, are managed by the forest departments. Supervision of the rakhs, or scrub forests of the Punjab, and control of grazing in forest areas in Baluchistan are vested with the revenue authorities.

The basic policy is to manage the forests primarily for the benefit of the public, particularly the rural population, whose economy depends upon them to a great extent. The Forest Act, therefore, divides the government forests into reserved, protected, and unclassed categories, depending upon the degree to which the rights and privileges of the farmers and other communities living near the forests are regulated. The term "forests" according to the Act, applies also to government lands that are devoid of trees but have been classed as forests for purposes of control.

Utilization of Forest Produce

Strictly speaking, forest industries in the sense in which they are understood in highly industrialized countries have not yet appeared in Pakistan. The partition of the Punjab and Bengal provinces deprived Pakistan of the best forest lands of these provinces. Apart from the fact that the proportion of the land area in forests is extremely inadequate, the forests are so distributed that they can meet the requirements of only a part of the country. Extensive stretches of land have no forest at all.

Pakistan has an essentially agricultural economy. The farmers are content to use backward methods of cultivation, and the standard of living of the rural populations is generally low. Utility services and communications are not sufficiently developed, except in and between towns. In a country where neither coal, electricity, nor gas are available to the farmers, the only standby for cooking and heating purposes is firewood. On the plains and treeless tracts where firewood is either unavailable or, if available owing to proximity to a road or town, sells at a price that the farmer cannot afford to pay, he is forced to burn animal dung for cooking. This vicious practice, although under present circumstances a necessary evil, deprives the land of fertilizer. The baneful effects of the scarcity of forests thus impinge directly on the agricultural economy and hinder attempts to raise the rural standard of living.

The principal use to which the forests in this country are put is for firewood and small timber for construction, and 75 per cent of the yield is consumed in these forms. Actual requirements for firewood and timber, including railway sleepers, are far in excess of the supply. The scarcity of timber near industrial towns or highways is largely responsible for the neglect of forest industries.

In West Pakistan practically all the irrigated and inundated forests of the plains and all the scrub forests of the foothills are worked for firewood. Utilization, especially in the plantations, is generally complete, with practically no wastage. Clear-felling with artificial regeneration is practiced in the inundated forests, where the principal tree species is babul (*Acacia arabica*), while the irrigated plantations are worked on a coppice-with-standards system. Standards of shisham (*Dalbergia sissoo*) are grown in three rotations and are used for furniture making, for which purpose shisham provides one of the most suitable timbers.

The timber requirements of West Pakistan are almost entirely met from the coniferous forests of the North-West Frontier Province, the Murree Hills, and the State of Jammu and Kashmir. The forests occur mostly on relatively inaccessible hills. Methods of exploitation are somewhat primitive and involve considerable waste. Forest working in the remote regions entails heavy investment, and hence the products marketed have to be of fairly high quality in order to make the operations pay their way. Inferior classes of timber, especially of small and medium sizes, are left in the forest because the high costs of handling and low price render marketing uneconomical. It is estimated that not more than 40 per cent of the standing volume of coniferous forests is actually marketed. For the same reason, management of these forests is also seriously handicapped, in that no thinnings can be carried out, to the detriment of the final crop. The comparatively accessible Murree Hills, near the market and served by a network of forest roads, are, however, an exception, and admit of an intensive and complete exploitation.

These forests are important in the local economy. The countryside is mountainous, agricultural land is scarce, and the pressure of population heavy. Forest operations, such as felling, logging, sawing, carriage, and floating, provide employment for thousands of farmers near their homes and are a mainstay of their economy.

In East Pakistan the forests cover comparatively large areas, but are mostly undeveloped, because means of transport are very difficult or nonexistent and only a small number of the tree species are of commercial value under the present market conditions. There is also a dearth of labor in some of these forests, a problem for which the solution seems to lie in the use of machinery for many operations. Mechanization has already been started on a modest scale, and it is confidently hoped that soon the hitherto untapped forest reserves will prove a great asset to the country.

As in West Pakistan, the scarcity of firewood and of small-sized timber is acute in the northern districts of East Bengal, which are devoid of forests and have a large population.

Forest Industries

Although the organization of major forest industries is on the whole in a backward condition, there are a number of small industries, the most important being the manufacture of sporting goods, furniture, matches, packing cases, umbrella handles, rifle butts, and boats, and the production of resin, pharmaceuticals, and paper.

The world-famous sporting-goods industry of Sialkot (Punjab) depends largely upon local supplies of mulberry, bakain (*Melia azedarach*), bamboo, and ash (*Fraxinus* spp.). Following the partition, the industry received a serious setback. Supplies of bat willow from Kashmir were completely cut off, and attempts are being made to tap alternative sources. Willows grown in Baluchistan and the North-West Frontier Province and some stocks imported from Afghanistan are being used as a substitute for the Kashmir willow.

Furniture making is perhaps the commonest industry drawing on the forests for raw material. Where shisham, teak, walnut (*Juglans regia*), or other suitable timbers are unavailable, any timber found locally is used for this purpose.

Before the partition, the match industry in India depended upon supplies of indigenous semal (*Bombax malabaricum*), while aspen (*Populus*) was imported from the Scandinavian countries. The factories were located in and near semal-bearing forests, although a few small plants were operated in the Punjab as well. Since the supplies from Bharat were cut off, the plants in West Pakistan have used substitutes such as poplar, blue pine (*Pinus excelsa*), and chir pine (*Pinus longifolia*), but with limited success. In Jammu and Kashmir willow and poplar are used for the manufacture of matches.

There is a great demand for packing cases for multifarious purposes, including crates for fruits and tea chests. Almost all of the lighter hardwoods are used for packing cases, and in West Pakistan a fir (*Abies pindrow*) with a nonresinous wood is also used to a limited extent.

Canes suitable for umbrella handles are found in large quantities in East Pakistan, and, despite difficulties of extraction and transport, the handles are manufactured largely as a cottage industry.

Among small-scale industries using wood are the manufacture of rifle butts and fore-ends, and boat building. For the former, walnut, maple, birdcherry (*Prunus padus*), and shisham are used; for the latter, timbers common in East Pakistan.

There are also industries based on minor forest products, the most important being the resin industry. Resin is obtained from the forests of chir pine (*Pinus longifolia*) of the Punjab and the North-West Frontier Province. A resin factory at Jallo (Punjab), owned by the government, has a distilling capacity of about 6,000 tons a year. The products of distillation, rosin, and turpentine are mostly exported. Local requirements are generally met from the produce of small distilleries installed by private enterprise.

Pakistan is very rich in plants of medicinal value, e.g., artemisia, belladonna (*Artropa belladonna*), podophyllum (*Podophyllum emodi*), ephedra (*Ephedra intermedia*), and kuth (*Saussurea lappa*). Large quantities of these are exported, but a flourishing pharmaceutical industry is fast developing, which aims at manufacturing drugs in the country. A factory has been constructed at Rawalpindi (Punjab) for the manufacture of santonine from artemisia, and another in Quetta (Baluchistan) for the manufacture of ephedrine chloride. The pharmaceutical industry based on forest products is one to which the Forest Department has rightly devoted a good deal of attention in recent years, and, although expansion must be gradual, the prospects are there and, if all goes well, it will only require effort along sound commercial lines to reap a good harvest.

A big paper mill has been completed at Chandragona in the Chittagong Hills of East Pakistan and is expected to produce annually 30,000 tons of fine paper. For the raw product it uses the bamboos of the Chittagong Hill Tracts, for which there was previously no market. If the Kashmir dispute, now pending before the Security Council of the United Nations, is settled in Pakistan's favor, a large mill for the manufacture of newsprint will be established at Jhelum (Punjab) and will utilize fir from Kashmir.

Annual Output and Foreign Trade

Tables 20–I and 20–II give recent data with regard to Pakistan's production and imports of forest products.

TABLE 20–I

PAKISTAN: ANNUAL FELLINGS AND REMOVALS, 1950-1953 [a]

| | Total | Industrial Wood | | | Fuel Wood, Including Wood for Charcoal |
		Total	Saw Logs, Veneer Logs, Logs for Sleepers	Other	
Fellings [b]					
1951: TOTAL	1,206	318	185	133	888
1952/53					
Conifers	149	74	50	24 *	75
Hardwood	1,374	174	124	50 *	1,200
TOTAL	1,523	248	174	74	1,275
Removals [c] Annual average, period 1950-52 ...	1,340	290			1,050

* Unofficial figure.

[a] Sources: for fellings, United Nations Food and Agriculture Organization: *Yearbook of Forest Products Statistics, 1953*, p. 26, *1954*, pp. 25, 29, 35; for removals the same: *World Forest Resources*, Rome, 1955, pp. 104-105.

[b] In thousand cubic meters, solid volume of roundwood.

[c] In thousand cubic meters, solid volume, without bark.

TABLE 20–II

PAKISTAN: VALUE OF ANNUAL IMPORTS OF FOREST PRODUCTS, 1951-1953 [a]

(In Thousand U.S. Dollars)

	1951-52	1952-53
Wood: lumber and cork	1,013	1,852
Wood and cork manufactures ..	171	259
Paper, paperboard, and manufactures thereof	6,619	7,701
TOTAL	7,803	9,182

[a] FAO, *Yearbook of Forest Products Statistics, 1954*, Table 41.

Imports of lumber have been mainly from Burma, Thailand, Malaya, and India. India supplies softwood, railway sleepers, and hardwoods, including teak for furniture, buildings, and railway wagons.

Forest Policy, Development Program, and Research

FOREST POLICY. The agricultural economy of the country makes it imperative that firewood and other small timbers be made available to the village communities. Our forests, however, as at present constituted, are so inadequate in area and so defective in distribution that they can neither supply forest produce in sufficient quantities nor exercise protective functions effectively. In the interests of a balanced economy it is necessary both to increase the forest area to the required minimum and to insure an equitable distribution of forests so as to cater to the needs of the rural and urban population and of industry. The problem was considered at length at the first Pakistan Forestry Conference in 1949. The decisions taken are embodied in a resolution (reproduced below) that lays down the basis on which forestry problems are to be tackled. The central and provincial governments are taking steps to implement the resolution, and some administrations have already made considerable headway in this direction.

RESOLUTION—Whereas it is essential to preserve in perpetuity for the benefit of the present inhabitants and posterity, sufficient land, as well distributed as possible, either already under forests or capable of afforestation, so as to supply the rural and urban population with fuel, fodder and timber for domestic and agricultural requirements, to produce a sustained yield of timber and other forest produce, to maintain regular flow in the rivers and mitigate the severity of floods, to sustain essential services and industrial development and to improve conditions for preservation of wild-life:

The Conference recommends that—

(1) A high priority be given to the national financial and economic plans to the claims of forestry and adequate facilities provided for large-scale afforestation and harvesting.

(2) The practice of sound management in privately owned forests should be ensured by legislation or negotiation and by technical and, if necessary, financial assistance.

(3) Legislation be enacted appropriate to the needs of the country to provide powers to control land use and define the scope of work of forest services in a co-ordinated programme of soil conservation and land utilization.

(4) It is of paramount importance to associate public opinion with the execution of forest policy, through education, propaganda and demonstration.

(5) Forests be classified, on the basis of their utility and objects.

(6) The commercial aspect of forestry be generally subordinated to the over-riding necessity of integrating it into the general context of the economy of the country as far as possible.

(7) In view of the acute deficiency of forest area in the country, a bold and well-planned action programme be undertaken for increasing forest area by:

    (a) reserving at least 10% of canal irrigated land and 10% water supply for raising irrigated plantations under new projects;

    (b) growing trees on canal banks, roads and rail-road sides and arable wasteland; and

    (c) farm forestry, on co-operative basis by village communities, in compact plots of cropland, set apart for the purposes.

(8) Existing forests be developed by encouraging the most economical utilisation of timber and other forest products.

(9) Policy be executed by the agency of Forest Service consisting of only trained foresters.

(10) Forest research, an important requisite for success of a dynamic science like forestry, be organised on suitable lines and be centralised in Pakistan Forest Institute, with ancillary field units in different problem areas of the country.

(11) More effective measures be taken for the preservation of the fauna of the country.

FOREST DEVELOPMENT PROGRAM. To carry out this resolution, which aims at increasing the forest area, one or more of the following alternatives will have to be adopted, depending upon particular conditions: (a) declaring all suitable "wastelands" and unclassed forests as reserved forests, and thereafter introducing effective measures for recuperation and the development of tree growth; (b) afforestation; and (c) bringing under scientific management forests owned by private individuals and tribal chiefs.

"Wastelands." Extensive tracts, miscalled "wastelands," occur in all of the provinces and states. They constitute generally depleted forests, which, with effective protection, supplemented by sowing and planting, could materially add to the forest wealth of the country. In this category are included the rakhs under the control of the revenue authorities. Some progress has been made in transferring the control of such areas to the Forest Department. As a result of past experience there is a growing realization that the existing system of control must change if these areas are to be brought into full productivity.

Afforestation. Some afforestation will undoubtedly be necessary in the unclassed forests and "wastelands" mentioned above. So much, however, has to be done in order to attain the minimum necessary for a balanced economy that afforestation by means of fast-growing trees will have to be undertaken on all marginal and submarginal lands, both publicly and privately owned. Where lands ordinarily unsuitable for agricultural purposes are unavailable, even agricultural land will have to be used for growing forest crops. In the past, agriculture was allowed to encroach on forest land to the ultimate detriment of both, especially in East Pakistan, where shifting cultivation still persists, but now our economy has reached a stage in which forestry must be given an important place in over-all land utilization.

Mention should be made here of the irrigated plantations and village forests. Afforestation over large areas of West Pakistan requires not only land but also water, because the rainfall is scanty and generally erratic. This principle is borne out by the allotment of lands to the Forest Department in the irrigation and colonization projects of the Thal in the Punjab and the Kotri Barrage in Sind. Growing shelter belts and windbreaks in the Thal seems to offer a means of arresting sand drift, which is a great menace to the canal system in that area. Similar action is under consideration in Baluchistan, where, moreover, agricultural land will have to be devoted to tree growth. It is a happy augury for the future that the people and the administration have both become aware of the important role that forests play in the economy of areas that are being colonized.

Afforestation receives special attention in the soil-conservation operations undertaken by the forest departments in various provinces, especially in the Punjab and the North-West Frontier Province. Besides the reclamation of deteriorating lands by check dams and bunds, emphasis is invariably laid on growing trees to stabilize the soil. This is a popular practice among the co-operating farmers. In the catchment areas, which are included in the soil-conservation program of the forest departments, special measures are adopted to conserve water for trees grown on bunds, in trenches, or in pits, according to local conditions.

Private and Tribal Forests. In East Pakistan and the North-West Frontier Province, there are large areas of private forests which, generally speaking, have suffered from lack of proper management. In the general interests of the country, the provincial governments are anxious to bring these forests under scientific management. With this object in view, the Private Forests Bill has been passed in East Bengal and rules for the management of the Guzara Forests have been framed for the North-West Frontier Province. These measures have already effectively reduced the damage.

Tree-plantation days and weeks have recently become a popular feature of the Forest Department's activities. They impress on every citizen the fact that there is a shortage of forest products in the country and that it is his or her duty to help in making good the deficiency. All governmental agencies, schools, and civic bodies play their part in espousing the cause of forestry and thus laying foundations for a prosperous agricultural economy, by integrating forestry with agriculture.

The Frontier states and tribal areas in the northern part of West Pakistan contain unexploited or partially exploited forests of great value. Some of the accessible areas have been overfelled and are badly depleted, but in general these potentially valuable sources of softwoods are waiting to be brought under scientific management. The government has already initiated action. Forest services are being organized in the Frontier states and rough inventories taken in order to have some workable basis until the forests are demarcated and working plans prepared.

Possibilities of legislative measures to utilize fully all marginal village lands and also to persuade villages to use part of their agricultural land to grow trees are being investigated. A gratifying feature of this enterprise is the co-operation that the Forest Service is receiving from the government and private agencies in its effort to increase the forest area. Village plantations, whether on marginal land or farmland, will ensure an equitable distribution of forests as well as an over-all increase in the forest area.

Steps are being taken to ensure the scientific exploitation of minor forest products, especially of the medicinal plants which occur in both parts of the country. The object is to standardize the products by systematic collection, processing, packing, and storage, as well as by laboratory analysis, and to explore markets in and outside the country. The importance of this work is now fully recognized, and a separate branch of the Forest Department called the Survey of Medicinal Plants has been organized. Its functions are:

(1) To survey the forests and to compile lists of plants of medicinal value.
(2) To carry out chemical analyses and ensure the marketing of only such products as conform to the pharmacopoeial standards.
(3) To carry out research on the time and method of collection, drying, and storage of important drugs.
(4) To advocate cultivation of important drugs which are not found naturally in marketable qualities.
(5) To keep liaison between trade on the one hand and the Forest Department on the other.

FOREST RESEARCH AND EDUCATION. To solve various forest problems confronting the Forest Department, a Research Institute was established in 1948 with the following branches: silviculture, forest utilization, forest entomology, forest chemistry, and forest botany. While the branches of forest utilization and forest chemistry deal with forest products, the other three deal with forestry. The research in forestry is further divided into research on production and research on protection. Research on production is mainly carried out in the silviculture branch and deals with silvicultural methods, growth, management, artificial methods of regeneration, plants, plant geography and forest ecology, and inventory methods.

Research on protection deals with pests and diseases of forest crops. Owing to difficulties in procuring laboratory equipment, the institute began on a humble scale. However, development has proceeded to the point where it is now possible to lay down a comprehensive research program dealing with all the forest problems of the country. With regard to forest products an immense amount of work is waiting to be done relating to the technology of the existing known timbers, their suitability for various uses, and the development of markets. The development of forest industries is urgently called for and will need a good deal of investigation and research work in order that standard methods may be adapted to local conditions and to available raw produce. The laboratories of the Research Institute are far from fully equipped at present, but fresh equipment is arriving every day and large orders have been placed abroad. It can be confidently expected that in the near future the Institute, which is now situated at Abbottabad, will be one of the finest organizations of its kind in the East. A Forest Products Laboratory is under construction at Chittagong in East Pakistan, to deal with the forest products of that area.

Along with the Forest Research Institute, there is also a college which provides training for professional and subprofessional staff. This college was started in 1947 at Upper Topa in the Murree Hills of the Punjab, but along with the Research Institute, it has also been removed to Abbottabad, which has a more salubrious climate. It is expected that the college will play a leading part in training forest officers for the whole of southwest Asia, and students are already coming to it from abroad. It has recently been decided to move both the college and the institute to Peshawar.

SOURCES FOR BOTANICAL NOMENCLATURE

BRANDIS, DIETRICH. 1906. *Indian trees, an account of trees, shrubs, woody climbers, bamboos, and palms indigenous or commonly cultivated in the British Indian Empire.* Archibald Constable & Co., London.

PARKER, R. N. 1924. *A forest flora for the Punjab, with Hazara and Delhi.* Government Printing Office, Lahore.

21. INDIA

M. D. Chaturvedi

The Aryans, who migrated into India from their northern homes about 2500 B.C., brought with them not only their cows and plows, their sheep and goats, but also their civilization and culture—the Vedas and the language in which they are written, Sanskrit. The Aryavarta, or "land of the Aryans" (modern Punjab), where they settled during the first period of their colonization, at that time was fairly well covered with tree growth, which gradually disappeared under the relentless pressure of an ever increasing population. In the ancient Aryan epics there are repeated allusions to the dark, dense, and dismal forests, their clearing, burning, and disappearance. The Aryans' innate love of nature, however, as typified by the worship of certain trees, such as pipal, deodar, and tulsi, led not only to their protection but also to their propagation. The religious merit to be earned from the planting of trees is indicated in the injunctions of the Agni Purana. In the locality where Gautama Buddha lived and preached, to this day, in deference to his teachings, no Hindu will fell a green tree. Land was cleared for cultivation and grazing, but the forests became the sacred abode of saints and sages, of poets and preachers, where every Hindu secretly hoped to spend his last days and shed his mortal coil. Arrian, the chronicler of the invasion of Alexander the Great (326 B.C.), described what is now a treeless tract east of the Jhelum River as a boundless forest shrouded "with umbrageous trees of stateliest growth and of extraordinary height; ... the climate was salubrious, as the dense shade mitigated the violence of the heat; ... copious springs supplied this land with an abundance of water." [1]

During the Brahmanic and Buddhist periods the forests were preserved, not by laws enacted for the purpose, but by religious injunction. By the close of the first millennium of the Christian Era, however, the Buddhist supremacy had declined and was supplanted by warring Hindu kingdoms, too weak to resist the later onslaught of the Mohammedan invaders. During the period of Muslim ascendancy, the forests of India suffered the same fate as those of Spain, Asia Minor, Persia, and other countries under the Crescent, for, unlike the Brahmin and the Buddhist, the Mohammedan had little compunction about felling trees. True, the Mogul emperors were fond of gardens, orchards, and roadside avenues,

[1] See E. P. Stebbing: *The Forests of India,* John Lane, London (1922), vol. 1, p. 30.

but their patronage was seldom extended to the forests, which drew their attention only for sport.

An unprecedented assault on the forests was made during the early and middle periods of the British regime in order to obtain, first, teak for the Royal Navy and, later, timber for railway sleepers. Vast forest areas were also signed away to British tea and coffee planters, and forest grants were freely given to all and sundry to be brought under the plough. Some of the most valuable state forests of today were not originally reserved as such, but are lands that have reverted to the government owing to the grantees' failure to bring them under cultivation within a specified period. The forests of the realm were considered inexhaustible, and the government, interested only in the royalties fetched by some of the more valuable species, such as teak, sandalwood, and sal, did nothing towards their preservation or perpetuation. Taking a cue from the previous rulers, the British declared these valuable species "royal trees," for the felling of which permits were required. Everyone was at liberty to hack, burn, and destroy trees of other species, and an appalling waste went on unchecked and unheeded.

FOREST TYPES AND REGIONS

Forest Types

The forest flora of India is rich, and varied both in composition and value. The number of species is estimated at 30,000, although the vast majority have no economic value. The distribution of forests and forest types (Fig. 46), as elsewhere, depends on climatic, edaphic (including relief), and biotic factors acting in combination. Hence, no one of these factors considered alone can give a satisfactory clue to the nature of the forest in any particular locality. Indeed, a forest itself is often a better index of climate, soil, and certain biotic conditions than vice versa.

THE CLIMATIC FACTOR. Marked climatic contrasts reflect pronounced differences in the relief of India. The mercury rises above 120° F. at Jacobabad in Sind and falls as low as −49° F. at Dras in Kashmir. A climb of only a few miles brings one from hot, moist marshes (tarai) along the outer foothills of the Himalayas to the temperate climate of the former British hill stations (*ca.* 6,500 feet), and thence to arctic cold above the snow line (*ca.* 12,000 feet). The contrasts in rainfall are even greater and have a profound effect on the vegetation, the extremes ranging from an annual mean of only 3 inches in Upper Sind to nearly 40 *feet* in the Khasi Hills.

Three seasons may be distinguished: winter (November–February), summer (March–June), and the rains (July–October). During the winter, winds of continental origin blow from the land toward the sea, in general from the northeast and northwest. This "northeast monsoon" becomes fully established by January, bringing cool, dry weather, although local disturbances cause occasional showers in northern India and in the eastern Deccan. The winter rainfall is heaviest in the northwest.

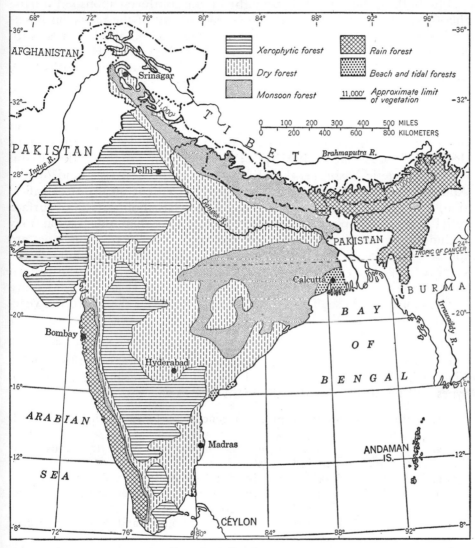

Fig. 46. India: forest types.

As summer advances, the wind direction is reversed. The winds now blow from sea to land, culminating in the "southwest monsoon," which sets in with the rainy season. The summer is characterized by progressively rising temperature and falling atmospheric pressure. Temperature maxima range from 100° F. in March in the Deccan, to 110° F. in April across central India and 115° F. in May and June throughout the Indo-Gangetic plains, reaching extremes of 120° F. in the northwestern desert.

Coinciding with the area of lowest pressure, this blazing furnace in the northwest induces indrafts of the monsoon from the Arabian Sea and Bay of Bengal.

The bulk of the rainfall is brought by the southwest monsoon during the four months July–October. One great current of the monsoon bursts against the Western Ghats and flows over the Deccan, another sweeps up the Bay of Bengal, and, combined, they flood the eastern Himalayas and outlying hills to the south. July and August are the rainiest months here. Northwestern India, away from the main paths of the southwest monsoon, gets the lowest rainfall in the country.

THE FACTOR OF RELIEF. For the purposes of the following description of its forest types, India will be divided into six major physical regions designated somewhat arbitrarily: (1) the Deccan, (2) the Indus Basin, (3) the Gangetic Basin, (4) the Himalayas, (5) the Seacoasts, and (6) the Andaman Islands. While these provide a convenient means of classification, it should be borne in mind that they are based on criteria of surface relief and not of phytogeography. Thus, more than one region may include representatives of a single forest type, and divers forest types are found within each region. The estuarine vegetation in the delta of the Ganges (or Ganga), for example, is like that of the deltas of the eastern coast of the Deccan; the evergreens of the Malabar Coast have far more in common with those of the northeastern Himalayas than with the vegetation of the rest of the Deccan.

MAIN FOREST TYPES. In describing the forests of these regions we shall follow Champion's classification in broad outline, omitting details. Five main forest types and several transitional, intermediate, and subtypes will be distinguished. The main types are:

1. Rain Forest—annual rainfall in general 80 to 120 inches; dense, tall evergreens.
2. Monsoon Forest—rainfall 40 to 80 inches; dominants deciduous; evergreens form the second story.
3. Dry Forest—rainfall 30 to 40 inches; deciduous; no evergreens.
4. Xerophytic Forest—rainfall 10 to 30 inches; low, stunted, thorny, deciduous species, and fleshy evergreens.
5. Mangrove Forest—rainfall varies; both evergreen and deciduous species.

Changes in the floristic composition of a given type brought about by edaphic and biotic factors and by rainfall and other climatic factors will be pointed out. For example, coarse, friable, porous soils require a much higher rainfall to support a rain forest than do soils with higher moisture retentivity. The presence of alkalis and salts may retard and even eliminate tree growth altogether, despite high moisture content. Human exploitation, fires, grazing, and lopping often act as limiting factors, affecting the character of the vegetation independently of the rainfall. The range of temperature, and, more particularly, minimum temperatures, sharp frosts, and snowfall have a profound influence. In the Himalayas the vegetation of the northern latitudes of the temperate zone is reproduced. The vegetation in the Deccan plateau, with its equable climate, differs from that of the Indo-Gangetic plains, which exhibit a continental range of temperatures, both seasonal and diurnal. The Nilgiri Hills, in the south, have a vegetation unlike that of the Himalayas at the same range of elevation. A distinction must often be made between tropical and Himalayan varieties of the same main forest type. The similarities between a given type of forest occurring in the Deccan and its counterpart in the north, however, may be fully as striking as the differences. The vegetation of the rainless Thar Desert is reminiscent of that of alpine wastes both in form and appearance.

The Forest Regions

THE DECCAN

The term "Deccan" should be here understood as embracing the whole of peninsular India and of the Central Highlands, with the exception of the northern and northwestern slopes of the latter, which will be considered as parts of the Gangetic and Indus basins, respectively.

The Deccan plateau rises above the Indo-Gangetic plains in a series of irregular terraces. Its principal rocks are of archean origin, comprising granites, gneisses, and schists, with basaltic lavas of more recent age capping them, particularly in the northwest. Decomposition of these lavas has given rise to the rich "black cotton soils." The plateau is buttressed on the north by the Aravalli, Vindhya, Satpura, and Kaimur hills, with characteristically flat tops. The Aravallis (*ca.* 5,500 feet), an extension of the plateau to the northwest, form an isolated, ancient, and much worn-down range flanking the desert of Rajputana on the east. Farther south, the eastern and western flanks of the plateau are fringed by the Ghats, which converge to an apex in the south. With an average elevation of about 1,500 feet, the plateau surface slopes down eastward from an altitude of about 3,000 feet in Mysore. The Western Ghats begin near the Tapti River and increase in elevation southward, reaching nearly 9,000 feet in the Nilgiri Hills. The Eastern Ghats average about 1,500 feet in altitude.

In considering the forest types of the Deccan, we may conveniently divide the region as a whole, exclusive of the seacoast, into three lesser regions: the West Coast, the Southeast, and the Central Plateau.

THE WEST COAST. The region comprising the Malabar and Konkan coasts, the Western Ghats, and the Nilgiri and Cardamom hills has the most luxuriant vegetation in the Deccan, owing largely to the heavy rainfall and to a soil rendered rich by the decomposition of a vast mass of leaf litter. The southwest monsoon floods the entire region. The mean annual rainfall increases with elevation on the Western Ghats; thus, while Bombay at sea level receives only 74 inches, Matheran at an altitude of nearly 2,000 feet some 25 miles to the east receives 200 inches. The higher altitudes of the southern portion of the Western Ghats also helps explain why the rainfall on the Malabar Coast (some 130 inches) is nearly twice as heavy as that on the Konkan Coast to the north (75 inches).

Of the main forest types, Dry Forest and Xerophytic Forest are not found in this region. The Mangrove Forest will be mentioned under another heading. Besides Rain Forest in the strict sense, there are two intermediate types: Shola and Semi-Evergreen Forest.

Rain Forest. Forests of this type are generally met with along the Malabar Coast and throughout the Western Ghats up to altitudes of 1,000 to 1,500 feet, wherever the mean annual rainfall is above 100 inches (with 120 inches as the optimum). In these areas the mean annual temperature varies from 80° F. to 100° F., the January minimum seldom goes below 65° F., and the mean annual humidity is about 80 per cent (e.g., at Cochin). Under such humid tropical conditions a bewildering variety of species flourish, their only common characteristic being their evergreen nature. These forests present several ill-defined stories, or tiers, the highest containing lofty trees, often buttressed, which reach a height of 150 feet and have girths of 15 feet or more. The lower tiers consist of an impenetrable mass of evergreens covered with a luxuriant growth of epiphytes (mosses, ferns, orchids) and climbers. The most typical genera are Dipterocarps and Hopeas, although the former are the less frequent and may even be locally absent. Species commonly met with are: *Dipterocarpus indicus,*[2] *Hopea parviflora, Hopea wightiana, Calophyllum tomentosum, Cullenia excelsa, Palaquium elliptica, Dysoxylum malabaricum, Cedrela toona, Vateria indica, Canarium strictum, Tetrameles nudiflora, Mesua ferrea, Mangifera indica, Sterculia alata, Artocarpus* spp., *Acrocarpus fraxinifolius,* and many other Myrtaceae and Lauraceae. The undergrowth, conspicuously free from grasses, is usually a tangled mass of cane, congested and creeping bamboo, and palms.

Sholas. Above the rain forests, related forests of a special intermediate type, locally known as sholas, are found up to about 4,500 feet in the valleys and on the slopes of the Nilgiri, Anaimalai, Palni, and other hills of southernmost India. At relatively lower elevations, these sholas usually consist of *Mesua ferrea, Vitex altissima, Artocarpus lakoocha,* and *Dysoxylum malabaricum,* often with *Strobilanthes* and *Selaginella* as a ground cover, and *Arundinaria* spp. and *Oxtenanthera* spp. as the commonest bamboos. At higher altitudes, the floristic composition changes to include such subtropical and temperate species as *Michelia nilagirica, Ternstroemia japonica, Eurya japonica, Gordonia obtusa, Eugenia* spp., *Ilex* spp., *Meliosma wightii, Photinia notoniana, Cinnamomum wightii, Euonymus crenulatus.* Here, owing to comparatively rigorous weather conditions, the tree growth suffers in height and the crowns are more rounded. Mention must also be made of artificial plantations of Aus-

---

[2] For sources of botanical nomenclature see below, p. 482.

tralian eucalyptus and of South African wattles (*Acacia* spp.). Exotic pines and cypress have also been introduced in the Nilgiri and Anaimalai hills. Farther north, on the Western Ghat slopes—as for example, at Mahableshwar—sholas are found in which the representative species are *Eugenia jambolana* (and *E. heyneana*), *Actinodaphne hookeri*, *Canthium didymum*, *Terminalia chebula*, *Olea dioica*, *Strobilanthes callosus*, and *Sideroxylon tomentosum*.

Semi-Evergreen Forest. Along gentle slopes, where the mean annual rainfall is between about 80 and 100 inches, the evergreen nature of the rain forest is further modified by the increasing association of deciduous species, typified by *Terminalia paniculata*, *Xylia dolabriformis*, *Stereospermum chelonoides*, *Trewia polycarpa*, *Eugenia* spp., *Diospyros* spp., *Lagerstroemia lanceolata*, *Schleichera trijuga*, *Vateria indica*, with *Bambusa arundinacea* as the representative bamboo in the lower story. The middle canopy is usually composed of evergreens, Myrtaceae, and Lauraceae, and the ground cover includes various species of Rubiaceae and Acanthaceae. Canes and climbers persist.

Monsoon Forest. The semi-evergreens merge imperceptibly into a moist, deciduous "monsoon forest," comprising comparatively few species but some of considerable economic importance, such as teak (*Tectona grandis*), rosewood (*Dalbergia latifolia*), *Xylia* spp., *Terminalia* spp., *Lagerstroemia lanceolata*, *Pterocarpus marsupium*, *Adina cordifolia*, *Stephegyne parvifolia*, and *Grewia leptopetala*, which occur in more or less gregarious associations. *Schleichera* and *Careya* are usually present in the second story. *Bambusa arundinacea*, *Dendrocalamus strictus*, and *Oxytenanthera monostigma* are the representative bamboos, although often locally absent. The undergrowth may consist of near evergreen shrubs (*Lantana*, *Clerodendron infortunatum*, *Helicteres isora*) but more frequently of grass. This monsoon forest occurs throughout the western Deccan in regions of 40 to 80 inches of rainfall, more particularly above the Palghat Gap. The mean annual temperature varies from 75° F. to 80° F., with the January mean often below 60° F. The trees, which reach a height of 100 to 120 feet, are generally leafless during March and April, putting on new foliage somewhat later. Along the Konkan Coast *Terminalia* spp. lend their name to the forest wherein they abound, in which teak may or may not be present locally.

THE SOUTHEAST. The southeastern subregion of the Deccan comprises the Carnatic, the Eastern Ghats, and the bulk of the plateau south of the Godavari River. During the period of the southwest monsoon, the region lies in the rain shadow of the Western Ghats. The rainfall, generally associated with the northeast monsoon, when the rest of India is dry, is relatively low and extremely variable. The annual precipitation seldom exceeds 40 inches (Mysore, northeastern Hyderabad), the average varying between 20 and 30 inches. Of the main forest types, only the two drier ones are represented here.

Xerophytic Forest. In the Carnatic and farther south in the lee of the higher Western Ghats the vegetation is of a dry, thorny, stunted type. The most representative genus is *Acacia,* with low (20 to 30 feet) crowns. The ground is usually bare, with thorny shrubs dotted here and there, and light grass appearing during periods of rain. The mean annual rainfall varies between 20 and 30 inches (with about eight months with less than 2 inches), and the mean annual humidity between 50 and 60 per cent. The mean annual temperature is about 78° F., the mean maximum about 105° F., and the hottest month is May (85° F. to 90° F.). Species that survive under these xerophytic conditions are few and far between, the commonest being *Acacia planifrons* (and *A. sundra*), *Mimusops* spp., *Azadirachta indica, Albizzia amara, Acacia latronum, Dichrostachys cinerea, Chloroxylon swietenia, Prosopis spicigera, Bombax insigne,* and *Osyris arborea.* Fleshy evergreen *Euphorbia* spp. also constitute a characteristic feature of the vegetation. *Cassia auriculata* (and *C. fistula*) occur here and there, and the chief among the thorny shrubs are *Capparis* spp., *Carissa spinarum, Aristida adscensionis L.,* and *Zizyphus* spp.

Dry Forest. The xerophytic thorn forest of the Carnatic gradually merges into a dry deciduous forest, where the mean rainfall is between about 35 and 40 inches, the mean temperature is close to 75° F., and the mean annual humidity is close to 60 per cent. This forest forms an intermediate stage between the monsoon and xerophytic forests, having characteristics of both. The trees are seldom more than 75 feet high. More species thrive under these conditions than in the xerophytic forest, and the dry forest includes the most valuable tree of southern India, sandalwood (*Santalum album*). Gregariousness is not common, unless artificially brought about. This type of forest usually occurs on shallow, sandy soils and laterites and in places where the rainfall is relatively heavy but rapidly drains off.

In the northern part of the region the dry forest is fairly dense. The representative species are teak (*Tectona grandis*) and associated *Terminalia* spp. and *Anogeissus latifolia.* Other species include *Dillenia pentagyna, Kydia calycina, Lagerstroemia lanceolata, Adina cordifolia, Bassia latifolia, Buchanania latifolia, Grewia asiatica, Odina wodier, Pterocarpus marsupium, Bombax malabaricum, Santalum album, Butea frondosa, Bridelia retusa, Diospyros melanoxylon,* and *Phyllanthus emblica.* The chief bamboo is the well-known commercial variety, *Dendrocalamus strictus.* Grasses are plentiful, including *Ischoemum angustifolium, Flemingia* spp., *Millettia auriculata, Lantana, Carissa spinarum,* etc.

Farther south, teak is less common and in many places absent, owing, perhaps, to past human exploitation. *Terminalia* spp. and *Anogeissus* spp. are associated with *Acacia catechu, Chloroxylon swietenia, Cleistanthus collinus, Hardwickia binata, Boswellia serrata,* and *Soymida febrifuga.* The ground cover is composed of grasses, usually *Andropogon* spp., *Panicum* spp., and *Aristida* spp.

THE CENTRAL PLATEAU. For present purposes the Central Plateau may be regarded as comprising the entire region between the Godavari River and the Bay of Bengal on the south and southeast, the Western Ghats and Aravalli Hills on the west and northwest, and the northern slopes of the Central Highlands on the north and northeast.

North of the source of the Godavari, the Western Ghats become progressively lower and finally disappear and, hence, no longer constitute an effective barrier to the southwest monsoon. The hill ranges of the Central Highlands run in an east–west direction, which allows a more even distribution of rainfall over this part of India than farther south. The climate becomes more continental, with marked extremes, as one goes northward.

Of the major forest types, xerophytic, dry, and monsoon forests are represented on the Central Plateau. At higher elevations the shola type, which is intermediate between the monsoon and rain forests, is also met with.

Xerophytic Forest (rainfall, less than 25 inches). Here, the general pattern of xerophytic vegetation found in the Carnatic is closely repeated. *Acacia leucophloea* (and *A. arabica*), *Balanites roxburghii, Cordia myxa, Zizyphus jujuba,* and *Calotropis procera* are characteristic species.

Dry Forest (rainfall, 35 to 40 inches). This is met with throughout the region, with low-quality teak much more frequent than in the corresponding dry forests farther south. Here, also, teak may be locally absent, suggesting human exploitation in the past. Any one of such species as *Hardwickia binata, Boswellia serrata, Butea frondosa,* and *Anogeissus pendula* may be locally preponderant. Babul (*Acacia arabica*) forests grow more particularly on the rich black cotton soils, notably in Berar and in the vicinity of Poona.

Monsoon Forest (rainfall, 40 to 80 inches). From the Maikal Hills eastward, and especially on the Chota Nagpur plateau, there is a copious rainfall due to the convergence of the two great currents of the southwest monsoon. Hence, the vegetation is rich and clearly assumes the form of monsoon forest. Where teak is more or less gregarious, the forest is known as "moist teak forest," and is not unlike the *Terminalia* forest of the West Coast region of the Deccan. Teak in this region of the Central Plateau is associated with *Terminalia tomentosa, Adina cordifolia, Pterocarpus marsupium, Dalbergia latifolia, Odina wodier, Lagerstroemia parviflora, Schleichera trijuga, Ougeinia dalbergioides,* and *Phyllanthus emblica,* with *Dendrocalamus strictus* as the common bamboo. *Helicteres isora* covers the ground, along with *Millettia auriculata* and *Bauhinia vahlii.* Where sal (*Shorea robusta*) predominates, in the so-called "moist sal" or "peninsular sal" forests, the associated species are *Pterocarpus marsupium, Terminalia chebula* (and *T. tomentosa*), *Anogeissus latifolia, Bassia latifolia, Eugenia jambolana, Phyllanthus emblica,* and *Indigofera pulchella,* with *Phoenix acaulis, Flemingia chappar,* and *Anthistiria ciliata* L. as the ground cover.

Sholas (rainfall, about 100 inches). On the upper levels of the Maikal Hills (e.g., near Pachmarhi) and of the Chota Nagpur plateau (e.g., near Parasnath), the sholas of the Western Ghats are repeated, with slight modifications due to soils derived from basaltic lavas. *Pterospermum acerifolium, Phoenix robusta,* and *Clematis nutans* are representative species.

THE INDUS BASIN

The Indus basin forms a vast area of low rainfall and high summer temperatures. The rainfall increases in a generally northeastward direction, for the clouds borne by the southwest monsoon current from the Arabian Sea tend to pass over the Thar Desert without dropping their moisture. In the Punjab the rain brought by this current is to some extent supplemented by rain from the Bay of Bengal. In the North-West Frontier region, however, the force of both monsoon currents is feeble, and, consequently, cold-weather rains account for more than half of the annual rainfall.

Recent excavations at Mohenjo-Daro in Sind and the discovery of elephant and rhinoceros remains along the right bank of the Indus point to a time when there must have been moist forests in this part of India, and the chroniclers of Alexander's invasion described the Larkana area in Sind as a "garden." Conditions are very different today. Two main forest types may be distinguished: dry forest and xerophytic forest.

Dry Forest. This type occurs in the northern Punjab where the mean annual rainfall is between 35 and 40 inches, the mean annual temperature between 75° and 80° F., the mean annual minimum and maximum are about 35° and 110° F., respectively, and both the diurnal and the seasonal ranges are wide. Owing to these severe conditions the trees seldom exceed 50 feet in height. In summer the lack of leaves gives a desolate look to these forests, but they turn bright green at the break of the monsoon. Among the species met with, *Anogeissus latifolia* is typical, its usual associates being *Buchanania latifolia, Sterculia* spp., *Bauhinia* spp., *Acacia catechu, Aegle marmelos, Limonia acidissima, Ehretia laevis, Kydia calycina, Ougeinia dalbergioides,* and *Terminalia tomentosa. Mallotus* spp. and *Nyctanthes* occur in the lower story. *Dendrocalamus strictus* is the usual bamboo. The undergrowth is composed of *Woodfordia floribunda, Indigofera* spp., *Carissa spinarum, Adhatoda vasica, Dodonaea viscosa, Bauhinia vahlii,* and *Acacia caesia.* Grasses are common. But for certain differences in emphasis, the dry deciduous type of the South is closely reproduced. Owing to the more pronounced climatic extremes, however, the teak, *Chloroxylon, Soymida,* and *Cleistanthus* met with in the dry forests of the Deccan are conspicuously absent, and the *Dalbergia latifolia* is replaced by its hardier cousin, *Dalbergia sissoo.*

Xerophytic Forest. Around the margins of the Indus Plain, wherever the mean annual rainfall is between 10 to 25 inches—as, notably, in Cutch and Kathiawar, along the base of the Kirthar and Sulaiman ranges, on the Salt Range, in the Sirhind Gap, on the Delhi Ridge, and along the lower western slopes of the Aravalli Hills—a scrub, seldom more than 30 feet high, is found, corresponding to the xerophytic forest of the Deccan. Here temperature conditions are comparable to those of the dry forest area of the Punjab. Various species of acacia abound, the chief being *Acacia arabica* and *A. leucophloea*, and are associated with *Prosopis spicigera* and the exotic *Prosopis juliflora*, which has come to occupy the Delhi Ridge and parts of Rajputana. *Acacia catechu* is found in considerable quantity in Cutch. In the southern Aravallis *Anogeissus pendula* occurs in fairly homogeneous patches. Farther north, typical species are *Salvadora oleoides*, *Tamarix articulata*, *Zizyphus jujuba*, *Grewia populifolia*, and *Ehretia laevis*. The undergrowth consists of *Capparis aphylla* (and *C. spinosa*), *Asclepias*, and *Calotropis*, with the fleshy *Suaeda* and *Salsola* growing on saline soils, and *Calligonum polygonoides* on sandy soils. Light grass flourishes only during the rains. On the floodplain of the Indus, which is periodically inundated, and in the regions with slightly higher rainfall, *Acacia arabica*, a species that adapts itself admirably to xerophytic conditions, occupies the ground, usually in association with *Populus euphratica*. *Dalbergia sissoo* and *Acacia catechu* are the first colonizers of the alluvial deposits along the river banks in their Himalayan reaches. Lower down (in southern Punjab and Sind), fresh alluvial deposits are first occupied by pure associations of *Tamarix dioica* and *Populus euphratica*, which give place in the course of time to *Acacia arabica* and *Dalbergia sissoo*, though the first two often persist in the understory. In the Thar Desert the xerophytic vegetation takes a more retrograde form, with fleshy evergreen *Euphorbias* as the most characteristic species.

THE GANGETIC BASIN

RELIEF AND RAINFALL. Lying like a moat along the wall of the Himalayas, the Gangetic basin has been filled with silt brought down from the mountains. It is drained by the river systems of the Ganges and Brahmaputra. By virtue of its fertility, gentle gradients, and mild climate, this great region supports an average population density of 400 to the square mile.

For the most part, the plain presents a dead-level appearance, with thousands upon thousands of acres under cultivation, whose monotony is relieved only by an occasional grove or artificial tank dug in the days of old for irrigation. The valley of the Brahmaputra is rendered picturesque by innumerable "islands" rising above the alluvium, but in the Ganges valley the level surface is unbroken except along the margins of the plain.

The most noteworthy of the marginal relief features in relation to the forest cover lie along the base of the Himalayas. Here the streams from the mountains have brought quantities of detritus which they have deposited in a series of alluvial fans along the fringe of the plain, forming a porous and consequently waterless tract known as the bhabar. The water that sinks into this mass of detritus travels beneath it and oozes out again where the bhabar meets the flat surface of the plain, giving rise to perennial springs and streams in a moist and malarious belt called the tarai. The upper parts of this Himalayan detritus were uplifted in comparatively recent geological time to form a subsidiary series of hills, known as the Siwalik Range, which parallels the Central Himalayas and in many places encloses green fertile valleys known as duns (e.g., Dehra Dun). The Siwaliks are rich in both flora and fauna.

Owing to the convergence of the two currents of the southwest monsoon, the mean annual rainfall increases progressively toward the east and southeast, and also toward the Himalayas (Delhi, 28 inches; Bihar, 50-52; Chota Nagpur, 54-56; Orissa, 58-60; East Bengal and Assam, 80-100). From the Rajmahal Hills eastward, the mean annual rainfall is nearly everywhere over 60 inches, and in the Brahmaputra and Surma valleys it is between 80 and 100 inches. These two valleys, with the Khasi Hills, form the wettest region in the world.

FOREST TYPES. The primeval forest that once covered the Gangetic plain has succumbed to the mounting pressure of population and receded to peripheral areas, where adverse climatic and topographic conditions render farming somewhat hazardous. With the exception of occasional patches of dhak (*Butea frondosa*), associated with *Phoenix sylvestris* on alkaline soils, groves of fruit trees (largely mango, *Mangifera indica*), babul (*Acacia arabica*), and sissoo (*Dalbergia sissoo*) along the rivers, the entire Gangetic plain is bereft of any forest growth worthy of the name. On higher ground around the margins of the plain, however, the following forest types may be distinguished: xerophytic, dry, monsoon, semi-evergreen, wet sal, and rain forest.

Xerophytic Forest (rainfall, 10 to 35 inches). The Delhi Ridge, the Jumna (Yamuna) ravines, and the whole tract in the lee of the Aravalli Hills extending eastward along the base of the Central Highlands as far as the Ken River, are characterized by a thorny xerophytic forest, of which the composition does not differ much from that of its more western counterpart on and around the Indus Plain. In Bundelkhand fairly gregarious patches of *Anogeissus pendula* occur. South of the Jumna mahaua (*Bassia latifolia*) replaces mango (*Mangifera indica*) in groves and roadside avenues.

Dry Forest (rainfall, 30 to 40 inches). Dry deciduous forests, which also correspond in general composition to their counterparts in the Indus basin, are found along the higher, eastern slopes of the Aravallis, in the northern Central Highlands, and on the bhabar and Siwaliks. Although mostly confined to areas having less than 40 inches of rainfall annually, forests of this type are also found where human interference,

or poor, friable soils, or both, have offset the effects of a heavier—in places
much heavier—rainfall.

Among these dry forests, mention need be made only of those where
sal (*Shorea robusta*) predominates, as does teak in the similar dry forests
of the Central Plateau of the Deccan. Such dry sal forests of low quality
occur in the Siwaliks, where the sal forms fairly large gregarious patches
associated with *Anogeissus latifolia* and *Buchanania latifolia* sprinkled
here and there. *Dendrocalamus strictus* is the representative bamboo.
Other species of a dry deciduous nature, such as *Terminalia tomentosa*,
Bauhinia variegata, *Acacia* spp., *Phyllanthus emblica*, *Erythrina suberosa*,
Bombax malabaricum, *Ougeinia* spp., *Cassia fistula*, and even *Pinus
longifolia* (along the upper Siwalik ridges), are also present, and the
undergrowth conforms to the type elsewhere, viz., *Woodfordia floribunda*, *Indigofera* spp. etc. Farther east, in Orissa and Bihar, *Adina
cordifolia*, *Terminalia* spp., *Lagerstroemia parviflora*, and *Chloroxylon
swietenia* are more in evidence.

Monsoon Forest (rainfall, 40 to 80 inches). A counterpart of the monsoon forests of the Deccan is found in the belts of relatively high rainfall
along the base of the Central Himalayas and, south of the plain, in Chota
Nagpur and Orissa. In the northern belt these monsoon forests grow on
the Gangetic alluvium and on the bhabar detritus up to altitudes of
about 2,500 feet, and, in the southern, on red lateritic soils. These tracts
have a mean annual temperature of about 75° to 80° F., a January
mean varying between 55° and 70°, and a mean annual minimum of
between 40° and 55° F. The trees attain an average height of 100 to 120
feet, and the period of leaf fall is usually limited to two or three weeks.
The undergrowth is semi-evergreen; canes and bamboos in most places
are conspicuously absent.

Where sal (*Shorea robusta*) occurs gregariously, rendered purer as a
result of preferential treatment, these forests are designated "moist sal"
and are not unlike the "moist teak" forests of the Central Plateau or
Terminalia forests of the Western Ghats. In the eastern zone sal is an
aggressive invader, well fitted for the struggle for existence. Among the
genera associated with it, *Terminalia*, *Pterocarpus*, and *Lagerstroemia* are
most common. *Schleichera* and *Careya* occur in the second story. In the
moist sal forests on the bhabar and Siwaliks characteristic associates are
Anogeissus latifolia, *Terminalia tomentosa* (and *T. belerica*), *Lagerstroemia parviflora*, *Mallotus philippinensis*, *Colebrookia oppositifolia*,
and *Dendrocalamus strictus*. In the tarai, *Eugenia operculata* (and *E.
jambolana*) and *Croton oblongifolia* abound. Sal, however, may be completely absent in some places and is replaced on heavier soils by *Terminalia* spp. Occasionally pure bamboo brakes may occur in comparatively
dry localities.

Semi-Evergreen Forest (rainfall, 80 to 100 inches). Where the rainfall
is somewhat heavier, as along the lower southern face of the Chota Nagpur plateau, at the foot of the Eastern Himalayas, and more particularly in

the upper Brahmaputra and Surma valleys in Assam, conditions favor a vast variety of species, the proportion of evergreens becomes larger, and canes, climbers, bamboo thickets, and epiphytes appear in the understory. Gregariousness, however, is far more common here than in the West Coast region of the Deccan, where the flora is even richer in variety. The soil is mostly Gangetic alluvium, but residual soils derived from crystalline and metamorphic rocks are also met with. Several species of Dipterocarps appear. Other evergreen genera include *Eugenia, Cinnamomum, Artocarpus,* and Magnoliaceae, the deciduous associates being *Terminalia* (*T. myriocarpa, T. citrina, T. tomentosa*), *Tetrameles,* and *Stereospermum,* with a sprinkling of *Shorea* frequent toward the drier margins of the forests. *Altingia-Magnolia-Cinnamomum* associations are common in upper Assam and Cachar, and near Chittagong. In northern Bengal we have a *Schima-Bauhinia* association, with *Cedrela toona, Stereospermum tetragonum* DC., *Ailanthus grandis, Castanopsis indica, Eugenia formosa, Tetrameles nudiflora, Michelia champaca,* and *Gmelina arborea.* The association is repeated in Orissa, with local emphasis on *Artocarpus lakoocha, Michelia champaca, Saraca indica,* and *Ficus* spp. In these semi-evergreen forests the undergrowth is generally composed of the genera *Phoebe, Machilus, Amoora, Actinodaphne, Polyalthia, Mesua,* etc., and the bamboo thickets of *Bambusa arundinacea, Dendrocalamus hamiltonii, Oxytenanthera nigrociliata,* and *Melocanna bambusoides.* Along hill slopes (as in the Cachar, Chittagong, and Arakan regions) oak is also found.

Wet Sal Forest (rainfall, 80 to 100 inches). Distinguished by the presence of sal groups, this type of semi-evergreen hill forest occurs along the upper bhabar tracts of the Eastern Himalayas (notably in eastern Nepal, Bhutan, and northern Bengal) and along the lower slopes of the Garo, Khasi, Mikir, and Jaintia hills of Assam, where the annual rainfall is over 80 inches. In it the sal is typically associated with *Schima wallichii, Dendrocalamus hamiltonii, Michelia champaca, Anogeissus latifolia,* and *Terminalia tomentosa.* In the Tisti valley of Sikkim *Garuga pinnata, Terminalia belerica, Schima wallichii, Lagerstroemia parviflora, Tetrameles nudiflora, Sterculia villosa, Cedrela* spp., *Bauhinia purpurea, Mallotus philippinensis,* and *Callicarpa arborea* are common associates of the sal.

Rain Forest (rainfall, 100 inches or over). With further increase in the rainfall, the semi-evergreens merge imperceptibly into an evergreen rain forest in the upper Brahmaputra and Surma valleys of Assam, along the slopes of the Eastern Himalayas (up to 3,500 feet), and on the hills farther south. This type of vegetation closely resembles the rain forest of the West Coast region. The mean annual temperature is 72° to 78° F., only slightly lower than in the West Coast rain forest, but the mean annual minimum temperature is lower by some 10° F., being under 50° F.; the January minimum is 50° to 60° F. The forest flourishes on bhabar, alluvial, and red lateritic soils, presenting a lofty appearance, with Dipterocarps prominently projecting above a vast conglomeration of varied species.

The preponderance of tall Dipterocarps, and the presence of oaks and sal trees not met with in the Western Ghats, distinguish the forest from its West Coast counterpart. Among families, the Meliaceae, Anacardiaceae, Lauraceae, Myristicaceae, and Magnoliaceae are well represented, and the characteristic bamboos are *Dendrocalamus hamiltonii* and *Bambusa tulda*. Canes, palms, climbers, and epiphytes occur freely. The following species are typical of the lower slopes of the hills in Upper Assam to the north of the Brahmaputra and of the Naga Hills to the south of the river: *Dipterocarpus pilosus, Artocarpus chaplasha* (and *A. integrifolia*), *Shorea assamica, Cinnamomum cecicodaphne, Dysoxylum binectariferum, Altingia excelsa, Mesua ferrea, Eugenia* spp., *Sterculia alata, Michelia champaca, Amoora wallichii, Cedrela toona, Ficus* spp., and *Kayea assamica*. Along the lower slopes of the Cachar, Khasi, and Jaintia hills around the Surma valley, *Dipterocarpus turbinatus* is found, along with oaks, *Dipterocarpus pilosus, Sterculia alata, Mesua ferrea, Bombax insigne, Artocarpus chaplasha,* etc. In northern Bengal, western Assam, and Bhutan typical genera of these evergreen forests are *Eugenia, Phoebe, Dysoxylum, Castanopsis, Terminalia,* and *Ailanthus*.

THE HIMALAYAS

The Himalayas extend over a distance of some 1,500 miles between the gorges of the Indus and the Brahmaputra. The main range, with Everest, Kanchenjunga, Dhaulagiri, and many other giant peaks, forms the core of the system, to which the Trans-Himalayas on the north, the Outer Himalayas on the south, and lesser subsidiary ranges give width and body.

The currents of the southeast monsoon from the Arabian Sea and the Bay of Bengal both strike the southern slopes of the Outer Himalayas, which receive the bulk of the rainfall. In general the rainfall increases eastward. Along the south slopes of the mountains, it increases with elevation to a zone of maximum precipitation between 3,000 and 5,000 feet above sea level. Few clouds pass the main range, north of which the slopes are dry and windswept. There is relatively little precipitation above 12,000 feet, and most of it is in the form of snow.

The Himalayas roll up the northern latitudes, as it were; within a relatively short distance they present tropical, temperate, and arctic types of flora. The character of the vegetation changes both with elevation and with the change to moister conditions eastward. Conifers like those of the north temperate zone of America and Europe constitute a noteworthy feature of the Himalayan forests, although the proportion of conifers progressively decreases eastward.

We shall deal with the Himalayas in terms of three regions: (1) the Western Himalayas, between the Indus and the Sutlej; (2) the Central Himalayas, between the Sutlej and the Gandak; and (3) the Eastern Himalayas, between the Gandak and the Brahmaputra. While the names applied to the forest types of the Deccan and Indo-Gangetic plains will be retained, the dry, monsoon, and rain forests of the Himalayas are distinct entities. Although they correspond in a general way to their counterparts elsewhere, they do not resemble the latter in points of detail.

THE WESTERN HIMALAYAS. In the western Himalayas the rainfall increases from the Indus valley (20 inches) eastward. The vegetation most characteristic of this region is best classed as Dry Himalayan Forest (rainfall, 20 to 40 inches). In the arid interior valleys in the lee of the main range we have such forests at altitudes of between about 5,000 and 11,000 feet. Here the greater part of the precipitation falls in winter as snow. Most of this forest is composed of pure associations of conifers, the broadleaf species being confined to sheltered and comparatively moist valleys. *Juniperus macropoda* and *Pinus gerardiana* are found throughout Kashmir in the dry interior valleys, with the junipers persisting farther eastward. Groups of deodars (*Cedrus deodara*) occur on the Outer Himalayas, more particularly in the relatively moister valleys of the Beas and Sutlej, associated with silver fir (*Abies pindrow*) at elevations of about 7,000 to 8,000 feet. Oaks are absent in Kashmir, the broadleaf species of the Western Himalayas being *Corylus colurna, Viburnum cotinifolium, Desmodium tiliaefolium, Lonicera quinquelocularis, Smilax vaginata* Dcne., *Rubus niveus, Berberis* spp., *Plectranthus rugosus, Fragaria vesca* L., *Viola canescens* Wall., *Thalictrum minus, Impatiens* spp., *Artemisia maritima* L., *Ribes grossularia, Rosa webbiana,* and *Abelia triflora.*

THE CENTRAL HIMALAYAS. A moister type of vegetation, the Himalayan Monsoon Forest, characterizes this region, which has an annual rainfall of between 40 and 80 inches. This forest occurs at elevations of between 5,000 and 11,000 feet. The rainfall is relatively less in the interior, toward the west, and above 10,000 feet, but increases eastward and more particularly in the Outer Himalayas. The conifers are typically represented by fir, spruce (which is notably absent in the Western Himalayas), cedar, hemlock, and pine, with occasional cypress and yew, and the broadleaf trees in the main by several species of oak, associated with rhododendron. Other genera met with commonly are *Acer, Carpinus, Aesculus, Prunus, Ulmus,* and *Betula,* and frequently *Litsaea, Lindera, Machilus, Euonymus* and *Ilex.* Bamboo is represented in *Arundinaria,* and the ground vegetation is composed of *Indigofera, Desmodium, Rubus, Viburnum, Impatiens, Plectranthus, Senecio, Dipsacus* and *Heracleum.* Within the monsoon forest, various species of oaks give clues to the following subtypes at different elevations.

Low-Level Oak Forest. Ban oak (*Quercus incana*) occurs gregariously in the Central Himalayas (Garhwal, Kumaun, and western Nepal) at elevations ranging from 6,000 to 8,000 feet, although relatively lower on northern slopes and in moist valleys and relatively higher along the warmer southern slopes. The ban oak prefers cool, shady, moist, sheltered slopes, decreases with the diminishing rainfall westward, and is conspicuously absent in Kashmir. In this zone chir (*Pinus longifolia*) occupies the hotter southern slopes, occurring more or less gregariously down to about 2,500 feet. Sought for leaf fodder and fuel in the hills, the ban-oak forests are gradually disappearing, yielding place to *Rhododendron arboreum* and *Pieris ovalifolia*, which yield neither fuel nor fodder. Other broadleaf species of the zone are: *Carpinus viminea, Cedrela serrata, Euonymus pendulus, Ilex dipyrena, Betula alnoides,* and *Litsaea umbrosa.* The ground cover is composed of *Viburnum cotinifolium, Desmodium tiliae-folium, Berberis lycium, Lonicera quinquelocularis, Rubus ellipticus, Indigofera gerardiana, Myrsine africana, Deutzia staminea, Vitis* spp., *Hedera,* and *Smilax parviflora.*

Mid-Level Oak Forest. In the next higher zone (roughly, 7,000 to 9,000 feet), which is somewhat cooler and drier, though snow is common, *Quercus dilatata* progressively replaces the ban oak, although the latter persists as an unhappy straggler. The representative coniferous associates, often occurring gregariously, are *Abies pindrow, Picea morinda,* and *Buxus sempervirens,* while *Pinus excelsa* replaces *Pinus longifolia.* Deodar is also found in this zone, but only on the inner ranges, where there is less rainfall and more snow, and often descending to the ban-oak level on cooler slopes. Occasionally, associations of cypress (*Cupressus torulosa*) colonize limestone outcrops that provide relatively dry conditions. The other broadleaf species are *Euonymus pendulus, Ilex dipyrena, Rhamnus purpureus, Lindera pulcherrima, Eurya acuminata, Rhododendron arboreum, Meliosma dilleniaefolia, Cedrela serrata, Pyrus lanata, Pieris ovalifolia, Machilus duthiei, Fraxinus micrantha, Betula alnoides, Carpinus viminea,* and *Acer caesium.* The representative bamboo is *Arundinaria,* and the ground cover most commonly is composed of *Rosa macrophylla, Rubus niveus, Viburnum* spp., *Berberis aristata, Strobilanthes wallichii, Deutzia corymbosa,* and *Hedera helix.*

High-Level Oak Forest. This zone (8,000 to 11,000 feet) is characterized by even more rigorous climatic conditions—less rain, heavier snows, and hail storms in spring—and hence has fewer species. The most typical is *Quercus semecarpifolia,* though other broadleaf species characteristic of the mid-level oak forest are also found here. Their coniferous associates are silver fir (*Abies pindrow*), deodar, and spruce (*Picea morinda*). Other leading species are *Quercus dilatata* at relatively lower levels, *Betula alnoides* (and *B. utilis*), *Pyrus lanata* (and *P. foliolosa*), *Prunus padus, Acer caesium, Meliosma dilleniaefolia, Rhododendron arboreum* (and *R. barbatum*), *Taxus baccata, Euonymus tingens, Rosa sericea* (and *R. macrophylla*), *Viburnum foetens, Cotoneaster acuminata, Strobilanthes wallichii,* and *Salix elegans.* The ground cover is largely composed of *Clematis montana, Vitis semicordata, Ribes glaciale,* etc., and the representative bamboo is *Arundinaria.*

THE EASTERN HIMALAYAS. In this region the rainfall progressively increases eastward from about 80 to about 120 inches annually. Snow seldom falls on the outer ranges. The vegetation comprises semi-evergreen and evergreen types.

Semi-Evergreen Forest (rainfall about 80 inches). This occurs in the 7,000- to 9,000-foot zone in Nepal, more particularly its eastern part, and in Sikkim. The oaks of the Central Himalayas are replaced by *Quercus pachyphylla* and *Quercus lineata* in association with groups of hemlock (*Tsuga brunoniana*) on warmer slopes and of *Abies densa* at high elevations. The chief among other species are: *Acer campbellii, Magnolia campbellii, Betula utilis, Taxus baccata, Rhododendron arboreum* (and *R. grande*), *Brassaiopsis alpina, Acer pectinatum, Daphne cannabina, Rubus niveus,* and *Berberis aristata.* Ferns are abundant and mosses cover the stems of the trees. In the understory *Rhododendron arboreum* is found. Oaks and other broadleaf species become less frequent with the diminishing rainfall in the interior. In the zone from 9,000 to 11,000 feet in the inner hills of northeastern Sikkim the conifers met with are *Picea spinulosa* Beissn., *Pinus excelsa, Larix griffithii, Juniperus wallichiana,* and hemlock (*Tsuga brunoniana*).

Himalayan Evergreen Forest (rainfall, about 100 inches). Sikkim, Bhutan, the Balipara frontier tract, and the outlying Patkai, Barail, Khasi, and Garo ranges support an evergreen type of vegetation, of which three subzones may be distinguished:

a) Laurel Forest (approximately 6,000 to 7,000 feet), consisting characteristically of *Machilus edulis, Beilschmiedia* spp., *Cinnamomum obtusifolium, Litsaea* spp., *Machilus* spp., *Michelia cathcartii, Magnolia campbellii, Engelhardtia spicata, Schima wallichii, Castanopsis tribuloides, Quercus spicata, Prunus nepalensis, Mallotus nepalensis, Betula alnoides, Acer laevigatum* (and *A. campbellii*), *Eurya acuminata, Symplocos theaefolia,* and species of Araliaceae.

b) Buk-Oak Forest (approximately 7,000 to 8,000 feet). Buk oak (*Quercus lamellosa*), with *Castanopsis tribuloides, Acer campbellii, Michelia* spp., and many of the characteristic species of the Laurel Forest.

c) High-Level Oak Forest (approximately 8,000 to 9,000 feet). *Quercus pachyphylla* intermingled with many of the buk-oak associates.

In the northeastern corner of Assam (rainfall about 80 inches) the flora above 5,000 feet includes oaks, maples, pears, magnolias, *Manglietia, Michelia, Bucklandia populnea, Alnus nepalensis, Betula alnoides,* and *Carpinus viminea.* On the outlying Khasi Hills and Shillong Plateau the characteristic species between 2,500 and 6,400 feet elevation are *Pinus khasia* and *Quercus griffithii.*

THE SEACOASTS

Trees are found on beaches [3] and sand dunes along the coasts of India, but the only coastal forests of any considerable extent and economic

[3] Beach forests occur in Orissa (at Puri) and in the Sundarbans. Species commonly met with are *Hibiscus tiliaceus, Thespesia populnea, Erythrina indica, Ixora parviflora, Vitex negundo* (and *V. trifolia*), *Trewia nudiflora, Tamarix gallica, Acanthus ilicifolius, Lippia geminata, Oryza coarctata* Roxb., *Caesalpinia bonducella, Derris scandens, Dalbergia torta, Vitis semicordata,* and *Ipomoea.* The sandy beaches and dunes along the coast support *Casuarina,* often artificially planted for fuel.

importance are the mangrove tidal forests of the Ganges, Mahanadi, and
Godavari deltas, on the Bay of Bengal.[4] Here differences in the floristic
composition are caused largely by the varying degrees of the brackishness
of the water and by the varying heights of the banks of estuary channels
and consequent differences in their liability to flooding. In the Sundarbans area of the Ganges delta, a region named from sundri (*Heritiera*
spp.) which grows there, the species generally met with in areas of brackish
and salt water are as follows:

a) Low mangroves: *Ceriops roxburghiana, Avicennia alba* (and *A. officinalis*), *Aegialitis rotundifolia, Excoecaria agallocha, Acanthus ilicifolius, Brownlowia lanceolata, Bruguiera caryophylloides,* and *Derris
uliginosa,* with *Rhizophora* spp. conspicuously absent.
b) Tree mangroves: *Rhizophora* spp., *Bruguiera, Ceriops,* and *Sonneratia.*
c) Salt-water *Heritiera* Forest in the lee of (a) and (b): *Heritiera, Excoecaria, Ceriops, Bruguiera,* etc.

Farther back, where the tidal flats are washed for only a short time at
high tides by slightly brackish water (quite fresh during the rainy season),
recently deposited river silts support what is known as a Fresh-Water
Heritiera Forest, comprising *Heritiera* and *Bruguiera,* with *Ceriops* in the
second story, the two former species reaching heights of about 100 feet.
On high banks *Pandanus,* canes, and ferns cover the ground. Under
brackish conditions near the sea *Phoenix paludosa* is common, while
Oryza grass colonizes newly formed high-and-dry mud banks washed by
fresh water only. Rhizophores, with their stilted stems, occupy the sea
face and are often associated with knee-rooted *Heritiera.* These mangroves are duplicated with minor modifications on the other east-coast
deltas.

THE ANDAMAN ISLANDS

The position of the Andaman and Nicobar Islands along an arc across
the Bay of Bengal suggests a former land connection between Burma and
Sumatra. The hilltops that constitute the Andamans comprise 204 islands,
the Nicobars being a separate group with 19 islands. In the present study
the Andamans only are considered, for little is known about the vegetation of the Nicobars.

The Andamans extend over a distance of some 220 miles from north to
south, with an average width of 15 miles. The land area is about 2,500
square miles. The surface is generally rough, cut by ranges of hills enclosing narrow valleys. In the North Andamans, Saddle Peak, the highest
point of the islands, reaches 2,400 feet. An equable, oceanic climate with
a heavy rainfall is reflected in generally moist types of forest vegetation, of
which three may be distinguished: Rain, Monsoon, and Shoreline Forests.

[4] Mention need only be made of the mangroves of the Indus delta. Low and of limited
extent, they have been adversely affected by the excessive heat.

Rain Forest. Of the type found in Assam and the western Ghats, the rain forest is at its best in the parts of these islands where the mean annual rainfall is approximately 100 inches and over, as, notably, along the west coast, which receives the full force of the southwest monsoon. Port Blair, on the east coast, however, registers a rainfall of 116.7 inches, with 177 rainy days and a mean annual humidity of 83 per cent. The mean annual temperature is 80° F., the mean April maximum 92° F., and the mean February minimum 74° F. A vast variety of species flourishes under these optimum conditions of growth, with trees reaching 125 feet in height and 15 feet and more in girth.

Dipterocarps predominate, as is not the case in the rain forests of the Western Ghats. The species most frequently met with are: *Dipterocarpus tuberculatus* (and *D. pilosus*), *Artocarpus chaplasha* (and *A. gomeziana*), *Calophyllum spectabile, Planchonia andamanica, Hopea odorata, Endospermum malaccense* Bth. ex Muell. Arg., *Sideroxylon longipetiolatum* King & Prain, *Garcinia andamanicum, Myristica andamanica* (and *M. glaucescens*), *Pterospermum aceroides, Caryota mitis, Euphorbia epiphylloides, Mitrephora prainii, Anaxagorea luzoniensis.* The ground cover is composed of *Dinochloa adamanica, Calamus palustris,* and *Gnetum scandens.*

In valleys protected from heavy rain, deciduous associates appear. In the south at lower elevations the evergreens consist of *Dipterocarpus costatus, Mesua ferrea, Canarium manii, Hopea andamanica* King ex C. E. Parkins, *Cratoxylon formosum, Euphorbia trigona* (and *E. epiphylloides*), and *Cryptocarya ferrarsi.*

Monsoon Forest. The moist deciduous forests of the Andamans, otherwise known as "Padauk Forests," like the moist sal and moist teak forests of the mainland, occupy low-level (below 300 feet) localities, which either have less rainfall, or coarse, porous soils derived from sandstone. The transition from the evergreens is imperceptible. The forest species characteristic of the region are: *Pterocarpus dalbergioides, Terminalia bialata* (*T. manii* and *T. procera*), *Canarium euphyllum, Sterculia campanulata, Bombax insigne, Lagerstroemia hypoleuca, Tetrameles nudiflora, Chukrasia tabularis, Albizzia lebbek, Odina wodier, Adenanthera pavonina, Dillenia pentagyna, Oxytenanthera nigrociliata,* and *Bambusa* spp. The ground cover is composed of *Alsodeia bengalensis, Mallotus acuminatus, Ventilago madraspatana, Delima sarmentosa,* and *Acacia pennata.*

Shoreline Forest. The shoreline is fringed throughout with beach forest and tidal mangrove forest. The former occurs on exposed seashores and is composed of *Mimusops littoralis, Pongamia glabra, Morinda citrifolia, Erythrina indica, Calophyllum inophyllum, Terminalia catappa, Barringtonia speciosa, Cordia subcordata, Thespesia populnea, Vigna retusa* Walp., *Mucuna gigantea,* and *Colubrina asiatica.* The ribbon-like tidal mangrove forest consists chiefly of *Rhizophora* spp., *Sonneratia, Heritiera, Ceriops* and *Bruguiera.*

FOREST RESOURCES AND FORESTRY

Forest Areas, Reforestation

FOREST AREAS. Reliable data relating to forest areas in India are available only for the government forests in regions that were formerly part of the British provinces. The figures for the private forests in these regions and for all types of forest in the former Indian States (which neither maintained forest departments nor carried out detailed forest surveys) are of doubtful value. For the country as a whole the ratio of forest area to total area amounts to about 22 per cent, as compared with the following percentages for other countries: Argentina, 25; Belgian Congo, 45; Brazil, 57; Burma, 58; China, 9; France, 21; the United States, 33.[5]

For India, where we have to contend with an oppressive tropical sun, desiccating hot winds, the periodic monsoons, a low forest potential, and a predominantly agricultural economy, an ideal forest ratio might be about one third of the total land area. In the mountains as much as 60 per cent should probably be kept under forests, because of their protective function, whereas on the plains the ratio might be as low as 20 per cent.

NEED FOR REFORESTATION. The lack of wood over large parts of India compels the farmers to burn their cow dung as fuel—dung that should go to fertilize their impoverished fields. The consequent diminishing harvests cause a further extension of cultivation, which tends to engulf not only the remaining village woodlands but grazing grounds, habitations, and even lines of communication, and condemn the average cultivator to a precarious existence in a congested mud hovel on the barest level of subsistence. The destruction of the forests, moreover, strips the land of its natural defenses against hot desiccating winds, dust storms, and erosion by wind and water; and this deterioration is the more serious because it is insidious. Hence, the campaign to grow more food must be inextricably tied to a "grow-more-fuel" campaign.

Measures must be put into effect for enlarging the forest area in the Indian states where it is deficient—measures involving not only the prevention of further encroachment of cultivation upon forest lands, but also the reservation for the production of timber and firewood of wastelands unfit for cultivation, and of such state lands as obsolete military camping grounds, canal banks, and railway and roadside lands. Success will be achieved partly by arousing mass tree consciousness and by enlisting the active cooperation of villagers in raising trees wherever the opportunity presents itself. In the Uttar Pradesh useful work has already been done in this direction, and many cultivators have been persuaded to raise a tree or two even on their own fields. The "Van Mahotsaya," or annual Festival

---

[5] United Nations: Food and Agriculture Organization. *World Forest Resources*, Rome, 1955, Table 1.

of the Trees, recently inaugurated by Shri K. M. Munshi, former Union Minister of Food and Agriculture, has done much to stimulate enthusiasm for tree planting throughout the country. Furthermore, wherever there is now a relatively high proportion of forest land, it should be utilized to the best advantage so as to make good the deficiency where climatic and edaphic factors militate against tree growth.

Production and Imports of Forest Products

In the former British provinces and in certain Indian states for which data are available, the annual production of timber and fuel wood during the three prewar years averaged about 4,379,000 tons. By 1945-46 it had increased by about 60 per cent to 7,115,000 tons, but during the four ensuing years it fell off to about 40 per cent above the prewar level, averaging some 6,151,000 tons each year. The increase, which would seem to have come to stay, may be accounted for by the following factors: (1) the opening up of inaccessible forests during World War II; (2) a general rise in the standard of living, with a corresponding increase in the demand for forest products; (3) the introduction of more speedy traction; (4) a closer conversion of logs to meet the increased demand; (5) the utilization of species unacceptable before the war; and (6) increased extraction from the Andamans.

The brunt of the fellings during World War II fell on such timbers as sal, deodar, chir, teak, and sissoo, which were in considerable demand to meet defence requirements. The excessive wartime cutting of these species, however, was largely balanced by diminished felling of them during the period 1945-51, when the increased general level of production was maintained by the utilization of hitherto little-used species and by the exploitation of timber—especially teak—from forests that had been unavailable before the war. Forestry, however, is a long-range enterprise. The current effort to introduce more scientific methods of management into the state-owned and private forests of India is not expected to yield speedy results. Except for improvement in the firewood situation, the influence of this effort on timber yields will hardly be felt to any great extent for the next 25 years.

The major imports are teak, paper, boards, and wood pulp. Teak comes largely from Burma and Siam, but steps are now being taken to replace it by timbers from the Andamans and by treated conifers. A 25-year lease was signed by the Government of India in August, 1951, for operations in the virgin forests of the North Andamans. While it is difficult to grow two cubic feet of timber where one grew before, it is easy to make a cubic foot last the life of two by treatment designed to preserve it against fungus and insect attack. Spread of the practice of timber seasoning and timber treatment is bound to be an important factor in the conservation of the forest resources of the country.

The bulk of the imports of paper, boards, and wood pulp comes from Sweden and Finland. India is now entirely dependent on imported newsprint, although efforts are being made, with the aid of technical assistance from the Food and Agriculture Organization of the United Nations, to bring about a domestic development of this industry within the next ten years. Recent surveys of the Himalayan fir, which has hitherto remained unexploited because of its inaccessibility, bid fair for the establishment of an indigenous wood-pulp industry on a modest scale.

Forest Management and Policies

PRE-BRITISH PERIODS. In pre-British times the forests of India enjoyed a measure of protection owing to their very inaccessibility—their lack of transport facilities, malarious nature, and wild beasts—and, above all, owing to the limited demand for timber in a country torn with strife and unrest. True, the Arabs carried on a trade in teak for building sea-going craft, but their requirements were small and easily met. Some measure of control was exercised by the rulers of the day, but with respect only to valuable species like teak and sandalwood, which were declared royal trees, for the felling of which permits had to be obtained. Otherwise, every one was free to fell what he liked, without let or hindrance.

THE BRITISH RÉGIME. As has been pointed out, destruction of the forests assumed menacing dimensions with the advent of the British and the consolidation of their power by the end of the eighteenth century. The havoc, however, proved a blessing in disguise, for the next fifty years witnessed widespread concern over the vanishing of forest resources that had been assumed to be inexhaustible. In 1805 the British government inquired of the Court of Directors of the East India Company regarding a sustained supply of teak logs for the British Navy. In 1806 a policeman was placed in charge of the Malabar teak forests, an appointment suggestive of the interest which the government of Madras took in their teak. During the first half of the nineteenth century the forests became largely the concern of the district administrative officers. The Collector (administrator) of Malabar established the famous Nilambur Teak Plantations in 1844, and the Bombay government appointed the then Director of the Botanical Gardens as the first Conservator of Forests in 1847. The government of Madras followed suit and appointed a Conservator in 1856. About the same time, a forest officer was appointed to look after the forests of Duns and Oudh; and the Commissioner of Kumsun worked as Conservator in addition to his other duties.

ESTABLISHMENT OF FOREST DEPARTMENTS. The introduction of scientific forest management and the organization of forest departments in India owe their inception to Dr. Dietrich Brandis, a professor of botany from the University of Bonn, who was engaged by the East India Company in 1856 as the superintendent of teak forests in Burma. His resource-fulness, ability, and consummate skill led to his appointment in 1864 as the first Inspector General of Forests for India, and as a result of his initiative forest departments were constituted in the then British prov-inces. A Forest Act, later replaced by the more elaborate Acts of 1878 and 1927, was passed in 1856, and in accordance with its provisions valuable timber-bearing regions were declared as either "reserved," "protected," or "unclassed" forests. In the main the difference lies in the degree of control prescribed. In especially valuable areas, declared as reserved because of the vital role they play in the national economy, only well-defined and limited private rights are recognized. In protected forests, private rights are admitted freely and restricted only in the interest of the right-holders themselves. In such forests, while the reasonable needs of the local population are met, the local people are not permitted to exercise rights and privileges in blissful disregard of the interests of the generations to come. Stated succinctly, the distinction consists in this: in a reserved forest everything is treated as an offense which is not permitted, whereas in a protected forest nothing is an offense unless it is prohibited. The "unclassed" forests, as their name signifies, are those awaiting classification as either "reserved" or "protected."

While the forest departments in the former British provinces of India were highly organized, such was not generally the case in the Indian States, where forests attracted attention more for the sport that they provided than for their protective and productive functions. Most of the states were too small and poor to afford full-fledged forest organizations, and the bulk of their forests were far from valuable. The integration brought about by recent constitutional changes since the dawn of independence has now made it possible for each group of states to have its own forest department.

PRIVATE FORESTS. During recent years attention has been focused upon the need for protecting private forests from the short-sighted policies of their owners, as a means of conserving an essential national economic resource. With no prospect of quick annual returns, an owner is fre-quently tempted to sacrifice his capital for an immediate gain. The pro-visions of the Indian Forest Act of 1927 did not suffice to arrest the destruction of these forests and the consequent physical deterioration of the areas in which they lie. Recent legislation for the control of private forests, however, has sought to establish the following procedure: (1) designation by the government of private forest areas over which control is to be exercised; (2) issue of felling permits, pending compilation of working plans for the areas so designated; (3) affording the owners of the private forests concerned the opportunity of managing them in accord-ance with approved working plans; and (4) vesting control of private for-ests in the government in cases where recalcitrant owners indulge in reck-less fellings in flagrant disregard of the working plans. While the title to such "vested" forests continues unaffected at present, existing trends point to the complete abolition of the private ownership of forests.

FOREST POLICY: 1894. Although the foundations of regular forest management were laid in the sixties of the nineteenth century, it was not until 1894 that the Government of India adopted the forest policy that constitutes the Magna Carta for the forests of India. Since then the vital role of the forests in relation to agriculture, industry, transportation, and defence, has received increasing recognition. Their protective functions have also come to be better understood.

The old forest policy was designed largely for the former British provinces. Its provision for the relinquishment of forest land "without hesitation" for the extension of agriculture—subject to certain conditions honored chiefly in the breach—led to undesirable consequences. In the original policy no mention was made of sustained yields, working plans, forest education, or forest research; nor was any cognizance taken of wildlife, an important and attractive feature of India's forests.

THE NEW POLICY. The recent constitutional changes have directed attention to the shaping of an over-all policy for the country. The government has revised the forest policy in relation to the progress that has been made in the physical, economic, and political fields. The New Policy of 1952 provides, among other things, for the classification of forests into: (1) Protection Forests, the preservation of which is directed by purely physical and climatic considerations; (2) National Forests, to be maintained and managed to meet the needs of defence, industry, and transportation; (3) Village Forests, to be maintained for their role in the agricultural economy of the country, such as provision of firewood and of small timber for agricultural implements and dwellings; and (4) Treelands, or areas covered with tree growth of some sort, which, though outside the scope of regular forest management, are essential to the amelioration of the physical environment. These classes are by no means mutually exclusive, since each forest usually fulfills functions subsidiary to those specifically assigned to it.

The notion, once widely entertained, that forests as such have no inherent right to land, but may be permitted on sufferance on residual land not required for other purposes, is being effectively dispelled. In the New Policy, the protective and productive role of the forests finds recognition in a directive to the effect that a proportion of the whole land area to be determined by each state should be permanently maintained under forest. Each group of villages is to have a complement of forest, constituting a fuel, fodder, and timber reserve.

Under the New Policy, moreover, attention is given to such matters as: (1) balanced land use; putting each type of land to such use that it will produce most and deteriorate least; (2) state control of private forests; (3) preservation of wildlife; (4) control of grazing; (5) control of shifting cultivation; and (6) provision against fluctuating budgets.

Special provision is also made for the training of forest personnel, for forest legislation, and for research. The principle of sustained yield and the need of setting up an organization for dealing with working plans have both been especially stressed.

Forest Education and Research

FOREST RANGERS' COLLEGES. The genesis of forest education in India dates from 1878, when a Forest Rangers' School was inaugurated by the government of the North-West Province (as the present Uttar Pradesh was then called) under the aegis of the Survey of India in Dehra Dun. This school, which enjoys the distinction of being the first of its kind in the British Empire, was intended for the training of forest rangers, and it has performed the function continuously ever since (except in 1933 and 1934, owing to the economic depression). In 1884 the school was transferred to the control of the central government, was designated the Imperial Forest College, and placed under the direct supervision of the Inspector General of Forests for India. To meet increasing demands for the training of forest officers, another Rangers' College was established in 1948, at Coimbatore, in the South, to cater to the special needs of that region. It is hoped that this new venture will develop into a regional center for forest research and education.

HIGHER INSTRUCTION IN FORESTRY. The first Forest Rangers' School was founded mainly to train Indians for recruitment to subordinate ranks in the forest service. The higher positions at that time were generally filled by British officers trained at the schools of forestry at Nancy in France, and, in the United Kingdom, at Cooper's Hill, Oxford, Cambridge, and Edinburgh. In 1912 advanced instruction in forestry was begun at Chandbag (Dehra Dun) for the training of Indians for somewhat higher positions than those previously open to them. With the advent of the reforms initiated in 1920 as a result of World War I, the Imperial Forest Service came to be progressively Indianized, although the higher Indian officers were sent for advanced training to Oxford, Cambridge, and Edinburgh until 1926. Thereafter it was no longer considered necessary to send Indian officers abroad for training, and until 1932 they were trained at the Forest Research Institute at Dehra Dun. Uncertain political conditions, however, led to the cessation of the forestry course at Dehra Dun during the ensuing six years. The new Indian Forest College, attached to the Institute, started functioning in 1938 after Congress governments had been formed in the various states, and this college has offered advanced instruction in forestry ever since.

THE FOREST RESEARCH INSTITUTE AND COLLEGES. Instructors in forestry at the Imperial Forest College at Dehra Dun from the beginning interested themselves in research, an interest that was recognized in 1906 by the creation of a research branch, from which the present Forest Research

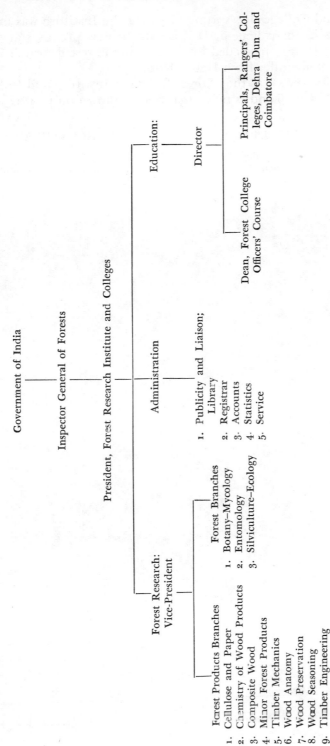

Government of India

Inspector General of Forests

President, Forest Research Institute and Colleges

Administration

Forest Research: Vice-President

Education:

Director

Forest Products Branches
1. Cellulose and Paper
2. Chemistry of Wood Products
3. Composite Wood
4. Minor Forest Products
5. Timber Mechanics
6. Wood Anatomy
7. Wood Preservation
8. Wood Seasoning
9. Timber Engineering

Forest Branches
1. Botany–Mycology
2. Entomology
3. Silviculture–Ecology

1. Publicity and Liaison; Library
2. Registrar
3. Accounts
4. Statistics
5. Service

Dean, Forest College Officers' Course

Principals, Rangers' Colleges, Dehra Dun and Coimbatore

Institute and Colleges has sprung. In 1914 the Institute was moved from its quarters in the college at Dehra Dun to new premises at Chandbag; and in 1929 it was superseded by the existing Forest Research Institute at Kaulagarh, four miles from Dehra Dun.

The entity known as the "Forest Research Institute and Colleges" was established in 1906 and is now organized as shown on p. 481.

SOURCES FOR BOTANICAL NOMENCLATURE

BRANDIS, DIETRICH. 1906. *Indian trees.* Archibald Constable & Co., London.
GAMBLE, J. S. 1881. *A manual of Indian timbers.* Office of the Superintendent of Government Printing.

22. CEYLON

Roman W. Szechowycz

Forest Zones

Although Ceylon lies entirely south of the Tropic of Cancer, no place in the island is more than seventy miles from the ocean and the temperatures are correspondingly moderate. The monsoons (northeast from November to February and southwest from May to October) and a hilly relief combine to create diverse climatic conditions that give rise to an exceptionally rich variety of plant communities. Between Colombo on the west coast and Batticaloa, 140 miles away on the east coast, there are no fewer than six main climatic and corresponding forest zones.

THE TROPICAL EVERGREEN ZONE. The southwestern part of the island is covered by tropical evergreen rain forest similar to that usually found in warm tropical regions of heavy rainfall and high humidity. This region benefits from both monsoons and receives a well-distributed rainfall of over 100 inches per annum; the mean annual temperature is approximately 80° F., with small diurnal and monthly ranges. The vegetation is luxuriant and trees usually attain a height of more than 100 feet; climbers abound. The forest growth consists of a large variety of species producing timber mainly of nondurable quality. Competition between species is so great that it is not easy to select any one as being typical of an area. In certain localities *Dipterocarpus zeylanicus* [1] (hora) produces almost pure stands. Other strong competitors are *Doona congestiflora* (thiniya), *Cyathocalyx zeylanicus* (kekala), *Calophyllum bracteatum* (kina), *Artocarpus nobilis* (del), *Cinnamomum multiflorum* (wal-kurundu), *Ficus* spp., *Melia composita* (lunumidella), *Palaquium grande* (mihiriya), and *Pericopsis mooniana* (nedun).

THE WET MONTANE ZONE. Northeast of the tropical evergreen forest zone lies the wet montane zone. A steady decrease in the luxuriance of the tree growth with altitude is observed. The species found at lower elevations begin to disappear and others take their place. The more prominent among the latter are *Michelia champaca* (sapu), *Syzigium umbrosum* (damba), *Acronychia pedunculata* (ankenda), and *Kurrimia zeylanica*

[1] Source for botanical nomenclature: H Trimen. *A handbook to the flora of Ceylon.* 6 vols. Dulau & Co., London, 1893-1931.

483

(palen). Above about 4,500 feet, the forest becomes a true montane ever-green forest with species such as *Syzigium umbrosum, Syzigium rotundi-folium, Gordonia zeylanica, Meliosma simplicifolia* (elbedda), and *Calo-phyllum walkeri* (kina). Higher still the trees are even more stunted and

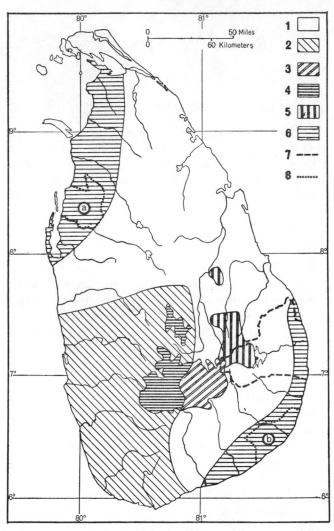

FIG. 47. Ceylon: forest types. 1. Dry zone (semi-evergreen monsoon forest area). 2. Wet zone (tropical evergreen rain-forest area). 3. Dry-zone uplands (montane evergreen forest and dry patanas). 4. Wet-zone uplands (montane evergreen forest and wet patanas). 5. Savanna forest. 6. Arid coastal-zone forest. 7. Boundary of area under administration of Gal Oya Development Board. 8. Boundary of national parks. *a.* Willpattu National Park. *b.* Ruhunu National Park.

branched. Dead and dying trees are seen practically everywhere. Al-though the annual rainfall is over 100 inches and is well distributed throughout the year, strong winds and very low temperatures from Decem-ber to February (26.1° F. recorded in February, 1914) prevent good forest development. This type of forest alternates with undulating grasslands locally called patanas, on which the only tree species is the sparsely distributed *Rhododendron arboreum* (ma-ratmal). The shifting cultivators who originally cleared the land of its forest cover, together with the annual grass fires that followed, may be responsible for the almost total absence of forest in these areas.

THE INTERMEDIATE MONTANE ZONE. East of the wet montane zone is an area of lower rainfall (about 75 inches yearly), shallow soil of low storage capacity, and droughts of four months or longer in duration—conditions not conducive to the development of trees. The montane evergreen forest of this intermediate zone is confined to watercourses, folds in the hills, and other places with a moist soil, and consists of a mixture of species found at both higher and lower altitudes. Below 3,000 feet occur species characteristic of the adjacent savanna forest of the lower elevations, such as *Terminalia chebula* (aralu), *Terminalia belerica* (bulu), *Emblica officinalis* (nelli), *Anogeissus latifolia* (dawu), *Butea monosperma* (gaskela), and *Pterocarpus marsupium* (gammalu). *Lantana aculeata*, originally introduced into Ceylon as a flower plant, has, in many places, become a persistent weed. The large extent of grassland (dry patanas) that alternates with these patches of forest is due to the enormous runoff over steep slopes, to long periods of drought, and to the shallowness of the soil above the gneiss rock, although in some localities shifting cultivation and subsequent grass fires have been responsible. The only tree species which survives in these dry patanas is *Careya coccinea* (kahata or patana oak).

THE SAVANNA FOREST ZONE. At approximately 1,500 feet one enters the parklike savanna forest, locally called damana or, in the wet zone, talawa, an apparently unending carpet of grass with a few scattered trees. The annual rainfall here is more than 75 inches, but the period of drought in some years lasts as long as five months. This country of indescribable beauty is still the haunt of the elephant, buffalo, and leopard. A paradise for the hunter, landscape painter, and poet, it is of no economic value as a forest. There is a total absence of undergrowth, and the herb layer consists of grasses, of which *Imperata cylindrica* (illuk) is the most prominent. Shallow, poor soil, long periods of drought, and the destructive activity of man have contributed to the making of this plant formation.

THE SEMI-EVERGREEN MONSOON DRY FOREST ZONE. This lies east of the savanna forest zone and has a similar climate. Most of the trees are deciduous, and their average height is about 60 feet. These forests produce some of the best timbers in the world—*Chloroxylon swietenia* (satinwood), *Berrya cordifolia* (Trincomalee wood, halmilla), *Vitex pinnata* (milla), *Diospyros ebenum* (ebony), *Alseodaphne semecarpifolia* (ranai), and *Manilkara hexandra* (palu). These valuable species grow in mixed stands with others less valuable, such as *Hemicyclia sepiaria* (wira), *Ficus* spp., *Walsura piscidia* (kiri-kon), *Pleurostylia opposita* (panaka), and *Aglaia roxburghiana* (kannakompu).

THE COASTAL JUNGLE ZONE. The arid coastal belt in the east, north-west, and southeast of the island is covered by a thorny scrub jungle, which does not exceed 25 feet in height. This zone receives less than 50 inches of rain concentrated in about four months of the year. The air humidity ranges from 60 to 75 per cent. The plant community consists of shrubs such as *Gmelina arborea* (et-demata), *Randia dumetorum* (kukuruman), and *Memecylon rostratum* (kuratiya). The scattered tree species found here are *Cassia fistula* (ehela), *Calophyllum calaba* (gurukina), *Manilkara hexandra* (palu), *Hemicyclia sepiaria* (wira), *Euphorbia antiquorum* (daluk), and *Chloroxylon swietenia* (satinwood). Commercially these forests are of no value, but merely provide cover for the poor sandy soil.

Since climatic changes are not abrupt there are few sharp divisions in the forest vegetation: the zones merge into one another, forming inter-mediate communities. The area between the tropical evergreen and the semi-evergreen monsoon dry forest is covered by a forest that has some of the characteristics of both, but most of this plant formation still awaits proper scientific description.

Destructive Factors

SHIFTING CULTIVATION. The activities of the shifting cultivator have contributed much to the establishment of certain of the present plant communities. Owing to its good accumulation of humus adapted to crops, high forest is invariably cleared and burned, and thousands of cubic feet of valuable timber go up in smoke every year. This method of cultivation, which ignores sound agricultural principles, is responsible for covering large areas with secondary forest (jungle) of no commercial value, or else with grasses. Accelerated soil erosion in such areas is enor-mous, especially on steep slopes. Tradition and lack of suitable land to satisfy all chena (shifting) cultivators have prevented the government from taking drastic steps. To localize shifting cultivation, however, and thereby to prevent the wholesale devastation of valuable forests, the government has divided the chena land into blocks, each of which is cultivated once in ten or twelve years, and has also made available irrigable land for permanent cultivation. Areas subject to heavy chenaing are now being reforested on a co-operative basis according to the "taungya forest system," which was first developed in Burma in 1856 and has been adopted in Java and other countries of Southeast Asia. Under this sys-tem government land is leased out rent-free for the raising of short-term food crops, and in return the lessee raises approved forest species along with his crops.

COMMERCIAL PLANTATIONS. Clearing for commercial plantations has been the second most important destructive human factor. Since 1873 more than half a million acres have been opened up for tea plantations, and since 1876 nearly 700,000 for rubber (*Hevea brasiliensis*). Most of these areas were previously covered by forest. Soil erosion on the plantations is heavy and has adversely affected rivers, tanks, irrigation channels, and the plantations themselves.

ILLICIT FELLING. A third factor altering the composition of plant communities in most forest areas is illicit felling and the extraction of poles for agricultural and building purposes. Illicit felling is locally looked upon as an honest trade, one that has come down from father to son. Extraction of poles, seldom properly supervised, tends to destroy nearly all valuable timber species in the round-pole stage. These sizes are extensively used for fencing cultivated land and the construction of semi-permanent buildings. Despite the fact that "the round pole of today is a log of tomorrow," removal of poles in other than silvicultural operations is still permitted.

Forest History and Administration

When Ceylon was ruled by the Sinhalese kings the entire forest estates of the island belonged to the Crown, and large areas were cleared for agriculture based on irrigation. After the eighth century, however, the forest came back, owing to the destruction and neglect accompanying continuous wars with invaders from the continent and to the ensuing ravages of malaria. The forest at first reclaimed the Anuradhapura area, including the large city of the same name, and, a few centuries later, the city of Polonnaruwa. But in the later forest history of Ceylon "man the destroyer" features prominently. Export of timber began with the Portuguese occupation in the sixteenth century. The Dutch destroyed much forest for the cultivation of cinnamon, in which they carried on a lucrative trade, and after 1830 the British undertook timber exploitation on an enormous scale. After several million cubic feet of the best timbers had been exported, a forest policy was initiated under British rule in 1885, and since then conservation and propagation of the forests have been promoted by the government.

The total forest cover is approximately 70 per cent of the island's area. Forest administration is at present the responsibility of four different bodies. The major portion of the forests is administered by the Forest Department, with a Conservator as head. The Department of Wild Life administers forests in the national reserves and sanctuaries for the flora and fauna. The Gal Oya Development Board, an autonomous body created for the multipurpose development of the Gal Oya valley, administers the forests in that area, and the Revenue Department administers village forests set apart for domestic needs. Private forests form a negligible part of the total forested area.

Care of the Forests

Timber extraction for domestic and commercial purposes has been heavy in the past, but the inroads made during and since World War II have contributed most toward the present depletion of timber stocks. A considerable period of rest and cultural treatment is necessary for the majority of the forests, except where inaccessibility, lack of drinking water in the dry seasons, and labor difficulties have prevented exploitation and thus helped to protect the stock. In the tropical evergreen zone the forests of the Sinharaja region are still intact. The stocks here, which consist mostly of *Dipterocarpus zeylanicus* (hora), could, on a rough estimate, produce half a million cubic feet yearly. In the dry-forest zone, the main source of valuable timbers, the only unworked forest is one of about half a million acres in the Northern Division (northwest of Trincomalee).

EXTRACTION AND REGENERATION. In Ceylon today modern machinery and methods applied in biblical times are found side by side. Owing to inadequate staff and consequent lack of supervision, timber contractors used to apply the "cut what you like" policy, and the present generation is paying heavily for the sins of its forbears. Now, however, the extraction of timber is usually done on a selective basis, and precautions are taken to leave sufficient trees of valuable species as seed bearers.

The heavy intermixture of species renders the removal of valuable timber, which seldom represents more than 5 to 10 per cent of the stock, both difficult and costly. The best forest tractor, one that can not only move easily between bushes and unwanted trees but also bring logs to the roadside and load them into trucks, is still the elephant, and elephants are also employed in almost every sawmill yard.

Regeneration of valuable species after extraction is quite satisfactory, although species of low commercial value, such as *Xylopia parvifolia* (netaw), *Ailanthus triphysa* (wal-bilin), and *Canarium zeylanicum* (kekuna), in the wet zone, and *Ficus* spp. and *Hemicyclia sepiaria*, in the dry zone, tend to overdevelop in areas that have been heavily exploited. Clear-cutting or excessive opening usually results in areas being overrun by forest weeds such as *Macaranga peltata* (kenda) and *Trema orientalis* (gedumba).

SILVICULTURAL OPERATIONS. Creepers and unwanted trees are removed by felling, girdling, or poisoning, and thinning is confined to plantations. Plantations in the dry and intermediate zones were started in 1890, as part of a plan for the co-operative reforestation of areas opened for shifting cultivation. About 15,000 acres of good forest have been planted. Species introduced with varying success are *Artocarpus integrifolia* (jak), *Swietenia macrophylla* (mahogany), *Tectona grandis* (teak), *Azadirachta indica* (margosa), *Vitex pinnata* (milla), *Felicium decipiens* (pihimbiya), *Alstonia macrophylla* (havari-nuga), and *Berrya cordifolia* (halmilla). In some areas the forest stock has been improved by plant-ing *Berrya cordifolia* in small clearings scattered within the original forest. These operations have been fairly successful. The afforestation of the grasslands (patanas) of the central hills comprising the montane zone was begun in 1929, and approximately 5,000 acres have been suc-cessfully planted with exotics (Australian gums and some conifers). Al-though no previous tests were made of the suitability of the species to local conditions, the choice has mostly proved good. The species that have shown themselves most adaptable are *Eucalyptus robusta, E. micro-corys* F. Muell., and *E. saligna* Smith. After trials the planting of *E. globulus, E. acmenioides* Schauer, and *E. maculata* was abandoned. Some areas in the montane zone have been planted with conifers, mostly *Cupressus macrocarpa,* and trials have been carried out with *Juniperus procera* Hochst ex. Endl., *Araucaria,* and *Pinus* spp. *Acacia melanoxylon* R. Br. has been successfully raised, but only on a small scale. Conifer plant-ing was abandoned for some years owing to the extreme susceptibility of the plantations to damage by fire. A fresh experimental attempt, however, is being made with *Pinus caribaea* Morelet. Except where strong winds prevail, all plantations on up-country grasslands show good promise. With the cooperation of the FAO, the Forest Department has embarked on an extensive scheme of mechanized afforestation of the patanas and low forests, and at present the target is a minimum of 2,000 acres per year.

Chief Timber Uses

In Ceylon timber is used not only for building construction, which makes heavy demands, but also in the manufacture of plywood, furni-ture, chests, safety matches, toys, and railway sleepers. The demand for nondurable light hardwoods is on the increase. A plywood factory run by the government utilizes such species as *Doona congestiflora* (kokun), *Calophyllum bracteatum* (walu-kina), *Palaquium petiolare* (kirihem-biliya), and *Myristica dactyloides* (malaboda). More than 150,000 cubic feet were used for this purpose in 1952. Species consumed in the manu-facture of chests, toys, and matches are all nondurable varieties such as *Alstonia scholaris* (ruk-attana), *Canarium zeylanicum* (kekuna), and *An-tiaris toxicaria* (riti). The furniture industry, on the other hand, uses the most valuable durable timbers, and there is a yearly demand for approximately 200,000 sleepers (600,000 cubic feet), which can be made only from primary hardwoods. Wood is also extensively used as fuel in the processing of tea and rubber and for domestic purposes, but this re-quirement should eventually be met by the development of hydroelectric schemes, one of which (Laxapana) is already under way.

The timber position of the island as a whole is unsatisfactory, extrac-tion at present exceeding the yearly increment. The population of Cey-lon, now well over 7,000,000, is growing rapidly and at the present rate of increase will double itself in another 25 years. Concurrently the demand per capita for timber, now approximately 10 cubic feet, is also rising. The problem of future supplies cannot be solved solely by afforestation and better forest management, which can never keep pace with the demand. During the last dozen years there has been an alarming increase in the import of timber, the value of which has jumped from Rs. 193,000 in 1942 to Rs. 21,000,000 in 1952. The only solution is the utilization of species that have hitherto been treated merely as forest weeds. The Gal Oya Development Board has taken the first step in this direction by installing a plant for the pressure treatment of timber, and even secondary species (light hardwoods) are now used successfully for building purposes. The Forest Department has also started experiments in timber treatment in a small experimental pressure plant and in open tanks, and steps are being taken to install a plant similar to that of the Gal Oya Development Board.

With a view to the utilization of waste timber material from sawmills and carpentry workshops, and of branch wood and inferior species, efforts are now being made to develop building bricks from a mixture containing timber and cement, and production on a small scale has already been begun.

Governmental and Public Interest

Of recent years both government and the public have shown an increasing awareness of the value of forests as a national asset and of the important role they play in the country's economy. To raise the standards of forestry a forestry field-training school was established in 1951 with two training centers, one in the wet and the other in the dry zone, and considerable research work is carried on by the Forest Department. The Soil Conservation Act, passed in 1951, empowers the Government to enforce anti–soil-erosion measures even on private lands. All these steps augur well and it is expected that in the not too distant future the present unsatisfactory timber position will be remedied.

There are three national parks, two of which—Ruhunu and Wilpattu—have been in existence since 1937. These abound in the fauna of the island and provide excellent relaxation and recreation for young and old. Ruhunu in particular, which is only 176 miles from the port of Colombo, has earned popularity in many parts of the world, and even casual visitors to the island find time to spend a few hours here. The third and most picturesque park, recently created under the Gal Oya scheme, shows promise of great popularity. The island has some of the most beautiful scenery in the world, and forest work is made especially interesting when the forester finds deep in the forest, as he often does, ancient ruined temples and other monuments to a splendid past.

23. SOUTHEAST ASIA

R. Sewandono

Southeast Asia is considered for present purposes as including the following countries on the Asiatic mainland and adjacent Indonesian archipelago: Burma, Thailand, Indochina, Malaya, British North Borneo, Sarawak, Brunei, Indonesia, Portuguese Timor, and all of New Guinea. Except for northern Burma, the entire area lies between the tropics.

Forest Types

Temperature and, especially, rainfall in Southeast Asia are the most important climatic determinants of the distribution of forest types. As the temperature falls gradually with increasing altitude, the natural vegetation undergoes corresponding changes in composition and form. The annual rainfall varies from about 50 centimeters in the drier regions to 500 and more in the mountains. Conditions are thus present for the development of highly divergent forest types.

The rainfall is largely influenced by the monsoons. The mountains of western Burma intercept the southwest monsoon and hence receive an abundant rainfall. The inland plains of Burma, Thailand, and Indochina, on the other hand, are in the rain shadow of these mountains during the southwest monsoon, and, consequently, the rainfall is here much less. In eastern Indochina the rainfall is again heavier, as a result of nearness to the South China Sea.

The Indonesian archipelago and Malaya lie in the sphere of the alternating monsoons. Close to the equator across central Sumatra, central Borneo, northern Celebes, and northwestern New Guinea there is a narrow belt with abundant rains during the whole year, north and south of which the typical monsoon climate is clearly marked by a rainy season alternating with a more or less extended dry period. There is also a marked tendency to increasing drought from west to east in the archipelago.

Mountains modify this general scheme. The moisture-laden clouds are forced upward by the slopes, causing oversaturation and higher rainfall. In these countries there are many mountain ranges lying at right angles to the direction of the prevailing winds. As a result, many areas in the mountains show an alternation of wetter windward and drier leeward sides.

The natural forest vegetation is markedly affected by these differences in climatic conditions.

Where the rainfall is abundant and evenly distributed during the whole year, or where the dry period is not very pronounced—not longer than one or two months, for example—evergreen rain forest appears as the climax of the natural vegetation. This forest is characterized by a great number of species and a luxuriant growth.

Examples of this general forest type are found in the *Tropical Lowland Evergreen Rain Forests* of western Burma, Malaya, Sumatra, Borneo, and New Guinea. These forests are dense and lofty. Some species reach a height of 50 meters and more, usually towering as scattered giants high above the general canopy. While the number of species is extremely high, most individual species contribute only a trifling percentage of the total number of trees. Occasionally, a few species more or less predominate—as, for example, the Dipterocarps—although pure stands of appreciable extent are rare. Normally every space is stuffed with vegetation. Epiphytes and climbers, including lianas, and also plank buttresses are common. Generally, most of the species are of soft wood. Besides the Dipterocarps, various species of the following families are often frequently represented: Apocynaceae, Asclepiadaceae, Burseraceae, Bignoniaceae, Rhamnaceae, Lecythidaceae, Leguminosae, Meliaceae, Anacardiaceae, Olacaceae, Rutaceae, Sapotaceae, etc.

Under similar rainfall conditions, in the mountains we find the *Tropical Lower-Montane* and *Upper-Montane Evergreen Rain Forests.* While the number of stems in these forests is higher, the number of species, although high, is usually less than in the lowland rain forests. The canopy is not so dense. Plank buttresses are scarce and found only in the lower parts of these forests. Lianas are fewer and smaller. These forests consist typically of oaks, chestnuts, and several species of Magnoliaceae, Lauraceae, Tiliaceae, Rubiaceae, Theaceae, etc., families seldom met with in the lowland forests. With increasing altitude, *Podocarpus,* a conifer, is found, and at still higher levels the trees become lower, smaller, and more branchy; in general the forest appears more and more dwarfed and little by little changes into an elfin-woodland, unsuitable for exploitation.

Besides *Podocarpus,* there are other conifers in the mountain forests, usually mixed with broadleaf species, but sometimes in pure stands constituting the *Tropical Montane Conifer Forests.* These pure conifer forests are mostly found in drier places. Examples are the forests of *Pinus merkusii* [1] and *P. khasya* in Burma and Thailand, and the *Pinus merkusii* forests in Indonesia. It is still a matter of dispute as to how far they constitute a real climax formation, for there are many indications that the distribution of *P. merkusii* in Indonesia is facilitated by fire. In the mountains of Celebes, Borneo, and the Moluccas, there are forests of

[1] For sources for botanical nomenclature in this chapter see below, p. 517.

Phyllocladus and other conifers, such as *Podocarpus, Dacrydium, Agathis,* and *Libocedrus.* The lower montane forests of New Guinea consist partly of *Araucaria;* the upper montane forests of *Libocedrus, Dacrydium, Nothofagus,* and *Podocarpus.* The forests in the mountains of southern Indochina include *Pinus merkusii, P. khasya, Podocarpus,* and *Keteleeria.* At higher altitudes *Dacrydium* is met with. In the montane forests of northern Indochina we find *Fokienia hodginsii* and *Podocarpus cupressinus.* Recently more conifer species have been discovered in the provinces of Laokay and Yenbay, viz., *Tsuga yunnanensis* Mast., *Abies pindrow* Royle, and a *Cryptomeria* species.

With longer dry periods, the evergreen forests are replaced by *Semi-Evergreen* and *Mixed Deciduous Forests.* The semi-evergreens are found in those regions where the dry periods last no longer than one, two, or at most three months; with a more pronounced dry period of two to five, or sometimes six, months mixed deciduous or monsoon forests occur.

The *Tropical Semi-Evergreen Rain Forests* consist of both evergreen and deciduous species, the former predominating. They are fairly dense high forests, in which the dominating trees sometimes run to large dimensions, although usually these forests are lower than the true evergreen forests. The number of species is high, but less so than in the true evergreens. Epiphytes and climbers, including lianas, are numerous. In general, this type of forest is very variable, but, as in true evergreen forests, Dipterocarps tend to predominate in them. This type of forest is found in large expanses in Burma and Thailand.

The *Tropical Mixed Deciduous* (or *Monsoon*) *Forests* are mainly characterized by the fact that during the dry period all or most of the trees of the upper canopy are entirely leafless. In the better parts of these forests, the trees reach a considerable height, some 35 to 40 meters or more. Although the canopy is less dense and the number of species smaller than in the tropical semi-evergreen rain forest, the percentage of precious hardwood species is usually higher. The teak (*Tectona grandis*) here calls for especial mention. Plank buttresses are rare, woody lianas and other climbers numerous. Epiphytes are mostly confined to the wetter places.

The composition of these forests varies considerably from place to place. Thus, to this group belong the mixed deciduous forests of Burma and Thailand, in which teak is accompanied by *Xylia, Pterocarpus macrocarpus* Kurz, *Homalium tomentosum* Benth., *Terminalia, Dalbergia, Vitex,* etc. In these two countries there are also extensive areas of mixed deciduous forests in which Dipterocarps predominate. In Java, on the other hand, teak grows mostly in pure stands, and only in the moister parts of the forests is it found to a greater or lesser extent mixed with other species. In Indochina the principal trees of the mixed deciduous forests are Dipterocarps and Leguminosae.

In tropical regions with a more strongly pronounced and longer dry period of some six to eight months, the *Tropical Savanna Forests* pre-

TABLE 23–I

SOUTHEAST ASIA: FOREST AREA IN RELATION TO TOTAL AREA AND POPULATION,
1947-1951 (INDONESIA, 1939)

Country	Date	Esti-mated Popula-tion, 1950 (Thou-sands)	Total Area	Forests				
				Forest Area			Productive	
				Total	% of Total Area	Per Capita	Total	Acces-sible
A		B	C	D	E	F	G	H
			1,000 Hectares				*1,000 Hectares*	
Burma	1950	18,490	67,802	39,094[a]	58	2.12	25,372	25,372
Thailand	1949	18,310	51,352	32,600	63	1.78	32,431	10,779
Indochina	1951	29,950	73,280	31,000[b]	41	1.03	...	...
Cambodia	1951	3,750[c]	17,600	8,000	45	2.14	...	...
Laos	1951	1,200	23,680	14,200	60	11.90	...	...
Viet-Nam	1951	25,000	32,000[d]	8,800[e]	25	0.34	...	...
Malaya	1951	5,230	13,129	9,717	74	1.86	7,340	2,034
Northern Borneo..	1950–51	956	20,379	16,178	79	16.9	...	...
Br. N. Borneo	1950	348	7,611	6,968	91	20.0	1,036	259
Brunei	1951	46	577	388	67	8.4	...	...
Sarawak	1951	562	12,191	8,822	72	15.7	3,885	3,885
Indonesia [f]	1947	75,000	190,435	121,000	64	1.61	70,000	11,000
Indonesia [f]	1939	68,600	190,435	123,761	65	1.80	...	...
Java	1939	47,700	13,217	3,061	23	0.06	...	...
Sumatra	1939	8,900	47,361	29,240	62	3.29	...	...
Borneo	1939	2,300	53,946	41,600	77	18.09	...	...
Eastern Indonesia [g] .	1939	9,700	75,911	49,860	66	5.14	...	...
New Guinea: Aus-tralian, and Papua	1951	1,070	47,400	33,000	70	30.9	...	...
TOTAL, S.E. Asia ..	1947–50	149,506	463,705	282,589	62	1.89	...	...
TOTAL, U.S.A.	1949	151,690	771,067[h]	252,530	33	1.66	191,828	170,784

Sources: Data for Indonesia, 1939, from Annual Reports, Forestry Service, Netherlands East Indies. Other data, except as otherwise indicated, as follows:

Column B: FAO, *Yearbook of Forest Products Statistics, 1953,* p. 120.

Columns C and D: FAO, *Yearbook of Forest Products Statistics, 1953,* pp. 123-125.
"   E and F: calculated from data in columns B, C, and D.
"   G and H: FAO, *Forest Resources of the World,* Washington, D.C., 1948, p. 17.

Dates in column A pertain to data in columns C to F.
[a] Includes inland water bodies.
[b] FAO *Yearbook, 1951,* p. 136.
[c] 1948.
[d] From *The International Year Book . . . ,* 1953, p. 135.
[e] Total for Indochina less sum of Cambodia and Laos.
[f] Includes Netherlands New Guinea.
[g] Celebes, the Lesser Sunda Islands, Moluccas, and Netherlands New Guinea.
[h] Land area.

vail, open forests, mostly with deciduous trees of low stature and a dense ground cover of grasses and shrubs. These forests are for the most part not economically productive, and are of local importance only. With still longer and exceptionally pronounced dry periods, the vegetation finally passes into *Thorn Forests* and true *Savannas*.

A brief account will now be given of the forest situation in each of the more important parts of Southeast Asia. This should be read in conjunction with the statistics presented in Tables 23–I, 23–II, and 23–III.

Burma

Although locally the tidal forests of Burma furnish large quantities of fuel wood, charcoal, and tanbark for home consumption, of far more importance are the evergreen rain forests and mixed deciduous forests. The former produce in the main relatively soft woods from such Dipterocarpaceae as *Dipterocarpus, Hopea,* and *Parashorea;* the latter, in the main, precious hardwoods, such as teak, pyinkado (*Xylia xylocarpa*), and padauk (*Pterocarpus macrocarpus* and *P. indicus*), and also considerable quantities of a secondary hardwood, gurjun (*Dipterocarpus*). The montane pine forests, with their pure stands of *Pinus khasya* and *P. merkusii,* also deserve mention. Although at present not exploited, in the future they should play an important role in the production of timber, resin, and turpentine.

In Burma elephants are indispensable in the extraction of timber, especially in the extensive swampy areas. They are used not only to drag logs in the forests and to the streams, but also for work in timber yards and at sawmills. During the Japanese occupation the elephant herds greatly diminished, and of the 6,000 domesticated elephants before the war, only 3,000 were left at its end. It will take a number of years before these casualties are replaced.

The Irrawaddy and the Salween rivers and their many affluents form a natural and cheap transport system for rafting timber to Rangoon and Moulmein. Here there are several big sawmills, where the wood can be processed before shipping.

Before World War II Burma had the greatest output of all the teak-producing countries, with an annual teak production of about 710,000 cubic meters, according to FAO statistics. Burma also produced other timbers, mainly pyinkado, padauk, gurjun, thitya (*Shorea obtusa*), ingyin (*Pentacme siamensis*), taukkyan (*Terminalia alata*), and pyinma (*Lagerstroemia flos-reginae*), as well as large quantities of fuel wood and charcoal. Of minor forest products bamboo, tanbark, cutch, and lac deserve mention. Annual exports of teak before the war varied between 284,000 and 355,000 cubic meters. India was the principal buyer, next came the United Kingdom, followed by South Africa, Germany, the United States of America, and Ceylon, all of which also imported considerable quantities.

TABLE 23-II

SOUTHEAST ASIA: PRODUCTION (FELLINGS) OF INDUSTRIAL WOOD AND FUEL WOOD, 1946-1953

(In Thousand Cubic Meters, Solid Volume of Roundwood)

Country	1946 I	1946 F	1946 T	1947 I	1947 F	1947 T	1948 I	1948 F	1948 T	1949 I	1949 F	1949 T	1950 I	1950 F	1950 T	1951 I	1951 F	1951 T	1952 I	1952 F	1952 T	1953 I	1953 F	1953 T
Burma	306	527	833	913	4260	5173	817	5040	5857	288[a]	1059[a]	1347[a]	400[b]	1062[b]	1462[b]	533[c]	1886[c]	2419[c]	694[d]	1318[d]	2012[d]	...	...	...
Thailand	(920)[e]	6257	(7177)	(687)	1906	(2593)	(780)	(1594)	(2374)	1327	952	2279	1350	1007	2357	1485	2128	3613	1514	1395	2909	1470	1825	3295
Indochina	358	1437	1795	...	...	...	278	463	741	300	685	985	134	305	439	446	722	1168	501	779	1280	516	626	1142
Cambodia	...	...	...	...	...	...	...	...	...	...	...	...	...	...	...	230	313	543	247	313	560	218	230	448
Laos	...	...	...	...	...	...	...	...	...	...	...	...	...	...	...	44	79	123	43	71	114	23	96	119
Viet-Nam	...	...	...	...	...	...	...	...	...	...	...	...	109	265	374	172	330	502	211	395	606	275	300	575
Malaya	488	280	768	786	592	1378	803	496	1299	906	854	1760	1155	919	2074	1310[f]	490[f]	(1800)[f]	...	...	...	1336[f]	412[f]	1748[f]
Northern Borneo	...	...	...	...	...	...	...	...	...	...	...	...	(425)	148	(573)	...	...	...	...	...	...	...	...	...
Br. N. Borneo	...	...	...	175	141	316	198	17	215	184	102	286	178	49	227	255	121	376	275	158	433	289	106	395
Brunei	...	...	...	(23)	107	(130)	65	113	178	(205)	68	(273)	16	12	28	...	...	...	...	...	...	...	...	...
Sarawak	14	(67)	(81)	...	...	...	...	...	...	...	...	...	(231)	87	(318)	238	46	284	394	47	441	...	...	...
Indonesia	179	276	455	387	592	979	797	1093	1890	1063	976	2039	1319	1556	2875	...	...	...	...	...	...	1517	2094	3611
New Guinea	...	...	...	...	...	...	...	...	...	(54)	...	(54)	(70)	(1)	(71)	94	(1)	(95)	86	(1)	(87)	97	(1)	(98)
Australian	...	...	...	...	...	...	...	...	...	(54)	...	(54)	(66)	...	(66)	78[c]	...	(78)[c]	74[d]	...	(74)[d]	91	...	(91)
Netherlands	...	...	...	...	...	...	...	...	...[g]	...	...	...[g]	4	1	5	16	1	17	12	1	13	6	1	7

Sources: FAO, *Yearbook of Forest Products Statistics*, as follows:

1946: from *Yearbook for* 1948, p. 26.
1947: " " 1949, p. 22.
1948: " " 1950, p. 28.
1949-50: " " 1951, pp. 20-21.
1951-52: " " 1953, pp. 26-27.
1953: " " 1954, pp. 24-25.

I: "Industrial wood," i.e, saw logs, veneer logs, sleepers, pulpwood, pit props, poles, piling, posts, etc.
F: "Fuel wood, etc.," including wood for charcoal.
T: Total, I plus F.
... No data.
( ) Incomplete data.
[a] Provisional figures for 1948-49.
[b] Estimate for 1949-50.

[c,d] 1950-51, 1951-52, respectively.
[e] Saw logs and veneer logs only.
[f] Commercial disposals only.
[g] Included in total for Indonesia.

TABLE 23-III

SOUTHEAST ASIA: IMPORTS AND EXPORTS OF FOREST PRODUCTS, 1946-1952
(In Roundwood Equivalents, Thousand Cubic Meters)

Country	Imports 1946	1947	1948	1949	1950	1951	1952	Exports 1946	1947	1948	1949	1950	1951	1952
Burma	1	35	30	30[a]	35[b]	40[d]	40[e]	2	40	270	200[a]	40[b]	150[d]	160[e]
Thailand	15	20	30	...	55	40	40	45	170	180	...	210	190	90
Indochina	7	...	35	50	...	280	290	5	...	...	*	100	293	352
Cambodia	...	...	...	...	3	–	–	...	...	...	...	100	290	350
Laos	...	...	...	...	...	–	–	...	...	...	*	*	1	2
Viet-Nam	...	...	...	...	55	280	290	...	...	...	*	*	2	–
Malaya	(70)	30	65	(120)	(280)[e]	500	630	(40)	40	80	160	330	270	230
Northern Borneo	...	...	...	...	...	...	...	...	100	140	160	240	230	230
British N. Borneo	...	2	*	3	2	3	3	...	...	...	...	20	...	...
Brunei	...	...	2	...	10	...	...	...	8	30	55	210	130	240
Sarawak	...	...	...	...	...	...	...	...	...	...	...	...	...	...
Indonesia	5	15	45	(60)[e]	(70)[e]	310	290	75	60	90	230	230	200	320
New Guinea	...	...	...	2	5	7	7	...	...	3	3	9	7	2
Australian	...	...	...	*	2	–	–	...	...	3	3	9	7	2
Netherlands	...	...	...	2	3	7	7	...	...	...	1	1	1	1

SOURCES: FAO, *Yearbooks of Forest Products Statistics*, as follows:

1946: From *Yearbook for 1948*, p. 148.
1947:   "   "   *1949*, p. 140.
1948:   "   "   *1950*, p. 131.
1949-50:   "   "   *1951*, pp. 126-127.
1951-52:   "   "   *1953*, pp. 114-115.

* Less than one half.
– None.
... No data.
( ) Incomplete data.
[a], [b], [c], [d] For years 1948-49, 1949-50, 1950-51, and 1951-52 respectively.
[e] Does not include paper and paperboard.

During the war, although cutting was somewhat extended, the actual production was not great, owing to military operations and the desertion of laborers caused by bombing by Allied forces. After the war, both production and exports increased until about 1948. Then internal disorders brought a marked slump (see Tables 23–II and 23–III). Indeed, the political complications of the last few years have been highly detrimental to the forest industries of Burma. These difficulties are now partly overcome, but owing to lack of personnel, funds, and equipment, rehabilitation is not easily effected.

Before the war, not less than 80 per cent of the total teak production came from European concessionaires, 12 per cent from small-scale licensees, 5 per cent from government fellings, and 3 per cent from indigenous lessees. Now the forests are nationalized, and the State Timber Board has taken over all the teak forests from the European and indigenous lessees. Recently, and with the help of foreign experts, investigations have been undertaken with regard to the preserving and new utilization possibilities of bamboo and of wood species hitherto considered useless.

The Forest Service in Burma was established in 1856 by the famous Sir Dietrich Brandis. Before World War II Burma had an adequate number of foresters, trained in England or at the University of Rangoon, but after the war the English foresters left the service, and hence the staff is now greatly depleted. For this reason, the facilities for forestry training in Rangoon have been expanded. During 1953 the Rangoon University produced its first postwar batch of forestry graduates, seven in number. Research work for Burma was formerly carried out by the Forest Research Institute of Dehra Dun, India, but a project for the establishment of an independent research station is now under way.

The forest policy, like that of India, is based on the Indian Forest Act of 1878. The main principles are: (1) maintenance of forests to preserve favorable climatic and other physical conditions; (2) preservation of the minimum area of forest needed for the general welfare; (3) preference given to agricultural use over forestry; (4) meeting the needs of the local population for wood, cost free or at low prices; (5) securing the greatest possible revenue, but only after the first four objectives have been met.

Thailand

In Thailand, as in Burma, the leading forest types from the commercial point of view are the evergreen rain forests and the mixed deciduous forests. Although the "yang" forests, consisting mainly of *Dipterocarpus alatus,* are outstanding among the former, there are also vast areas of evergreen rain forests characterized by other Dipterocarps, such as *Dipterocarpus pilosus, D. costatus, Hopea odorata, Cotylelobium lanceolatum* Pierre, and *Anisoptera cochinchinensis* Pierre, mixed with species of other families, for instance *Amoora* spp., and in the southern parts also *Balanocarpus heimii.* Among the mixed deciduous forests, teak forests, with *Tectona grandis* as the predominating species, are of first importance; in addition, there are mixed deciduous forests with Dipterocarps predominating and consisting of *Dipterocarpus tuberculatus, D. obtusifolius, Shorea obtusa, Pentacme siamensis,* etc. In the montane forests, we find oaks, *Castanopsis,* and *Eugenia,* and locally *Pinus khasya* and *P. merkusii.*

Logging operations in the teak forests are conducted according to the Brandis selection system, with a felling cycle of thirty years. To this end, the area of each concession is divided in two parts, which must be felled in two successive periods of fifteen years. Each part is further divided into five blocks. Felling in each block lasts three years. Exploitation is strictly prohibited in blocks not yet opened for felling. The minimum girth for felling is 7 feet. Trees considered for felling are selected and girdled by special girdling parties of the Forest Department. These trees remain girdled for at least three years.

Since this system of exploitation results in felling considerably in excess of the annual growth, the teak forests of Thailand are being seriously overcut. Hence, it is urgently necessary to reduce the amount of the annual felling for some time to come and to increase the productivity of the forests by such appropriate means as improvement fellings and plantations. The total teak area, however, is said to be more than 12 million hectares and therefore large enough to warrant greater production in the future.

Logging is carried out mainly by manual labor. Although elephants are now used for transporting the logs to the rivers and railroad stations, experiments are being made with tractors for this work, at least in the drier areas. The logs are rafted down the Salween River to Moulmein in Burma, down the Mekong to Indochina, and down the Menam to Bangkok, after first being floated individually to so-called "rafting points" below the rapids, where they are collected and combined into rafts of about 200 logs each. As a rule, it takes four or five years before the logs arrive at Bangkok. It is customary to reckon with a loss of 25 per cent due to thefts during transport.

Figures concerning prewar production are difficult to obtain. According to a paper submitted by the Thailand delegation at the Fourth World Forestry Conference in Dehra Dun, December 1954, the average annual production of teak during the period 1938–42 was 140,128 cubic meters, and of other woods 485,834 cubic meters. From 1943 to 1946 the corresponding figures were 66,605 and 509,860, respectively. The period after the war has shown an important rise in production. During 1947–51 the average annual production of teak rose to 206,392 cubic meters and of other woods to 929,434. In 1952 production of teak was 261,306 cubic meters and of other woods 1,237,111; in 1953 these figures were respectively 328,172 and 1,209,817 cubic meters.[2]

[2] These figures differ rather considerably from those in Table 23–II, taken from the FAO *Yearbooks.*

The production of non-teak timber in Thailand is thus very considerable. Until 1932 the annual production of teak was always higher than that of all other species together. But the ever-increasing demand for wood forced a steady rise of the exploitation of other species and since that year production of non-teak timber has exceeded that of teak. Among the non-teak species must be mentioned primarily yang (*Dipterocarpus alatus*), teng (*Shorea obtusa*), and rang (*Pentacme siamensis*).

In addition to timber, the forests of Thailand produce considerable quantities of fuel wood, charcoal, bamboo, rattan, tanning bark, gutta percha, lac, gum benzoin, wood oil from the yang, and various other products.[3]

Exports in 1936 are stated to have been 126,406 cubic meters, of which 99,601 were teak, 9,284 yang, 8,042 pradu (*Pterocarpus macrocarpus*), 3,105 phayung or rosewood (*Dalbergia latifolia*), and 351 maklu or ebony (*Diospyros burmanica*). The above-mentioned paper of the Thailand delegation records as average annual exports during 1948–51 a volume of 117,788 cubic meters, of which 76,037 were teak, 37,804 yang, 423 pradu, and 502 phayung. In 1952 exports came to 57,694 cubic meters, of which 57,403 were teak; in 1953 to 73,195 cubic meters, of which 65,497 were teak and 5,765 yang.[4]

During the war there was comparatively little destruction of property in Thailand. The production of timber in the period after the war has considerably exceeded prewar levels. Exports, however, have not yet reached prewar quantities, probably because of exchange difficulties and the diminishing activities of foreign exporters. Yet, since 1952, export figures have tended to increase, and it is hoped that this tendency will continue; the new trade policy of the government is aimed at the promoting of exports.

The Forest Department in Thailand was organized in 1896 in much the same way as in Burma. All the teak forests are the property of the government, which grants concessions to private operators. Before the war about 85 per cent of the production was in the hands of foreign firms, about 14 per cent in the hands of Thailand operators, and the government retained only 1 per cent. Today, however, there is a strong movement to increase the government share. For this purpose the Forest Industrial Organization has been established, and the foreign concessionaires' share has been fixed at 45 per cent, the Thailand operators' at 33, and the government's at 22.

The Thailand foresters are trained at the Forestry School at Phrae. The number of foresters, however, is insufficient for adequate management of the forests and effective supervision of the concessions. The FAO mission to Thailand in 1948 recommended the following with re-

[3] At Uban, in eastern Thailand, there is a turpentine distillery plant, but its production is still of little importance.

[4] These figures differ rather considerably from those in Table 23–III, taken from the FAO *Yearbooks*.

gard to forestry: reorganization and strengthening of the Forestry Department; increase in the field staff; an aerial survey of the country; reservation as soon as possible of all forests important to the economy of the nation; a rapid preliminary survey of the forest resources; stricter enforcement of existing forestry laws and regulations; setting up of uniform grading rules for exports; undertaking of a large-scale program of artificial and natural regeneration of forests; more vigorous suppression of illicit cutting and theft; and strengthening of the Research Division of the Forestry Department.

In 1951 a five-year Forestry Development Program was submitted to the government. Although public declaration is still awaited, most of the essential projects were approved and financed by the government in the 1952 and 1953 budgets. This program provides for the following measures: setting aside at least 270,000 square kilometers of forest as permanent forest reserves; protection of the reserved forest areas; preservation of protection forests; forest management based on a sustained yield; recognition of the principle that all forest products should be used primarily to meet the needs of the local inhabitants and only secondarily to serve agricultural, industrial, and commercial purposes; surveying marginal forest lands and waste lands as a basis for the formulation of an appropriate land-use policy; promotion of basic and higher education in forestry; study of the utilization possibilities of various timber species and other forest products; stimulating forest-mindedness in general; and encouragement of private tree planting.

Indochina

In view of the differences in climatic conditions, a distinction must be made between the forests in southern Indochina and those in northern Indochina.

Apart from mangrove and fresh-water swamp forests along the coast, the forests in the southern part of the country may be divided into two groups: lower-altitude and higher-altitude forests. At low elevations we find mixed forests, in which Dipterocarpaceae and Leguminosae predominate. Among the former are various species of *Hopea, Dipterocarpus, Shorea, Vatica,* and *Anisoptera,* and among the latter, *Pterocarpus, Sindora, Pahudia, Dalbergia, Dialium,* and *Xylia.* Among other important species are: *Lagerstroemia* spp., *Mesua ferrea, Calophyllum* spp., *Palaquium* spp., etc. In the mountains, above 1,000 meters, there are mixed forests consisting of *Dipterocarpus obtusifolius* and oaks, and locally conifers. In some places pure stands of *Pinus merkusii* and *P. khasya* occur. At still higher altitudes on Mount Bokor in the province of Kampot vast areas are found with the conifers *Dacrydium elatum* and *Podocarpus neriifolius.*

In northern Indochina, also, mangrove forests are found along the coast. In contrast with those of southern Indochina, these mangrove forests are of a very low stature, usually less than 3 meters. The other forests of northern Indochina are divided into forests of middle and higher altitudes. The former are very mixed in composition and consist mainly of *Erythrophloeum fordii, Quercus* spp., *Vatica tonkinensis, Chukrasia tabularis, Melia* spp., *Aglaia gigantea, Talauma gioi, Manglietia* spp., *Cinnamomum* spp., *Mallotus cochinchinensis, Canarium* spp., *Bassia pasquieri,* etc. The latter are found more especially in the northwestern part of Tonkin, near the Chinese boundary, and usually consist of species of *Quercus, Pasania,* and *Castanopsis,* mixed with such conifers as *Fokienia hodginsii* and *Podocarpus cupressina.* Above 2,000 meters *Cunninghamia sinensis, Tsuga yunannensis* Mast., and *Abies pindrow* Royle are found. Mention must also be made of the *Pinus merkusii* forests in northern Annam and in Tonkin, and of *Pinus merkusii, P. khasya,* and *Keteleeria* sp. in Laos.

Before World War II, forest exploitation in Indochina was not very systematic. Production was almost entirely in the hands of small Chinese and Malayan operators, and even the big concerns—for example, the Compagnie Bien-hoa Industrielle et Forestière—acquired their stocks through the intermediary of small contractors. Total timber production in 1934 was about 370,000 cubic meters and the production of fuel wood about 820,000 cubic meters. The annual fellings increased gradually, and in 1941 production of timber came to 875,000 cubic meters and of fuel wood to 1,750,000 cubic meters. Postwar data are given in Table 23–II. These figures are still far below the prewar levels. Indeed, the rehabilitation of forest production in Indochina is a difficult and slow process, because of the civil war.

Exports before World War II were never very important, a circumstance that may have been due partly to the prevalent confusion regarding the nomenclature of the various wood species. Exports of timber in 1939, 1940, and 1941 were estimated at 32,000, 15,200, and 4,880 cubic meters, respectively, and were mainly to Hongkong, France, South Africa, and Japan. Of these quantities, 70 per cent or more was teak, produced in Burma and Thailand and transported to Saigon by rafts, Indochina thus serving merely in a transit capacity. Besides teak, the exports consisted mainly of Dipterocarps and pines. Postwar data are given in Table 23–III. During the period 1950-52 the export volume surpassed that of the prewar period, but in view of the troubles caused by the civil war, it is very doubtful whether this gain will be maintained in the immediate future.

The logs are either dragged to the roads or rivers or hauled by special timber lugs (triqueballes) pulled by oxen or buffaloes. Twenty pair of buffaloes are often necessary for the extraction of the bigger logs. In Annam and Cambodia elephants are also used. From the gathering places the logs are moved also by truck, or floated down the rivers to the sawmills and markets, the cheap river transportation being especially popular. The Mekong, Tonle Sap, and Red rivers are the natural waterways for log transport, and on them rafts are often towed by tugboats. Large quantities of teak come down the Mekong from Thailand.

Special mention must be made of the production of resin and turpentine from *Pinus merkusii*. Before the war this industry had made a satisfactory start, and during the period 1935–41 the annual production of resin increased from 585,000 to 965,966 kilograms. Postwar figures are not obtainable, but in view of the vast areas covered with *Pinus merkusii* in Tonkin, Annam, Laos, and Cambodia, the industry may have a great future.

Besides the products mentioned, the forests of Indochina also produce large quantities of fuel wood, charcoal, and bamboo, and other products, such as rattan, tanbark, wood oil, gutta percha, and gum benzoin.

Before World War II there were ten European sawmills, a great number of smaller local sawmills, six match factories, one plywood and veneer factory, and five wood-pulp factories. During the turbulent days after the Japanese capitulation, however, most of the European-owned factories were destroyed.

The members of the higher staff of the Department of Forests and Waters are graduates of the École Nationale des Eaux et Forêts at Nancy, France. Ranger personnel is trained at Pnompenh.

Since the war the rehabilitation of forest exploitation and the lumber industry has been seriously hampered by unsettled conditions. The French Government has tried to stimulate production by creating a special company known as "Socafor." Modern equipment has been imported for several important logging operations and sawmills, and far-reaching programs for expansion and modernization have been developed, including plans for extensive cultivation and reafforestation and for the conversion of low-value mixed deciduous forest into teak forest. The annual production of wood is to be expanded, and also the production of resin and turpentine. To stimulate exploitation several roads will be constructed in hitherto untapped areas. The civil war, however, has been an insurmountable hindrance to recovery.

Malaya

Mangrove and fresh-water swamp forests are found in many places along the coast, behind which tropical lowland evergreen rain forests extend to the hills. The latter are represented by lowland Dipterocarp forests with an upper limit of 1,000 feet and lower hill Dipterocarp forests from 1,000 to 2,500 feet above sea level. On higher altitudes tropical montane rain forests are found, also represented by two forest types: the upper Dipterocarp forests, ranging from 2,500 to 4,000 feet, and montane oak forests between 3,500 to 5,000 feet.

Although the mangrove forests produce considerable quantities of fuel wood and charcoal, from the point of view of wood production the lowland Dipterocarp forests are the most outstanding forests of the country. The economic value of the lower hill Dipterocarp forests is still unimportant, because of their inaccessibility to present means of exploitation. The upper Dipterocarp and the montane oak forests have not as yet been considered for exploitation.

The lowland Dipterocarp forests are characterized by such predominating Dipterocarpaceae as the red merantis (*Shorea* spp.), white merantis (*Shorea* spp., *Parashorea* spp., and *Pentacme* spp.), keruing (*Dipterocarpus* spp.), kapur (*Dryobalanops* sp.), merawan (*Hopea cernua*), and resak (*Vatica* spp.). Important, too, are chengal (*Balanocarpus heimii*) and merbau (*Intsia* spp.), two hardwood species with outstanding qualities. The following are also often very common: nyatoh (*Palaquium* spp.), geronggang (*Cratoxylon arborescens*), kempas (*Koompassia* spp.), and jelutong (*Dyera costulata*). The last-named produces a latex used as a substitute for chicle in the chewing-gum industry.

Before World War II Malaya had a well-organized and carefully supervised forest industry, and since the end of the hostilities it has made a rapid recovery. Production in 1937 amounted to about 400,000 cubic meters of saw logs, 400,000 of other industrial woods, and 600,000 of fuel wood, or a total of some 1,400,000 cubic meters. Since the war production has risen to somewhat higher levels (Table 23–II).

Singapore is the principal center in Southeast Asia for the timber industry and timber commerce. Singapore's supply of roundwood comes not only from Malaya, but also in considerable quantities from Indonesia, British North Borneo, Thailand, and Indochina; in 1939 more than 250,000 cubic meters were imported from Sumatra alone. These imports consist mainly of softer wood species, such as merantis, keruing, nyatoh, seraya (*Shorea* sp.), and geronggang. In the last few years there has been an increasing demand for merantis because of its suitability for plywood and veneer.

Before the war there were 12 to 15 big sawmills and several smaller ones in Singapore. Only one mill was damaged during the war and the others suffered little. After the war the lumber industry made such a rapid recovery that about thirty sawmills were already in operation in Singapore before the end of 1946. At that time the number of sawmills in the whole country was 110, and they had produced nearly 500,000 cubic meters of lumber in that year. In addition, there were four match factories, and in 1951 a new modern plywood factory went into production.

The supply of logs from neighboring countries, however, sank temporarily to a very low level during the first postwar years, partly because about half of the prewar fleet of some hundred Chinese sailing vessels used for log transportation had been lost during the war and partly because of unsettled conditions in the exporting countries. Furthermore, supplies from fellings in Malaya itself were sometimes hampered by the activities of extremists.

In 1935 the export of lumber amounted to 25,000 cubic meters and in 1938 to 23,800. Of these quantities only a small part went to Great Britain. The principal customers were China, India, and Arabia, since these countries did not make such high demands as to the quality of the product. Table 23–III shows a substantial increase in exports after 1948. The percentage of exports to Europe has also been going up by leaps and bounds, and during the last years has greatly exceeded the total export to Asiatic ports. This success has been due to the accurate inspection and grading now carried out by forest officers of all the wood before shipment. Modern methods of seasoning and preserving have also been adopted.

At the end of 1953, however, the timber export to England received a deadly blow by the abolishing of the currency restrictions. Malaya now has to compete in England with other wood-exporting "non-dollar" countries, such as the Baltic states, France, and Yugoslavia, and, without a drastic reduction of the existing ocean freight rates, it will be impossible for Malaya to maintain its place in the British market. Exports of light hardwoods showed an especially serious decline. During the eight months January–August 1954 such exports to Great Britain were only 917 tons, as compared with 15,243 tons in the corresponding eight months of 1953. The total export of graded timber—light and medium hardwoods—to all countries during the same period decreased by about 50 per cent to 15,499 tons, a decline that would have been even more pronounced had it not been for the special export to Britain of keruing wagon planks. Since, however, keruing has to compete with oak from European countries for use as wagon planks, it is uncertain that this export can be continued.

The Forestry Department in Malaya consists of British foresters, assisted by local foresters trained at the Forestry School at Kepong, near Kuala Lumpur. At Kuala Lumpur, too, there is a Forest Research Institute that has done considerable work in the development of grading rules, in wood technology, and in silviculture and the management of mixed Dipterocarp forests. The well-known "regeneration improvement fellings," as practiced in Malaya, serve as an example to other tropical countries. After the war a new system of regeneration of the Dipterocarp forests was adopted.

Although the rehabilitation of forest exploitation and of the timber industry is thus making good progress, there are still many problems with regard to the expansion of timber production. These are due principally to the shortage of labor, to the need for replacing worn-out sawmill machinery, and, not least, to the competition of non-dollar countries in the English timber market.

Northern Borneo

This section will deal with the whole northern, or British, part of the island of Borneo, consisting of British North Borneo, Sarawak, and Brunei. The forests here are of much the same type as those of the neighboring parts of Indonesia and Malaya.

The mangrove forests produce considerable quantities of fuel wood, charcoal, and tanbark. The fresh-water swamp forests and the mixed Dipterocarp forests in the lowlands are the areas of timber production. Here Dipterocarpaceae predominate, among them, notably, merantis (*Shorea* and *Parashorea* spp.), seraya (*Shorea* spp.), and keruing (*Dipterocarpus* spp.). Other very common species are: ramin (*Gonystylus bancanus*), nyatoh (*Palaquium* spp.), and sepetir (*Sindora* spp.). In some places belian or ironwood (*Eusideroxylon zwageri*) is frequent, and also another group of precious hardwood species, merbau (*Intsia*).

Before the war, exploitation was mostly confined to broad strips along the rivers. On account of the swampy ground and low percentage of usable species in the mixed forests, logging was mainly done by manual labor. Since the war modern equipment has been used in North Borneo and Sarawak, especially for exploitation of hitherto inaccessible forest areas.

In *British North Borneo* proper the annual timber production was more than 350,000 cubic meters before the war and since then has been of comparable magnitude (Table 23–II). The two biggest sawmills at Sandakan were completely destroyed during the hostilities, but have been rebuilt, and new mills have been established, notwithstanding the difficulties in obtaining necessary accessories. At the end of 1948, 19 sawmills were in operation, of which the biggest, owned by the British Borneo Timber Company, is capable of producing 500 cubic feet of sawn timber per day. The cutch factory at Sandakan was severely damaged, too, but could resume production as early as April, 1947. The greatest handicap limiting forest production, however, is the scarcity of labor. An experiment with elephants imported from Thailand, and also with indigenous elephants, for extraction work failed mainly because of the lack of suitable food and feeding grounds, and perhaps also because the logs cut in North Borneo are often too big for elephants to drag. On the other hand, the mechanization of timber extraction has been a great success. Metalled roads are constructed to the hills, where there are vast areas of valuable forests unexploited until now because of their inaccessibility. Extraction in these areas is now done by high-lead skidding, and in addition, a great number of tractors are in use.

Prewar exports amounted to 250,000 cubic meters annually, the greater part of which went to Japan, China, and Britain, with smaller quantities to Australia and Africa. More than 95 per cent of the timber exported consisted of Dipterocarpaceae. There was, in addition, a fairly important export of fuel wood, especially to Hongkong, and also of tanbark, cutch, and dammar, and of jelutong for chewing gum. After the war, exports of timber made a rapid recovery and since 1950 have reached prewar levels (Table 23–III). Japan is again the leading importer, now followed by Hongkong and Australia. The export of fuel wood to Hongkong is still important, the demand for cutch is satisfying, but the jelutong trade is depressed.

An outstanding event in the history of forestry in North Borneo was the termination on June 30, 1952, of the concession of the British North Borneo Timber Company. Hitherto, this company had complete control over the exploitation and export of all the timber in North Borneo. With the end of this monopoly, the Forest Department gained full control over all the forests and can now take all measures regarded necessary for appropriate forest management.

Sarawak, too, has an output of timber and exports comparable to those of British North Borneo (Tables 23–II and 23–III). During the war, little damage was done to industrial properties and at the end of 1946 twelve sawmills were already in operation. This number had increased to 23 by the end of 1948. Postwar production has also greatly increased in spite of shortages of capital and equipment. Since 1951 a start has been made in the mechanization of logging operations: one of the concessionaires is working an area by means of high-lead winching.

The main forest products, besides timber, are fuel wood, charcoal, rattan, dammar, and jelutong.

Table 23–III shows that exports of timber have recovered satisfactorily since the war. From 8,000 cubic meters in 1948 they increased to 240,000 cubic meters in 1952.[5] The bulk went to Britain, Hongkong, Australia, and Borneo ports; smaller quantities were sent to Singapore and South Africa. Among the species exported, ramin (*Gonystylus bancanus*) was the most outstanding, with more than 60 per cent of the total; then came merantis (*Shorea* spp.), sepetir (*Pseudosindora* spp.), jongkong (*Dactylocladus stenostachys*), and kapur (*Dryobalanops rappa*).

Brunei is by far the smallest country in northern Borneo. Logging here is still done primitively by means of manual labor and buffaloes. Before the war there were only two sawmills, but in 1953 the number was 23. Hand sawing has thus been largely replaced by mechanical sawing, but most of the sawmills are very small, with capacities of only 2 to 4 tons of timber per day. The biggest sawmill, owned by the British Malayan Petroleum Company, has been closed down since 1949, because its modern equipment had proved to be too complicated to run by unskilled hands. Shortages of equipment and labor are not beneficial to timber production. Laborers prefer to work in the oil fields. Since the domestic production of timber is insufficient to meet local demands, particularly of the oil industry, considerable quantities of timber are imported from Sarawak. The cutch factory in Brunei town closed down in April 1952 and is now dismantled. In the mangrove forests, fuel wood and charcoal are produced. The export of fuel wood to Hongkong amounts to about 1,500 tons monthly. Production of jelutong is of no importance because of little demand.

---

[5] These FAO figures from Table 23–III do not correspond with data in the *Malayan Forester*, 1954, p. 87, according to which total timber exports in terms of round timber in 1952 and 1953 were 127,814 and 204,223 Hoppus tons, respectively, or about 180,000 and 290,000 cubic meters, respectively.

Forest production in British Borneo as a whole has regained its prewar levels. According to FAO estimates [6] annual fellings in North Borneo before the war were already more than 50 per cent in excess of the estimated net annual growth. It would be interesting to know to what extent this still holds true.

Indonesia

Indonesia consists of a great number of islands, with very varying densities of population and ratios of forest area per capita. The figures presented in Table 23–I show that Indonesia has by far the largest forest area of all the countries of Southeast Asia.

Locally, mangrove and fresh-water swamp forests are found along the coasts, with lowland evergreen rain forests behind them. In Sumatra and Borneo, Dipterocarps form a high percentage of the composition of the swamp and lowland evergreen forests, but in the eastern part of the archipelago—east of the "Wallace line," from the Straits of Bali via the Straits of Macassar northwards—representatives of this typical Malayan family are seldom met with, and, indeed, only a very few species of this family are found in Java, which is in the western part of the archipelago. However, on that overpopulated island practically the whole area of the lowland forests has long since been converted into farmlands. In some places in Borneo we find in the lowland forests another conifer, *Agathis borneensis*, often occurring in fairly pure stands. This is much sought after because of its suitability for veneer, plywood, pulp, and matches. Generally, conifer stands in tropical lowland forests are somewhat out of the ordinary, and probably represent an edaphic climax in this case, as implied by the marked podsolization of the soil in the *Agathis* forests.

Above 1,000 meters in Indonesia we find montane evergreen rain forests, often composed of *Quercus* spp., *Castanopsis* spp., *Altingia* spp., *Michelia* spp., *Manglietia* spp., *Nyssa javanica* Wangerin, *Pometia tomentosa*, etc. In North Sumatra pure stands of *Pinus merkusii* also occur locally at these altitudes—the only pine with a natural distribution area stretching south of the equator. In many places in the mountains of eastern Java and the Lesser Sunda Islands extensive areas of *Casuarina* are found. In Borneo and the islands east of Borneo, we find several conifers, such as *Agathis* and *Phyllocladus*, among the species in the montane forests.

In the drier lowland regions of eastern Java and the Lesser Sunda Islands vast areas are covered with mixed deciduous forests and savannas. The most important species in the mixed deciduous forests in Java is djati, or teak; in the Lesser Sunda Islands we find a few eucalyptus species and, locally, sandalwood (*Santalum album*).

Among the forests in Java, the teak forests are undoubtedly the most important in terms of exploitation. Before the war, they had an area of

[6] *Unasylva*, 1948, 2(6).

about 824,000 hectares. The other Javanese forests, however, are also regularly exploited, insofar as fellings can be carried out without undue damage to the slopes and streams of this overpopulated island. Where possible, afforestation work has as its primary object the creation of plantations of species for industrial uses, notably teak, mahogany, *Pinus merkusii, Acacia decurrens* Willd., *Ochroma, Agathis,* etc.

During the last part of the Japanese occupation, felling in Java was largely extended. Table 23–IV shows the production during the years 1942-44 as compared with 1939. The building of wooden motor vessels consumed large quantities of valuable teak wood, especially from the biggest trees. Some two hundred vessels of about 250 tons each, and a great number of smaller craft, were built each year, and in addition large quantities of fuel wood had to be produced to meet the demands of the railways and industries, in substitution for coal. The damage done to the forests in Java, however, was much greater than might be inferred from the figures in Table 23–IV. In their fellings the Japanese totally ignored

TABLE 23–IV

JAVA: PRODUCTION 1939, 1942-1944
(Roundwood Equivalents in Thousand Cubic Meters)

Year	Timber		Fuel Wood		Total
	Teak	Non-Teak	Teak	Non-Teak	
1939	504	34	738	284	1560
1942	456	26	1340	141	1963
1943	917	63	914	279	2273
1944	908	106	1636	466	3116

prewar working plans, and the easily accessible forests, especially, were the ones that suffered. Fine, long boles were cut for fuel wood, and to get it out as quickly as possible many excellent young teak plantations were sacrificed. At the end of the occupation hardly a teak plantation more than thirty years old was left. In the last year of the occupation, a vast area of teak forests, equivalent to 8½ times the usual annual felling, was girdled and killed. The tending of forests was neglected, and finally all afforestation was stopped. Moreover, large areas of forest land were given to the personnel and laborers as compensation for insufficient pay and to promote the cultivation of food crops. Of a total forest area of about 3,000,000 hectares, no less than 500,000 were deforested.

Java, with a forest area of no more than 0.06 hectare per capita, produced before the war, in roundwood equivalents, about 1,500,000 cubic meters of teak and non-teak annually, of which about 500,000 were timber and 1,000,000 fuel wood and charcoal. The annual teak production was about 500,000 cubic meters of timber and 800,000 of fuel wood; the production of non-teak timber was of no importance (Table 23–IV, year 1939). The postwar production of teak and non-teak during the period

1951-53 totalled 1,947,000 cubic meters annually, of which 575,000 were timber and 1,372,000 fuel wood and charcoal. The average annual teak production during the mentioned postwar period was 490,000 cubic meters of timber and 825,000 of fuel wood.

Before the war, Java exported 15,000 to 25,000 cubic meters of teakwood annually. Postwar exports of teak in the years 1950-53 amounted to 6,230, 6,660, 4,000, and 6,500 cubic meters respectively, mainly to Holland and West Germany.

The timber production of Java is not nearly enough to meet local demands, and large quantities must be imported from other parts of Indonesia, especially from Borneo. Since Java's need of wood will certainly increase, only the other islands of the archipelago can really contribute to the net export of wood to foreign countries.

Outside Java exploitation is greatest in the mangrove and swamp forests on the east coast of Sumatra and adjacent islands near Singapore, whence large quantities of timber, fuel wood, and charcoal are exported to Singapore. This exploitation is almost entirely in the hands of Chinese operators, working exclusively with Chinese laborers. At the end of 1940 there were 74 licensees for timber exploitation, 148 for fuel wood, and 238 for charcoal.

The mangrove forests produce considerable quantities of fuel wood and charcoal, and the fresh-water swamp forests mainly soft-wooded species, such as *Shorea* and other Dipterocarpaceae, *Palaquium* spp., *Tetramerista glabra*, *Cratoxylon arborescens*, etc. The logs are transported by Chinese sailing vessels to Singapore. Some years before the war there was a Japanese concession, with a big sawmill, on one of the islands in the neighborhood of Singapore, but it soon closed down. The production in 1939 in this part of the country alone amounted to 233,446 cubic meters of timber, 102,026 tons of fuel wood, and 32,009 tons of charcoal. During the first years after World War II forest activities were hampered by unsettled conditions, but in 1952 felling reached prewar levels again, with a production of about 225,000 cubic meters of timber in that year. Several new sawmills have been established in this area since the war, and, if this trend continues, the region may become of no little consequence to the lumber industry of Singapore.

Another important exploitation center is in eastern Borneo, where in 1939 about 337,000 cubic meters of timber were produced; after that year production declined because of the closing of a large Japanese concession. Since the war, production has been increasing again, but prewar levels are not yet attained: in 1952 the timber production was 168,950 cubic meters. Timber production in southern Borneo is also of great importance, with a volume of 230,390 cubic meters of timber in 1952. There is a modern sawmill in Sampit, and logging in the *Agathis* forests is done by tractors.

The exploitation of the *Pinus merkusii* forests of Achin in North Sumatra for resin and turpentine is another interesting project. A plan is being studied for the establishing of a big paper mill, with this pine as raw material.

As for eastern Indonesia, mention must be made of the production of teak in southern Celebes, ebony in central and northern Celebes, and sandalwood in Timor.

The whole of Indonesia produced in 1939 about 1,917,000 cubic meters of timber and 2,213,000 of fuel wood and wood for charcoal, totaling about 4,130,000 cubic meters in roundwood equivalents. In addition, there was a considerable yield of minor forest products, such as tanbark, rattan, dammar, copal, jelutong, and gutta percha. Postwar production has shown a rapid gain since 1948, and in 1950 reached about three quarters of the 1939 level (Table 23–II). In 1953 production is stated as totaling nearly 3,500,000 cubic meters, but until now the products have been used mainly for home consumption; exports are still far below the prewar figures (Table 23–III).

Exports in 1939 came to 400,286 cubic meters of timber, 4,551 tons of fancy woods, 96,324 tons of fuel wood, and 29,634 tons of charcoal, or, in roundwood equivalents, to a total of about 625,000 cubic meters. Before the war Singapore, the best customer, received from Indonesia nearly 250,000 cubic meters of timber annually, and Japan, another good client, received about 100,000 cubic meters. Smaller quantities went to Hongkong, China, India, South Africa, the Netherlands, Germany, France, and elsewhere. Singapore and Japan imported soft-wooded species almost exclusively, while the Netherlands and other European countries imported more precious species, such as teak, ironwood (*Eusideroxylon zwageri*), bangkirai (*Hopea cernua*), and ebony (*Diospyros celebica* Bakh.). Fuel wood and charcoal went almost entirely to Singapore. After the end of the war the export of logs from Bengkalis, on the east coast of Sumatra, to Singapore recovered quickly, amounting to 207,570 cubic meters in 1952.[7] Japan came into the market again, and also the Netherlands and West Germany. Australia proved to be a good customer for *Agathis* wood from Borneo. Tables 23–III and 23–V show exports during the postwar years.[8]

Indonesia has to import large quantities of lumber and also various articles made of wood. In 1939 these imports, in terms of roundwood equivalents, were as follows, in cubic meters: lumber, 135,947; tea chests and other packing cases, 47,165; matches, 8,175; rayon, 3,120; newsprint, 49,800; packing paper, 12,210; total, 256,417. According to FAO sources imports in 1952 were as follows (cubic meters): saw logs and veneer logs, 1,000; sawn wood, 5,000; wood pulp, 2,000; box boards, 6,000; newsprint, 5,000; printing and writing paper, 27,000; other paper, 39,000; paper board, 5,000; total, 90,000.

[7] *Unasylva,* 1948, 2(6).

[8] Figures obtained from Indonesian Forest Service. The FAO figures in Table 23 V for sawlogs and veneer logs are, very likely, too low.

Before World War II the Forest Service of the Netherlands East Indies was very well organized in accordance with the usual forestry principles. Its higher staff was trained at Wageningen in the Netherlands. Considerable work was done with regard to forest exploitation, silviculture, and management. The Forest Research Institute in Buitenzorg (Bogor) carried out many investigations in the fields of silviculture, forest botany, wood technology, erosion control, forest mensuration, thinnings, forest zoology, etc.

TABLE 23–V

INDONESIA: EXPORTS OF CERTAIN FOREST PRODUCTS, 1947-1952

Year	Saw Logs and Veneer Logs	Lumber: Sawn, Planed or Dressed	Fuel Wood	Charcoal (Thousand Metric Tons)
	Thousand cubic meters			
1946	21	–	48	–
1947	23		38	–
1948	17		74	–
1949	134	4	60	16
1950	127	9	86	20
1951	107	15	22	8
1952	175	16	47	12
1953	178	17	31	10

Sources:

1946-47: FAO, *Yearbook of Forest Products Statistics, 1948,* pp. 124-125.
1948:   "   "   "   " *1950,* pp. 106-107.
1949-50:   "   "   "   " *1951,* pp. 102-103.
1951-52:   "   "   "   " *1953,* pp. 102-103.
1952-53:   "   "   "   " *1954,* pp. 100-101.

After the government of the islands was handed over to the Republic of Indonesia, the Dutch foresters, except for a few who have remained as advisers, left the service. Thus the new Indonesian Forest Service has had to face the difficult task of reconstruction with a depleted staff. It is planned to meet the deficiency of graduate personnel by expanding the training of foresters under the faculties of forestry of the Universities of Djokja and Djakarta, but it will take a number of years to accomplish this. Besides, there is a great lack of machinery and of means of transport. The technical equipment has been destroyed or worn out, and new modern equipment is difficult to get. Unsettled political conditions have also been a serious handicap, especially during the first years after the war.

In spite of these difficulties, the Indonesian Forest Service has energetically initiated the rehabilitation and modernization of forestry. A special accelerated program of reforestation is being carried out to replace the losses during the Japanese occupation and for the plantation of wood species for industrial purposes. According to this plan, 40,000 hectares are planted annually, or about three times the prewar average. Modern sawmills have been built in Samarinda and other exploitation centers, metalled roads are being constructed in remote forest areas, and exploitation is being modernized by the introduction of tractors and arches for logging. Furthermore the network of forest railways in the teak forests is being considerably expanded.

New Guinea *

Western New Guinea is under Netherlands, eastern New Guinea under Australian, rule. The Australian part consists of Papua and the mandated territory of New Guinea.

On this vast island all possible forest types peculiar to the tropics are represented. The mangrove and swamp forests resemble their counterparts in Indonesia and Malaya. On drier places along the coast we find many tracts with *Casuarina equisetifolia*. Special mention must also be made of *Agathis labillardieri* Warb., which occurs on sandy soils behind the mangrove forests; this species is usually mixed with *Tristania* and *Dacrydium*.

The lowland rain forests also show a striking resemblance to the corresponding forests of Malaya and Indonesia, though with this conspicuous difference: Dipterocarpaceae are seldom met with, only a few species having been found up to now (viz., *Vatica papuana*, *Anisoptera polyandra*, *Hopea* sp., and *Shorea* sp.). In these forests, however, occur a great number of other valuable species, of which the most outstanding are: merbau (*Intsia* spp.), *Planchonia valida* Bl., *Fagraea fragrans*, *Palaquium* spp., *Calophyllum* sp., *Garcinia* sp., *Horsfieldia* sp., *Metrosideros* sp., *Myrica* sp., etc. In the monsoon forests there are found among other species, linggua or angsana (*Pterocarpus indicus*), *Albizzia procera*, *Homalium* sp., and *Eucalyptus deglupta* Bl., and in the savanna forests, *Eucalyptus deglupta* Bl., and *Melaleuca leucadendron*.

On the mountains of middle elevations (700 to 2,000 meters above sea level) the forests are composed largely of oaks (*Quercus spicata*, *Q. pseudomolucca*, etc.) and chestnuts (*Castanea* spp.), and at some places the hoop pine, or *Araucaria cunninghamii*, is found. In the upper montane zones above 2,000 meters there are locally forests of other conifers, such as *Podocarpus* sp., *Dacrydium* sp., *Nothofagus* sp., *Phyllocladus* sp., and *Libocedrus* sp.

Although representatives of both the Asiatic and the Australian flora occur among the forest trees of New Guinea, the Asiatic species are far more prominent, especially in the lowlands. Generally speaking, our knowledge of the forests of New Guinea, their composition and capacity, is still very limited, although it has been somewhat augmented by aerial

---

* Some aspects of New Guinea's forestry situation are also discussed by Dr. Egler in his chapter on Oceania (see below, pp. 611-630).

photographs taken on a large scale during the war, and by considerable work in the field of forest botany.

Forestry activities in the Netherlands New Guinea are aimed primarily at the mapping of productive areas, mainly of *Agathis* forests. Exploitation is being carried out only to a very small extent, the species used being chiefly *Agathis, Intsia amboinensis, Adina,* and *Metrosideros.* Lack of personnel, labor, and equipment are serious hindrances. The total production of industrial wood amounts to less than 20,000 cubic meters annually (Table 23–II). In 1954 a new forestry program was adopted as a part of a general development scheme for this country, and, accordingly, several experts and other personnel have already been sent to New Guinea. The exploitation in the accessible parts of the forests will be considerably expanded, and a big sawmill is to be established in Manokwari.

In Australian New Guinea, exploitation is being carried out on a somewhat larger scale. Production, which in 1952 amounted to nearly 75,000 cubic meters of industrial wood, will be expanded considerably, not only to meet the country's local needs, but also to obtain a surplus for export. At Bulolo, Morobe District, a plywood factory has been built recently, with a capacity of 10,000 sheets of ply per day. The forests in the Bulolo valley consist for a large part of hoop pine and klinki pine (*Araucaria klinki*). But, all things considered, forestry is still in its infancy both here and in the Netherlands part of the island.

The Outlook

Exact data about the forests of some of the countries of Southeastern Asia are difficult—and in certain respects impossible—to obtain. We must also take into account the fact that gigantic masses of fuel wood and small timber are acquired from uncontrolled fellings in gardens and farmyards. A city of the size of Djakarta consumes several hundred thousand cubic meters of this unrecorded wood annually. The figures cited in this paper are taken mainly from various FAO sources. Although largely based on rough estimates only, they are accurate enough to enable one to make certain broad comparisons.

Table 23–I shows that, although Southeast Asia had a total land area of about two thirds of that of the continental United States, its population and forested area are both much the same as those of the United States.

In the United States, however, timber production in 1950 amounted to 150 million cubic meters, compared with 5 million for all the countries in Southeast Asia. The average annual consumption per capita during the period 1947-50, converted into roundwood equivalents, was, for the United States, 2.08 cubic meters, but for Southeast Asia only about 0.08 cubic meters. British North Borneo, Sarawak, Brunei, and Malaya had the highest averages in Southeast Asia, with, respectively, 0.39, 0.29, 0.46 and 0.30 cubic meters. The other countries all averaged much less, the lowest figures being those for Indonesia, with 0.03, and for Viet-Nam, with 0.02 cubic meters.[9] The average annual consumption for the whole world is about 0.66 cubic meters per capita.

Although the home consumption of forest products in Southeast Asia is extremely low, the ratios of the forest area to total area are high, and under efficient management the forests of the region should be capable of producing a surplus of wood for export. Because of the great distances and high costs of transportation, only the most valuable species, such as teak, padauk, ebony, rosewood, sandalwood, and probably also veneer logs, can be considered for export to Europe and America. The case is different with nearby India, China, Japan, and Australia, where the production of wood is wholly insufficient to meet domestic needs, and considerable quantities must be imported. Southeast Asia is favorably situated in relation to these adjacent consuming markets, because of the shorter distances and lower freight rates.

In 1950, the last year for which reasonably complete data are available, the total output was equivalent to some 10,275,000 cubic meters of roundwood, of which 5,068,000 cubic meters were timber. Total exports were equivalent to 1,389,000 cubic meters of roundwood, and total imports to 515,000 cubic meters.

In estimating Southeast Asia's wood-producing capacity, account must be taken of the peculiar composition of the tropical mixed forests. Usually such a forest consists of some hundreds of species, of which only a few are commercially exploitable. Thus a forest with a standing crop of more than 200 cubic meters per hectare may often produce not more than 20 to 30 cubic meters per hectare. Means must be found, therefore, to increase production.

New uses must be found for many species which, until now, have not been merchantable. Cost price and transport rates could be reduced by the establishment of sawmills and lumber industries in the immediate vicinity of the forests. Wood preservation and seasoning also offer means of improving the products of many species now considered inferior. The plantation of valuable species must be promoted, and low-value mixed forests, with a high percentage of inferior species, should be converted into more productive ones. Logging methods need modernizing. Where possible, manual labor must be replaced by machinery. The construction of roads and the use of trucks, tractors, and other modern means of transport would enlarge the area of accessible forests. The industry needs stimulation through the establishment of new factories for the manufacture of plywood and veneer, matches, fiberboard, chests, and many other articles.

For such expansion and modernizing, competent administration and large funds are essential, and hence, it seems unlikely that the countries of Southeast Asia, handicapped as they now are, can achieve these objectives within a short period. Before the war, most of these countries had

---

[9] The real average consumption per capita in Southeast Asia would be very much higher, were we to include the large quantities of uncontrolled fellings in these countries.

well-organized forestry services, but during the war there was mismanagement and overcutting, especially in the best forests. In Java the teak forests in many places were completely wiped out. Steep mountain slopes were stripped of their cover, causing severe deterioration of the water supply in many catchment areas, and technical equipment was almost entirely destroyed or worn out. Burma, Indochina, and Malaya, also, underwent particularly serious losses. Furthermore, the great majority of the European foresters have left. For all these reasons, forestry in Southeast Asia has suffered so grievously that re-establishment of proper forestry management seems an almost impossible task. Certainly, without foreign assistance the total output for the near future is likely to remain at the present level of about 5 million cubic meters of timber a year.

How far this production could be increased by outside technical and financial assistance is difficult to estimate, especially since our knowledge of the forests, their areas, composition, and capacity, is insufficient, and the data given to the FAO are far from complete. For the nearer future, it would seem conservative to consider the directly exploitable area as about 10 per cent of the total forest area (Table 23–I)—that is, as about 28 million hectares—and the average annual growth as approximately 0.5 cubic meter per hectare.[10] On this basis, with moderate financial and technical assistance, aimed only at the rehabilitation of prewar forestry and the exploitation of existing accessible resources, it should be possible to raise the total annual output of timber from 5 million to about 14 million cubic meters. On the assumption that home consumption would also increase, about 4 million cubic meters of timber might then be available for export.

Production could conceivably be raised to a much higher level by opening up areas now classed as inaccessible, but since these possibilities are limited by various factors of the terrain—especially the mountainous character of so much of the region—it seems unlikely that more than a third of the forest area, or about 100 million hectares, could ever really prove suitable for regular exploitation.

On the other hand, the average annual growth in this third might well be increased considerably by appropriate silvicultural measures—notably, as already suggested, the cultivation of the more valuable species and the conversion of low-value mixed forests into more productive forests. Some trees here tend to grow much faster than they do in the temperate zones, especially the softer-wooded species, which show a strikingly rapid growth. In Java, for example, in plantations of *Acacia decurrens* Willd., *Agathis loranthifolia* Salisb., and *Eucalyptus deglupta* Bl., average annual growths of 16, 25, and 34 cubic meters per hectare have been reported, respectively. Although these figures relate to the best producing species—those growing on the most favorable sites—and the general average would be far less,

[10] The average production per hectare of natural teak forests in Thailand is stated to be 0.01 cubic meter timber, in Java 0.5 to 1 cubic meter. No reliable data are obtainable regarding natural mixed forests.

it does not seem extravagant to estimate a possible future average annual growth of 2 cubic meters per hectare, which, for 100 million hectares of productive forests would mean an annual timber output of about 200 million cubic meters.

Should, then, internal consumption increase *pari passu* with the improvement of forestry and the growth of industrialization, the quantity that could be set apart annually for export would probably come to somewhere between 30 to 50 million cubic meters of timber.

To reach such a goal, the countries of Southeast Asia would obviously require technical and financial assistance on a very large scale. First and foremost, however, is the need of ending the unrest and insecurity that prevail in most of these countries, in order that constructive work may proceed undisturbed.

SOURCES FOR BOTANICAL NOMENCLATURE

CHEVALIER, A. J. 1919. *Premier inventaire des bois et autres produits forestiers du Tonkin.* Imprimerie d'Extrême-Orient, Hanoi-Haiphong.

CORNER, E. J. H. 1952. *Wayside trees of Malaya.* 2d ed. Government Printing Office, Singapore.

MASON, FRANCIS. 1883. *Burma, its people and productions; or notes on the fauna, flora and minerals of Tenasserim, Pegu, and Burma.* Vol. 2: Botany. Stephen Austin & Sons, Hertford.

MERRILL, E. D. 1921. "A bibliographic enumeration of Bornean plants," *Jour. Straits Branch Roy. Asiatic Soc.* (special number).

———. 1929. Plantae Elmerianae Borneenses. *Univ. Calif. Publications in Botany,* 15:1-316.

24.   THE PHILIPPINES

Florencio Tamesis

The forests of the Philippines constitute one of the most valuable re-plenishable assets of the Republic. This natural wealth plays a particularly important part in the country's economy because at least 97.5 per cent of the forest area is government-owned and managed by a well-organized forest service. Of 21,021,955 hectares of government-owned forest, 3,109,728 are licensed for exploitation.

The total land area of the Philippines is 29.7 million hectares, 72.5 per cent of which is temporarily classified as forest land (see Table 24–I), divided into four categories: (1) commercial forest, (2) noncommercial forest, (3) open forest and grassland, and (4) marsh and mangrove. Forest land, once definitely classified as such, cannot be alienated, and the present 72.5 per cent of forest land may not be reduced to less than 43 per cent.

TABLE 24–I

THE PHILIPPINES: LAND USE

		Area in Hectares	Percentage
Commercial forest		11,415,020	38.4
Noncommercial forest		4,459,920	15.0
Open forest and grassland			
Agricultural land	2,727,235		
Pasture	955,495		
Reforestation	1,390,570	5,073,300	17.0
Marsh			
Fresh water	169,340		
Mangrove swamp	443,400	612,740	2.1
Cultivated land		8,179,992	27.5
TOTAL		29,740,972	100.0

Geographical Distribution and Composition of Forest Land

The bulk of the Philippine forests occurs in large tracts in the principal islands (Mindanao, Luzon, Palawan, Samar, Negros, Mindoro, Leyte, Panay, and Masbate). Most of it is tropical rain forest, complex in com-position. There are more than 3,000 species that attain a diameter of one foot or more, but fewer than 60 species find their way to the market. Dipterocarpaceae comprise 75 per cent of the stands ("Philippine mahog-any" belongs to this family). The frequent occurrence of merchantable species in stands averaging 100 cubic meters per hectare makes possible the use of modern mechanical methods of lumbering.

The volume of the standing timber is more than 464 billion board feet, 97 per cent of it hardwood. The remaining 3 per cent represent softwood species, the most important of which are Benguet pine (*Pinus insularis*) [1] and talupau (*Pinus merkusii*). The major Philippine forest species are listed in Table 24–II.

TABLE 24–II

THE PHILIPPINES: MAJOR FOREST SPECIES

	Stand (Thousand Cubic Meters)	Per Cent of Total Stand
1. White lauan (*Pentacme contorta*)	240,956	19.5
2. Apitong (*Dipterocarpus grandiflorus*)	152,684	12.4
3. Tañgile (*Shorea polysperma*)	116,884	9.5
4. Mayapis (*Shorea palosapis*)	112,485	9.1
5. Red lauan (*Shorea negrosensis*)	108,232	8.8
6. Guijo (*Shorea guiso*)	62,420	5.1
7. Yakal (*Hopea* sp.)	43,317	3.5
8. Benguet pine (*Pinus insularis*)	28,397	2.3
9. Manggachapui (*Hopea acuminata*)	25,288	2.0
10. Palosapis (*Anisoptera thurifera*)	16,365	1.3
11. Bagtikan (*Parashorea malaanonan*)	16,152	1.3
12. Narra (*Pterocarpus* sp.)	14,615	1.2
13. Almon (*Shorea almon*)	13,714	1.1
14. Malugai (*Pometia pinnata*)	9,889	0.8
15. Makaasim (*Eugenia* sp.)	8,837	0.7
	980,235	78.6

The broadleaf trees supply the bulk of commercially valuable timber, and the majority are hardwoods of much the same category as the walnut, mahogany, beech, or oak of other countries. The predominant species of commercial value belong to the Dipterocarpaceae, but the Leguminosae, although next in importance by volume, are generally more valuable and highly priced than the dipterocarps.

Most of the commercial timber found in such stands is comparable to the best merchantable timber of its class in the world and ranges from 30,000 to 60,000 board feet to the acre. The existence of trees of merchantable sizes has offered an opportunity for extensive exploitation. Operators make use of the most modern equipment in the form of tractors, trucks, heavy cranes, steam donkeys, and gasoline or diesel yarders. Locomotives are also used for certain operations.

[1] Source for botanical nomenclature: Merrill, E. D. *An enumeration of Philippine flowering plants.* 4 vols. Bureau of Science, Manila, 1925-26.

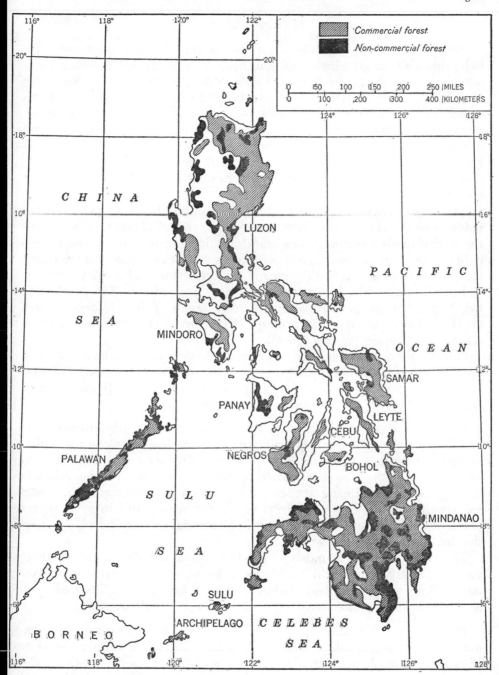

FIG. 48. Philippine Islands: distribution of commercial and noncommercial forests. Based on "Forest Map," compiled under the direction of Florencio Tamesis, former Director of Forestry, Republic of the Philippines, Jan. 1, 1951.

Forest Types

DIPTEROCARP FORESTS. These forests are found throughout the rain-belt region where growing conditions are the most favorable. Their composition is complex, consisting, as a rule, of several stories. The first story is occupied by large dominant trees, usually dipterocarps. Below, is an understory containing a great variety of small subdominant trees of lesser commercial importance. Below these again are smaller tree species and a heavy undergrowth of shrubs and herbs. Through the whole mass of forest runs a tangle of lianas, large and small, among which the climbing palms or rattans are the most conspicuous of the economically important species.

The dipterocarps in more or less pure stands form 75 per cent (in volume) of the timber resources of the country and about 70 per cent of the entire lumber output. The stands, which produce from 100 to 200 cubic meters per hectare, are considered sufficiently valuable to warrant the use of modern mechanical means for extraction. The chief commercial species are: white lauan (*Pentacme contorta*), almon (*Shorea almon*), bagtikan (*Parashorea malaanonan*), red lauan (*Shorea negrosensis*), tañgile (*Shorea polysperma*), apitong (*Dipterocarpus grandiflorus*), yakal (*Hopea*), and guijo (*Shorea guiso*).

Other principal species are dao (*Dracontomelum dao*), malaikmo (*Celtis philippensis*), *Canarium* spp., ilang-ilang (*Canangium odoratum*), kalantas (*Toona calantas*), malugai (*Pometia pinnata*), katmon (*Dillenia*), alupag (*Euphoria*), and taluto (*Pterocymbium tinctorium*).

MOLAVE FOREST. This forest is more open than the dipterocarp type and its volume of timber per unit area is much less, averaging 30 cubic meters per hectare. It occurs where there are distinct wet and dry seasons of several months' duration. During the dry season the vegetation is largely leafless, but in the wet season it makes a luxuriant growth. Local soil conditions intensify the effects of the dry season and in some places produce almost desert-like conditions. The molave (*Vitex parviflora*) predominates on dry limestone ridges.

Most of the species found here produce woods highly valued for their natural beauty and durability. Among the most important are molave, narra (*Pterocarpus*), tindalo (*Pahudia rhomboidea*), ipil (*Intsia bijuga*), akle (*Albizzia acle*), and banuyo (*Wallaceodendron celebicum*).

PINE FOREST. The Philippine coniferous forest offers an interesting example of economic utility. *Pinus insularis* and *P. merkusii* are found at high altitudes and, as a rule, above the upper limit of the dipterocarps, the boundary between the two species being noticeably clear-cut. It also happens that most of the pines are found in the gold mining regions, and this is an important factor in the development of the mines. The miners prefer pine timber to any lowland hardwood for pit props because it gives warning of imminent collapse.

Another important conifer is almaciga (*Agathis alba*), which produces resin. It grows to be one of the biggest trees in the Islands, but may not be cut for lumber because of its value as a source of gum copal, exported for the manufacture of high-grade varnish.

MANGROVE FOREST. This type occurs on tidal flats at the mouths of streams and on the shores of protected bays. It could serve for construction purposes if the wood were made more durable by treatment. The stands are composed mostly of Rhizophoraceae, consisting of the following species: bakauan-babae (*Rhizophora mucronata*), bakauan-lalaki (*R. candelaria*), busain (*Bruguiera conjugata*), pototan-lalaki (*B. cylindrica*), pototan-babae (*B. sexangula*), langarai (*B. parviflora*), and tangal (*Ceriops tagal*). There are also other species of other families, such as pagatpat (*Sonneratia caseolaris*), api-api (*Avicennia officinalis*), tabau (*Lumnitzera littorea*), tabigi (*Xylocarpus granatum*), piagau (*X. moluccensis*), and duñgon-late (*Heritiera littoralis*).

Mangroves are the principal sources of firewood, tanbark, cutch, dyebark, and charcoal.

Along streams in many parts of the tidal flats occurs a palm known as nipa (*Nipa fruticans*), whose leaves are used principally for thatched roofs and walls of houses. It also produces a sap used for the manufacture of vinegar, alcohol, wine, and sugar.

BEACH FOREST. Above high tide are found sandy beaches, where the original form of vegetation has been left undisturbed, making a distinct "beach type." The frontal zone usually has a tangle of vegetation, of which pandan (*Pandanus tectorius*) forms a conspicuous part. The principal trees are talisai (*Terminalia catappa*), dapdap (*Erythrina variegata* var. *orientalis*), botong (*Barringtonia asiatica*), duñgon-late (*Heritiera littoralis*), palomaria (*Calophyllum inophyllum*), agoho (*Casuarina equisetifolia*), bani (*Pongamia pinnata*), and tawalis (*Osbornia octodonta*).

MOSSY FORESTS. These forests, in high and very rough mountainous regions, are essentially protection forests. As a result of the combined effects of heavy rainfall, high relative humidity, and strong winds, the trees are mostly short-boled and their trunks and branches are generally covered with mosses, liverworts, filmy ferns, and epiphytic orchids. Among the principal species are *Dacrydium* spp., *Podocarpus* spp., *Eugenia* spp., *Decaspermum* spp., *Quercus* spp., *Myrica* spp., *Symplocos* spp., and *Tristania decorticata*.

Forest Products

PRINCIPAL TIMBER SPECIES. From a commercial viewpoint, the principal timbers may be grouped in six general classes: (1) lauans, (2) apitongs, (3) guijos, (4) yakals, (5) other dipterocarps, and (6) legumes.

The lauans, or "Philippine mahogany," are the softer members of the dipterocarp family and are subdivided into the red lauans and the white lauans. The former includes tañgile (*Shorea polysperma*), tiaong (*Shorea teysmanniana*), and true red lauan (*Shorea negrosensis*), which constitute the dark-red Philippine mahogany, while the white lauan (*Pentacme contorta*), almon (*Shorea almon*), bagtikan (*Parashorea malaanonan*), manggasinoro (*Shorea philippinensis*), kalunti (*Shorea kalunti*), and mayapis (*Shorea palosapis*) constitute the light-red Philippine mahogany. The red and white lauans are moderately heavy and durable for interior work when used without sapwood. They are not suitable for heavy structures and exposure to the weather, except when the structure is such that water sheds off, as in shiplap, or siding of buildings. The lauans are suitable for siding, partitions, and ceilings and would be excellent for light ship planking.

Apitong, the most abundant of the heavier and stronger structural timbers of the dipterocarp family, lasts for a long time when used without sapwood and not exposed to the weather or to contact with the ground. Apitong responds admirably to processing. It is now the most important wood used as frame work in wooden constructions. Properly treated apitong is the equal in durability to molave, duñgon (*Tarrietia sylvatica*), ipil, and yakal for structures exposed to the weather and is superior to any of these for salt-water piling.

Guijo is similar to apitong in many respects, especially in color. Apitong, however, has larger pores and tends to be more resinous. The wood of guijo is strong, relatively easy to work, and has good wearing qualities. It is best suited for interior framing, vehicles, automobile and truck framing, beams, and joists. For flooring it appeals to lovers of reddish-brown colors. Like apitong, the wood shrinks much in the process of seasoning and should, therefore, be properly dried if the best service is to be expected. Once dried, however, both woods "stay put."

The hardest and strongest member of the lauan family is yakal. This wood is resistant to decay, which makes it particularly suitable for structures exposed to the weather. It shrinks about as much as guijo, and best results can be obtained only when it is thoroughly seasoned before using. It is an excellent substitute for ipil for house posts and bridge timbers. It is recommended wherever great strength and durability are required.

Some of the less abundant members of the lauan family are palosapis (*Anisoptera thurifera*) and manggachapui (*Hopea acuminata*). Real manggachapui is fine-textured, straight-grained, hard and heavy, pale white when fresh but dark-reddish-yellow when exposed to the sun. Palosapis, which is often substituted for manggachapui by unscrupulous dealers, is coarse-textured, moderately hard and heavy, and yellowish in color, often with rose streaks. Manggachapui possesses most of the properties of guijo and can be used interchangeably with the latter, whereas palosapis has uses similar to the lauans.

Akle (*Albizzia acle*), narra (*Pterocarpus* spp.), ipil (*Intsia bijuga*), and tindalo (*Pahudia rhomboidea*) all are legumes and furnish most of the

valuable cabinet woods. Akle is brownish in color and excellent for
cabinet making. It has many of the qualities of walnut, with the further
advantage of being more resistant to termites. Narra is reddish-yellow
to dark red. The yellow variety is more common and more readily obtainable than the red for high-grade work. For persons who can afford
the price, a still better wood is available in tindalo, a beautiful hard red
wood which gets darker with age. Tindalo keeps its shape remarkably
well and, like most members of the legume family, has not only a beautiful grain but is very durable.

Another very popular wood is ipil. This is the most commonly used
wood for house posts, on account of its great durability and strength.
Before house posts were set on top of concrete or stone foundations, there
were few woods that withstood the ravages of decay and termites, but,
with the adoption of concrete foundations, even woods of moderate durability can be expected to last for many years. Dao (*Dracontomelum
dao*), of the family of Anacardiaceae, is a beautiful wood with distinct
black and brown markings resembling walnut, and is now in demand for
cabinet and furniture work. It shrinks badly when fresh, so that it should
be perfectly dried before using. It finds a good market abroad for plywood manufacture, being a high-class wood.

MINOR FOREST PRODUCTS. Philippine forests yield not only timber but
also minor products with great commercial possibilities. Among the most
important are palm products, cutch and tanbarks, firewood, charcoal,
fibers, resins, gums, rubber and gutta-percha, beeswax, medicinal plants,
and orchids.

Palm Products. Among the palms, rattan occupies the most important
place in trade and industry. Rattans are found in all forests of the
Philippine Islands. There are many species, with plants ranging in size
from 4 millimeters to 10 centimeters in diameter. Sika (*Calamus spini-
folius*), the best rattan in the Philippines and equal to the best in other
countries, abounds in Palawan Island. Other species of nearly the same
quality are widely distributed.

Rattan is indispensable in the economic life of the Filipinos. It enters
into the manufacture of tables, lamp shades, chairs, baskets, walking
sticks, horse whips, ropes, grocery baskets, cradles, sewing baskets, and
other important household articles. The bud of some species of rattan
is edible and makes delicious vegetable salad.

Another valuable palm is kaong, or cabo negro (*Arenga pinnata*).
This grows at low and medium altitudes in the forests and is sometimes
cultivated. Among its products are a sweetmeat from the young fruits;
sugar and vinegar from the sap tapped from the stems of young flowers;
flooring, broomsticks, wood strips from the stiff trunk; flour extracted from
the pulpy portion of the trunk; delicious materials for making salads
and pickles from the tender tips of the palm, and thatching materials
from the leaves. The most important product, however, is the black

fiber around the growing portion of the palm. This is used for roofing materials, ropes, brushes, and doormats, and is resistant to mild acid.

Still another palm of high economic value is the buri (*Corypha elata*), which furnishes fiber for the famous "lukban" and "buntal" hats and for other articles. The leaves of the plant are woven into bags, and also furnish the raffia for weaving. Sugar, vinegar, and buri wine are fermented from the sap. The young fruits are used in the preparation of sweetmeats, and starch is extracted from the pith. It is an interesting palm in that it flowers only once, producing the largest inflorescence of any plant.

A palm that is beginning to attract attention in the manufacture of fishing rods is anahaw (*Livistona rotundifolia* var. *luzonensis*), known as "palma brava." Anglers claim that fishing rods made of this are stronger and more durable than any in the market. Other articles that can be made from the leaves of this palm are fans, hats, and thatching materials. The wood is used for arrow shafts, spear handles, polo clubs, and walking sticks, and has great possibilities for fancy interior finishing. The seedlings of this palm are valued as ornamental plants.

Other forest products, similar to palms, which are important sources of materials for household industries are pandan (*Pandanus* sp.) and bamban (*Donax cannaeformis*). Among the articles made of these are book bags, grocery bags, lunch baskets, slippers, telescope cases, hats, mats, and bamban fish traps.

Among ferns of economic importance are nito (*Lygodium*), diliman (*Stenochlaena palustris*), and kilob (*Gleichenia linearis*). From nito are made baskets, salakots (hats), cigarette cases, horse whips, and helmets. Diliman is a coarse climbing fern, 2 to 4 meters in height, from a commercial viewpoint the most important of our ferns. Its stem is noted for its tensile strength and durability when submerged in salt water and is therefore in demand for tying bamboo frames used in fish corrals. Kilob is also used for tying, but it is more important as a source of material for household industries. Belts, hats, and baskets are made from kilob. Other ferns are used for food.

The roots of a fern locally known as "pako" are now extensively used in orchid culture as a substitute for the imported *Osmunda* fiber.

Medicinal Plants. The Philippine flora comprises a large number of medicinal plants. Among them are *Hydnocarpus* spp. and *Taraktogenos* spp., from which chaulmoogra oil for the treatment of leprosy is extracted. The St. Ignatius bean (*Strychnos ignatii*) yields strychnine, and *Derris* roots produce rotenone, a powerful insecticide. *Oleandra, Donax,* and *Lygodium* neutralize the poison of venomous reptiles and insects; *Ficus* and *Eurycles* yield antirheumatic medicine; *Orthosiphon aristatus* is effective against urinary ailments.

Soap Substitutes. Gogo (*Entada phaseoloides*), a vine belonging to the bean family, is an important source of soap substitutes and shampoo ingredients. The bark is also used for cordage, while the kernel of the seed is used for medicinal purposes. Gogo is common and widely distributed throughout the Islands, but the Manila supply comes principally from the provinces of Batangas, Cavite, Quezon, Palawan, Mindoro, Bataan, and Bulacan. The gogo plant is cultivated in several towns in Cavite.

Most firewood and charcoal are produced from mountain species, but the best fuel woods are the mangroves, tañgal (*Ceriops tagal*), bakauan (*Rhizophora* spp.), pototan or busain (*Bruguiera* spp.), lañgarai (*B. parviflora*), and pagatpat (*Sonneratia* spp.). These occur in very great quantities and could readily be exploited for fuel in conjunction with the extraction of tannin from the bark.

Cutch and Tanbarks. The manufacture of cutch was one of the principal industries in Zamboanga Province before the war. Cutch is a trade name for tanning extracts from the bark of various mangroves, notably bakauan (*Rhizophora* spp.), pototan (*Bruguiera* spp.), and tañgal (*Ceriops tagal*). The barks of camachile (*Pithecolobium dulce*), kalumpit (*Terminalia* spp.), anabiong (*Trema orientalis*), oak (*Quercus* spp.), etc., also contain a large amount of tannin and are used locally for its extraction.

Resins, Oils, and Gutta-percha. Pili (*Canarium* spp.), an important resin-producing tree, is found principally in the provinces of Quezon, Sorsogon, Masbate, Marinduque, Bohol, and Zamboanga. The resin, known by the Spanish term "brea blanca" (white pitch), is obtained by tapping the bark.

Almaciga (*Agathis alba*) produces Manila copal, a resin used chiefly in the manufacture of high-grade varnish, patent leather, and sealing wax. Almaciga resin is used in cheap soap and nonabsorbent paper, as incense in religious ceremonies, for torches, starting fires, and caulking boats, and in paints, varnish, and linoleum. The tree is widely distributed in the Islands, but the resin itself is principally produced in the provinces of Quezon, Camarines, Davao, Palawan, and Cagayan.

Lumbang oil (from the kernel of *Aleurites moluccana*) is closely related to the Chinese tung oil of commerce and is highly valued by varnish manufacturers because of its transparency and resilient qualities.

Gutta-percha is produced from the gutta-percha tree (*Palaquium ahernianum*) of the chico family and is used for insulating underground and submarine cables. Owing to the fact that it softens at temperatures a little higher than those at which the ordinary gums do, gutta-percha is mostly used in the manufacture of dental and surgical appliances. Its great resistance to acids makes it suitable for the manufacture of acid containers. There is no organized gutta-percha industry. The gum is collected by small-scale gatherers, mostly non-Christians.

Forest Policies

The Philippine forests are classified as either protective or productive. The government aims to maintain all protective forests intact and to bring the remaining forests under sustained-yield management. The country is fortunate in having an acreage of valuable forest adequate for its own use. Lumbering has developed considerably since the end of the war and is now one of the main industries. In most areas the forests now provide ample soil cover and could even be reclassified to release more land for agriculture. Comprehensive soil and forest surveys are now under way, but it will require from ten to twenty-five years to complete them and draw up detailed development plans, which will, it is hoped, provide land for agricultural expansion and also ensure the establishment of national parks and permanent forest reserves for a wide variety of uses.

Not widely known to the people is the influence of the forests upon their daily lives. The facts that the forests stabilize soils on hills and mountain sides, ameliorate the rigors of the seasons, conserve and maintain even stream flows, and afford retreats for recreation and repose, are little appreciated. Nor very clearly understood is the incontrovertible fact that forested watersheds guarantee permanent agriculture in the valleys and the plains.

The government, cognizant of the part that forests must play in agricultural and industrial development programs, has geared forest conservation with such programs. The great task ahead is one of education and information, and, at the same time, of taking active steps to conserve the watersheds without detriment to the use of the land and its products. The land must be put to its optimum use in the interests of the people—both for the present and for the years to come.

25. CHINA[*]

D. Y. Lin

China is a large country, approximately one twelfth of the land surface of the world and only a little smaller than Europe. Within its boundaries it has nearly every known type of relief, climate, soil, and vegetation. In Tibet there is the highest inhabited area in the world, while parts of the oasis of Turfan in Chinese Turkestan are more than 200 meters below sea level. The temperatures range from arctic rigor to torrid heat. The mean annual precipitation varies from less than 5 millimeters in the Tarim basin to more than 7,900 millimeters on Mount Omei in Szechwan. There is a great number of different species and varieties of forest trees in China.

Although there are vast alluvial plains, deserts, lowlands, and loess formations within its boundaries, China is predominantly mountainous. It is estimated that 68 per cent of the total land area consists of mountains and plateaus over 1,000 meters above sea level, 18 per cent of hilly land between 500 and 1,000 meters in altitude, and only 14 per cent of level land below 500 meters. Because of the large proportion of upland, more suitable for tree growth than for the production of agricultural crops, forests could and should play a major part in the land economy of the country.

Historical Background

Foresters of the West have often been told how Europe before the Christian Era was well wooded, how the forests then were more a hindrance than a help to settlers, how Alexander the Great (330 B.C.) regulated forest use because of wasteful exploitation, how the Romans sought to conserve timber and shipbuilding, and how in Asia Minor, Greece, and Palestine the forest cover had vanished to such an extent that timber for palaces and temples had to be brought long distances, notably from the cedar forests of Mount Lebanon.

Similar events also took place in China, but with one difference: what was happening in Europe and Asia Minor 2,000 years ago had already occurred in China some 2,500 years previously. The regions in northern and northwestern China along the Yellow River, where the Chinese first settled, were once extensively wooded. There were "boundless stretches

[*] This chapter was written in the spring of 1952 and statements therein that are in the present tense should be interpreted accordingly. EDITOR.

529

of *tsao mu* (grass and forest) everywhere." These original forests were not only the homes of the ancients, where wood and food were obtained, but also pleasure spots and hunting grounds. Tribal chiefs vied with one another in establishing *yu* (woodlands set aside for hunting), similar to the "paradises" of the Persian kings and the "nemora" of the Romans and Carthaginians; and in these *yu*, birds, fish, turtles, and other beasts were kept for food and for amusement. To cultivate and sustain the loyalty of their people, certain benevolent chiefs threw open the *yu* for popular use and, hence, were praised in classical literature and called "exemplary rulers" by Confucius, Mencius, and other philosophers. In the course of time, however, the early Chinese found it necessary to "burn, destroy and open up" forests and to "drive away the wild beasts and turtles" in order to make *tien* (fields) for agriculture, and this destruction was continued for more than 1,500 years, until the establishment of the Chou Dynasty (1127-255 B.C.).

The period of the Chou was a golden age in Chinese history, not only because of its general culture and wise "laws and rites," but also in the domain of forestry. During this time a well-organized "Mountain and Forest Service" was established, forestry as a public function was recognized, and forest administration and management reached a high degree of efficiency.

After the Chou another decline set in; there were constant wars, and much of the settled area along the Yellow River was laid waste. The demolition of the forests by axe and fire has formed a sad theme for poets and historians, who have described the "ruthless destruction" and its "devastating effects," of which "China's Sorrow" (flooding by the Yellow River) was one. The forest area was reduced to such an extent that, as in the Mediterranean world, timber for *yamens* (public offices), palaces, and temples had to be brought from "high remote mountains" in Szechwan and other parts of central China.

During the Tang (A.D. 618-907) and Sung dynasties (A.D. 960-1128) some interest was shown in forestry, but the efforts were sporadic and often perfunctory. In the succeeding centuries the destruction of the forests was continued and accelerated as a result of dynastic wars and of a growing population's need for farmland, and soon extended from the Yellow River basin to the basins of the Yangtze and the Pearl rivers.

So, after more than 5,500 years of destructive action, interrupted though it was by the enlightened conservation of the Chou, the forests in China today are no longer "boundless stretches." They have shrunk to only about 9 per cent of the total land area of the country.

Land Use: General Categories

Experts disagree as to the areas of forest and of cultivated land in China because no systematic survey has yet been undertaken either by the government or private agencies, and all available figures are only estimates.

Whether the actual areas have been overestimated or underestimated is difficult to say, and it will take years of intensive and extensive investigation and survey before the estimates can be reasonably checked. It is generally recognized and accepted, however, that of the total land area of some 982,063,500 hectares in China, 99,534,000, or about 10 per cent are cultivated land, 66,000,300 (7 per cent) are *hwang ti*, 88,921,700 (9 per cent) are under forests, 292,868,200 (30 per cent) are *li lin ti*, and 434,739,300 hectares (44 per cent) are other areas.

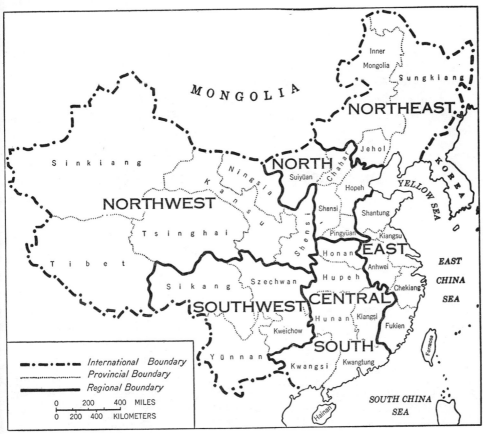

FIG. 49. China: provinces and major regions.

The figures given for the cultivated land and the *hwang ti* are taken from a recent report made public by the Peking Government, while those for the forested area and the *li lin ti* are revised estimates derived from data that have been accumulated by the writer over a period of more than thirty years. (Many of these data have been published in the *China Year Book* during the past twenty years.)

The so-called *hwang ti* is cultivable but uncultivated land, which may or may not have been cultivated before. Much of the abandoned farmland in Kansu, Ningsia, and Suiyüan belongs in this category.

The *li lin ti* is land that is either too dry, too high, or too steep for the practice of agriculture but is *li lin,* or "suitable for forestry work." Most of these areas were no doubt once forested (*tsao mu*), but, as they stand now, some produce only grass, bush, and scrub, while others are so denuded and eroded that even grass and shrubs do not grow. Comprising, as they do, approximately 30 per cent of the total land area of China, these *li lin ti* areas will be for many years to come not only an economic loss, but a physical problem to the nation.

Some of the *li lin ti* areas along the upper reaches of the Yellow River are so eroded that they have become a real menace to the farm population there. The erosion, both by wind and water, has resulted in increasing the frequency and severity of floods and droughts, in the silting up of canals and rivers, and in a general deterioration of farmland, causing great losses of food crops and making life and farming extremely difficult and precarious. It would take hundreds of years to re-establish on these *li lin ti* areas their former *tsao mu* cover, and to bring the land back to its former habitability and prosperity.

FOREST RESOURCES AND OPERATIONS

Extent and Character of the Forests

FOREST AREA. Of China's total forested area of about 88,921,700 hectares, about 77 per cent may be classified as susceptible to management, and the forests thereon are in the present work called "productive forests" (Table 25–I). The other 23 per cent consist of alpine scrub land, tundra areas, deserts, moorland, bush-savanna, etc., where conditions are unfavorable for the normal growth of the trees.

The provinces of the Northeast and Southwest regions comprise by far the best and the largest timbered areas remaining in China today (see Table 25–I and Fig. 50). These two regions have more than 59,030,000 hectares of forests, representing more than 66 per cent of the total forested area in the country. The Manchurian forests alone have a total of 26,010,000 hectares. In the Southwest Region only 28 per cent of the productive forests are classed as accessible; the development of transportation and the introduction of modern logging devices, however, may soon reduce their relative inaccessibility.

The provinces in the North Region are the most depleted of forests, with a total forested area of only some 1,013,800 hectares, representing only 1.4 per cent of the land area. Although the forested area for the Northwest Region appears large, it represents only 2.6 per cent of the total land area there. The East Region and Central South Region, with an aggregate of 17,426,400 hectares of forest, are most important on account of their proximity to, and role in meeting the local requirements for wood of, the most densely populated part of the country, for, together with the Szechwan Province, which is adjacent, they contain more than 65 per cent of China's entire population. It is likely that the hitherto inaccessible forests in these two regions will be made accessible much sooner than will those in the other regions.

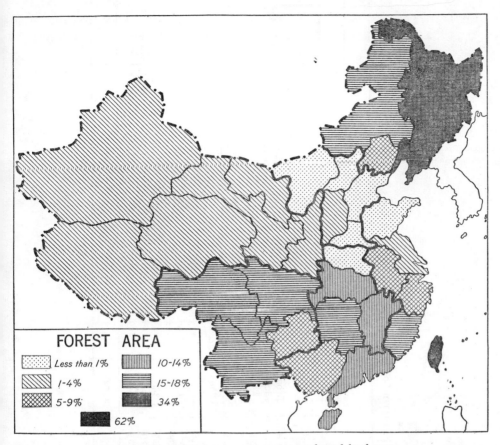

FIG. 50. China: forest area as percentage of total land area.

FOREST ZONES. The forests of China may be grouped according to four climatic zones, each with its characteristic vegetation. In order from south to north, and also as one ascends from lower to higher altitudes, these are: (1) the subtropical, (2) the warm-temperate, (3) the cold-temperate, and (4) the tundra-and-alpine zones.

The subtropical zone includes Taiwan (Formosa), Kwangtung (with Hainan), the southern half of Yunnan, Kwangsi, and the southern end of Fukien. Most of it lies south of latitude 26° N. and is of moderate elevation. The tree species in this zone are too varied for enumeration, including banyans, palms, tree ferns, bamboos, and all kinds of ever-green broadleaf trees, such as species of oaks (*Quercus*),[1] *Diospyros*, *Machilus*, *Castanopsis*, mangroves, lichee (*Litchi chinensis*), and camphor

[1] For sources of botanical nomenclature see below, p. 550.

TABLE 25–I

CHINA: ESTIMATED FOREST AREAS AND VOLUMES, BY REGIONS, ca. 1950

Region	Total Forests		Productive Forests								
	Area (Thousand Hectares)	Per Cent of Total Land Area	Area					Volume			
			Conif-erous	Broad-leaf	Mixed	Total	Acces-sible Forests (Per Cent of Total Forest Area)	Conif-erous	Broad-leaf	Mixed	Total
			Thousand hectares					*Million cubic meters*			
Northeast	35,680	22.6	21,226	10,613	273	32,112	65	3,502	934	34	4,470
Northwest	11,449	2.6	5,108	1,703	58	6,869	10	450	281	7	738
North	1,014	1.4	188	63	2	253	2	31	6	0.3	37
East	6,249	10.5	1,755	3,511	45	5,311	75	290	309	6	605
Central South	11,177	9.7	1,529	6,118	66	7,713	35	252	538	8	798
Southwest	23,353	16.1	10,034	5,017	129	15,180	28	1,656	441	16	2,113
TOTAL	88,922	9.0	39,840	27,025	573	67,438	45	6,181	2,509	71	8,761

(*Cinnamomum camphora*). Some planting has been done of such species as *Cinchona*, rubber (*Hevea brasiliensis* M. Arg.), teak (*Tectona grandis*), and *Eucalyptus*.

The warm-temperate zone comprises Kiangsi, Chekiang, Kiangsu, Hupeh, Honan, Kweichow, Szechwan, Sikang, most of Fukien, most of Tibet, and the southern portions of Shensi, Kansu, and Tsinghai. The tree species typical of this zone are also numerous and include such deciduous broadleaf trees as oak, maple (*Acer*), poplar (*Populus*), *Hovenia*, *Bischofia*, *Catalpa*, *Albizzia*, boxwood (*Buxus*), locust (*Gymnocladus* and *Gleditsia*), *Zelkova*, tulip (*Liriodendron chinense*), *Pterocarya*, *Liquidambar*, *Melia*, and such softwoods as pine (*Pinus*), *Cryptomeria*, *Chamaecyparis*, *Cunninghamia*, and cedar (*Libocedrus*).

The cold-temperate zone includes the provinces along the Yellow River and its tributaries—and all of China to the north thereof, except for patches of tundra north of latitude 45° N. Typical trees are pine, spruce (*Picea*), hemlock (*Tsuga*), fir (*Abies*), larch (*Larix*), birch (*Betula*), maple, *Sophora*, tulip poplar, oak, ash (*Fraxinus*), and elm (*Ulmus*).

Corresponding to the horizontally arranged climatic zones from south to north as just described, there are vertically arranged climatic belts on the mountains. As has been mentioned, China is a very mountainous country. The Altyn Tagh, the Nan Shan, the Tien Shan, and the Tibetan Plateau have mean altitudes ranging between 3,500 meters and 6,000 meters. At these levels only such vegetation as rhododendron bush, alpine scrub, and tundra forms occur.

Fine examples of the vertical zonal range can be found in Taiwan and in southern Yunnan, which borders Burma and Indochina. According to a botanical report published by the Fan Botanical Institute of Peking, as many as 14 distinct types of vegetation are recognized within the four climatic zones in southern China, as follows:

1. Subtropical zone, below 1,200-1,500 meters: (*a*) rain forest, (*b*) riparian vegetation.
2. Warm-temperate zone, 1,200-1,500 to 2,500 meters: (*a*) lacustrine vegetation, (*b*) oak forest, (*c*) pine forest.
3. Cold-temperate zone, 2,500 to 3,500 meters: (*a*) sphagnum moor, (*b*) birch-maple forest, (*c*) spruce forest, (*d*) fir forest, (*e*) juniper forest.
4. Tundra-and-alpine zone, above 3,500-3,800 meters: (*a*) rhododendron bush, (*b*) alpine scrub, (*c*) alpine meadow, (*d*) tundra.

CONIFEROUS AND BROADLEAF FORESTS. According to the best estimates available, of the 67,438,000 hectares of productive forest land in the country, coniferous forests occupy some 39,840,000 hectares, or 59 per cent, broadleaf forests occupy some 27,025,000 hectares, or 40 per cent, and mixed forests only about 573,000 hectares, or less than 1 per cent (see Table 25–I).

In the North, Northeast, and Northwest Regions conifers predominate, while in the East and Central South, broadleaf species occupy a larger area than do the conifers. The high elevation and mountainous character of the Southwest Region may account for the fact that conifers are reported to occupy about two thirds of the forested area there; but there are also vast areas of pure oak and birch-maple forests at altitudes of between 1,700 and 2,800 meters.

In Taiwan the broadleaf forests cover more than 65 per cent of the forested area of the island. In the Northeast, where conifers predominate, there are also broadleaf species, such as elm, birch, oak, maple, tulip, ash, and walnut (*Juglans*), which in many places comprise 30 per cent or more of the stumpage.

IMPORTANT TREE SPECIES. Owing to its generally mountainous relief, its wide range of climates, and the copious rainfall over large areas, China is extremely rich in arborescent flora. According to reports published by the Chinese Botanical Society, there are 134 families of trees, as many as 685 genera, and more than 2,000 species in the country. Nearly every important genus of the coniferous and broadleaf trees known in the temperate regions of the northern hemisphere is represented in China.

Among the coniferous trees *Cunninghamia lanceolata,* commonly known as sha mu (or sha shu), and to foreign merchants as "Chinese fir," is undoubtedly the most valuable tree in China. It is found in temperate parts of the country; its range extends from southern Kwangtung along the coast, and throughout the provinces touching, and south of, the Yangtze—namely, Kwangsi, Chekiang, Kiangsi, Fukien, Hupeh, Anhwei, Yunnan, and Hunan. About the fastest growing coniferous tree in China, in good soil its sprouts often attain 3 or 4 feet in the first year, and up to 6 or 7 feet in the second. They are generally cut for commercial purposes when they are twenty to thirty years old and about 50 feet high. The logs, often called "Foochow poles," vary from a few inches to a foot or more in diameter. Because sha mu has such sprouting vigor, rendering it particularly adaptable to coppice management, reproduction by seeding is seldom used for establishing new stands. The wood, light, soft, fragrant, and fairly tough, is used for house building, general carpentry, and the manufacture of pulp, for pillars, masts, coffins, boat building, and many other purposes. Extensively grown for trade and for local consumption, sha mu accounts for more than 90 per cent of the economic timber found in the lumber markets in China, except in the North and Northwest Regions.

Another important coniferous tree, wrongly called hwang hwa sung or "yellow pine," forms nearly 75 per cent of the forests in Heilungkiang, Manchuria. It is really a larch (*Larix gmelini*), or loh-yeh-sung.

BAMBOO. The Chinese generic name for bamboo is chu. Many genera and species have been identified and described. The most common of these are: moa chu (*Phyllostachys edulis, P. niger*), tan chu (*Phyllostachys puberula, P. bambusoides*), tsie chu (*Bambusa arundinacea* Willd., *B. aspinosa, B. beecheyana* Munro), and nan chu (*Dendrocalamus giganteus*).

Bamboo is very fast growing and flourishes in all the southern provinces and along the Yangtze Valley up to 1,000-meter altitudes. It occurs in groves, in farm wood lots, in ravines, and along rivers and canals in both *sen lin* (forested) and *li lin ti* areas. In the rain forests of southern Yunnan there are vast jungles of pure bamboo, where different species grow to great height.

Bamboo is by far the most useful "timber" in China: those who have lived there will appreciate the multitudinous uses to which it is put. It is used for food, in building houses and bridges, for drilling pipes, for fishing gear and boats, and in the manufacture of paper, furniture, sedan chairs, ropes, umbrellas, mattresses, scrolls, chopsticks, toys, musical instruments, baskets, curtains, combs, undershirts, hats, raincoats, and all kinds of farm implements and household utensils. The West certainly does not possess any tree or shrub which for all around general usefulness can compare with the bamboo of China. The Chinese people are indeed fortunate in having such a valuable plant to take care of their daily needs.

During World War II the wartime capital city of Chungking was subjected to daily air raids by the Japanese. Many times much of the city was completely devastated, but each time, surprisingly enough, the city was quickly rebuilt. Bamboo walls and roofs plastered with cement or mud make attractive, inexpensive houses and last anywhere from ten to fifteen years.

Many paper factories using bamboo as the chief material have been in operation from time immemorial. If modern mechanical and chemical methods are developed for the manufacture of pulp from bamboo, it will not be surprising if someday bamboo becomes one of the world's most important pulp-producing plants.

Some long bridges in China have been built entirely of bamboo ropes, the longest, in Kwanhsien, Szechwan, being more than 350 feet in length.

Most of the salt wells in Szechwan, some of which are 3,000 feet deep, are operated by means of bamboo pipes.

Ownership

During the days of the monarchy all "mountains, forests, and wild lands" in the country belonged to, or were controlled by, the Imperial Government, but things have changed since the establishment of the Republic. When the various provinces became politically more independent, they claimed ownership of such "mountains, forests and wild lands" as came within their boundaries, while the local communities and private interests struggled to gain possession of accessible forested areas through their provincial authorities. There was no forest law to stop or regulate all this. Although there was a Ministry of Agriculture and Forestry in the central government in Peking, it existed only in name and was reorganized and abolished many times, and the power of granting forest concessions and establishing ownership of forests in practice remained in the hands of local *hsien* (district) magistrates or of the tax collectors. Hence there was great confusion.

When Nanking became the capital some improvement was made; the old National Forest Law was revised in 1945, and the entire forest administration was put on a more effective basis. According to the provisions of the revised law, the forests were classified as *kuo yu* (nationally owned), *kung yu* (publicly owned), and *si yu* (privately owned), but "in principle" all forests were *kuo yu,* or nationally owned.

Kuo yu forests belong to the central government. *Kung yu* forests include forests owned and controlled by provincial governments, *hsien* forests, temple forests, and forests of villages, cities, guilds, communes, and other public corporations. The management of *si yu,* or privately owned, forests is not subject to state or public control, except when they are classified as protection forests.

Kuo yu forests are "managed and operated" by regional officers established for the purpose by the Ministry of Forestry; or, if necessary, such management and operation may be entrusted to the forest administrative organs of provincial and municipal authorities. *Kung yu* forests are managed and operated by local official organizations under the *hsien* governments, or by legal bodies on being entrusted to so act. *Si yu* forests are managed and operated by private individuals or groups of individuals, i.e., *kung si* (companies) or *hong* (commercial firms).

Kung yu and *si yu* forests may be nationalized, by the procedure of "selection and designation," (1) if and when nationalization becomes necessary for reasons of national territorial security or to facilitate the operation of *kuo yu* (nationally owned) forests, or (2) if and when such forests are related to the sources of stream flow or have benefits that extend beyond the limits of the provinces in which they are located. Compensation in money must be given for such nationalization.

It is obvious that the ownership of forests in China will be for some time subject to much change. Since, however, all forests are "in principle" *kuo yu* or nationally owned, and since the process of nationalization has been legally defined and will continue to operate, it is likely that all forests, whether productive or otherwise, and all the *li lin ti* areas will again eventually become nationally owned and nationally managed as in the days of the monarchy.

So far, no attempt has been made to demarcate the boundaries of the existing national, public, and private forests, or to determine their areas. The work is a prodigious one, and will take a long time to accomplish.

Some "authorities," however, have tried to estimate the area in private forests, and put more than 43 per cent of the country's productive forests in that category. This is much too high and very misleading. Even in areas where sha mu (*Cunninghamia lanceolata*) is extensively planted by private interests, the percentage of privately owned forests as compared with the total productive forests is extremely small.

Until more data are available, it seems preferable to say that about 88 per cent of all the forests in the country today are nationally and provincially owned, less than 9 per cent privately owned, and 3 per cent communally owned.

Timber Resources, Logging, and Transport

STANDING TIMBER. The existing forests in China today are mostly *tien yen* (natural) forests, except in certain parts of the East and Central South Regions, where they have been described by some authorities as "secondary" or *jen tsao* (man made). The best examples of the latter are found in Fukien province, along the Min River, where *Cunninghamia lanceolata*, the main species grown, is generally managed on short rotation of about thirty years. The yield of these forests is high, and their average volume of standing timber per hectare is generally greater than that of the *tien yen* forests.

Tien yen forests predominate not only in the Northeast and Southwest, where the population is sparse, but also in those areas of Hunan, Hupeh, Kiangsi, and Taiwan where transportation and modern logging facilities are still lacking.

It would be conservative to state that the average volume per hectare of standing timber in the country is 165 cubic meters for the conifers, 88 for the broadleaf species, and 124 for the mixed forests. The total volume is estimated at 8,761 million cubic meters, of which 6,181 million, or 70.6 per cent, are in coniferous, 2,509 million (28.6 per cent) in broadleaf, and 71 million (0.8 per cent) in mixed forests (Table 25–I).

The Northeast Region, with a total forested area of 35,680,000 hectares, has a total volume of more than 4,470 million cubic meters, representing a little over 50 per cent of the total volume of the standing timber of the country.

GROWTH. No statistics on growth have been gathered for either the *tien yen* or the secondary forests of China. Although studies have been made at certain places around Peking, Nanking, Canton, and Chungking by the forestry departments of universities, the resulting figures are too local and fragmentary to justify any estimate of the total, or the average, growth for the country.

In general, we may assume that there is almost no net growth in the *tien yen* forests. This is to be expected, as only a very small percentage of the volume has been exploited. But if and when these forests are opened up, under proper cutting plans, their net growth should be enormous.

Much planting has been done during the past thirty years, and planting is now being accelerated both in the secondary forests and the *li lin ti* areas. The plantations will greatly increase the volume of current timber growth of the country as time goes on.

ANNUAL CUT. The average annual cut of timber in China for the 25 years up to 1950 is estimated at about 9,482,000 cubic meters. This meant less than 0.02 cubic meters per person for a population of 480 million persons, an exceedingly small ratio compared with the prewar European average, which was fifty times as much, or even with the all-Asian average of 0.3 cubic meters per person. Although the annual cut has been increased since V-J Day as a result of the rapid industrial development, the shortage of wood is obvious, and China must open up her *tien yen* forests as soon as possible if she is to meet the wood requirements for her industries and for the millions of adobe farm houses, in the construction of which more wood must be used if they are ever to be made into satisfactory living quarters.

Of the average annual cut before 1950, about 3 million cubic meters came from the Northeast, one million each from the Northwest and the Southwest, 2.8 million from the Southeast, including Taiwan, and 1.7 million from coastal and southern localities.

LOGGING AND TRANSPORT. Logging in the *tien yen* forests is extremely wasteful. Only the best trees are cut, and the less valuable or faulty ones, which should, nevertheless, be utilized, are left. Hitherto, this has been unavoidable because of the difficulties of removal, but there is no doubt that scavenging on the cutover areas could produce logs for plywood and match manufacture, railway ties, mine timbers, firewood, roof shingles, pulpwood, bolts for tool handles, pencil manufacture, and wood distillation.

The Chinese woodsmen use narrow, single-bitted axes and short saws to fell and buck the trees. These implements are very primitive and their use is time-consuming. From the standpoint of forest conservation, however, they may have been a blessing in disguise, for they have slowed down the process of deforestation.

Most of the timber cut in China comes from the vicinity of rivers, which play an important part in facilitating logging operations and the transport of logs. In high, rugged areas of heavy precipitation, where the *tien yen* forests are located, water transport is the main reliance; and where no such transport is available, the forests will long remain inaccessible.

When the trees have been cut into logs ranging from 10 to 30 feet long, they are skidded down to the streams by manpower or by cows or donkeys. They are then tied into rafts and stored until floodwater, when they are floated down to the markets along the rivers. Rafting, especially in mountainous areas, requires great skill. Depending on precipitation and other climatic factors, it may take months, or even a year or two, to float a raft to the lumber market.

WOOD-USING INDUSTRIES
Major Industries

THE LUMBER INDUSTRY. Practically all lumber for house construction in China is sawn by hand on the building site with thin whipsaws. Makers of various wood products generally buy their timber in log form and cut it up themselves. Hand-sawing is accurate and economical, and makes close utilization possible.

While there are many water-driven sawmills and also in some of the larger markets medium-sized modern mills equipped with circular or band headsaws and band or gang resaws, trimmers, edgers, and other machinery, they often cannot compete with hand-sawing, which is preferred for close utilization and because of the abundance of cheap labor.

There are no statistics on the number of sawmills in the different forest regions of China, but an annual cut of 9.5 million cubic meters of timber implies several thousand mills in operation. If Taiwan, with a total forested area of only 2,232,000 hectares, has as many as 460 sawmills, with a total output of about 400,000 cubic meters, an estimate of about 4,500 mills for the entire country would seem conservative. Nearly all sawmills except those in the North, Northwest, and Northeast handle not only softwood and hardwood but also bamboo, which, as already explained, is important "timber" for general construction, especially in rural districts.

Since no data are available, it is difficult to estimate how much of the annual cut in China is used for house building, and what proportions of it are consumed for making railway ties, bridges, poles, mine props, agricultural implements, and various other purposes.

THE PULP INDUSTRY. An enormous amount of wood pulp and bamboo pulp is produced in China. Shortly before World War II, the value of forest products chiefly in the form of paper and wood pulp imported into China totaled annually more than $39,000,000 (U.S.), but since then the demand has been met by native manufacturers.

Until recently, Manchuria and Taiwan were producing 225,000 metric tons of wood pulp annually. Hundreds of mills in central and southern China, producing pulp from wood, bamboo, straw, and grass, now take care of the country's need for paper. The largest of these mills is at the mouth of the Pearl River, in a suburb of Canton.

Much has been written about spruce, fir, pine, hemlock, and aspen as the leading woods in the world's production of paper and pulp. China has all of these and, in addition, the fast growing sha mu (*Cunninghamia*), which other countries do not have and which experiments have shown to contain a high proportion of cellulose comparable in quality to cellulose from spruce. The future of the pulp industry in China, therefore, is potentially encouraging.

FUEL WOOD AND CHARCOAL. For domestic cooking and heating for a population of 480 million persons, for rural industries and agricultural processing, such as making noodles and beancurd, curing tea, raising silk-worms, and manufacturing bricks and tiles, an enormous amount of fire-wood and charcoal is consumed annually throughout the country. Although there are no statistics concerning the annual production of fire-wood and charcoal in the country as a whole, we may conservatively say that it totals more than 20 million cubic meters. Most of it comes from the accessible secondary forests and the *li lin ti* areas along the Yangtze and in the East and Southwest regions. The Northwest Region is so depleted of tree growth, and firewood there is so scarce, that the rural population has occasionally been forced in extreme cases to burn refuse, cow dung, and other poor substitutes for cooking and for heating their *kang* (dried mud beds).

In the warm, temperate regions of China, ma-wei-sung (*Pinus massonia*) and all kinds of bamboo and fast growing broadleaf species are raised for firewood. Ma-wei-sung is generally kept low and pruned, to produce as much branch wood as possible.

Charcoal burning is a very old enterprise in China. Farmers and local merchants produce much charcoal in small kilns or pits. Charcoal burn-ing is also carried on as an independent trade in certain areas and as a follow-up job after commercial logging operations. In certain districts south of the Yangtze hardwood coppice is maintained and cut on a three- or four-year rotation for charcoal wood. Unlike firewood, which is con-sumed near the place of cutting, charcoal is shipped to cities and indus-trial centers all over the country. During the war, when gasoline was scarce, large quantities of charcoal were used for driving motor cars and buses in the interior provinces.

The amount of fuel wood and charcoal produced in China is far from sufficient to meet the fuel requirements of the population. For cooking and heating in the cities, coal and electricity are to be had in limited quantities; but what about the 380 million farmers who do not have coal or electricity? To answer this question, a word must be said about the typical farm stove.

This is usually built of bricks and is about $2\frac{1}{2}$ feet high, 3 feet long, and 3 feet wide, with an open top for a cast-iron pan, a tall chimney lead-ing through the roof, and a big side opening for bulky fuel. Unable to obtain sufficient firewood and charcoal for their domestic cooking, the farmers in China through the centuries have ingeniously solved their daily fuel problem by devising a cook stove suitable for using grass and shrubs, of which they can get an ample supply from the hills and mountains in most of the rural districts. The writer has estimated that in South China a farm family of five persons with a hog (the Chinese generally cook the food for their hogs) uses approximately 14,100 catties [2] of grass and 1,900

---

[2] 100 catties = 60.48 kilograms, or 133.333 pounds.

catties of shrubs and bamboo twigs per year for cooking. This means that 68 million farm families would require 6.6 billion kilos of bulky grass and shrubs, or the equivalent of 9,430,000 cubic meters of wood.

Miscellaneous Products

Among the many miscellaneous secondary forest products the following may be mentioned:

Tung Oil. Perhaps the most important is tung oil, from the tung yu or wood-oil tree, of which three species are known: *Aleurites fordii, A. montana,* and *A. cordata. A. fordii* occurs throughout the Yangtze valley, while *A. montana* is found in South China. *A. cordata,* known as Japanese tung tree, is of little account. Ninety per cent of the tung oil produced in China comes from *A. fordii.* The total tung-tree area in China is about 200,000 hectares, and the average tung-oil production per year is 110,000 metric tons.

Vegetable Tallow. Wo chiu (*Sapium sebiferum*), a member of the spurge family, yields the valuable Chinese vegetable tallow of commerce. The tree is remarkable for the beautiful red color of its foliage in the fall and is found in all the warm parts of China. The fruits are collected in the fall, and, when dried, liberate seeds that yield both fat and oil used in China for the manufacture of candles, and, when exported, used for the manufacture of soap.

Camphor. Chang shu (*Cinnamomum camphora*), another important tree, yields camphor. Found all over Taiwan, Fukien, Kiangsi, Kwangtung, and other southern provinces in the subtropical zone, the tree is valued both for its wood and for the camphor crystal and oil that it produces. More than 80 per cent of the world's camphor supply comes from China. The center of this production is in Taiwan, where the planting of chang shu has been systematically encouraged for many decades.

Lacquer. This is prepared from the sap of a tree called chi shu (*Rhus verniciflua*). "Chi" means varnish or lacquer. Although the tree grows wild in the woods, it is abundantly cultivated on the hillsides and along the margins of fields throughout Central China. The varnish is used in many handicrafts, on woodwork, and as an interior finish. Lacquer articles are exported to foreign countries in large quantities.

Silk. Besides the silkworms that live on mulberry leaves, there are two other kinds: one lives on the leaves of oak trees in Shantung province and produces a silk commercially known as "pongee," and the other feeds on the leaves of camphor and liquidambar trees in Kiangsi and Hainan and produces a kind of silk valuable for fish line, a superior type of surgical suture, and strings for musical instruments.

Incense. An enormous amount of incense is used in the homes and temples of China. The best is manufactured from the sap tapped from *Liquidambar formosana.* The wood of this tree is used for making high-grade furniture and tea chests.

Kwei Pi, or Cassia Bark. This is obtained from *Cinnamomum cassia,* a tree found in Kwangtung and Kwangsi. It is valued as a tonic or stimulant in Chinese medicines. Recently it has become an important article of commerce in foreign trade.

Tea Oil. This is extracted from the seed of a low-growing tree, *Thea oleosa,* and is widely used as hair oil, in cooking, in making candles, and for medical purposes. The tree is widely grown in Kiangsi, Fukien, Kwangsi, and Hunan. Its oil has also become an important article in international trade.

Wax. This is the product of a kind of scale insect which lives on the ash (*Fraxinus chinensis*) and the privet (*Ligustrum lucidum*). Large quantities are produced in Szechwan.

Tannin. This is obtained from the bark of oak, chestnut, or hemlock, and from nutgalls found on the leaves of *Rhus chinensis* and *R. potanini.*

Edible fungi. A delicacy in Chinese diet, these are grown in large quantities on dead branches or logs of pine and oak. The annual output is valued at millions of dollars.

Cork. This is obtained from the bark of *Quercus variabilis* and *Phellodendron amurense.*

Dyeing Materials. These are obtained from the flowers of *Sophora japonica* and *Koelreuteria paniculata* var. *apiculata,* and from the fruits of *Platycarya strobilacea* and other species.

Besides these, there are hundreds of other products, including fruits, nuts, berries, sung hsiang (resin), fibers and basts, rattan and canes, drugs and spices.

FOREST ADMINISTRATION, LAW, AND POLICIES

Forest Administration

NATIONAL ADMINISTRATION. Not until the early twentieth century was an organized national effort initiated to put forestry in China on a modern basis. After the Republic was established in 1911, the forest administration was at first only an insignificant subdivision of the government, initially in the Ministry of Agriculture and Commerce, then in the Ministry of Industries, and then in the Ministry of Economic Affairs. In 1938, when the Ministry of Agriculture and Forestry was formed, forestry work first received due recognition with the organization in the new Ministry of a Department of Forest Administration. Ten years later, in 1949, this department was elevated to the status of a Ministry, and the Chief Forester was made a Minister of Cabinet rank. First known as the *Lin Khen Pu* (Ministry of Forestry and Reclamation), this Ministry was changed in November 1951 into the *Lin Yieh Pu* (Ministry of Forestry).

This rapid development is indeed gratifying and bespeaks the great emphasis the government has placed on the need for and work of reclaiming and utilizing the vast areas of nonagricultural land in the country, and its determination to carry out forestry plans on a large scale.

The new Ministry is not only continuing but greatly strengthening the work started by the Department of Forest Administration. Its four divisions—Forest Administration, Extension, and Protection; Forest Planting; Forest Management; and Forest Districts and Stations—carry out their specific duties and collectively give effect to and administer the forest policies for the whole country. Thus through its Division of Forest Management the Ministry manages or supervises protection forests, military-protective forests, sand-fixation forests, and soil and water conservation forests.

In addition to the four main divisions, the Ministry maintains six "economic" forest districts in various parts of the country, nine watershed-protection forest districts, one forest extension station, one soil-erosion experiment station, and seven *tien yen* forest districts—all organized and managed according to the needs and suitability of the regions in which they are located. The economic and *tien yen* district offices grant cutting licenses, supervise cutting, and apply certain forest treatments to the valuable species within their regions, while the watershed-protection district offices demonstrate to the local people the importance of safeguarding the hills and mountains from soil erosion. China will need hundreds of such forest districts and stations to meet the forest needs of its people.

The central government has done much planting work. According to a report made by the Minister of Forestry, more than 4,800,000 hectares of denuded land, including some of the loess desert areas in the Northwest, were planted in 1950 and 1951, and the Ministry plans to carry out much greater planting projects in Honan, Hopei, and other North China provinces.

PROVINCIAL ADMINISTRATION. Every province has either a Provincial Reconstruction Bureau or an Agricultural and Forestry Bureau, in which a department administers the forests of the province, maintains nurseries and forest stations in mountainous and watershed areas, and carries out planting or cutting work. There is no direct relationship between the provincial and central forest administrations except through the headquarters of the regional political area to which each province belongs.

Since the establishment of the Republic much practical work has been done in the various provinces. Reforestation has been greatly accelerated in central, southern, and northern China. According to a government report on operations in 24 provinces and a few special areas during the period 1945-48, more than 2,330,166,000 seedlings and young trees were planted, more than 25,800 hectares of nurseries were started, and a total of 1,478,580,000 seedlings were raised in these nurseries.

In the Northeast, the regional government has conducted an air survey of the Manchurian forests and is now making preparations for an ambitious ten-year program of planting 20,000,000 hectares of denuded land, a tract approximately 1,100 kilometers long and 300 kilometers wide, extending from the Hingan Mountains across seven provinces to Shanhaikwan.

FOREST MANAGEMENT. So far, no effort has been made to develop long-range plans for forest management. Planting in cutover and *li lin ti* areas is, and for many years will be, the main job for the central, the provincial, and the *hsien* governments.

In the *tien yen* forests, in which cutting permits have been granted to private interests by the regional offices of the central government, clear-cutting or selective cutting followed by planting is, generally speaking, the usual method of handling. However, although planting after cutting is required, it is not always done, and there is not enough supervision to enforce it. During the war, when the capital was moved to Chungking, as many as 1,205 cutting permits, and 89 more for charcoal making, were granted by the central government. This gives some idea of the vast amount of cutting that goes on daily in the accessible *tien yen* forests all over the country.

Although nearly all the *tien yen* forests are nationally owned, so far no management and regulation plans to assure a sustained yield of timber have been worked out for any of them. This, however, is to be expected because of the amount of preliminary work that must be done. As to protection forests, only the prohibition or restriction of cutting in these forests is enforced, but no working plans have been developed for achieving the maximum value of soil and water conservation and flood control.

In *jen tsao,* or "secondary," forests, especially where *Cunninghamia* is the principal species, a very intensive coppice system of management is practised. Rotations are commonly 25 to 40 years. The stands are regularly thinned every two or three years for poles and firewood, and at the end of rotation they are clear-cut. The *Cunninghamia* forests in Kiangsi and along the Min River in Fukien have been under such intensive management for hundreds of years.

The forests owned by temples, guilds, and private interests are generally managed on short rotations to insure permanent supplies of firewood and building timber for their owners. Thousands of farmers have small patches of woodland, consisting of pine, bamboo, oak, or other species, which are managed on short rotations for poles and small timber for building and a variety of farm uses. Others raise crops of firewood under an intensive coppice system of management. Short rotations (10 to 25 years) are more common in most private woodlands, and still shorter rotations (2 to 10 years) for firewood coppice. For charcoal making 2 to 5 year-old sprouts are commonly used. In pure bamboo groves, cutting is done almost yearly.

Forest Law and Regulations

The National Forest Law, first written and promulgated some 25 years ago, was to a great extent modeled after the Forest Act of Japan. It has been revised twice, the last time in 1945, and, as it stands, deals separately with nationally owned, publicly owned, and privately owned forests, protection forests, the use and appropriation of land, government supervision, forest protection, rewards, and penalties. As a whole, the law is comprehensive and serves to express the forest policy of the Chinese government.

In addition to this National Forest Law, many supplementary forest regulations have been drawn up, the chief of which pertain to forest planting along the national highways and rivers, and on steep lands; reforestation work by soldiers and by schools and colleges; observance of "Memorial Forest Week"; compulsory forest planting; rewards for forest work done; forest management of watershed areas; the management, investigation, and survey of nationally owned forests; logging and lumbering on nationally owned forests; registration of public and private forests; and forest police regulations.

Forest Policies

PROTECTION FORESTS. In recognition of the importance of maintaining a protective cover on watersheds for the conservation of the soil and water resources, the Chinese government has fittingly emphasized the role of "protection forests" in the National Forest Law, and has made special provisions therein for the establishment and preservation of forest cover on the hills and mountains. According to the law, all forests that are necessary for any of the following reasons are to be designated and included among the protection forests: "for protection against danger from floodwaters, winds and tides"; "in the regulation of water supply"; "for the prevention of soil erosion and damage from sandstorms, rolling stones, snow, and ice"; and "to facilitate fisheries." Even bare mountains and other bare lands meeting any one of these conditions may be included among the protection forests.

The power of establishing protection forests is vested in the central government and may be given effect either upon the initiative of the government or upon application by interested parties. As soon as an area is designated as a protection forest, no person may "cut or damage the trees or bamboos, develop the land, graze livestock or collect or dig out soil, stones, turf and roots of trees" in that forest without the approval of the forest authorities. When cutting is thus prohibited, the owner of the land or of the trees and bamboos may claim compensation for direct losses sustained in consequence of the prohibition. If forestation work is done by the owner, the government may order the people benefited by the

establishment of such a protection forest to bear part or all of the forestation expense incurred.

These protection forest laws are drastic and inclusive. If properly enforced, they should go far toward preserving the forest cover on the hills
and mountains, and toward conserving soil and water.

FOREST RESEARCH. In 1941 the government organized a National
Forestry Research Bureau, with headquarters in Koloshan, Chungking.
After V-J Day the Bureau was moved to Nanking, and the government
also set aside a vast tract of land on the Purple Mountain for the Bureau's
use in experimental work and for the erection of a suitable building.

The activities of the Bureau are divided into three categories, as follows:

1. Silviculture, including nursery practice, reforestation, ecology, taxonomy, forest protection, and soil and water conservation techniques.
2. Forest utilization, including wood technology, lumbering, forest products, and forest industries.
3. Investigation and extension, including the study of forest conditions
   throughout the country and the devising of ways and means of promoting forest planting and forest protection, especially in the mountainous
   districts.

Although the Bureau has been organized for only a short while, it
has started much research work. Demonstration planting and nursery
work in the different forest regions has been launched, and preparations
for establishing arboretums in Nanking and Peking have been completed.
In view of the great variety of tree species in the country, and the need of
studying their distribution and soil and moisture requirements, such
arboretums are important.

In the field of forest utilization, the Bureau is co-operating with the
forestry departments of the various universities, and has made much progress in, and published many reports on, (1) the physical properties of
certain more important timber trees of China, and (2) methods of utilizing
such secondary forest products as camphor, tung yu, lacquer, tannin,
edible fungi, nutgalls, and cassia bark. In extension work the Bureau is
co-operating with private persons and with institutions, including temples,
for the promotion of experimental planting on various sites and for the
introduction of better methods of thinning and protecting farm woodlots.

Perhaps the most significant aspect of the Bureau's research work—in
progress since 1942—has been the establishment of experimental demonstration areas in the use of farm, grazing, and forest lands in the Northwest along the Yellow River. The purpose is to discover the most practical
and prompt ways of improving upon existing measures of soil-erosion
control and soil and water conservation. These projects should have a
far-reaching effect in determining future forestry and land-use policies
for that part of the country.

FOREST EDUCATION AND RELATED POPULAR ACTIVITIES. Modern forest
education in China is almost as old as the Chinese Republic itself. It

began when the Shantung Provincial Agricultural College first introduced forestry courses into its agricultural and sericultural curriculum. The step so taken in Shantung was soon followed by other provincial agricultural colleges. These so-called colleges, however, were merely of high-school grade and the adding of forestry courses to their curricula was done in a haphazard manner, without any direction from either the central or the provincial governments.

In 1915, when the central government established the so-called Sen Lin Chuan Shi So (Forestry Training School) and enrolled students selected from Anhwei, Shantung, Kiangsu, Hopei, Yunnan, and other provinces, a more definite and substantial start was made in forest education. The Sen Lin Chuan Shi So, however, did not last long, for immediately after its reorganization all the students of the school were sent to Nanking University, where a forestry department of college grade was established under the joint leadership of the late Joseph Bailie and the present writer, using Purple Mountain as a laboratory for field work for the students. The growing interest in forestry at the time prompted other universities and colleges to follow in the footsteps of Nanking University, so that today all national universities and colleges have established forest departments or courses and certain public and private technical schools in various provinces also offer similar instruction. Some of the principal subjects taught in these universities and colleges are:

Silvics	Nursery Practice
Dendrology	Forest Economics and History
Wood Technology	Forest Law and Policy
Forest Protection	Forest Management
Mensuration	Forest Administration
Silviculture	Forest Finance
Forest Entomology	Forest Utilization

A word should also be said about popular activities that have done much to develop public interest in forestry. Among them are:

1. Popular lectures by teachers and students from universities and colleges with forestry departments.
2. The annual observance of "Forest Week" throughout the country.
3. The consistent work of the Chinese Forestry Association.

The "Forest Week" (March 11 to 18) was initiated in 1930 in commemoration of the death of Dr. Sun Yat-sen, March 12, 1924. In his *San Min Chu I*, Dr. Sun pointed out the relation of forests to floods, droughts, stream flow, and soil erosion, and emphasized how important forests are to the life and happiness of the Chinese people, and how reforestation work in central and northern China must be carried out simultaneously with other constructive measures. Forest Week is designed to perpetuate these teachings and injunctions and to translate them into action.

The Chinese Forestry Association was founded in 1917 in Shanghai and now has branches in all the principal cities in China. By co-operating with agricultural colleges and the agricultural forestry departments of universities, by publishing an organ known as *Lin Hsioh (Chinese Forestry Journal)*, and by constantly issuing pamphlets and suitable articles relating to forests and the need of reforestation. the Association has done much to arouse a public sentiment favorable to forestry. This sentiment, no doubt, accounts for the widespread recognition of the importance of forestry as a public function in the government and for the rapid elevation of the forest administration of the country from a small division to the status of a Ministry. The Chief Forester of China is a Cabinet Minister.

SOURCES FOR BOTANICAL NOMENCLATURE

CHUN, W. Y. 1921. *Chinese economic trees.* Commercial Press, Ltd., Shanghai.

HANDEL-MAZZETTI, HEINRICH. 1929-1936. *Symbolae sinicae, botanische Ergebnisse der Expedition der Akademie der Wissenschaften in Wien nach Südwest-China, 1914-1918.* Part VII. Julius Springer, Vienna.

REHDER, ALFRED. 1940. *Manual of cultivated trees and shrubs hardy in North America.* The Macmillan Co., New York.

26.   JAPAN

Laurence J. Cummings

Japan is a country of rugged mountains, which occupy two thirds of the land area, and of small plains, narrow mountain valleys, and limited agricultural land. Much of the interior is over 1,000 meters in altitude; several peaks rise to about 3,000 meters, Fuji-san reaching 4,300 meters. The mountainous region is wild and rugged, with numerous narrow, canyon-like valleys cutting a thousand or more meters below the mountain crests.

Forest Areas

Forest lands comprise 24,952,000 hectares, or 68 per cent of the total land area of 36,848,000 hectares.[1] Of the forest lands, 23,682,000 hectares are considered potentially productive and the remainder (1,270,000 hectares) as waste land not capable of producing crops of usable wood. Table 26–I shows the area of the forest lands as classified according to five major

TABLE 26–I

JAPAN: FOREST LAND OWNERSHIP, AREAS, 1948

Ownership	Area	
	1,000 Hectares	Per Cent
National	7,768	31.1
Nonnational	(17,184)	(68.9)
Private individual	12,678	50.8
Community	3,218	12.9
Prefecture	914	3.7
Shrine and Temple	125	0.5
Other	249	1.0
TOTAL	24,952	100.0

categories of ownership and Table 26–II the same as classified in terms of primary land uses. From Table 26–II it may be ascertained that the national forests comprise 22 per cent of the area supporting saw timber, 28 per cent of the fuel wood forest area, 56 per cent of the area classed as inaccessible, and 30 per cent of the area in need of reforestation.

[1] The source of all data used in this report, unless otherwise indicated, is the Forestry Agency, Ministry of Agriculture and Forestry.

TABLE 26–II

JAPAN: PRIMARY FOREST LAND USES, AREAS, 1948

Forest Land Use	Area			
	National	Nonnational	Total	
	In 1,000 hectares			*Per cent*
Saw Timber	1,507	5,228	6,735	26.9
Coniferous	(848)	(2,807)	(3,655)	(14.6)
Broadleaf	(659)	(2,421)	(3,080)	(12.3)
Fuel Wood	2,546	6,457	9,003	36.1
Inaccessible	1,433	1,100	2,533	10.2
Area in need of reforestation ...	833	1,911	2,794	11.2
Bamboo	0	98	98	0.4
Genya	235	1,594	1,829	7.3
Wasteland	865	405	1,270	5.1
Other	299	391	690	2.8
TOTAL	7,768	17,184	24,952	100.0

There are more than 5,000,000 individual private forest landowners in Japan, whose holdings are distributed by size classes as shown in Table 26–III. Of the 72.7 per cent with holdings of less than one hectare each,

TABLE 26–III

JAPAN: INDIVIDUAL PRIVATE FOREST LAND OWNERSHIP BY AREAL SIZE CLASS, 1948

Size Class	Area			Owners	
	Hectares	Per Cent	Hectares per Owner	Number	Per Cent
Under 1 hectare	1,952,412	15.4	0.5	3,634,644	72.7
1-5 hectares	3,245,568	25.6	2.8	1,053,729	21.1
5-20 hectares	3,118,789	24.6	10.8	256,462	5.1
20-50 hectares	1,546,716	12.2	32.0	42,153	0.8
Over 50 hectares	2,814,516	22.2	171.7	14,645	0.3
TOTAL	12,678,000	100.0		5,001,633	100.0

the vast majority are farmers, who maintain wood lots incidentally to other activities. The table discloses that 41 per cent of the total area of the private forests belongs to the 93.8 per cent of the owners who own less than 5 hectares apiece, and the remaining 59 per cent to the 6.2 per cent who own 5 or more hectares each; those who own 20 hectares or more each constitute 1.1 per cent of the owners, but between them possess 34.4 per cent of the area in private forests.

The forest land is rather evenly distributed throughout the country, occupying more than 60 per cent of the total area of each of the four main islands (Table 26–IV). In 38 of the 47 prefectures more than 50 per cent of the total area is forested, and in 20 prefectures more than 70 per cent.

TABLE 26–IV

JAPAN: REGIONAL DISTRIBUTION OF FOREST LAND, 1948

Island	Area		
	Total	Forest land	
	In 1,000 hectares		Per cent of land area
Hokkaido	7,847	5,407	69
Honshu	23,042	15,580	67
Shikoku	1,878	1,394	74
Kyushu	4,081	2,571	63
TOTAL	36,848	24,952	68

Forest Zones

The Japanese forests may be classed according to three climatic zones: a warm, or evergreen-broadleaf, zone occurs in Kyushu below 800 meters elevation, in Shikoku below 700 meters, and in Honshu, south of latitude 36° N, below 500 meters. The most characteristic trees of this zone are the live oaks (*Quercus* spp.,[2] *Lithocarpus* spp., *Shiia* spp.) and two members of the laurel family, laurel (*Machilus* spp.) and camphor (*Cinnamomum* spp.). Zelkova (*Zelkova serrata*), elm, and ash occur in the colder portion of this zone. The conifers include pine, momi fir (*Abies firma*), southern Japanese hemlock (*Tsuga sieboldii*), and some sugi (Japanese cedar or redwood, *Cryptomeria japonica*).

The temperate, or deciduous broadleaf, zone occurs in Kyushu at altitudes above 800 meters, in Shikoku from 700 to 1,600 meters, in central Honshu from 500 to 1,300 meters, in northern Honshu from sea level to 900 meters, and in Hokkaido, south of latitude 43°30′ N., below 500 meters. It is the most important zone for timber production. Sugi, hinoki (Japanese cedar or cypress, *Chamaecyparis obtusa*), pine, Japanese larch (*Larix kaempferi*), fir, spruce, and hemlock grow in this zone. Broadleaf species are represented by beech, oak, maple, ash, chestnut, magnolia, walnut, alder, elm, cherry, and birch.

The cold, or coniferous, zone occurs in Shikoku above 1,600 meters, in central Honshu above 1,300 meters, in northern Honshu above 900 meters, and in southern Hokkaido above 500 meters, while in northern Hokkaido this zone occupies most of the entire area. The characteristic trees are fir, spruce, Japanese yew (*Taxus cuspidata*), birch, alder, aspen, and willow.

Character of the Forests

The forests of Japan are said to contain more tree species than are found in any area of comparable size in a similar climatic zone. The *Japanese Foresters' Manual* lists more than 1,100 species and more than

[2] Sources of botanical nomenclature: Rehder (1940), Matsumura (1905), and Makino (1940). For full references see p. 560.

800 additional varieties, most of which are broadleaf. In general composition Japan's forests resemble those of eastern North America, where
counterparts of many Japanese trees are to be found, usually different
species of the same genera. Japan's forests also contain many indigenous
trees that have no generic counterparts in America.

Aboriginal Japan was heavily covered with extensive virgin forests,
most of which probably were of broadleaf species. Heavy drain to meet
the needs of the population has profoundly altered the character of most
of the accessible forests, which today bear little resemblance to the
original stands. Except in the national forests, sizable tracts of virgin
forest are found only on the higher mountains, where they are beyond
physical, or at any rate, economic accessibility. The accessible forests have
been depleted by poor forest management, prolonged overutilization, insufficient reforestation, soil erosion, and insect pests. As a result, the
annual supply of industrial wood is derived from only 27 per cent of the
total forest area (the part that contains accessible saw timber, Table 26–II),
and the remainder of the forest land either supports fuel-wood forests, is
inaccessible, or is nonproductive waste land.

INACCESSIBLE FORESTS. The forest areas classed as inaccessible in Japan
are those lacking transportation facilities which would permit economical
timber exploitation. Because there have been no comprehensive forest
surveys and because existing statistics are not dependable, there is wide
difference of opinion as to the condition, size, and potentiality of Japan's
inaccessible forests as a source of timber supply.

Rough estimates indicate that there are about 2,535,000 hectares of
inaccessible forests, containing 392,000 cubic meters of timber, or 10.2
per cent of the total forest area and 23.6 per cent of the estimated total
timber volume of the country.

These inaccessible forests are mostly located on steep mountains at the
headwaters of streams and, hence, play an important role in watershed
protection; yet, in spite of their protective value, many enthusiastic plans
are being advanced for their exploitation. A government road-develop-
ment program for the inaccessible forest areas has been under way, but
progress has been slow and has fallen far short of goals since 1945, owing
to the steepness and rockiness of the terrain, the greater distances to the
timber, and the consequent mounting costs of road construction as the
remoter districts are opened up.

There is reason to doubt, indeed, that the inaccessible forests can ever
be developed as a major timber source. Recent aerial reconnaissance
and detailed observation on the ground have revealed that the timber
volume and the quality of the inaccessible forests have been grossly ex-
aggerated. Most of the timber is virgin, overmature, and of such poor
quality as to be suitable for fuel wood only.

Air surveys have disclosed a few large, continuous bodies of merchantable timber in the inaccessible forests of Hokkaido and on the mountains

of central Honshu, but generally such forests are broken by patches of subalpine scrub timber that is valuable for soil protection only.

SAW-TIMBER FORESTS. Although less than 15 per cent of the total forest area is occupied by accessible coniferous timber, this small area provides 85 per cent of the saw logs cut annually. The coniferous forests, 78 per cent of which are in nonnational and, for the most part, private ownership, are largely plantations. Scattered over the mountains, they consist principally of sugi, hinoki, pine, larch, fir, and spruce, and constitute Japan's principal source of construction and building material and of wood for pulp. While the national forests still retain some mature coniferous timber, heavy cutting has so reduced the private coniferous forests that little mature timber is left. Potentially, however, Japan is still a good coniferous timber country, capable of becoming one of the major producing areas of the east-Asiatic and Pacific world. Surveys are needed to determine the areas that ought to be devoted to coniferous timber, but it is safe to say that 75 per cent of Japan's productive forest area could well be used for this purpose.

The principal broadleaf species in Japan are beech, oak, birch, and maple. Although the broadleaf forests contain about 50 per cent of the standing accessible timber in Japan, they supply only 15 per cent of the annual timber harvest. The broadleaf trees of saw-timber size are characteristically short-boled, crooked, and forked, and are also predominantly old, ranging in age from 100 to 300 years. These forests long ago reached their maximum growth, and net increment cannot be expected, owing to natural losses in volume from disease, insects, fire, and wind throw.

The stocking ratio [3] of these stands can be rated as medium in most instances, and the volume growth is much lower per acre than is that of coniferous timber. The inherent characteristics, particularly the space requirements and branching habits, of the broadleaf trees result in much smaller accumulations of timber per acre than those of the coniferous stands.

The broadleaf forests are generally on steep mountain slopes and are valuable for watershed protection. Clear-cutting has been the general practice, with regeneration by natural sprouting of the stumps. This practice has resulted in the conversion of most of the original high-timber stands to low, brushwood coppice forests suitable only for fuel wood.

FUEL-WOOD FORESTS. The fuel-wood forests cover more than 36 per cent of the forest land of Japan. They are principally coppice forests, although approximately 10 per cent are pine plantations maintained primarily for the production of fuel wood.

The coppice forests consist of stumps of a variety of hardwood species which send forth sprouts from the root crowns. These are cut periodically

---

[3] The ratio of the actual volume on a given forest area to the maximum volume that could be produced there under ideal conditions.

for fuel. In many cases the sprouts are harvested every year. Most of the privately owned fuel-wood stands adjacent to roadways and villages have been subjected to continuous overexploitation by owners who, needing ready cash to meet current living expenses, have found it necessary to cut the trees before they reach maturity. The inevitable result is evident in the accumulation of low brushwood on partially stocked hillsides which have lost their water-holding and soil-protective values and are producing only a fraction of the timber that could be produced under good management.

GENYA. *Genya* is defined by the Japanese as wild land primarily in grass, either treeless or containing scrub or scattered tree growth. The area classified as *genya* comprises 1,829,000 hectares, or 7.3 per cent of the total forest land of Japan. On the basis of general observation and ocular estimates by Japanese and American forestry specialists, the larger part of this area appears suitable for conversion to timber production. The advisability, however, of such conversion on a broad scale is doubtful, owing to the present use of some of these areas for grazing and producing cut grass for domestic purposes, and also because of the high cost of establishing new forests as compared with that of reforesting the more accessible cutover areas. Hence any action in this regard should be carefully planned in the co-ordinated national land-use program.

BAMBOO. Although bamboo (*Bambusa* spp.) as a forest type comprises less than one half of one per cent of the forest land of Japan, it is highly important to the Japanese people because of its versatile qualities and numerous uses. Bamboo products are in great demand for both domestic use and export. Bamboo is utilized for house construction, furniture, household articles, baskets and containers for transporting produce, and also in the manufacture of special paper and as an important vegetable food.

Bamboo is grown primarily by the farmer in small patches on good agricultural land. Although some bamboo is found on the higher slopes of mountain ranges in nearly all parts of central and southern Japan, it does not ordinarily extend in commercial quantity beyond the lower slopes of the foothills. The principal commercial species are madake (*Phyllostachys reticulata*), mosochiku (*P. mitis*), medake (*Pleioblastus simoni*), and kurodake.

Ninety-two per cent of the bamboo acreage is owned by private individuals and 6 per cent by communities.

Exploitation of Forest Products [4]

LOG PRODUCTION. An adequate supply of wood for industry is extremely important to Japan's economy. Timber for logs and lumber is

[4] Dates refer to the Japanese fiscal year, April 1 of the named year through March 31 of the following year.

an essential requirement. The native forests provide nearly all of the household fuel consumed, of the lumber used for housing, shipbuilding, furniture, and manufactured wood products, and of the raw material used in the making of pulp and rayon textiles. Forestry and forest industries give employment mostly to seasonal workers, principally farmers who are free to engage in such work during the winter. Continued emphasis on production to meet demands—especially during the past two decades—has resulted in overexploitation of Japan's forest resources. In 1950, for the first time in postwar Japan, production of wood and wood products was insufficient to meet the demand. Figure 51(A) shows that between the two world wars Japan was primarily a timber-importing country. Imports continued to increase until 1928, when they reached a maximum of over 8,000,000 cubic meters, as compared with 11,900,000 cubic meters of indigenous production. After 1933 timber imports declined as foreign-trade credits were required for purchasing other essential raw materials, and they were virtually eliminated in the late 1930's. They were again resumed on a small scale in 1948, but Japan's lack of trade credit and the unfavorable relationship between timber import prices and prices on the Japanese market make it difficult for her to expand these imports.

Wood for Fuel. Japan has always depended heavily upon her forests as the main source of fuel. Firewood is used for cooking and for heating bath water, and in winter the houses are warmed with charcoal. Just after the end of World War II, many of the automobiles in Japan were operated on gas generated from wood and charcoal, although this use has declined as liquid fuels have again become available. Even the industries of Japan supplement the coal supply with charcoal. The wartime demands on the forests for fuel were great, and postwar demands are still heavy and, in view of relatively low indigenous production of coal, petroleum, and natural gas, will continue to be heavy. Figure 51(B) shows the estimated annual production of fuel wood and timber. More wood has always gone into fuel than into timber, and in the past twenty-five years fuel-wood production has been nearly two and one half times timber production. During this period, log production has generally increased, whereas, except for the war years, fuel-wood production has remained relatively constant.

Consumption per Capita. Because the pressure of population on Japan has been steadily increasing, the per capita production and consumption of wood products [Fig. 51(C)] are of particular importance. The marked decline during the war years 1942–45 is striking. Until 1942 a high proportion of the fuel wood was consumed by industry, but bomb destruction and decreased industrial military production substantially reduced the demand. The interruption of transportation by war destruction, together with the low priority for the distribution of fuel wood for domestic civilian requirements, reduced urban deliveries.

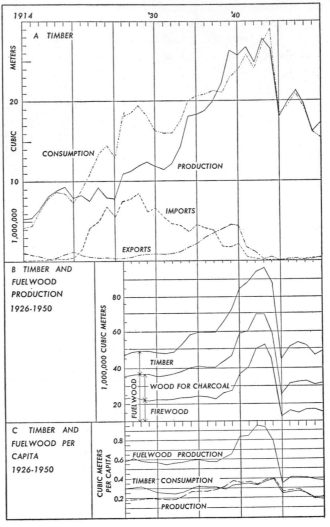

Fɪɢ. 51. Japan: timber and fuel wood, production, consumption, and foreign trade, 1914 (1926)–1950.

The Future

Since the end of the war, needs for wood have increased steadily. The reconstruction of war-damaged areas, the resumption of house building, and the need for more wood for the pulp industry, for the operation of mines and of transportation and communication systems, and for fuel and other uses have created an enormous demand on the forests. Wood has been used primarily for essential reconstruction and rehabilitation. The greatest drain has occurred in the coniferous timber stands, which are being overcut at an annual rate more than two and one half times the growth—a situation which may have serious consequences.

Timber production without proper soil-stabilization safeguards has created a major drain on Japan's postwar economy. During 1949 Japanese government expenditures for controlling floods and erosion and for repair of damages exceeded 40 billion yen, and in 1950, 60 billion yen were required, more than 60 per cent of the total Japanese budget for public works. Despite such vast expenditures on downstream defenses, Japan is losing her struggle against mounting losses from floods and erosion owing to a lack of an adequate preventive program in the flood source areas. The extent of damage to agricultural areas by flood waters is shown in Fig. 52. Japanese government officials recognize the problems involved and are working toward a solution.

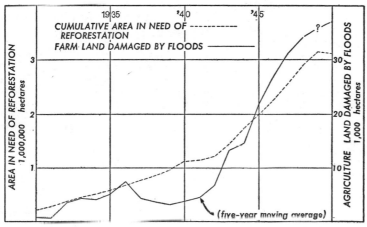

FIG. 52. Japan: area in need of reforestation, farm land damaged by floods, 1930-1950.

There are no quick or easy solutions of the problems created by poor forestry practices in the past, but through aggressive action, supported by a well-informed and sufficiently advised public, material benefits from improved forestry programs can be realized immediately. The urgency for immediate action is emphasized by the fact that less than 15 per cent of the forest area constitutes the major source of industrial and construction timbers. The preservation and increased productivity of this area are essential if the Japanese forests are to be rehabilitated. In recent years the forest situation has been intensively studied. Data gathered by the forestry technicians of the Supreme Commander for the Allied Powers show the complete reliance of the Japanese on their forests, the inadequacy of the present forest yield, and the urgent need for remedial action. On the basis of this information the Japanese have been encouraged to formulate an over-all forest-development policy, and have been furnished guidance and assistance in the establishment of an adequate program to solve their forest and timber-supply problems. According to recent reports, the forestry programs developed during the Occupation are being actively and effectively carried out by the Japanese government —a gratifying circumstance.

SELECTED REFERENCES

BRUCE, H. D. 1949. *Forest fuel production in Japan.* General Headquarters, Supreme Commander for the Allied Powers, Natural Resources Section, Preliminary Study No. 33. Tokyo.

CUMMINGS, L. J. 1951. *Forestry in Japan, 1945-51.* General Headquarters, Supreme Commander for the Allied Powers, Natural Resources Section, Report No. 153. Tokyo.

———, et al. 1950. *Forest area, volume, and growth in Japan; statistical summary.* General Headquarters, Supreme Commander for the Allied Powers, Natural Resources Section, Preliminary Study No. 37. Tokyo.

GILL, TOM. 1951. *Forest policy and legislation for Japan.* General Headquarters, Supreme Commander for the Allied Powers, Natural Resources Section, Preliminary Study No. 49. Tokyo.

——— and DOWLING, E. C., comps. 1949. *Forestry Directory, 1949.* Amer. Tree Assoc., Washington, D.C.

HAIBACH, D. J., et al. 1949. *Important trees of Japan.* General Headquarters, Supreme Commander for the Allied Powers, Natural Resources Section, Report No. 119. Tokyo.

KIRCHER, J. C., and DEXTER, A. K. 1951. *Management of private coniferous forests of Japan.* General Headquarters, Supreme Commander for the Allied Powers, Natural Resources Section, Preliminary Study No. 43. Tokyo.

KRAEBEL, C. J. 1950. *Forestry and flood control in Japan.* General Headquarters, Supreme Commander for the Allied Powers, Natural Resources Section, Preliminary Study No. 39. Tokyo.

MAKINO, TOMITARO. 1940. *An illustrated flora of Nippon with the cultivated and naturalized plants.* Publisher unknown, Tokyo.

MATSUMURA, J. 1905. *Index plantarum japonicarum.* Maruzen Bibliopolam, Tokyo.

REHDER, ALFRED. 1940. *Manual of cultivated trees and shrubs hardy in North America.* The Macmillan Co., New York.

27. KOREA

Min Sim Hyun

Korea is largely mountainous. From the Changpai Mountains, along the Manchurian border, a lofty range runs southward along the east coast to the southern end of the peninsula, of which it thus forms the backbone and watershed. Its deviation from the center makes the eastern side of the peninsula steep, rock-bound, and without plains or important streams, whereas the opposite side, though broken by many ridges, slopes more gently and in many places opens out into wide, fertile valleys traversed by large rivers. The southern part of the country has much more level land suitable for agriculture, while the northern part is hilly, rich in timber and minerals, and holds greater potentialities for industrial development.

Area, Volume, and Ownership of the Forests

About 16,000,000 hectares, or 72 per cent of the total area of Korea (20,074,000 hectares), is classed as forest land. In South Korea, an area of about 6,845,000 hectares (see Table 27–I), or 73 per cent of the total (9,363,000 hectares), is classed as actual or potential forest land. Though South Korea contains roughly 42 per cent of the land area and 42 per cent of the forest area of the entire peninsula, it has only 33 per cent of the timber volume.

TABLE 27–I

SOUTH KOREA: FOREST AREAS, BY AGE CLASSES, 1950

	Per Cent	1,000 Hectares
Barren, denuded, or poorly stocked	30	2,055
Trees, up to 20 years old	45	3,083
20 to 40 " "	15	1,027
40 to 60 " "	5	340
over 60 " "	5	340
TOTAL	100	6,845

South Korea supports a population of 20 million persons. This implies 0.34 hectares of forest land per capita. The requirements of a dense population and the need for soil stabilization call for the most intensive use and the best possible management of the forests. The mini-

561

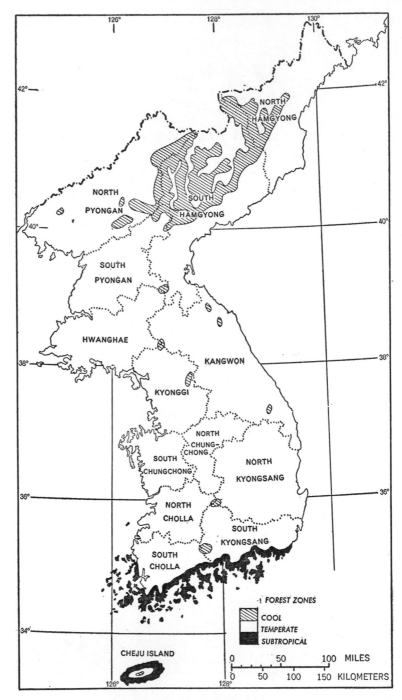

FIG. 53. Korea: forest zones.

mum annual wood requirement is estimated at 4.1 million cubic meters. Thirty per cent of the forest land of South Korea is denuded or poorly stocked and needs restocking. Table 27–I shows areas by age classes.

If all the forest land in Korea were producing wood at the maximum rate possible, there would be more than enough material to meet domestic needs for fuel, lumber, and wood products. Unfortunately, heavy demand and lack of control have resulted in great devastation. The growing stock has been reduced, large areas have been denuded, serious erosion is taking place, and the productive capacity of the forest has been so lowered that yearly cutting removes at least twice as much wood as is being replaced by growth. Almost as serious as the cutting of the trees is the continual raking up of the needles and leaves for fuel almost as soon as they fall. It takes more than trees to make a forest. Even where timber stands are fully stocked, erosion may take place unless the needles and leaves are allowed to accumulate into a protective mulch on the forest floor to absorb moisture.

Much of the volume is in small trees which should not be harvested in the near future, nor should equivalent amounts be taken from the dwindling supply of old timber. In 1942 the average standing-timber volume per hectare in Korea was 13.7 cubic meters; in 1952 it was only 5 cubic meters. The calculated allowable annual cut from the forest is approximately 1.7 million cubic meters, or about 41 per cent of the annual requirement. Current annual growth is estimated to be 1.84 million cubic meters. Tables 27–II, 27–III, and 27–IV, respectively, show for South Korea the annual requirements and allowable cut, the forest area and timber volume by provinces, and the forest area by types of ownership.

TABLE 27–II

SOUTH KOREA: ANNUAL REQUIREMENT AND ALLOWABLE CUT, 1950

	Annual Requirement (Thousand Cubic Meters)	Allowable Cut	
		Thousand Cubic Meters	Per Cent of Annual Requirement
Fuel wood	2,627	1,365	52.0
Charcoal	609	220	36.0
Saw logs	840	95	11.3
TOTAL	. 4,076	1,680	41.2

There are twelve national forests north of the thirty-eighth parallel, but only two south of it. Both of the latter are in the province of Kangwon, with headquarters at Seoul and Kangnung respectively. A small amount of national forest land in the other southern provinces is handled by the provincial forestry sections for the Bureau of Forestry.

TABLE 27–III

SOUTH KOREA: FOREST AREA AND TIMBER VOLUME BY PROVINCES, 1950

Province or Forest Station	Area (Hectares)	Coniferous Volume	Deciduous Volume	Total Volume
		(Cubic meters)		
Seoul	5,832	4,107	2,747	6,854
Kyonggi	723,783	790,476	1,084,052	1,874,528
N. Chungchong	624,754	854,913	1,191,606	2,046,519
S. Chungchong	497,730	455,624	354,189	809,813
N. Cholla	741,210	541,210	491,397	1,032,607
S. Cholla	805,119	2,283,238	741,218	3,024,456
N. Kyongsang	1,389,601	3,950,758	2,025,818	5,976,576
S. Kyongsang	845,185	2,068,208	1,344,839	3,413,047
Cheju	48,929	151,781	799,858	951,639
Kangwon	660,120	2,666,013	712,639	3,378,652
Kangnung Forest Sta.	384,662	1,547,886	1,672,933	3,220,819
Seoul Forest Sta.	116,075	807,835	3,164,250	3,972,085
TOTAL	6,843,000	16,122,049	13,585,546	29,707,595

TABLE 27–IV

SOUTH KOREA: FOREST AREA BY TYPE OF OWNERSHIP, 1950

Type of Ownership	Area (Thousand Hectares)	Per Cent
National	953	14
Vested	430	6
Provincial and other public ...	561	8
Lee household	67	1
Temple	67	1
Private	4,757	70
TOTAL	6,835	100

There is a Central Forest Experiment Station near Seoul, with excellent buildings and facilities and some very good equipment. Associated with it are a small experimental forest, an arboretum, a forest nursery, and housing facilities for a training school, as well as wood-testing and seed storage facilities and a library. Twenty miles northeast of Seoul there is a branch station, an experimental forest of 3,130 hectares. At two other branch stations, in North Cholla and South Kyongsang, a little work has been done. There are also several provincial experimental stations.

Most of the vested forest lands and also the former royal Lee household forest land, all of which have good forest cover, have now come under intensive government control. The vested land formerly belonged to Japanese owners. Seventy per cent of the total forest land is owned by Koreans as private holdings, most of it in the form of small holdings, and a great deal has been denuded and is of little value at the present time.

Forest Zones

SUBTROPICAL ZONE OF MIXED EVERGREEN AND DECIDUOUS FOREST. This zone is characterized by *Quercus glauca*,[1] *Castanopsis cuspidata* var. *sieboldii, Cinnamomum pedunculatum, Machilus thunbergii,* and *Vaccinium bracteatum.* Much of the standing timber has been cut or destroyed by human activity or forest fire. These harvested or denuded areas were once occupied by deciduous trees, mixed forest with deciduous trees, and coniferous trees such as Japanese red pine (*Pinus densiflora* Sieb. et Zucc.). Recommended species for the zone are: *Quercus acutissima, Pueraria triloba* Makino, *Buxus microphylla* var. *koreana, Pinus densiflora, Zelkova serrata, Cryptomeria japonica, Chamaecyparis obtusa,* and *Pinus thunbergii.*

TEMPERATE ZONE OF DECIDUOUS FOREST. The forests of this zone, which comprises about 85 per cent of the total forest area in Korea, occur north of 35° N wherever the mean annual temperature is not less than 5° C. and not more than 14° C. The upper limits vary from between 600 and 1,500 meters. The chief species is the oak, although Japanese red pine has replaced the oaks in many places. The mineral soils are granitic and schistose.

The southern section of the zone is characterized by the following species which occur naturally: *Cephalotaxus koreana* Nakai, *Platycarya strobilacea, Euonymus radicans, Acer palmatum* var. *coreanum,*[2] *Xanthoxylum simulans.*

In the middle section, the characteristic species are *Styrax japonica, Quercus glandulifera* Thunb., *Quercus mongolica, Juniperus chinensis, Abies holophylla, Betula davurica,* and in the northern section *Betula costata, Acer tegmentosum, Abies holophylla, Tilia amurensis* var. *glabra, Betula schmidtii, Quercus mongolica, Pinus koraiensis, Larix olgensis* Henry. Recommended for artificial reafforestation in the northern section are. *Pinus densiflora, Larix gmelini* var. *olgensis, Larix leptolepis, Pinus koraiensis, Abies holophylla, Castanea crenata, Quercus acutissima, Zelkova serrata, Juglans sinensis, Paulownia tomentosa, Alnus japonica, Robinia pseudoacacia, Fraxinus mandshuria, Forsythia densata* Nakai, *Betula schmidtii.*

COOL ZONE OF CONIFEROUS TREES. This zone comprises the plateau and mountain areas of the provinces of North Pyongan and South Hamgyong where the mean annual temperature falls below 5° C. The lower limits of this type of forest range from 600 meters in the Changpai Mountains, to 1,150 meters in the Diamond Mountains, and to 1,500 meters in the Hanra and Sollack mountains. The zone·is characterized

---

[1] For sources of botanical nomenclature see p. 572.

[2] The seeming inconsistency of the spellings *koreana, coreanum, koraiensis,* etc., in this chapter results from the botanical rule that the spelling adopted by the author of a name must be retained.

by *Picea jezoensis* Carriere, *Abies nephrolepis, Larix koreana, Picea koyamai, Pinus koraiensis,* and *Abies holophylla. Pinus pumila* is found only in the Changpai, Rangrim, Sollack, and Diamond mountains, above heights ranging from 1,200 meters to 1,600 meters.

At one time this region maintained a coniferous climax association, but many trees have been destroyed by forest fire and human activities. These denuded or destroyed forests have been replaced by deciduous species, such as *Picea jezoensis, Betula ermani, Betula latifolia* var. *niponica, Populus tremula* var. *davidiana, Populus maximowiczii,* Ulmaceae, and Tiliaceae, by mixed wood of deciduous species and larch, or by pure larch forests.

Commercial Tree Species

Among the native conifers, the Japanese red pine is the most common and most widely used. Usually very crooked, although in a few areas growing straight and tall, it is primarily used for firewood, construction timber, and sawn lumber. The nutting pine (*Pinus koraiensis*) has a limited range in South Korea and grows in the cooler locations on good, well-drained soil. The tree is straight and has an even-grained wood which makes it the most valuable of the Korean pines. It is used for window sashes, interior trim, furniture, and construction lumber, and its seed is highly prized for food. The native larch (*Larix gmelini* var. *olgensis*) has a wide distribution, is straight, fast-growing, and durable, and is used for poles, piling, mine props, and construction timbers. The needle fir (*Abies holophylla*) is fast-growing but does not have a wide distribution south of the thirty-eighth parallel. Formerly cut primarily for pulp, it is now used for lumber. Spruce (*Picea koyamai*) is likewise not found abundantly south of the thirty-eighth parallel. It can be used for pulp, masts, lumber, and construction timber.

The Japanese larch (*Larix leptolepis*), imported from Japan and planted in Korea, has all the virtues of the native larch and is faster growing. Pitch pine (*Pinus rigida*), imported from the United States, grows fast on poor soils and is straight, whereas the native Japanese red pine is crooked. It is also one of the few pines that will reproduce by sprouting after cutting or being killed back by fire. It is a general-purpose wood, but very little of it has reached maturity. Black pine (*Pinus thunbergii*) from Japan is tall and well suited to the southern part of Korea. Cryptomeria is an excellent and fast growing tree valuable for shipbuilding and other special uses, and more effort should be made to find areas in South Korea suitable for its growth.

Among the native broadleaf species the oaks are most common and most widely used. The principal species in order of importance are *Quercus glandulifera, Q. dentata, Q. acutissima,* and *Q. variabilis.* They are used for charcoal, railroad ties, furniture, cork (*Q. variabilis*), and tannin (*Q. dentata*). The Japanese chestnut (*Castanea crenata*), an excellent tree from every standpoint, is widely distributed. The wood is principally used for railroad ties and the nut is an important source of food. The poplar *(Populus maximowiczii)* is common. It is used for temporary building, and roadside trees are pollarded to provide fuel. The Japanese alder *(Alnus japonica)* is widely planted for stream bank protection and erosion control. It is a soil builder and improves bare sites so that better trees will grow upon them. Sumac or varnish-tree *(Rhus verniciflua)* is found in northern and central South Korea. The wood is of little value, but the galls are distilled to secure tannin and the sap is made into lacquer. The zelkova *(Z. serrata)* is of limited distribution but highly prized for making the rims of wagon wheels. The Manchurian walnut *(Juglans mandshurica)* is used for gunstocks and furniture, but its distribution is limited. Maple *(Acer sizuense)*, hickory *(Pterocarya rhoifolia)*, basswood or linden *(Tilia amurensis)*, and elm *(Ulmus sp.)* are occasionally found.

The black locust *(Robinia pseudoacacia)*, introduced from the United States many years ago, has escaped from cultivation and is now widely distributed. It forms a dense cover, propagated by seed and suckers, and sprouts vigorously when cut for fuel. It is recognized as a soil builder and a good erosion-control species. But, while it thrives on better soil and moisture conditions where more valuable species would also grow, it does not do well on the barren, dry sites where it is really needed. The sycamore or plane-tree *(Platanus acerifolia)* is widely found along city streets and country roads. Like the black locust and cottonwood it is pollarded each fall to furnish fuel. *Paulownia tomentosa*, found on the island of Ulong Do, and *P. coreana*, which is a native, are widely planted. Their wood is used to make wooden shoes and boxes for silverware.

Recreational and Other Uses of the Forests

The Korean forests have not long been used for other than economic purposes, and no outstanding provisions for such use have been made, except for a few recreational areas. The Diamond Mountains and the great natural beauties of their waterfalls, woods, and rocks, are widely known, and recreational facilities have recently been provided there. Mount Chiri, in South Korea, is a very popular summer resort. The natural forests in the Mount Chiri area are protected and maintained for research work under the supervision of the Central Forest Experiment Station. A number of hot springs, such as Yangtock and Chuul in the north, are well provided with recreational facilities and surrounded with natural scenic views, and in the south, the hot springs of Onyang, Tongnai, and Haiuntai are also known as recreational centers. The Central Forest Experimental Station near Seoul has an arboretum used by the people of Seoul for picnics. Other resort areas of the south are Cheju Island and the Hanra Mountains. The Tai-kwan Pass and Sambang Valley in the north are used for skiing in the winter. Plans are now being put forward for the establishment of a National Park in Kyongju, in the province of North Kyongsang.

Much of the forest land in South Korea is used for purposes other than the production of forest crops. Table 27–V shows such economic use by provinces.

TABLE 27–V

SOUTH KOREA: POTENTIAL ECONOMIC USES OF FORESTS FOR PURPOSES OTHER THAN THE PRODUCTION OF FOREST CROPS, BY PROVINCES, 1950

Province	Area in Hectares Adaptable for:					
	Shifting Cultivation	Conversion Into Non-irrigated Farm Land	Pasture	Hay and Green Manure	Other Uses	Total
Kyonggi	1,076	9,311	12,730	17,601	17,655	58,373
N. Chungchong	1,341	2,895	4,116	10,400	8,469	27,229
S. Chungchong	61	3,058	3,524	4,554	8,945	20,141
N. Cholla	1,000	7,218	2,649	7,805	17,213	35,885
S. Cholla	251	11,420	27,689	13,103	7,990	60,453
N. Kyongsang	2,281	6,398	487	49,879	31,702	90,747
S. Kyongsang	–	8,236	4,891	48,980	32,000	94,107
Kangwon	20,361	7,816	9,170	10,749	7,352	55,448
TOTAL	26,371	56,352	65,256	163,071	131,326	442,383

Afforestation

Korean tree species are hardy and very prolific. Had the forests been properly managed, little artificial reafforestation would be needed. But they have been decimated and nearly two million hectares must be replanted to young trees if the soil is to be kept from washing down over the rice fields and the productivity of the forest lands is to be restored. If fertilizer is made available, South Korea can produce sufficient food to feed her people. It is just as important that she grow enough wood to cook their food, house them, warm them, and furnish material for the ties, poles, paper, and other wood products that are vitally necessary to the welfare of the country. It can be done.

Between 1909 and 1945, 7.5 billion trees were planted in South Korea, an average of about 200 million per year. In 1946, 200 million trees were planted; in 1947, 86 million; in 1948, 104 million; in 1949, 217 million; and in 1950, an estimated 230 million. The ten-year plan of 1947 contemplated the planting of 550 million trees a year on 200,000 hectares. The number and areas of forest nurseries were increased to give an estimated annual capacity of 550 million seedlings and transplants, but shortage and uncertainty of funds to develop the nurseries and take care of the stock in them have prevented attainment of this goal. Except on the publicly owned lands young trees are raised in private nurseries and then purchased by the Bureau of Forestry and supplied free to private timberland owners for planting. For several years past, hundreds of millions of such trees have been available, but the Bureau has had no funds with which to purchase them. Private-forest nurserymen consequently are turning to other means of livelihood.

Arbor Day has been officially established as April 5. From 1946 through 1950 special programs were held on that day throughout South Korea. The planting season lasts each year from about March 10 to April 20. No fall planting is done.

More than three million hectares in South Korea bear trees less than twenty years old (Table 27–I). A large proportion of this area is in trees less than 10 feet high that grow from 8 to 15 inches per year. Many people with little knowledge of forestry refer to such growth as "brush" instead of as young timber, and some wonder whether it should not be plowed up to make room for agricultural crops. Few foresters would object to so using land that can be truly classed as agricultural, but it may be doubted if there is as much as 400,000 hectares of such land in South Korea not now used for agriculture.

Erosion Control

The forest lands of Korea are usually steep and the soils are largely decomposed granite and are very unstable. Land reclamation and flood and erosion control have become vitally important because areas that should be covered with protective forests have been denuded or so continuously raked over that they cannot now act as efficient watersheds and, hence, their soils are being washed down onto the agricultural lands below. But even the most extensive and costly programs of reclamation and flood and erosion control will not solve the basic problem, which is how to restore and maintain the forest cover, hold the soil in place, and control the runoff by natural means. Unless denuded lands are quickly recovered with protective vegetation, erosion becomes progressively worse and eventually replanting is successful only if preceded by terracing.

Korean foresters do excellent erosion-control work, but it is expensive. Terraces a foot or two wide are built at appropriate intervals on the side of the mountain and faced with sod or stone. Eroded terrain is smoothed out, drainage lines are sodded. Erosion-control plants such as *Lespedeza* and black locust are planted, together with Korean or Japanese alder and Japanese red pine. If properly protected and maintained, such an area can be completely healed and covered with vegetation in from five to seven years. But on the average about 100 man-days of work are required to terrace and plant one hectare, and the total cost runs from $37 to $74 per hectare.

In 1949 intensive erosion-control operations were carried forward by the Bureau of Forestry on 6,000 hectares at a total cost of 91,600,000

hwans or a little more than 123,500 *hwans* (about $74) per hectare. The
work was done in the main on privately owned lands, and the government
will get 80 per cent of the crop when the timber is eventually harvested.
The Bureau of Forestry also supervises stream-control work along the headwaters of mountain streams. Both check-damming and revegetation are
resorted to. In 1949 and 1950 stream-control work was done on about
200 kilometers of mountain streams. When the Korean War broke out
in 1950 something like 400,000 hectares needed erosion-control work and
5,000 kilometers of stream-control work remained to be done.

Protection

The forests must be protected from theft, indiscriminate cutting
(whether with or without permit), leaf raking, fire, insects, and disease.
More and better trained forest protectors will be needed but, above all,
the people must be educated as to their own personal stake in the forests
and as to why and how they should protect them. Organization of local
forest protective associations has in some instances proved highly effective
and should go forward on a large scale. In reafforestation and erosion
control the government should offer the most help to those who are willing to help themselves.

Forest Products

LUMBER AND FUEL WOOD. The forests in Korea were excessively overcut during the period of Japanese occupation. Since 1945 South Korea
has been deprived of a supply of saw logs and fuel woods from the North
and overcutting is continued year by year.

Climatic conditions, the structure of the houses, and the lack of coal
for domestic purposes are all unfavorable to the conservation of forest
resources. The annual consumption of domestic fuel in South Korea
is estimated at 11,266,400 metric tons, of which coal and peat supply only
a small proportion (510,000 metric tons) of the total. There are more
than 3¾ million households; hence the annual consumption of fuel per
household is approximately 3 metric tons. Most of the annual forest cut,
therefore, is used for domestic fuel, and the demand for such fuel increases
with the growth of population.

To relieve the pressure on forest cut for fuel wood the government is
making every effort to produce peat as a substitute. According to an
investigation made by ECA, there are about 78 million tons of peat
in Korea. The United Nations Civil Assistance Command in Korea
(UNCACK) is continuing the investigation, and developing a project for
a large expansion of peat production. By the middle of June 1950,
150,000 tons of peat had been produced. When production reaches one
million tons per year the pressure for wood will be greatly reduced. The
possibilities in Korea seem almost limitless. In fuel value a ton of peat is

equal to at least 2 *pyung* of wood.   (A *pyung* is 6′ × 6′ × 27″, or about
two thirds of a cord.) Hence there is no difficulty in selling peat if its
cost per ton does not exceed that of 2 *pyung* of wood. Costs have been
reasonable with hand-produced peat, and with machinery a better product can be obtained even more cheaply.

Concurrently with peat production a detailed survey of peat deposits
should be undertaken to determine the location, quantity, and quality
of peat available. This is extremely important. Not only can peat be
used for fuel and to produce valuable tar products, but, if it exists in
large enough quantity, it can also be used to generate electricity. The
production and use of peat on a large scale would be the greatest single
step toward the preservation and restoration of the Korean forests. It
would lessen the terrific pressure for domestic firewood, which accounts
for more than 80 per cent of the forest drain, and it would reduce the
need for raking up needles and leaves from the forest floor. It would
offer a period of respite during which good forestry practices could be
put into effect to make possible, eventually, the production of sufficient
wood for all domestic uses. But unless advantage were taken of this
period to organize, finance, and practice good forestry, the respite would
be largely wasted.

The annual requirement for logs in South Korea is approximately 1.2
million cubic meters, of which 45 per cent goes for lumber, 12 per cent
for construction logs, 11 per cent for railroad ties, 10 per cent each for
box boards and pulpwood, 5 per cent for veneer and plywood, and 7
per cent for miscellaneous uses.

Since the war the demand for logs and lumber for ties, bridge timbers,
dwellings, stores, factories, and public buildings has been tremendous.
The forests of South Korea cannot supply this demand, and logs must
be imported in large quantities, mostly from the Philippines.

It would be a mistake to assume that unification of the country would
solve all forestry problems or that ample supplies of fuel wood and timber
for all needs could flow down from North Korea. Even before the war
the Korean peninsula was not self-sufficient in its supply of wood. The
war and subsequent occupation of North Korea must have gravely depleted the timber stands there except in the most inaccessible areas. It
is possible that some lumber and timber could be brought into South
Korea from north of the thirty-eighth parallel, but lack of an accessible
supply and the transportation costs of the long haul would make it difficult to secure much fuel wood, except, perhaps, for the city of Seoul.

WOODWORKING INDUSTRIES. In general the woodworking industries in
South Korea are small. There were 1,074 sawmills in 1944 for the
country as a whole, and milling capacity was approximately 3.7 million
cubic meters per year. These mills were equipped with small circular
saws or band saws. The 1948 figures show that there were 972 sawmills
in South Korea and that the annual production was 424,380 cubic meters.

There are only five mills equipped with more than 100 horsepower; the rest have less than 30 horsepower.

In 1944 there were five plywood factories in Korea as a whole, the largest of which was in the north. This plant was equipped with five 6-foot rotary machines and produced annually more than one million pieces of 3′ × 6′ plywood. The main species used in the factory were ash, maple, and oak. One factory at Inchon was destroyed during the war and is being reconstructed at present. There are two other plants in South Korea, having between them three 6-foot rotary machines and five 3-foot rotary machines. The monthly production capacity per machine is approximately 150 cubic meters. Until 1944 Korea exported plywood to China (including Manchuria) and India.

Korea has a long tradition of paper manufacturing. There are more than 200 small mills using the paper mulberry (*Broussonetia papyrifera*). Fifteen pulp-using mills have a combined annual pulp requirement of 55,500 metric tons. Only one plant in South Korea, located at Kunsan, is equipped to produce pulp. This mill has an annual capacity of 12,000 metric tons and has had to augment an inadequate supply of red pine by the collection of waste paper. Some pulp was brought into South Korea by the Military Government and ECA, but supplies have been inadequate.

An excellent pressure treating plant at Pusan for ties and poles can handle poles more than 60 feet long and 700,000 ties annually on a one-shift basis. Shortage of creosote has, however, caused a bottleneck at this plant. There are smaller plants in Taegu and Taejon.

SOURCES FOR BOTANICAL NOMENCLATURE

BAILEY, L. H., and BAILEY, E. Z. 1953. *Hortus Second.* The Macmillan Co., New York.
REHDER, ALFRED. 1940. *Manual of cultivated trees and shrubs hardy in North America.* The Macmillan Co., New York.

28. AUSTRALIA

D. A. N. Cromer

The distribution and the character of the Australian forests are largely controlled by the climate. Luxuriant vegetation is confined to a comparatively narrow strip around the coast which receives over 760 millimeters average annual precipitation. In this region, rarely more than 160 kilometers wide, lies almost the whole of Australia's forest resources. With decreasing rainfall as one proceeds inland, dense forest gives way to savanna woodland, which forms a wide belt within the coastal strip. Further inland, savanna woodland gives way on the east and north to savanna, while in the south and west it is replaced by mallee (dwarf, multiple-stemmed eucalypts), shrub steppe, and arid scrub formations. The whole of central Australia is occupied by desert or by dry sclerophyllous grassland, desert steppe, sclerophyllous grass steppe, and mulga (*Acacia aneura*) [1] scrub. This huge area is practically uninhabited.

Location and Extent of Forested Areas

Only about 115,600,000 hectares, or 15 per cent of the total land area of Australia, receives rainfall sufficient for forest growth. This area, however, also contains all the cultivated and dairying land of the Commonwealth, and in it is concentrated almost the whole of the population of some 8,350,000 persons.

The forest resources of Australia have not yet been completely assessed. A considerable body of information is available concerning areas under state forestry legislation, but little is known of the resources on other Crown land or on private property. Considerable timber is at present derived from the latter sources, but how much private property and unreserved Crown land will be devoted to timber production in the future is a matter for conjecture, since no equilibrium between agriculture and other types of land use has yet been reached.

An estimate of the forest area in each state is shown in Table 28–I, which includes all lands carrying trees of any kind in forest formations except savanna woodland. The quality of these forests varies greatly. Western Australia, for example, possesses more than 7,700,000 hectares of forest land in the Goldfields region, which supplies huge quantities of

---

[1] For sources of botanical nomenclature see below, p. 590.

firewood and mining timber, and an additional 4,900,000 hectares of forest in the southwest capable of providing rough material only. The figures for Victoria and South Australia include several million hectares of mallee, which provides firewood, mallee roots, and eucalyptus oil, while the total for New South Wales includes 1,600,000 hectares of poor forest on the infertile Hawkesbury sandstone formation and a considerable area of noncommercial forest.

TABLE 28–I

Australia: Forested Areas, Totals and by Types of Forest, by States [a]

(In Thousand Hectares)

	Total	Eucalypts	Rain Forest	Cypress Pine
Queensland	7,006	5,320	1,014	656
New South Wales	12,141	11,354	243	532
Victoria	7,000	6,975	–	–
South Australia	2,670	2,617	–	–
Western Australia	15,820	15,814	–	–
Tasmania	2,833	2,527	304	–
Australian Capital Territory	98	92	–	–
TOTAL	47,568	44,699	1,561	1,188
PER CENT	100	94.0	3.4	2.6

[a] Does not include certain poor forests in the Northern Territory and approximately 125,000 hectares (0.2 per cent) in coniferous plantations (see Table 28–II, columns 2 and 3).

Forested land amounts to only 6 per cent of the total area of Australia, a ratio little greater than that for the United Kingdom, but the percentage of forested land in the inhabited area is 38. The forest area per capita, 5.7 hectares, is considerably greater than the world and European averages. The consumption of timber in the round for industrial purposes is approximately 0.9 cubic meters per capita annually, or about one half of the corresponding figure for North America and slightly more than that for Europe.

When productive forest land alone is considered, however, a different picture emerges. Table 27–II gives the area of all forests of sawmilling quality, including not only forests at present capable of sustained-yield management for saw logs, but also areas from which saw logs have been extracted in the past, those from which saw timber is being exploited at present, and those carrying saw timber which may be utilized in the future.

Productive forests of sawmilling quality cover 2.3 per cent of the total land area of Australia (14.4 per cent of the "inhabited area") and amount to 2.2 hectares per capita.

TABLE 28–II

AUSTRALIA: AREAS OF PRODUCTIVE FOREST, OF PLANTATIONS, AND OF PLANTATION PROGRAMS, BY STATES

(In Thousand Hectares)

| | Productive Forest of Sawmilling Quality | Coniferous Plantations, 1950 | | Plantation Programs for State Forest Services |
		Forest Services	Private	
Queensland	2,800	17	–	81
New South Wales	4,900 [a]	15	3	81
Victoria	4,900	20	5	81
South Australia	100	44	7	81
Western Australia	3,200	5	small	40
Tasmania	2,000	2	1	20
Australian Capital Territory	[b]	6	–	16
TOTAL	17,900	109	16	400

[a] Includes A.C.T.
[b] Included in New South Wales.

Approximately 65 per cent of the productive forest area is under some form of reservation, and of this portion 8,000,000 hectares have been permanently dedicated to timber production by the different states. The highest-quality forests have already been thus dedicated, but not all the Crown forest area is of high quality; indeed, some of it is even treeless and much poor land is included under the headings "Timber Reserves" and "Other" of Table 28–III.

TABLE 28–III

AUSTRALIA: DEDICATED CROWN FORESTS, AREAS BY STATES, JUNE, 1950 [a]

(In Thousand Hectares)

	Total	State Forests [b]	Timber Reserves [c]	Other [d]
Queensland	2,925.5	1,659.8	1,265.7	–
New South Wales	2,925.5	2,398.6	526.9	–
Victoria	2,080.2	1,723.1	290.4	66.8
South Australia	103.1	103.1	–	–
Western Australia	2,528.6	1,380.2	728.3	420.1
Tasmania	1,130.7	722.1	55.5	353.3
Australian Capital Territory	53.0	–	–	53.0
TOTALS	11,746.7	7,986.8	2,866.7	893.2

[a] Does not include national parks, state parks, and flora and fauna reserves.
[b] Permanently dedicated under Forestry Acts.
[c] Temporarily dedicated under Forestry Acts.
[d] Pulp concessions and temporary reservations under other acts.

Reserved forests occupy only 1.5 per cent of the total land area of the Commonwealth, or 1.4 hectares per capita. These figures are less than those given for productive sawmilling forest because considerable un-reserved Crown land carries commercial forest and because little infor-mation is available for alienated forest land. Most of the private forests are neither managed nor protected, and it will be a long time before they play a large part in Australia's timber economy. This is in direct contrast to the situation in certain European countries, where private forests managed on a sustained-yield basis often constitute the major forest resource.

Forest Trees

Figure 54 shows the regions in which forests cover a significant pro-portion of the total area and are the chief sources of Australian saw timber, hewn timber, and veneers. Areas of low-quality forests or of merely local importance for firewood and mining timbers are not shown on the map.

The Australian forest flora consists predominantly of evergreen hard-woods, the characteristic genus being *Eucalyptus,* embracing more than 600 species and varieties, most of them endemic to Australia. Of more than 100 eucalypt species commercially sawn, only 30 to 40 are exten-sively exploited. A limited and discontinuous area of favorable soils and rainfall carries a rain-forest admixture of broadleaf trees of Indo-Malayan affinities, which constitutes a valuable supply of cabinet timbers and veneer logs.

The indigenous softwood resources were never very large and are now seriously depleted. Only about one million hectares of cypress pine (*Callitris*) is likely to be maintained as permanent forest; the remainder is being cleared for agriculture or is too remote or scattered for profitable forest operations. The other conifers are either too slow in growth for re-forestation, or, like hoop pine (*Araucaria cunninghamii*), are better suited to artificial regeneration in plantations.

Commercial Forests

The main commercial forests may be grouped into three classes: Euca-lyptus, Rain, and Conifer Forests.

EUCALYPTUS FORESTS. These forests are of three distinctive types.

1. *High-rainfall forests* (mean annual rainfall greater than 920 milli-meters). The eucalypts in these forests are mainly species which attain greater size and show more luxuriant growth than those in the drier areas. There are forests of this type along the coast from Sydney north to Bundaberg in Queensland, in the Australian Alps and in the Otway Ranges and southern Gippsland in Victoria, in Western Australia (karri [*E. diversicolor*] forests), and in Tasmania.

2. *Low-rainfall forests* (rainfall less than 920 millimeters). These forests in general are more lightly stocked and the trees are smaller than is the case in the high-rainfall forests. They contain many very durable species.

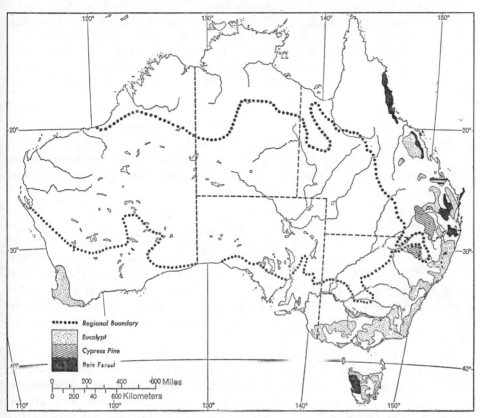

FIG. 54. Australia: forest regions. Based on "Map of Australia showing Principal Commercial Forest Regions," compiled by Forestry and Timber Bureau from information supplied by State Forest Services, 1950. The dotted line (from map "Timber Supply in Australia, 1941," Australian Forest School, Canberra, revised 1950) separates the interior region of desert (with occasional scrub growth) from areas in which sparsely distributed trees are found; in the north and northeast timber from these trees is suitable for sawmilling, and in the southwest for farm and mining timbers, light railway sleepers, and firewood.

Included in this category are the inland eucalypt forests of Queensland, the highland and south coast forests of New South Wales, the lowland and foothill forests of Victoria, small regions in South Australia, and the jarrah (*E. marginata*) forests of Western Australia.

3. *Riverain forests,* represented solely by the floodplain red gum forests of the Murray River area.

RAIN FORESTS. All the rain forests of Australia are alike in the great diversity of their species composition. They may be subdivided as follows:

1. *Tropical rain forests,* in northern Queensland, an important source of cabinet timbers. Both botanically and ecologically these rain forests are

closely allied to the jungle of New Guinea. Hoop pine and kauri are also found in them.

2. *Subtropical rain forests,* commonly termed "scrub" in southern Queensland and "brush" in New South Wales. These carry fewer high-grade cabinet timbers than do the tropical rain forests, but contain numerous species that are useful commercially. Hoop pine occurs throughout.

3. *Cool-temperate rain forests,* restricted to one district in Tasmania. These contain fewer species than do the northern forests and are botanically closer to New Zealand forests than to those of tropical areas.

CONIFER FORESTS. Hoop pine, although it does not occur as a pure type throughout any large region, is the principal or secondary species in some of the rain forests. The principal commercial areas of cypress pine are in northern New South Wales and southern Queensland on the inland side of the Dividing Range. No other indigenous conifer forests are significant in Australia today.

Distribution of Forests by States

QUEENSLAND. The commercial forests of Queensland extend 950 miles from the New South Wales border north to Cooktown. The rainfall ranges from 500 to 4,000 millimeters and hence a great variety of tree species occurs in Queensland. As is the case throughout Australia, the best forests are within 160 kilometers of the sea, though the cypress-pine areas extend to 400 kilometers inland.

Hoop and bunya pine (*Araucaria bidwillii*) have been Queensland's most important sawmilling timber, but the supply is rapidly diminishing, and in recent years the cut of the eucalypt hardwoods has correspondingly increased. Cypress pine and cabinet timbers together constitute about 15 per cent of the total cut. The cabinet timbers of Queensland, especially maple and walnut, have a worldwide reputation and in the past have been exported.

NEW SOUTH WALES. Originally densely forested, that part of New South Wales between the Great Dividing Range and the coast still remains one of the most valuable and productive forest areas in Australia. Although most of the fertile valleys have been cleared, there are still large tracts of continuous forest. Good-quality commercial forests extend along the coast from Queensland to Victoria, except for the area around Sydney underlain by the Hawkesbury sandstone. This rock formation produces a very poor, shallow soil, especially on the plateaus and ridge tops, and good-quality saw timber is rare on it. Inland from the Dividing Range the forests are more open and scattered. The cypress-pine forests, mainly in the north, are the most important of these interior forests.

Eucalypts represent about two thirds of the present saw log production in New South Wales, cypress pine (*Callitris cupressiformis*) and "brush-wood" (subtropical rain-forest trees, mainly on the northern coast) making up the bulk of the remainder. Hoop pine is still cut in this state, but in negligible quantities.

VICTORIA. A larger proportion of Victoria than of any other state except Tasmania receives an adequate rainfall; consequently, Victoria has a large forest area in relation to her total area. The principal commercial forests, except for the red gum, are in the southern half of the state.

A pulping industry established at Maryvale in 1939 has become an important adjunct to the economy of the state. Eucalypt species used include *E. regnans, E. sieberiana, E. scabra* and related species, *E. obliqua, E. goniocalyx, E. baxteri, E. muelleriana,* and *E. consideniana.*

State forests produce about three quarters of the sawn timber. Mountain ash (*Eucalyptus gigantea*), alpine ash (*Eucalyptus regnans*), and shining gum (*E. nitens*) together make up about 40 per cent of the sawn-timber production, stringybark messmate (*E. obliqua*) accounts for about 35 per cent, and red gum (*E. tereticornis*) for less than 5 per cent.

In contrast to New South Wales and Queensland, where native softwoods and rain-forest species contribute an appreciable volume to the annual cut, the commercial forests of Victoria are almost exclusively eucalypts. Small patches of temperate rain forest in the Otways and southern Gippsland are of more botanical than commercial interest.

TASMANIA. About 80 per cent of Tasmania was forested before white settlement, and a larger proportion of the area still remains under forest than in any other state of the Commonwealth.

In addition to supplying sawmills, the forests help support a pulp and paper industry, which contributes substantially to the economic wealth of Tasmania. Two pulp and paper companies hold large timber concessions from the Tasmanian government.

The forests are of two distinct types. Certain regions are characterized by a limited number of commercial eucalypts. In these, where the rainfall exceeds about 1,100 millimeters, an understory of rain-forest species develops. Other regions contain cool-temperate rain forest, in which the most important species are myrtle beech (*Nothofagus cunninghamii*), southern sassafras (*Atherosperma moschatum*), and leatherwood (*Eucryphia billardieri*). Of the saw-log production in Tasmania, eucalypts account for about 90 per cent, with myrtle beech and native conifers such as huon pine (*Dacrydium franklinii*), celery top pine (*Phyllocladus rhomboidalis*), and King William pine (*Athrotaxis cupressoides*) next in importance.

SOUTH AUSTRALIA. The aridity of most of South Australia accounts for the absence of high-quality native forests and for the necessity of importing hardwood timber from other states, as well as softwoods from abroad. The limited forests mainly produce posts, poles, and firewood for local consumption. South Australia has concentrated, however, on the establishment of exotic coniferous plantations.

WESTERN AUSTRALIA. Western Australia has a very small proportion of its total land area under good-quality commercial forests. These are located in the extreme southwest corner of the state, between Perth and Albany and within the 500–1,400 millimeters rainfall zone. (Evaporation in the far north of the state makes the high rainfall there insufficient for the growth of forest.) The forests contain only two important commercial species, jarrah (*Eucalyptus marginata*) and karri (*E. diversicolor*). The jarrah forest (occurring mainly in the 760–1,000 millimeters rainfall zone) yields three quarters of the log timber of the state. Thus it is one of the most important timber species in Australia. The wood has a beautiful grain and color and is suitable for furniture and cabinet work, but because of its strength and great durability it is also extensively used for structural work, transmission poles, and railway sleepers. Wandoo (*Eucalyptus redunca*) is increasingly utilized for the production of tannin extract.

Coniferous Plantations

Softwoods constitute only a small proportion of the indigenous forests, and consequently Australia has long been a substantial importer of coniferous timber. To make good this deficiency, numerous coniferous plantations have been created. The first steps were taken about 1870 in South Australia, but planting was not carried out on a large scale until after 1918. Extensive plans for new plantations since World War II have in many cases been held up by labor shortages and other economic difficulties.

The approximate area of coniferous plantations in June 1950 was 125,000 hectares, distributed as shown in Table 28–II.

More than half of these forests consist of *Pinus radiata,* a pine introduced from California. Plantations of this species are restricted to the winter-rainfall area, which extends along the southern coast from the southwest corner of Western Australia to the southern half of New South Wales. Other pines which have been planted in this area include *P. pinaster* (maritime pine), *P. nigra* var. *poiretiana* (Corsican pine), and *P. ponderosa* (western yellow pine). In the summer-rainfall area of northern New South Wales and Queensland different species have been used, including indigenous softwoods like hoop pine (*Araucaria cunninghamii*), bunya pine (*A. bidwillii*), and kauri (*Agathis robusta*). Two pines introduced from the southwest of the United States, *P. taeda* (loblolly pine) and *P. caribaea* Morelot (slash pine), have grown promisingly in Queensland; some plantations have been first-thinned.

On the basis of actual imports and expected yields from plantations, the Australian forest services have estimated that the present population of Australia requires about 405,000 hectares of coniferous plantations. The programs of the various state forest services call for 400,000 hectares, distributed as shown in Table 28–II. A thousand hectares a year are also being planted privately.

Timber Supply and Demand

PRODUCTION. Table 28–IV shows sawmill production of native timbers (excluding sawn sleepers) by states and also suggests the increase in utilization of Australian grown timber over the period 1919-53.

TABLE 28–IV

AUSTRALIA: SAWMILL PRODUCTION OF NATIVE-GROWN TIMBERS, BY STATES, AVERAGE ANNUAL AMOUNTS, 1919-1944; ANNUAL AMOUNTS, 1944-1953

(In Thousands of Cubic Meters)

	Total	Queensland	New South Wales, Including A.C.T.	Victoria	South Australia	Western Australia	Tasmania
1919/20–1923/24	1,430.2	312.1	363.2	272.5	8.4	343.5	130.5
1924/25–1928/29	1,465.2	286.3	367.2	245.3	9.1	436.5	120.7
1929/30–1933/34	786.0	163.1	184.8	154.8	13.9	165.5	103.9
1934/35–1938/39	1,502.9	379.6	353.7	277.3	32.2	275.2	184.9
1939/40–1943/44	1,991.5	485.4	555.0	408.5	67.5	270.1	205.0
1944/45	1,913.7	443.8	594.8	395.3	87.7	194.4	197.7
1945/46	2,031.6	435.2	602.3	493.7	85.2	201.4	213.8
1946/47	2,393.5	495.8	719.9	590.6	108.5	236.9	241.8
1947/48	2,572.7	537.7	806.5	600.4	111.7	257.5	258.9
1948/49	2,725.6	561.9	858.0	648.7	121.7	252.8	282.5
1949/50	2,831.3	557.8	832.3	792.8	129.3	280.9	298.2
1950/51	2,909.5	559.7	821.8	764.1	140.1	329.2	294.5
1951/52	3,202.3	641.7	909.6	817.5	158.4	377.5	297.7
1952/53	2,933.1	615.4	809.6	666.8	161.5	420.3	259.4

IMPORTS AND EXPORTS. Production, consumption, exports, and imports of sawn timber are shown in Figure 55.

Australia's eucalypts are so varied and diverse that they satisfactorily meet present requirements in heavy constructional timbers, poles, piles, girders, railway sleepers, constructional scantlings, weatherboards, and hardwood flooring. Other species meet requirements in fancy veneers and cabinet woods. Australia's forests cannot, however, supply her needs with respect to plywood, softwood pulp, case timbers, light structural timbers, and softwood flooring.

For several decades, Australia has had to make up her softwood deficiency by importing coniferous timbers. The great bulk of undressed timber imports, consisting of Douglas fir (*Pseudotsuga taxifolia*), hemlock (*Tsuga* spp.), redwood (*Sequoia sempervirens*), and western red cedar (*Juniperus scopulorum*), have come from Canada and the United States. Smaller amounts of kauri, rimu (*Dacrydium spp.*), and white pine (*Podocarpus dacrydioides*) have been imported from New Zealand, and deals from the Baltic countries.

Since World War II Borneo and Sarawak have provided dipterocarp timber for plywood manufacture, Parana pine (*Araucaria angustifolia*) has been imported from Brazil, *Pinus radiata* from New Zealand, and various species of pine for saw timber from Central Europe.

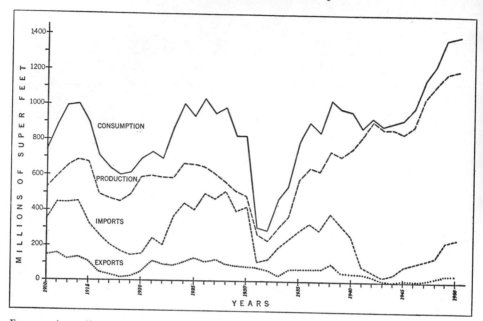

FIG. 55. Australia: consumption, production, and foreign trade in sawn timber, 1910-1950. 1,000,000 super feet = 2,360 cubic meters of sawn timber.

Just before World War II, annual imports amounted to between 700,000 and 950,000 cubic meters. They fell to one tenth of that figure during the war, but had risen to 1,000,000 cubic meters by 1951-52.

Exports of sawn timber have followed the same pattern, on a much smaller scale. In 1938-39, 137,000 cubic meters (including 53,000 cubic meters of sawn sleepers) left the country; exports fell off to 12,000 cubic meters during the war, but had risen to 77,000 cubic meters (including 9,000 cubic meters of sleepers) by 1949-50. Most of the exports—railway sleepers, piles, poles, hewn timber, and undressed sawn timber—have gone to New Zealand, with South Africa, the Pacific Islands, the United Kingdom, and the United States of America as subsidiary markets.

The species exported include jarrah and karri from Western Australia and mixed hardwoods from the east coast of Australia. Other exports are ironbark (*Eucalyptus paniculata*), turpentine (*Syncarpia laurifolia*), ironbark piles, and sawn ironbark for the North American shipbuilding industry.

INTERSTATE TRADE AND CONSUMPTION. Two states, Western Australia and Tasmania, have exportable surpluses beyond local requirements. South Australia, despite its sparse population, is deficient in indigenous timbers, while densely populated New South Wales and Victoria cannot meet their present requirements. There is consequently considerable interstate trade, mainly from Western Australia and Tasmania to South Australia, Victoria, and New South Wales, although smaller quantities of special-purpose woods move in other directions. Queensland exports a limited quantity of sawn timber to all states, but particularly to New South Wales. Trade between states is unrestricted under the Commonwealth Constitution. Most timber moves from state to state by sea.

The annual per capita consumption of sawn timber for the Commonwealth as a whole before World War II was about 0.31 cubic meters, but it has risen during the postwar years (1948-52) to approximately 0.41 cubic meters in spite of an accelerated increase in population due to immigration.

Forest Policies, Programs, Research, and Education

POLICIES AND PROGRAMS. The individual Australian states have long been autonomous with respect to forestry and have maintained separate and distinct forest services, whose administrative status and policies differ. Eventually, however, the Commonwealth government appointed a Forestry Adviser, and in 1930 it created the Commonwealth Forestry (now Forestry and Timber) Bureau, a branch of the Commonwealth Department of the Interior. The Bureau supplies advisory service, furnishes advanced training in forestry for personnel of the state services, and carries out forestry research. Its powers and functions may be summarized as follows:

a) Advising the administrations of Commonwealth Territories (New Guinea, Norfolk Island, and the Northern Territory) on the management of forests.
b) Managing forests placed under its control by the Governor-General (e.g., in the Australian Capital Territory).
c) Establishing experimental stations.
d) Collecting and distributing forestry information.
e) Providing professional forestry education.
f) Carrying out research on the supply, production, distribution, and use of timber.
g) Collecting statistics and information and advising on matters relating to the supply, production, distribution, export, and import of timber, and formulating programs thereon.

Although the states differ in their organization and their forests contain different species, their respective programs are, with minor exceptions, fundamentally the same.

One of the main common objectives is to increase softwood production. Indigenous conifers were never extensive and exploitation has considerably reduced the growing stock. To meet the deficiency, plantations of both exotic and indigenous conifers have been established, as already pointed out.

With respect to the hardwood forests, the most serious problem is that of protection from fire, and the objective is to bring the whole of the productive forest area under complete protection. At present it is not possible to prevent the occurrence of fires even within "protected" zones. The public is being educated as to the danger of bush fires, and legislation concerning fire prevention is being strengthened.

A national forest inventory is another desideratum, especially in view of the rapid rise in population and the reduction in timber imports. Current requirements have been met by increased annual production of local timbers, but complete data are not available to determine whether these record cuts can be sustained, or whether local timber production will meet requirements in the future. While plans for a national inventory await executive action, state forestry services are going ahead with surveys of limited areas.

Natural stands should, in the long run, be brought under sustained-yield management and accorded the silvicultural treatment required for maximum production. Progress in this direction hinges largely on the extent to which fire protection can be afforded, and hence has been slow. There is need for stand improvement and silvicultural operations, but the problems of access and fire protection must be solved for each individual area before intensified treatment can be justified.

Before 1939 logging operations were restricted to prime logs of the species producing high-quality timbers, but since then the utilization of secondary species has increased enormously, while at the same time the size and standard of logs accepted by sawmills has progressively decreased, resulting in greater total utilization. This trend has been more marked in some localities than in others, but greater utilization both of secondary species and substandard logs throughout the whole country will eventually be attained.

The problems of the increasing demand for plywood and of the technical difficulties of producing it from species not previously used are being tackled. In the meantime, the plywood shortage is being met by the importation of peeler logs. Shortages also exist in pulp and fiberboards.

Although they form only a small part of Australia's forest estate, the tropical rain forests are a valuable asset, producing cabinet woods and veneers of world renown. The southernmost forests are being converted to pure stands of *Araucaria cunninghamii,* but the proper silvicultural management for the other rain forests is still to be determined. Research programs have been initiated in order to ascertain how to obtain selective regeneration and growth of the desirable species in the rain-forest mixture.

RESEARCH. Australian forestry research began before the turn of the century with systematic botanical investigations and experimental work on the introduction of exotic conifers to meet the softwood deficiency.

After World War I the state forestry departments commenced laying down sample plots to determine the rates of growth of indigenous species, a job still in progress.

By 1925, when the Commonwealth Forestry School was founded, it was generally recognized that there was a need for fundamental forestry research on a much wider basis. The activities of the Commonwealth Forestry Bureau were extended to cover general forestry research, and in 1928 research scholars were appointed to go abroad for postgraduate study before beginning work in Australia.

The experimental station for the study of silviculture, forest management, and forest production which was established at Canberra in 1930 has been followed by others in South Australia and Tasmania, and plans are now under way for stations in other states and territories. With an increasing number of trained foresters available, considerable expansion of research activities should be possible.

The research activities of the Forestry and Timber Bureau were extended in 1946 to the supply, production, distribution, and use of timber. The results of the Bureau's research work are published in bulletin and leaflet series. State forest services have also conducted research into growth rates, reforestation, nutrition, and the practical aspects of nursery work, and have done some outstanding work on the pathology and the mycorrhiza of forest trees.

Forest-products research, inaugurated in 1919, is now carried on by the Commonwealth Scientific and Industrial Research Organization in a well-equipped laboratory with a staff of approximately 250, who devote themselves to the study of wood structure, wood chemistry, timber physics, timber mechanics, seasoning, preservation, veneer and gluing, and utilization.

In addition to its fundamental research, much of the work of the Forest Products Division is devoted to solving the practical problems of the industry throughout Australia. Close liaison is maintained with commercial firms, some of which supplement government funds with contributions of their own. Smaller laboratories have been established by some state forestry departments.

EDUCATION. Advanced forestry education was inaugurated at the University of Adelaide in 1911, but the University withdrew its program in 1925 in favor of the Australian Forestry School established by the Commonwealth government. The School, which continued to function at Adelaide until transferred to its present site in Canberra in 1927, is administered by the Director-General of the Forestry and Timber Bureau. State trainees are nominated by forest services, and, in addition, the Commonwealth government awards ten scholarships annually for higher forestry education.

Students successfully completing a two-year science course in selected subjects at an Australian university, followed by a two-year course in forestry subjects at the Australian Forestry School, are awarded the diploma of the school, and, by agreement with the universities, this may lead to a bachelor's degree in science or in forestry.

The Forests Commission of Victoria maintains a forestry school at Creswick for the training of field staff for that state. Here university training is not prerequisite for the three-year course leading to a diploma. The University of Melbourne, however, accepts Creswick graduates for a forestry degree course, recently instituted, which calls for two years of further study at the University.

There are at present no schools for the training of the subprofessional grades in forestry, such training being carried out by the individual forest services as required.

Present Economic Use of the Forests and Their Products

The sawmilling industry in most Australian states consists of a large number of small rural sawmills which cut hardwood scantlings. Few country mills are equipped with drying kilns, and wood is seasoned by stripping out in drying yards. Some of the mills have planing machinery for dressing flooring, weatherboard, and moldings, but most timber is so treated at the larger distribution centers.

Owing to the lack of softwoods, hard, heavy, and durable eucalypt timbers are used for house framing and even for roof construction. Many species produce high-quality flooring and weatherboards, while the lighter eucalypts are employed for the manufacture of furniture.

Certain species of eucalyptus, especially as young trees, are used for case making, and a large number of small mills are engaged in producing cases for the distribution of agricultural products. The production of lighter cases from coniferous timbers is increasing rapidly, as softwood plantations reach exploitable age.

The durability and strength of some eucalyptus species makes them eminently suitable for hewn girders, railway sleepers, and heavy constructional timbers, and these items have been used locally as well as exported throughout the world. The hewing of sleepers with a broad axe is gradually being replaced by mill sawing, and in one state (Western Australia) all sleepers are now sawn.

Many durable species are also highly suitable for use in the round, and large quantities of telephone and electric-light poles are used locally as well as exported to New Zealand. Turpentine (*Syncarpia laurifolia*) and ironbark (*Eucalyptus paniculata*) are superior pile timbers, used in many harbors throughout the world. Many species are employed for pit props and other mining timbers.

The rain forests of northern Queensland contain a number of species which provide fancy veneers of superior quality, for example Queensland walnut (*Endiandra palmerstoni* C. T. White) and maple (*Flindersia bray-*

leyana F. Muell. These fulfil Commonwealth requirements and provide limited quantities of veneer for export. A thriving plywood industry in Queensland produces about 9,000,000 square meters annually, more than do all the other states put together. But plywood manufacture is also expanding in the southern states, as the technical difficulties of peeling new species are overcome, while in New South Wales logs are imported from Borneo and Sarawak for peeling. Production is well below current requirements, but this is not due to limited plymill capacity so much as to shortages in suitable peeler logs and labor. The forestry departments are seeking to divert suitable logs from the sawmills to the plymills.

Two factories, both in New South Wales, manufacture wallboards, and, although production has increased over the last few years and there is a small export to New Zealand, the demand for hardboard, accentuated by the plywood shortage, has necessitated importations from Scandinavia.

Intensive research conducted from about 1920 overcame the difficulties of producing pulp and paper from eucalypt timbers, and there are now two mills in Tasmania and one in Victoria. One of the Tasmanian mills, at Burnie, produces pulp by the soda process and manufactures writing and printing papers. The other, at Boyer, manufactures newsprint from groundwood with the addition of a small proportion of imported sulfite pulp. At Maryvale, in Victoria, production is mainly of kraft paper and is expanding toward a goal of 67,000 tons of pulp per annum. In addition, a pulp and paperboard mill has been established at Millicent, South Australia, employing plantation-grown *Pinus radiata* as groundwood. Nevertheless, the production of all classes of paper is below Commonwealth requirements, the balance being made up by imports.

Large quantities of fuel wood are consumed both for industry and for domestic heating in the cold regions, but statistics are not available of the quantities removed from lands other than reserved forest. However, it is estimated that the annual consumption is between 7,000,000 and 9,000,000 cubic meters.

Minor forest products are produced to a limited extent, the most important of which is tanning material. In Western Australia an industry is established for the extraction of tannin from *Eucalyptus wandoo* Blakeley. The logs are chipped into fine pieces, treated in vats to extract the tannins, and the extract is then concentrated to a solid mass. In the same state the bark of mallet (*E. occidentalis* var. *astringens*) is stripped for tanbark, and the Forests Department has ensured the continuity of this industry by establishing mallet plantations. In the eastern states the stripping of wattle (*Acacia* spp.) bark has declined since 1939; Australia now imports wattle bark and wattle-bark extract from South Africa in considerable quantities.

Eucalyptus oil and tea oil are extracted from the leaves of suitable species by a simple distillation process. The oil contents of the various species differ considerably; from only a few is oil extracted commercially, and none of these is economically important as a timber tree. The industry is very small.

A limited amount of sandalwood (*Santalum* spp.) is exported to Singapore and Hongkong, mainly from Western Australia, but this product is obtained from drier areas beyond the forest zone.

The majority of the forest areas are leased for grazing, which brings in revenue to the forest services, but increases the danger of fires, which are sometimes deliberately set by leaseholders endeavoring to improve feed.

Potentialities for Development

PRESENT POSITION. Land use in Australia is still extremely fluid. Certain areas that were thrown open to intensive agricultural settlement only a few decades ago have proved unsuitable for agriculture, have been abandoned, and are reverting to forest. At the same time, pressure is being constantly applied for the alienation of land reserved for forests and of unoccupied Crown land carrying timber.

Scientific forestry has thus far made little headway in Australia. Proper management of indigenous hardwood forests is unfortunately still in its infancy, and to be economic must await a reasonable degree of protection from fire. Owing to the large spreading crowns of the eucalypts, their intolerance, and the limited number of mature trees per acre, few of the conventional silvicultural systems are applicable to eucalypt forests, but selection and group selection systems have been employed on limited areas. For the most part, however, eucalypt management has been confined to tree marking to preserve vigorous growing stock for a second cycle and to setting minimum cutting sizes for commercial exploitation.

Natural stands of eucalypts are at present rarely in a fully productive state. This is due to the peculiarities of the genus *Eucalyptus,* the method of exploitation, and the cost of treatment. The eucalypt in later life usually develops a variety of defects, notably a central rotten core, which may be up to 60 centimeters in diameter. Defective trees are not felled by commercial loggers but are left in the forest, where they take up potentially valuable growing space. The cost of treatment, which must include the removal of these defective trees of large size and hard timber, is very high. Some states partly subsidize the felling of trees that prove unfit for milling, but it would not pay at present to extend such subsidies to all logged-over natural stands, especially in remote areas where there is no demand for fuel or minor timber products. Yet it remains an essential for sustained-yield management at a fully productive level.

On good sites many of the commercial eucalypts are capable of producing very high volumes of timber. One tree of *E. regnans* in Victoria contained a merchantable volume of 33 cubic meters, with a total height of 100 meters and center girth of the millable log of 4.08 meters. Another tree in Tasmania, with a girth of 19.8 meters and a height of 76.5 meters to its broken crown, contained 191.7 cubic meters, while a karri (*E.*

diversicolor) in Western Australia contained 212.4 cubic meters. In one area of 565 hectares in Victoria the average gross merchantable volume under mark was assessed at 1,133 cubic meters per hectare.

Nevertheless, the great bulk of the eucalypt forests do not carry a merchantable volume of more than about 70 cubic meters per hectare. Conversion of the poorer eucalypt stands to coniferous plantations is desirable for many reasons, but chiefly because of the higher merchantable volumes which can be harvested from the latter.

The characteristics of mature eucalypt timbers are not fully developed in the timbers from immature trees, and small young trees of many species when felled are subject to splitting and other defects. For these reasons, eucalypts must usually be allowed to grow to large size before harvesting. On the other hand, softwoods can be sawn and utilized down to very small diameters.

POTENTIALITIES AND FUTURE PRODUCTION. At present approximately one third of the indigenous sawn timber production is derived from private property, and it is unlikely that much of this alienated forest land will be dedicated to timber production once the existing crop is removed. State-owned forests are subject to regulated cutting, and the number of sawmills is restricted by license. There is sufficient evidence to doubt the wisdom of increasing the cut on state forests, which, without such increase, will be unable to make good the loss of production that will ensue when the alienated land becomes unproductive. On the other hand, the acceptance of inferior logs and the use of secondary species hitherto regarded as valueless will permit higher yields per acre.

The production of exotic coniferous plantations, many of which are now being thinned, will be offset by a decrease in the production of indigenous softwoods, principally hoop pine in Queensland, which is reaching exhaustion and is being replaced by plantations. The annual cut of cypress pine (*Callitris*) is likely to remain at approximately the same level on a sustained-yield basis. In the next ten to twelve years these factors will roughly cancel one another out, and sawn-timber production will remain approximately at its present level.

Table 28–V shows estimates of sawn-timber production for 1956 and 1961. It is expected that by 1976 there will be a falling-off in hardwood production and a further increase in softwood production, owing to decreased production from private holdings. Australia's better hardwood forests could be made to yield far greater increments, however, given adequate timber-stand improvement and other silvicultural operations. But even if lack of labor and money did not prevent it, immediate treatment would hardly be reflected in sawn-timber production within the next quarter of a century.

Estimates have not been made of future production in plywood, pulp and paper, and fiberwood, but it is expected that all of these will fall short of requirements during the next ten years. By that time, however, the expansion of existing industries may have altered the situation.

It has been estimated that the population of the Commonwealth will reach 12,000,000 by 1970, owing to the immigration policy as well as to natural increase. The necessity for providing homes for an additional population of four million will accentuate demands created by the present housing shortage. Even if the per capita consumption remains static, a larger volume of imports will be needed to meet requirements. All of these deficiencies will have to be made up by imports, and, in view of the world shortage, it is unlikely that the requirements will be met in full.

TABLE 28–V

AUSTRALIA: ESTIMATED SAWN-TIMBER PRODUCTION BY STATES FOR 1956 AND 1961

(In Thousand Cubic Meters)

	Total		Softwoods		Hardwoods	
	1956	1961	1956	1961	1956	1961
Queensland	578	569	182	130	396	439
New South Wales	807	843	75	111	732	732
Victoria	578	628	45	95	533	533
South Australia	161	257	149	245	12	12
Western Australia ...	342	347	5	7	337	340
Tasmania	312	359	5	5	307	354
Australian Capital Territory	31	30	26	28	5	2
TOTAL	2,809	3,033	487	621	2,322	2,412

SOURCES FOR BOTANICAL NOMENCLATURE

AUDAS, J. W. 1949. *Native trees of Australia.* Whitcomb & Tombs Pty., Ltd., Melbourne.
EWART, A. J. 1930. *Flora of Victoria.* University of Melbourne Press, Melbourne.
REHDER, ALFRED. 1940. *Manual of cultivated trees and shrubs hardy in North America.* The Macmillan Co., New York.

29. NEW ZEALAND

A. R. Entrican and J. T. Holloway

Primitive New Zealand was essentially a land of forests. The first European colonists, a little more than a century ago, found these islands largely clad with dense and seemingly subtropical rain forests from the shores to the timber line on the inland mountain ranges. But there were exceptions to this rule. In the South Island tussock grasslands replaced forests on the windswept eastern plains in the rain shadows thrown by the higher ranges, notably on the Canterbury Plains and Otago intermonts. In the North Island the grasslands were of more restricted distribution and limited extent, but were supplemented by extensive scrublands occupying, in part, the pumice-covered central volcanic plateau. To the west the forest cover was luxuriant and complete, broken only by the swamps and bogs of the coastal plains and by open mountain tops, snowfields, icefields, and glaciers. But even the scrublands and the grasslands must have been forest-covered, in some districts at least, when the islands were settled by the Polynesians a thousand years ago; for the imprint of these earlier forests persists to this day in the soil profiles of the grasslands, and traces of charred timbers and stump and log mounds may still be found.

Over the past one hundred years considerably more than half of the indigenous forests (1850, about 30 million acres; 1950, 12 to 14 million acres) have been destroyed, and this loss has fallen mainly on the accessible, merchantable forests of the plains and foothills. Possibly less than one million acres of fully merchantable forest remains—beech, podocarp, or mixed. The loss is explained in part by the creation of the exotic softwood forests of higher sustained productive capacity and, overwhelmingly, by the development of highly productive farmlands on the sites of the vanished forests. The mistakes of the past appear as small in the light of these achievements.

Forest Distribution, Past and Present

With but few exceptions the climates of New Zealand are true forest climates. But the term "subtropical" is a misnomer, despite the density and luxuriance of the forest undergrowth, the frequent abundance of lianas and epiphytes, and the subtropical affinities of many of the forest species. Climates range from near subtropical or Mediterranean in the extreme north, through warm- to cool- and cold-temperate in the far south, with superimposed high mountain climates, and local areas of subcontinental climate in inland range and basin country isolated from the prevailing temperate oceanic influences. An understanding of this marked diversity in local and regional climates is the main key to an understanding of the forests of today. To cite but one extreme example, it is possible to pass in less than one hundred miles from a region with an annual rainfall exceeding 200 inches, where winter frosts are light and rare, across mountain ranges carrying permanent and considerable ice-fields, to grassland country of semidesert character, where the annual rainfall is less than 20 inches and ground frosts may occur on more than 200 days each year.

The distributional patterns of the various types of indigenous forest are therefore confused and complex. With but one major exception, the main types of forest are distributed in patchwork fashion throughout the country from the far north to the far south, in accordance with the dictates of local and regional climates. Moreover, recent studies strongly suggest that even this intricate pattern is not stable but in part the outcome of distributional changes still in progress, consequent on effective changes in regional climates dating approximately from the twelfth or the thirteenth century. In brief, it might be stated that disturbed ecotonal conditions prevail over the entire country and that, consequently, the local occurrence of any one type of forest is not necessarily wholly related to local factors of site, but may be conditioned by historical accidents unrelated to the site. This implies that no general description of the forests can pretend to accuracy. The broad outlines may be indicated, but exceptions are numerous and often significant.

To the northern-hemisphere observer the forests are unusual in type, though they are by no means peculiar to New Zealand. They are much like the forests of southern Chile and Patagonia and of Tasmania, though they lack the characteristic eucalypts of the latter country. Broadly speaking, they are evergreen podocarp–southern-beech forests (*Podocarpus*,[1] *Dacrydium*, *Nothofagus*), though other conifers (*Agathis*, *Libocedrus*) or hardwoods (*Weinmannia*, *Metrosideros*, *Beilschmiedia*, *Griselinia*, and others) may assume local dominance. The term "podocarp-beech" used here covers any type of forest from pure beech to pure podocarp forest. Any possible admixture of any of the podocarps with any of the beech species can and does occur in one region or another. The following broad forest types may be distinguished.

Forest Types

INDIGENOUS FORESTS. *Beech Forests*. The beech forests are characteristic of regions possessing cold, wet, mountain climates and are widely developed on the higher mountains of the North Island and in the north-

---

[1] For sources of botanical nomenclature see below, p. 609.

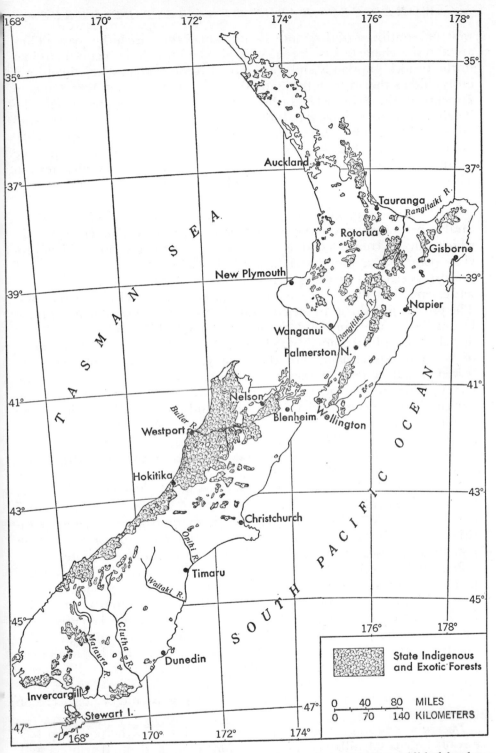

FIG. 56. New Zealand: map showing areas of state forests. Based on maps published by the
New Zealand Forest Service, 1952.

west and southwest of the South Island, where they reach the coast. They are also the characteristic forests of regions with drier climates marginal to the tussock grasslands and they extend (though somewhat discontinuously) along the eastern flanks of the main ranges from East Cape to Foveaux Strait. Five species of beech (*Nothofagus*) are represented. The beech may occur in pure stands of a single species or in mixed forest containing all five. These forests are, above all, watershed-protection forests, but at least three of the species are commercially significant and amenable to intensive silvicultural management. Select forests on suitable terrain within the areas of optimum range are being placed under sustained-yield management.

Beech-forest soils, save in exceptional cases, are unsuited to agricultural or permanent pastoral use. Cleared land reverts fast to scrub growth, which can be controlled only by excessive use of fire and which provides poor and rapidly deteriorating hill grazing. Considerable areas of the dry beech forests were destroyed by fire during the early years of settlement. But this process has of late been brought virtually to a halt. The present real threat to the continued existence and well-being of these forests lies in the damage done by the uncontrolled browsing of introduced game animals, notably red deer. From six to eight million acres of beech forests remain. For the most part they are permanently reserved as state forests or included within national parks and scenic reserves. Little more than 500,000 acres of this total is likely to prove of any considerable commercial significance, and the greater part lies in the South Island.

Podocarp Forests. These may be considered under two main heads, though the distinction on the ground is by no means clear. In inland regions of the North Island, with humid warm summer and mild winter climates, the physiognomic species are commonly *Podocarpus spicatus* and *P. totara,* with *P. dacrydioides* and *Dacrydium cupressinum* in lesser amount. Forests of this type have long been the source of large quantities of valuable multipurpose softwoods, but they appear to be true postclimax forests. The physiognomic species do not regenerate in significant volume even in the absence of any form of exploitation, and the podocarp stands give place to poor-quality hardwoods, of which only *Beilschmiedia* has any commercial value. Where topography permits, the forest soils are good agricultural soils. The greater part of the entire area formerly occupied by these forests is now under permanent highly productive pasture. Residual stands are limited, and the last lap in the exploitation of this wasting asset is now being run. Pockets of this forest type also occur throughout the South Island but, in general terms, they are remnants only. The ancient forests of the grassland region were of this type.

Dacrydium cupressinum is the normal dominant in the podocarp forests of the coastal hills and plains, regions of humid, mild winters and cool summers. In the hill country this forest type, also, appears as postclimax. The forest dominants are universally old and in various stages of replacement by the scrub hardwoods *Weinmannia* and *Metrosideros*. The plain land, in the North Island, where satisfactory regeneration of *Dacrydium cupressinum* might be expected, is required for agriculture. In the South Island, where, under very high rainfall, forests of this type are widely developed on the narrow coastal plains of the west coast, the soils are strong podsols with heavy iron pans, and logging of the virgin stands is frequently followed by rising water tables and the development of bogs. *D. cupressinum* has long been the staple New Zealand softwood, but, for the above reasons, sustained-yield management on any significant scale must prove difficult. Attempts at artificial re-establishment of the stands have been rendered abortive by the high cost of seed collection and by difficulties in transplanting. Growth rates are extremely slow, with long periods of stagnation, and an optimistic view would place the minimum rotation at 300 years. It is difficult to escape the view that as a renewable resource the *D. cupressinum* forests can make only a minor contribution to the national timber economy: considerable reserves still exist, though not enough to meet all demands. The urgent need is curtailment of output and the translation of *D. cupressinum* timber from a staple commodity to a special-purpose timber, coupled with continued research into the difficult silvicultural problems involved in restoring to productivity the logged lands not required for agriculture.

One minor forest type is also worthy of mention. Swamps developed on recent alluviums formerly carried heavy stands of *Podocarpus dacrydioides*. On such sites this species is most vigorous, regenerates freely, and displays comparatively rapid growth—the only podocarp to do so. Undoubtedly sustained-yield management here would prove possible and profitable; but these swamps, when cleared of forest and drained, become the richest dairy lands in the country. Continued production of *P. dacrydioides* timber must be passed over for butterfat, except on very limited sites.

Kauri Forests. The kauri (*Agathis australis*) forests of the North Auckland and Coromandel peninsulas are distinct from the podocarp and beech forests, though over wide areas podocarps occur in association with kauri, and one species of beech locally enters the kauri stands. These kauri forests are no longer of economic significance as a national timber resource, though they are undoubtedly the most renowned of all New Zealand forests, on account of the immense size of the trees and the high value of the timber. At one time there may have been as much as one million acres of kauri-dominant stands, but these were early devastated by uncontrolled logging and by the fires of the gum diggers. Today perhaps less than 50,000 acres of true kauri forest remains, distributed in small parcels over wide areas, while the former kauri lands carry worthless scrub growth. Nevertheless kauri, of all New Zealand indigenous softwoods, possesses under management the greatest potential as a timber-producing species. When special techniques are used, it can be handled in forest nurseries, and its growth rates are comparatively satisfactory. It could be grown as a forest crop on rotations equivalent to those used for hardwoods in Europe, and it can be grown far to the south of its natural range.

Probable Future Developments. The above classification of the forests is, of course, a most arbitrary one. On the ground, the various forest types intermingle with one another and merge with interspersed areas of minor types not described here, and, as already indicated, active changes in species and forest-type distributions are in progress. One species displaces another. One type of forest stagnates, with temporary luxuriant development of the minor species of the forest understories. One type of forest persists under present unfavorable regional climates by virtue of its own internal microclimates and in default of invasion by a logical successor group of species. In effect, no two indigenous forests in New Zealand, despite superficial resemblances, are of exactly the same degree of stability or behave in strictly comparable fashion under management. But out of this confusion the broad outlines of future forest development emerge clearly. The podocarp forests, where they lend themselves to really promising management, occupy soils required for agriculture. On sites other than these the podocarps are difficult to manage as a renewable resource, and the New Zealand forester must seek the means whereby the scrub hardwoods succeeding the podocarps can be replaced by species economically more valuable. Hardwood supplies can be maintained, and stepped up, from the beech forests, but maintenance of remote watershed-protection beech forests in the face of pressure from introduced browsing animals is in many cases likely to prove most difficult. Finally, kauri, the special-purpose softwood, may again in the future play a significant part in the national timber-use economy.

EXOTIC, OR INTRODUCED, FORESTS. This outline must serve to focus attention upon the most critical problem of all—the problem of maintaining a supply of the all-important softwoods. The natural solution—the introduction of well-proven exotic species—was early undertaken. This led to the formation of an Afforestation Branch of the Lands Department in 1896, when forest-tree nurseries were established in both main islands. Even earlier, the land-settlement laws of the province of Canterbury provided for free grants of land on condition that plantations were established, though this was done in an attempt to improve living conditions on the windswept plains as well as to forestall prospective timber shortages. At first this work involved a long period of trial and error. In the South Island almost all the best-known commercial trees of the northern hemisphere were tried. Species early used in the North were *Larix decidua, Pinus nigra* var. *austriaca, P. nigra* var. *poiretiana, P. ponderosa,* and a number of eucalypts.

On the basis of experience so acquired, however, the main species planted in the North today are *Pseudotsuga taxifolia, Pinus ponderosa,*

P. radiata, and *P. nigra* var. *poiretiana,* with *P. caribaea* Morelot, *P. palustris* and *P. taeda* in the far north. In the South Island the main species employed are now *Pseudotsuga taxifolia, Pinus radiata, P. ponderosa,* and *P. nigra* var. *poiretiana.* Locally and on special sites such species as *Pinus contorta, P. strobus, Cupressus macrocarpa, Chamaecyparis lawsoniana,* and *Thuja plicata* are frequently used.

Perhaps the outstanding feature of these plantations of northern hemisphere conifers is the rapidity of growth of many of the species. In some instances, notably *Pinus radiata,* rotations for saw-log production may be as low as 30 years. In most cases the first rotation will be less than 50 to 60 years. These forests must rank among the fastest producers of wood cellulose in the world. Natural regeneration of the stands after logging is generally from free to profuse, and the stands, once established, can be maintained without the need for replanting. That is not to say that the forests are without their serious silvicultural problems. For many years planting proceeded faster than tending, and many of the present stands are of unnecessarily poor quality. Overplanting during the decade 1925-35 has created problems in age-class distribution, and overplanting with the single species *P. radiata,* particularly by private companies, has laid the forest open to the risks inherent in all monocultures. The correction of these faults is the task of the future. The worth of the exotic softwood forests is, however, already amply proven.

Afforestation work received an impetus with the establishment in 1920 of a separate department of state, now the New Zealand Forest Service. Today the exotic forest estate stands at approximately 890,000 acres, 450,000 of which represent state planting and the remainder the interests of various commercial afforestation companies and local government bodies. By and large, the period of trial and error is now over. Many mistakes were made—faulty selection or siting of species and, in a few instances, even faulty siting of forests. But production from these planted forests is already effectively shielding the remaining podocarp forests against the ever-expanding demands for softwood timbers.

The exotic forests, which are of necessity sited on soils marginal or submarginal for agricultural purposes, have been most widely developed on the former scrublands of the central North Island pumice country. In the South Island the submarginal soils of the Moutere Gravels in the Nelson Province will grow, and are in part growing, promising timber crops. Afforestation on the Canterbury Plains has not been equally successful. The soils are poor and the climate adverse, though the better lands on the plains will grow profitable timber crops. This is proven by the success of the local government bodies, which, since they are concerned as much with wind shelter and amenity planting as with timber production, are not restricted in their operations to the poorest soils. Other exotic forests have been established on selected sites from North Auckland to Southland, though not all centers of population are yet served with exotic forests within economic range.

Forest Land-Use Problems

THE LAND-USE PROBLEM IN GENERAL. In the realm of national economics, forestry is essentially a land-use problem. Almost 100 years of an extensive-farming philosophy saw not merely the valley bottoms and the river flats converted to crop and pasture, but many millions of acres of hill country cleared of forest, only, so to speak, to grow one blade of grass where two trees grew before—and temporarily at that. Fire was the universal implement of conversion. Only recently has it become widely recognized that its use has been almost as damaging to the farming economy of the country as to the forest wealth.

For every cubic foot of wood converted into sawn timber ten cubic feet went up in smoke for nothing more than wood ash. In the hill country it was the wood ash which gave to the new grass such a lushness of growth that the pioneers were deceived into the belief that a permanent pasture of high animal-carrying capacity was assured. Few stopped to ponder that the same fire which had produced the wood ash from the forest had largely destroyed the very soil that had grown the forest and was now supposed to produce even more valuable grass. So it is that many millions of acres of the original hill forest country have reverted to weed and scrub.

Of the area remaining under grass much has been stabilized by good management, more particularly in districts of moderate rainfall, but accelerated erosion of all types has become so extensive in areas of high rainfall and on country of heavy topography as to necessitate the formation of a Soil Conservation and Rivers Control Council, with Dominion-wide coverage by Catchment Boards, to correct the menace of low productivity and flooding.

Contrary to popular belief, extensive areas both in the North Island and in the South were treeless immediately prior to the British occupation, or even before the Maori invasion. Great areas of tussock and low scrub stretched from central Otago up the eastern side of the South Island and surrounded Lake Taupo on the central volcanic massif of the North Island. In the South Island the high fertility of the coastal plains and the moderate rainfall of the foothills made it so easy to establish crops and English grasses and to raise sheep that farming developed into a slow but steady exhaustion of soil fertility. Slowly but surely bottom lands were transferred from high- to low-fertility use, but in the hill country fire-stick farming became prevalent, in the naïve belief that by burning the native tussock the forage would be improved. Instead, the soil continued to deteriorate, and the effect became accentuated by over-grazing—at first by sheep and later, as well, by rabbits. Much high country has deteriorated so badly that complete closure from grazing is the only means of rehabilitation, though eventually it will be entirely practicable to return it to production through controlled grazing. So great has been the damage by rabbits that at long last an active policy of extermination has been substituted for the old, established practice of pest control.

In the North Island most of the treeless areas were largely on pumice soils. Although these are friable and workable with extreme ease, several factors combined to defer until quite recently their development for farming purposes. Their fertility was not high. They were deficient in unknown trace elements, resulting in cattle sickness. In many cases the pumice deposits were so deep that extensive areas were almost entirely devoid of surface-water supplies, the rivers of the central volcanic massif drawing the greater part of their water from subterranean sources.

Over recent years two developments have occurred, with profound and far-reaching effect upon this general and long-established pattern of land use. The discovery of cobalt as the missing trace element required to eliminate cattle sickness has made practicable the extensive development of well-watered pumice lands for farming purposes. Because of the lateness of this discovery, more than 200,000 acres of such lands had been established in trees. But already some farmers have begun to change them again to farming land, as they clear-cut their older stands for milling. The evolution of aerial top-dressing or manuring techniques has been equally important. As a result, much hill country has not only been stabilized but made so much more productive that less of the low country is now required for the fattening or topping of sheep and cattle for the market. Indeed, these developments have changed the farming philosophy from one of extensive development to one of intensive pastoral and agricultural techniques. Forestry must thereby lose significant areas which otherwise would have been devoted to highly productive tree growing.

CONSERVATION AND THE MULTIPLE-USE CONCEPT. Although the National Forest Survey was not scheduled for completion until 1956, at the time of writing sufficient progress had already been made to indicate that the remaining indigenous resources—both of softwood and hardwood—are very much smaller than the national forest reconnaissance carried out in the early twenties had implied. The need for their conservation is correspondingly more urgent, but unfortunately the present difficulties of implementation are great. Following the suspension of normal building activities during both the great depression and World War II, the accumulation of deferred house and other building construction became so large by the end of the war that the postwar period has been characterized by a demand for timber that is even more spectacular than the increased production of exotics.

Even the production of indigenous timbers has increased over the postwar period, that of softwoods from 230 to 310 million board feet (or by 35 per cent) and that of hardwoods from 20 to 35 million board feet (or by 75 per cent). Estimates differ as to the size of the remaining backlog of deferred construction. Sooner or later the backlog will dis-

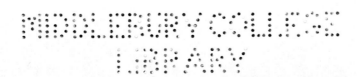

appear, and, though the replacement of obsolescent construction may for a short time sustain building activities above normal, some recession in timber demand is soon likely to occur. It should then be more practicable to reduce the annual cut of the indigenous softwoods. Meantime, methods of reducing wastage in conversion both in logging and in milling are being closely studied as another means of conservation.

The National Forest Survey has confirmed the extremely slow rate of growth of the indigenous conifers. In contrast, it has disclosed some promising management areas for the sustained management of beech stands, with a higher annual rate of growth than has previously been anticipated. None the less, there is a very real need for increasing the timber-production potential of the indigenous forests by enlarging the area of the national forest estate. One movement, however, threatens the attainment of this objective.

Down the years there has been an increasing clamor by enthusiastic minorities for the dedication of large areas of forest land for a variety of single-purpose uses—as national parks and scenic reserves for recreation, as catchment reserves for soil stabilization and conservation of water resources, as wildlife reserves for game, etc. Some single-use forestry is unavoidable in order to give a feeling of purpose in the management of bird sanctuaries, and for reserves for scientific purposes, etc., but only by putting as much as possible of the nonagricultural or forest lands to a multiplicity of uses can forestry make the greatest possible contribution both to the social well-being of the people and to the national economy of the country. By appropriate management the same forests can produce timber and also provide recreation, sport, and inspiration for the people, and ensure the maximum productivity of the agricultural lands through maintenance of climatic equilibrium, regulation of stream flow, and control of erosion. Multiple-use management under unified control is therefore the essential objective of forest land-use policy.

National Forest Policy

EARLY DEVELOPMENTS. To the early pioneers, with the exception of the Canterbury settlers, the forest appeared inexhaustible and a deterrent to their very existence, since its clearing on even the small areas required for growing food and raising domestic animals was a heavy task. As the kauri gradually gained a world-wide reputation for general building as well as for boat making, so did the country develop not only a virile logging and sawmilling industry but a strong coastal and trans-Tasman Sea shipping trade, which contributed largely to the Colony's early economy. *Podocarpus totara* likewise gained an early reputation for its high natural durability, though more on the local than on the export market.

During the period of the provincial legislatures desultory fears were expressed from time to time—more in Auckland than elsewhere—about

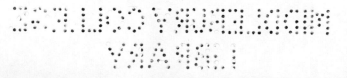

the possible exhaustion of the country's forest resources. But only in Canterbury, with its negligible supplies of indigenous forest, was corrective action taken, by encouraging tree planting for farm shelter and for moisture conservation against the drying effect of the prevailing northwesterly winds. After the formation of a colonial legislature in the late fifties, increasing concern was expressed down the years as the industry expanded almost spectacularly to meet the ever-growing domestic and export demands of the rapidly increasing populations in both New Zealand and Australia. With the development of refrigeration and its fillip to the dairy and meat industries, the fame of New Zealand non-tainting kahikatea (*Podocarpus dacrydioides*) timber for the packing of butter, cheese, and tallow became almost as widespread as that of kauri. Large mills equipped with the most modern machinery were soon making serious inroads into the kahikatea stands, and for many years the dairy produce of both New Zealand and Australia was shipped overseas in boxes and crates of this timber.

By the nineties of the last century, the fallacy of inexhaustible forest supplies had been exposed, and the first conscious evolution of national forest policy became evident in Prime Minister Richard Seddon's determination to plan against the increasing depletion of indigenous supplies by establishing exotic forests. Although sixty-odd years have passed, most of the numerous re-examinations and re-estimates of the exhaustion of indigenous forests and of the future timber requirements of the country have been in close agreement, and broad policy has remained remarkably consistent through the years.

ESTABLISHMENT OF THE FOREST SERVICE. Not until the end of World War I, however, were the implications of this policy fully appreciated. By this time New Zealand's grand old statesman of the twentieth century—Sir Francis Bell—had come to the conclusion that the steps taken meantime to provide for the future were woefully inadequate. Under his guidance, a national forest authority was brought into being in 1919. It is now known as the New Zealand Forest Service and is charged with conserving the indigenous resource and assuring the country of an adequate future supply of suitable timber. In accordance with precept, the first Director of Forestry, L. McIntosh Ellis, a Canadian forester, ascertained by a national forest reconnaissance that the existing indigenous resource was incapable of furnishing the Dominion's future timber requirements. Following this, he inaugurated in 1925 a ten-year programme of exotic forest establishment, using rapidly growing exotic conifers to assist in meeting an estimated annual demand for 675 million board feet of timber by 1965. Not only was his target of 300,000 acres achieved ahead of time, but private forestry companies, as well, planted another 300,000 acres, no inconsiderable part, however, being on what is now farmable land, as explained above. How much of it will remain permanently dedicated to forestry only time will tell.

Up to 1935 the whole emphasis on national forest policy had been on the bulk requirements of the Dominion by the early date of 1965 when only insignificant supplies would still be drawn from the indigenous forest. As planting experience was gained and the practical problems of future utilization loomed up, it became necessary to examine policy and all its implications more closely. In order to reach the various targets involved, both state and private plantings had been concentrated in a relatively few large areas and had used virtually one species, *Pinus radiata,* as the most rapidly growing softwood and the most widely proved exotic conifer in the Dominion.

PLANTING POLICIES. Wood-use problems soon demonstrated the inability of radiata pine to provide adequately for the whole of the country's future timber requirements. In addition, many sites on the land already secured for planting were unsuitable for this species, and investigations overseas indicated not only that the species was susceptible to numerous insect and fungal pests, but that, on the general principle that it is most inadvisable to put all one's eggs in one basket, the Forest Service should diversify its plantings and not rely upon even the best species to the extent of more than one third of its requirements. With the onslaught of the great depression of the 1930's and the availability of unemployment funds, the Forest Service was enabled to plant another 150,000 acres, using mostly Corsican pine, ponderosa pine, lodgepole pine, Douglas fir, and European larch. This was done primarily as a security measure, but with the national forest policy broadened to provide for the growing of additional supplies for export to Australia.

The next step in the evolution of forest policy was the abandonment of concentrated planting—concentrated in terms both of area and time. With virtually the complete exhaustion of indigenous supplies in such intensively developed farming districts as Hawkes Bay, Wairarapa, Taranaki, and the Gisborne area, and with rapidly increasing road and rail freights, the false economy of having these consuming areas dependent upon the Putaruru and Kaingaroa forests, 400 miles distant by rail, became obvious. The government of the day agreed to a policy of local forests for timberless areas, leaving the larger state exotic forests to service the export trade when local forests would eventually come into production.

Policy was further modified to spread the planting of any one forest over a minimum of twenty years, with an objective of forty or more years. Not only had the more rapid establishment of older forests involved high growing costs through the impact of compound interest charges and poor establishment techniques, but it had made much subsequent silvicultural treatment largely impracticable and thus defeated the basic objective of producing high-quality logs. In contrast with the untended stands of the older forests, no trees may be established in the new forests while other trees still require tending.

FOREST RESEARCH AND FOREST EDUCATION. Concurrently with these latter developments a Forest Research Institute has been brought into existence to study the silviculture and establishment of indigenous and exotic forests. One of its major projects is a national forest survey of the indigenous resources, using aerial photography and ground sampling.

In the realm of forest education, the policy has been to train professional officers—up to six annually—at overseas forestry schools, including Canberra (Australia), Oxford (England), Edinburgh (Scotland), Nancy (France), and Berkeley (California). As a prerequisite, they are required to have three years practical forestry experience and a B.Sc. degree in selected subjects. Administrative and executive staff are trained at a Forest Training Center maintained at Rotorua. Formal training is also given to foremen and leading hands, and a Woodsmen's Training Scheme, giving a four-year apprenticeship with superannuation rights, recruits annually seventy youths of between fifteen and seventeen years of age, in order to provide a hard core of skilled craftsmen trained in the highest traditions of forestry.

The Manufacture of Wood Products

THE WOOD-USE PROBLEM. As in North America and Scandinavia, both plentifully supplied with standing timber, wood has been used in New Zealand for a wider variety of purposes than in most other countries. Ninety per cent of the houses and other forms of light building construction are of wood. This is because ample supplies of durable heartwood of high quality and defect-free indigenous timbers have been available at low cost for over a century. In these circumstances the basic philosophy of wood use in New Zealand has been one of limitless abuse. All the important indigenous softwoods were relatively so dense, so hard, and so homogeneous, with heartwood so durable, that in the early days of the Colony buildings were often left unpainted. Even their sapwood could be carelessly treated during conversion and seasoning. This preference for a timber which would stand endless abuse during both conversion and use has made the switch from indigenous to exotic timbers an extremely difficult one.

Small quantities of logs secured from farmers' shelter belts have been converted into sawn timber ever since the turn of the century. Because of the old age and branchy nature of the trees, the timber was characteristically both knotty and hearty. Only a very small portion was used for wooden buildings. The greater part was used for boxes and crates, but some for wooden forms for concrete construction. Prior to the 1930's the annual production of exotic softwood had only rarely exceeded 10 million board feet, but by 1940 the shortage of kahikatea for boxes, crates, and concrete boxing had become so acute and the demand for radiata pine as a substitute so great that the annual production increased to almost 50 million board feet. Log supplies from shelter belts rapidly declined. Even the older state exotic forests established before World War I could give little relief. There was no alternative but to turn to the state and private exotic forests established in the mid-twenties. With few exceptions these were unthinned and unpruned, and they remain so today. Before World War II little finance had been available for tending operations, and during the war and postwar periods little manpower has been available. Even with the rapid growth of radiata pine—often exceeding one inch in diameter annually for dominants—these young forests yielded only small-diameter logs, which were very knotty and wholly sapwood.

ADAPTATION OF SCANDINAVIAN TECHNIQUES. The first problem was how to convert these logs economically to sawn timber. By using the orthodox type of logging and sawing equipment of the indigenous logging and sawmilling industry, no difficulty had been experienced previously in converting the large-diameter exotic logs secured from farmers' wood lots. For the small-diameter logs from immature stands, however, all equipment was too heavy and too slow to allow of economic conversion. By the mid-thirties the Forest Service had satisfied itself by searching studies overseas that the only satisfactory solution lay in the adaptation of Scandinavian sawing practices, using log and deal frames of inherent sawing accuracy. It was finally left to the government to demonstrate this equipment through the erection of two large-scale demonstration mills, which between them now produce nearly 30 million board feet of frame-sawn timber annually. As a result of this pioneering effort, the use of frame-sawing equipment is spreading and is likely to become dominant in the export mills if not in the domestic mills as soon as less expensive machines can be developed for use by small operators. Concurrently, another solution has been sought through the use of highly mechanized Pacific carriages and fast-cutting American band saws as head rigs and resaws, though deal frames are retained as secondary production units in some cases. The results have been disappointing.

Scandinavian sawing techniques are based on the classification of logs into diameter classes and the setting-up of log and deal frames to cut several hundred logs of the same diameter to exactly the same pattern of boards, scantling, etc. Success has been achieved through the adaptation of the equipment to New Zealand raw material. Scandinavian logs are characteristically straight. In New Zealand, owing to the great annual height growth of between 4 and 6 feet, radiata-pine logs from immature stands carry a characteristic sweep or bend, as many as 70 per cent from some stands having a gradual sweep of as much as 5 inches in a length of 16 feet. These logs are sawn in the first or log frames, with the sweep in the vertical plane so as to produce a central cant and on each side one or more inch boards and a thin slab. The side boards are edged and cross-cut, but the central cant has a sweep of anything up to 5 inches and is sawn in the second or deal frame by following the sweep.

This yields boards and other products of full length but with a longitudinal bow, which is removed by piling the timber flat and either kiln-drying or air-seasoning it to yield perfectly straight timber. This, of course, is an example of wood bending in reverse: the principle ordinarily used to bend wood into a curve is here used to straighten it.

The net results of these modified techniques have been spectacular. For logs of comparable sizes they yield an average of one more board foot of sawn timber per cubic foot of log than does the use of the orthodox carriage and circular head rig with circular resaw. The band-saw equipment gives results intermediate between these two types of sawing. On the principle that a tree saved is a tree grown, the new sawing techniques, if universally applied, would produce the equivalent of an increase in the effective area of the exotic forests of about 15 per cent. The superior accuracy in dimension of frame-sawn timber is already widely recognized in Australia and New Zealand. Because of the immaturity of the stands being cut, almost the whole of the timber is knotty and sappy, but, fortunately, owing to the rapid height-growth of radiata pine, the larger knots are separated by as much as 4 to 6 feet lengthwise in the boards, though late or autumn flushes of growth sometimes produce very small knots at intermediate points. In some of the more extensive stands many of the knots are encased, and the percentage of boards with tight or intergrown knots only is relatively small. To raise the grade of these boards for use as flooring and weatherboarding a knot-plugging technique has already been successfully developed, and the practicability of applying paper overlays is now being studied to improve paintability. The problem of effectively substituting such raw material for the highly durable defect-free timber produced from the indigenous species has been extremely difficult, but with increasing age the forests should yield much superior timber. When between thirty and forty years old radiata pine trees lose much of their sweep, and, with interim pruning and thinning of elite stands, the exotic forests should eventually furnish the softwood traditionally needed to supply up to 90 per cent of the country's total timber requirements.

USE OF PRESERVATIVES. With wooden construction playing such a dominant part in the national economy, the first difficulty to be overcome was that of low durability. During logging, conversion, and seasoning, as well as in construction and other uses, the sappy exotic softwoods develop mold, stain, and incipient decay so readily that the extensive use of wood preservatives is necessary. Not until an effective supply of properly treated wood was available for the building industry was any great success achieved in substituting the exotic softwoods for the indigenous timbers. Today, more than twenty pressure-treating plants, producing about 30 million board feet annually, are in operation. They use a number of the better-known metallic salt preservatives for the treatment of exotic softwoods intended for use in building construction.

The best preservatives in common use are Boliden Salts, Celcure, and Wolman Salts, all of which are both insecticidal and fungicidal. Boric acid treatments are also being accepted, though more for their insecticidal than their fungicidal qualities. In order to ensure the observance of proper standards of treatment, a Wood Preserving Authority has recently been set up by the government, with responsibility for the policing of wood-treating operations resting with the Forest Service. All of the water-soluble preservatives, of course, are being approved only where leaching is unlikely to occur. Creosote is the dominant preservative for exposed usages, though increasing quantities of pentachlorphenol are being employed.

GRADING. A wide range of grades for the exotic softwoods has already been established to service both the domestic and export markets. Grading specifications are being constantly improved with experience. The basic problem is to adapt the raw material produced to as many types of use as practicable. Not all of the timber requirements of New Zealand, and still fewer of those of Australia, can be met by the New Zealand exotic softwoods, but there is little doubt that, with the present development of suitable grades, 60 per cent and eventually 80 per cent of New Zealand's domestic requirements and at least 30 per cent of Australia's import requirements can be so met. The grading bases for the principal requirements of use are essentially: knot size for constructional timber, grain tightness for flooring, watertightness for weatherboarding and sheathing, yield of maximum-length clear-cuttings for shop and factory grades (e.g., freedom from knots, for recutting purposes for industrial use, such as furniture), and ability to withstand shipment for boxing grades.

That the problem is well on its way to solution is best evidenced by the fact that, from an annual production level of about 30 million board feet in the mid-thirties, production of exotic softwoods had risen to 230 million board feet in 1954. This means that more than 200 million board feet are being used annually in New Zealand, as exports to Australia are of the order of only about 20 million board feet.

OUTLOOK FOR TIMBER PRODUCTION AND DISTRIBUTION. Figure 57 shows the estimated production and distribution of indigenous and exotic timbers in New Zealand for the year 1952-53. The total production amounted to 340 million board feet of indigenous and 232 million of exotic timbers. It has been estimated, however, that by 1975 the former figure would decrease to about 100 million and the latter would increase to about 740 million. It is believed, though, that in 1975 New Zealand will still require substantial importations of Australian hardwood for construction and specialty purposes, and, likewise, limited quantities of North American softwoods for similar uses, together with some supplies of decorative woods from tropical countries, although none of these demands will be large enough to be significant in relation to the supplies available. Incidentally, the estimates also envisage a drop in the produc-

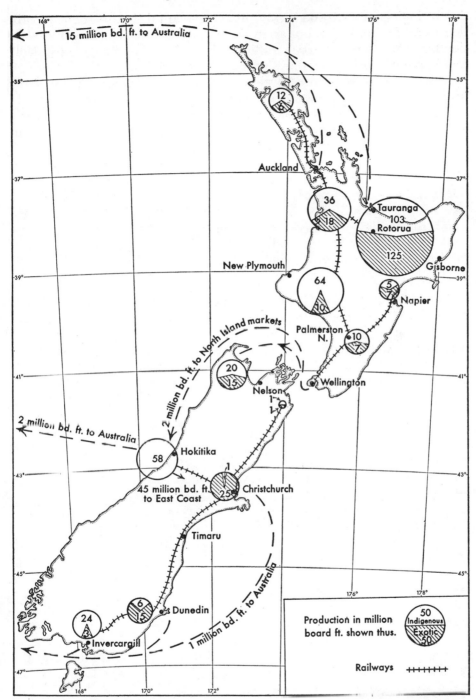

FIG. 57. New Zealand: production and major distribution of sawn timber, 1952-1953.

tion of indigenous softwoods from just over 300 million to about 60 million board feet annually, but an increase in indigenous hardwood production from 30-odd to at least 40 million, with an ultimate increase still later to something more like 70 million board feet annually.

Although eventually the South Island should become self-supporting in timber supplies—except, of course, for import needs—by 1975 it should be drawing upon the North Island for some 20 million board feet of exotic softwoods in exchange for a somewhat larger quantity of indigenous softwoods which will be required to meet essential needs in the North Island.

It has further been envisaged that, to put the remaining supplies of high-quality indigenous softwood and hardwood logs to their most effective use, the supply of peeler logs will be maintained at about the present level of some 1½ million cubic feet annually. Defect-free veneers and plywood from indigenous logs may then be combined with low-quality core stock from the exotic softwoods, as a substitute for the prodigal use of solid defect-free indigenous timbers for furniture, interior fittings, and the like.

THE WOOD-PULP AND PAPER INDUSTRY. Before World War II New Zealand had no wood-pulp industry, and only a small paper industry based on the importation of long-fibered chemical pulp for the manufacture of less than 10,000 long tons of wrappings annually. Just at the outbreak of war the production of groundwood pulp and its manufacture into paperboard began and attained about 15,000 long tons annually. Imported long-fibered chemical pulp was used. After the war the country entered upon the production of unbleached sulfate pulp and its manufacture into kraft wrappings and container board. The newly erected plant is already producing pulp at the rate of 45,000 long tons annually and manufacturing 25,000 long tons of kraft paper annually, with its surplus pulp going to both domestic and Australian users. At the time of this writing, an integrated sawmill and pulp-and-paper plant was under construction for operation before 1956. It consists of a groundwood pulp mill with an annual rated capacity of 60,000 long tons, a sulfate pulp mill of 51,000 long tons (31,000 long tons unbleached and 20,000 long tons semibleached), and a one-machine newsprint mill of 75,000 long tons (using groundwood and semibleached pulp). The integrated sawmill will have an annual capacity of 36,000,000 board feet on a one-shift five-day-per-week basis, or 72,000,000 on a two-shift basis. It is hoped to install within a short period a second newsprint machine to bring production up to 150,000 long tons annually. In the one-machine stage it is likely that at least 30, if not 40, per cent of the newsprint will be used locally and the remainder exported to Australia. That country will have an import demand several times greater than even the part of the two-machine production that is surplus to New Zealand's domestic requirements.

The sulfate process has been adopted in preference to the sulfite, largely because it is the only one entirely suitable for the reduction of all the principal exotic softwoods. The New Zealand sulfate pulps must be semi-bleached for use in newsprint, and when fully bleached are also suitable for many qualities of white paper. Australia is estimated to have an immediate annual demand for 70,000 long tons of sulfate pulp. Within the foreseeable future this will probably increase to one of over 100,000 long tons, which is much greater than the 50-odd thousand long tons likely to be available from existing and planned New Zealand plants.

The Export Potential

Calculations based on existing and planned resources and on the maintenance of adequate reserves against the risk of fire and of insect and fungal attack indicate that the annual cut of raw forest material surplus to New Zealand's domestic requirements and available for export in one form or another of finished product will amount in 1975 to 50 million cubic feet of logs (inside bark). According to current thinking, half of this is likely to be converted to 150 million board feet of sawn timber, largely for export to Australia. That country's softwood import requirements will be several times this figure. Another 13 million cubic feet is likely to be exported in the form of 100,000 long tons of newsprint and similar papers, leaving the remaining 12 million cubic feet (together with sawmill waste) to yield 70,000 long tons of sulfate pulp. Both pulp and paper are likely to be absorbed largely in Australia.

SOURCES FOR BOTANICAL NOMENCLATURE

CHEESEMAN, T. F. 1925. *Manual of the New Zealand flora.* Government Printer, Wellington.
REHDER, ALFRED. 1940. *Manual of cultivated trees and shrubs hardy in North America.* The Macmillan Co., New York.

30. OCEANIA

Frank E. Egler

Ten thousand islands—thirty million square miles of sea—less than 2 per cent of the surface land. One island alone, New Guinea, has three times the land area of all the others. Those others are as if an area equal to that of Great Britain had been fragmented and scattered over one third the world. Such is Oceania. Yet its islands and their forests, specked on some of the earth's most critical airways and seaways, of strategic importance in peace and war, command attention.

Origins

The origins and relationships of the floras of Oceania have challenged the ingenuity, imagination, and fact-finding capacities of botanists. A drop of only 60 feet from present sea level would join New Guinea and Australia. Such a united continent of Papualand is believed to have existed 30,000 years or less ago. As a result of this or earlier unions, the forest flora of New Guinea bears a marked Australian character, especially as to casuarina, eucalyptus, and oak. A lowering of only 60 or 70 feet more would expose the Sunda Shelf, uniting Southeast Asia with Sumatra, Java, and Borneo. Such a union in the past must have brought the continental flora far east before its overseas migrations were launched.

THE COMING OF THE PLANTS. Although the last word has by no means been said, it would appear that the lesser Pacific islands obtained their original plants from across the seas, with all the hazards and uncertainties and failures of a man seeking to cross in a rowboat and trying to perpetuate himself if he could land. Hurricanes, rafts of floating logs, stray birds, and other "accidents," continuing to this day, have contributed to the origins of the present floras.

There is now a consensus that the floristic invasion of Oceania has come from three main regions: the Americas, most obviously in Hawaii; a now vanished Antarctic continent, with the remnants of its flora found in southern South America, South Africa, Australia, and New Zealand; and Indo-Malaysia, which in turn is basically Asiatic. Despite the prevailing easterly winds, however, the tropical cyclones from the west have been most influential.[1] As one proceeds from the western borders of the Pacific,

[1] Visher (1925, 1926). For full references see p. 630.

the flora becomes more and more impoverished in genera and appears obviously to be a fraying-out, an attenuation of the Asiatic plant world, as the chances of successful immigration become less and less over the tremendous distances of water. Fosberg [2] has analyzed the Hawaiian flora with regard to its origins, basing his discussion on the number of assumed original immigrants. For the seed plants, he finds that 40.1 per cent are Indo-Malaysian, 18.3 per cent American, 16.5 per cent Antarctic, and the remainder boreal, cosmopolitan, or obscure.

Offsetting in part this paucity in genera and larger categories, there has been an extraordinary speciation in certain groups. Whatever be the causes, the original immigrants, including trees, have sometimes indulged in endless morphologic variation, often with each valley developing its recognizable form. Certainly many of the named forms are ecologic modifications and many more would interbreed and lose their identity if placed in a related population; but many others are undoubtedly established genetically, and the recognition of them as desirable strains in forest trees is an open field for silvicultural research. Immigration and speciation are probably continuing now as in the past, but on too slow a time scale to be of practical importance. The striking effects of introductions by man will be considered later.

The above discussion holds for what one might term the "inland flora," for species that cannot tolerate salt, die when submerged in salt water, and shun the strand. It is these species which pose the problem of overseas migration to the botanists.

The "strand flora," [3] entirely to the contrary, seems to have evolved capable of overseas migration. Buoyant seeds that withstand many days of floating—even as germinated seedlings—are found in totally unrelated plant families. This flora is remarkably constant in all the islands—evidence of the success of these adaptations; and this flora is adapted not only to migration but also to growth under saline conditions, either in soil or air. Indeed, the plants are frequently incapable of terrestrial migration (though many grow well where planted). For all these reasons, the strand flora forms the entire vegetation on countless low islands. On the high islands it tends to predominate only in the plant communities near the seacoast.

Among all these native plants, as well as among naturalized species, there are innumerable kinds of trees of distinct value to the forester, especially in the islands close to Southeast Asia. No manual of dendrology exists for this territory, although Kraemer [4] has published a volume for part of Malaysia, including some of Melanesia. The book describes more than 100 important species, said to be about one per cent of the total tree flora.

2 Fosberg (1948).
3 Merrill (1945) 27-58.
4 Kraemer (1951).

THE EFFECTS OF MAN. *Black Men and Brown Men.* The first peoples to be pushed out of Asia into the islands, either by deterioration of climate during the last glacial period or by more aggressive tribes, or both, were Negroids, Ainoids, and Veddoids. As they entered Melanesia ("black islands"), the black fuzzy-haired Negroid element was predominant. Hunters and food-gatherers of an Old Stone Age culture, they probably had no marked effect on the forests of their islands.

Four to five thousand years ago, the New Stone Age culture spread to the Negroid islands of Oceania, a culture that turned the people into farmers practicing a destructive shifting cultivation that has persisted to this day and is of great significance from the standpoint of world forestry. To these folk the forest was and still is a hindrance. They cut and burn the trees and plant crops for a few years, until soil fertility presumably lessens. Then the site is abandoned, and a new forest is cut. In the meantime the old site grows up to secondary forest. In a decade this is recleared and reused, but for a shorter period. Fire is omnipresent. Rhizomatous grasses invade, which successive fires only encourage by burning the tree seedlings. The grassland, encroaching on the surrounding forest even without agriculture, is unmanageable, and the farmer moves away permanently to new forest sites. New Guinea today is a patchwork of forest and grassland wherever (which is almost everywhere) a "burn-dry season" occurs, from sea level to the frost regions above the mossy forest. Forest remains only in swamps, along stream sides, and where the natives have not yet entered, as in a no-man's land between warring tribes. When such tribes annihilate each other, the forest replaces the grassland, to be destroyed by some future tribe. Since the roving agriculture is a one-way process, especially with increasing population, this destruction of much timber of high commercial value is a problem of first importance to forestry. In addition, it poses a more general problem: the Melanesian in effect destroys his own habitat, for the grassland is useless to him.

After the New Stone Age had spread to Melanesia, but still before the Christian Era, paler, more Mongoloid people invaded the islands to the north, the area now known as Micronesia ("tiny islands"). And then the far-flung islands from Hawaii to Samoa and New Zealand were populated by the handsome race known as Polynesians ("of many islands"), who conquered vast distances in frail canoes. Ethnologists now consider these folk to have migrated through Melanesia toward the east and to have emerged with their present bronze skin. The theory that they came from Peru, by the Kon-Tiki route is not fashionable. All these invasions were barely completed by A.D. 1400, the date of the first entering of Hawaii.

The Micronesians and Polynesians radically altered the forests of the high islands with regard to both flora and vegetation. They brought with them a limited number of plants; these included a few weeds, but for the most part were food plants, of which the coconut has done the most to change the landscape. It is now dominant on practically every low island

and at the lowest elevations of the high islands too. What the forest was originally, or would be now if left to itself or planted to other trees, is a matter of conjecture and future experimentation.

A shifting upland cultivation, such as that of Melanesia, was not part of the culture on the high volcanic islands, and consequently the mountain forests were but seldom entered. On the other hand, fire—as always with primitive peoples—was uncontrolled and often started for pleasure and hunting. It is the author's opinion that on many islands fires burned as frequently and as far up the hills as the vegetation and the climate would permit, destroying not only large areas of original forest but also the evidence of present forest potentialities.

White Men and Yellow Men. In 1520 Magellan passed through the straits that bear his name, and, the following year, landed at the Mariannas. Thus was opened a new chapter in the exploitation of Oceania, a chapter of conflict that continues today between two fundamentally opposed philosophies of social living, a conflict that every forester faces squarely when he tries to administer tribal forest lands.

The original natives lived in small social units. Theirs was an agricultural and subsistence-barter economy, based on few material wants. With the crudest of tools, they fashioned a satisfying existence on infertile specks of land. Living under a form of "communalism," the individual had no incentive to amass personal wealth, for he would only have to share it with his tribe. To this day and for these reasons it is difficult to lure natives to forest work, unless they make a total break with their home villages.

In striking contrast, the new invaders were members of large social units. Theirs was a complex money economy, based on many and ever-growing material "necessities." Under the guise of "individual liberty," each man had every incentive for personal gain, and thus wave after wave of Occidentals has passed over Oceania, each intent on its own brand of personal gain: souls, morals, and modesty; loot and trade. The invaders streamed in from Europe, the United States, and Japan, and, when native muscle was not co-operative, Hindus, Chinese, Malayans, Filipinos, Javanese, Tonkinese, and Puerto Ricans were herded in. World War II, however, left Oceania with a new political geography and under a "trusteeship" philosophy that has shown itself more altruistic and more humanitarian than history has usually known. Such elements make the Oceania of today the unusual stage that the forester must know if he is to act effectively.

Sandalwood, 1790-1850, is a finished case history of forest "mining." Undoubtedly, the value of island sandalwood was discovered independently on several occasions, and the period of its exploitation is filled with double-crossings. Many a chief succumbed to the money lure, assuming island monopolies and forcing his people to work at gathering the wood in the unhealthy rain forests. Either by nature or with the connivance of the gatherers, who are said to have pulled up all the seedlings they saw, commercial sandalwood disappeared. Apparently the plant has some silvicultural peculiarities, for it has not reappeared in any quantity, either naturally or by artificial means.

The introduction of large naturalized mammals is another aspect of the Occidental invasion that is having a continuous and most important effect on the forests. Only the continental islands possessed a native fauna of large animals; the oceanic islands apparently developed their biotic communities in the complete absence of hoofed animals. It appears that the native forests have extremely shallow root systems, critically located in a moist surface layer. The slightest disturbance to the ground vegetation, as by grazing or browsing, kills the trees, in turn opening the adjacent forest to drying, and destroying it, with an effect almost of a chain reaction. Cases are on record in Hawaii where grazing stock was put into a forest for a matter of a few weeks and then removed, but the forest died thereafter. If such destruction were on land planned for grazing, no unexpected problem would result.

Unfortunately the early white settlers introduced cattle, sheep, goats, and horses. The islanders placed a taboo upon them, but some escaped to the hills and showed remarkable fertility. In addition, missionaries and traders often released animals on small uninhabited islands, for the sustenance of shipwrecked individuals. The destruction of the native vegetation by these feral animals and by pigs, earlier naturalized, has been tremendous. Wholesale slaughter of thousands of animals has since taken place in some islands; and to this day one of the most useful activities of a local forest service is the building and upkeep of border fences, not only to keep out adjacent high-quality stock, but to prevent reinvasion by feral animals. Although rabbits have in general been less of a problem, Christophersen has made an interesting report on their history in Laysan, in the Hawaiian Islands. Until 1903 this little island had a flora of 28 species and a solid vegetation of grass and shrubs. In 1911 rabbits were swarming "over the island by thousands." By 1923 only four species of plants could be found and Laysan was described as a "desert of sand," with no mention of rabbits, alive or dead—another example of an introduced mammal annihilating itself by destroying its own habitat.

Much more than half of the flora of some of the islands is composed of species that have been introduced and naturalized since the white invasion. Moist uplands have been less affected, but arid lowlands—with their original vegetation already destroyed—were fair prizes for hordes of weeds. In many islands the bulk of the lowland vegetation is now composed of alien species, and one must search carefully for the indigenes. Furthermore, on destruction of the native forest by grazing, the land is taken over almost at once by alien grasses and shrubs which, as on the grasslands of New Guinea, form a strong deterrent to the return of the native trees. This situation has given rise to egregious comparisons between the native flora and the native cultures that disintegrate before the onslaught of aggressive aliens. The contrary, however, would seem to prevail in the case of the flora. The writer (1942), in accord with Allen's interpretation for New Zealand (1936), has presented field evidence in support of the thesis that most of the alien plants are pioneer species expanding into "open" lands and forests that have already been disturbed, whereas the native trees are largely of end-stage (climax) species that will hold their own against most of the invaders. The critical need in reforestation is for a "nurse tree," [5] native or alien, which can naturally invade the grassland and scrub, forming a growth that can in turn be invaded by the native forest trees.

Climates

Oceania comprises three main kinds of islands: (1) "oceanic coral low islands," composed entirely of coral limestone and presumably capping submerged volcanic deposits; (2) "oceanic volcanic high islands," composed of active or extinct volcanoes, arising from the floor of the ocean basin, and usually complicated by fringing reefs; and (3) "continental high islands," composed of sedimentary strata overlying a granite base, usually complicated by volcanoes and coral reefs.

The low islands partake of what might be called regional climates, controlled by the warm moist trade winds blowing diagonally from the horse latitudes (at about 30° N and S) westward toward the equator. These winds, as they pass over warm, low, sandy islands, may be sufficiently heated so that no rain falls, even when there is precipitation on the surrounding ocean. In general, within five degrees of the equator there is a dry zone, which includes the Phoenix and Gilbert islands, and at higher latitudes a moister zone. At still higher latitudes, the seasonal shifting of the trade-wind belt with the prevailing westerlies modifies the climate, as in Hawaii. In the western Pacific, especially in New Guinea, the influence is predominantly that of monsoons, related to the greater seasonal warming and cooling of large land masses than of the adjacent ocean.

The climates of high islands may vary markedly even within distances of less than a kilometer. The moist trade winds, striking a volcanic island, are deflected upward, where they cool to condensation. Passing over and beyond the summit, they drop, are warmed, and dry up. The result is a series of concentrically arranged precipitation belts, placed askew on the contour pattern. The center of highest precipitation is slightly to windward of the peak, and each rainfall belt is tipped down to windward so that at any one elevation there is less rainfall and a drier vegetation on the lee than on the windward side of the island. Each valley and ridge adds its minor complications. The majority of these climates exhibit a great variety of physiognomic vegetation types, depending largely on human activities, especially management practices. Consequently, any climatic classification which invokes a single vegetation type as the "climax" for its zone runs immediately into inconsistencies.

[5] Egler (1939), 53.

Soils

Few generalizations can yet be drawn on the soils of Oceania. Those of the continental islands are probably as varied and as complex as in any continental area, though they are today little known. The low limestone islands have invariably a thin and poor soil, occasionally favored by a layer of organic matter from the vegetation or from bird colonies. More has been published on the soils of the high volcanic islands, especially as regards agricultural Hawaii.[6] It is probable that many of the forest soils are ferruginous laterites. Aside from a surface crust, sometimes present, aluminum and silicon increase downward, iron concentrates at an intermediate position, and titanium remains abundant at the surface.

Soil erosion can be critical, often spectacular, but as yet has failed to arouse the governmental authorities, as in other parts of the world. Perhaps this is because most of the erosion has been in unpopulated areas from the start and has not resulted in the displacement of contemporary populations and agricultures. Much of it apparently was consummated before the advent of the white men, or else immediately after—owing to the naturalization of grazing mammals—but before European land managers began to look more critically at the land. Within a few miles of Honolulu there was a valley forest a few years ago half buried with debris from the hills. Elsewhere entire coastal plains are said to have been formed in recent years, and relict soil patches hanging on rocky mountains attest to past conditions. Unlike that in temperate regions, the decomposition of the volcanic rocks in the tropics may be rapid, and some lands may be amenable to management practices that would restore seminatural forests to areas now completely barren. The research on this remains to be done.

Island Types

Recent figures for forest areas in Oceania [7] are presented in Table 30–I. It should be noted, however, that these are not only incomplete, but are not indicative of potential forest land, since there is much grassland and savanna that could be converted to forest under rational management practices. Such grasslands include not only those of New Guinea and the Solomons, already mentioned, but also those of Hawaii, Guam, and even Yap and Palau.

OCEANIC LOW ISLANDS. Where volcanic or other materials have formed the sea floor at depths of less than 150 feet in tropical waters, they have been subject to colonization by coral and related organisms. These have built up calcareous deposits as living reefs at, or slightly below, sea level. Surmounting such a reef, generally at its margins, an atoll is usually a more or less circular group of small islands, produced by wave and wind action, enclosing a "lagoon." To the geomorphologist atoll islands seem ephem-

---

[6] Sherman (1950), and others there mentioned.
[7] Source: FAO, *Yearbook of Forest Products Statistics, 1954*, p. 124.

eral, subject to rapid destruction, especially during storms. Forestry practice must reckon with the hazards to which such islands are subject.

TABLE 30–I

OCEANIA: LAND AREA AND FOREST AREA FOR CERTAIN ISLANDS, 1950-1953

(In Thousand Hectares)

		Forest Area		
	Land Area	Accessible	Inaccessible	Total
British Solomon Islands, 1953 ..	2,890	20	2640	2,660
Fiji, 1953	1,828 *	140	815	955
French Oceania, 1950	360	50 [a,b]	65 [a,b]	115 [b]
Hawaii, 1950	1,665	450	325	775
New Caledonia, 1952	1,582	10 [a]	70 [a]	80
New Guinea (Australian) and Papua, 1951	47,400	3,000 [a,b]	30,000 [a,b]	33,000 [b]

[a] Unofficial figure.
[b] Includes brushland.

As a habitat for plants, atoll islands, despite their almost infinite number, their human populations, and their emotional appeal, do not hold much for the forester interested in quantity. Their vegetation normally comprises a series of belts from sea to lagoon. Back of the sea beach is a scrub 2 to 5 meters high. Next is a narrow forest zone of *Messerschmidia argentea* and *Pandanus* spp. In the Marshalls and Carolines *Terminalia litoralis* is found in this *Messerschmidia* zone. The greater part of the typical atoll is a forest which today is almost entirely composed of *Cocos nucifera,* topped sometimes by huge breadfruit trees (*Artocarpus altilis*) where the rainfall is heavier. The timber of breadfruit is excellent in almost every respect, but the tree is seldom cut since it serves primarily for food. It would appear that the original forest vegetation was composed of such trees as *Pisonia grandis,*[8] *Pandanus* spp., *Ochrosia parviflora, Pipturus argenteus, Hibiscus tiliaceus, Messerschmidia argentea, Calophyllum inophyllum, Barringtonia asiatica, Eugenia* spp., and others. *Pisonia* may be the sole dominant on dry islands, such as Vostok.[9] Some of the isolated eastern atolls [10] may have floras composed of as few as five species, or even less, seemingly the result of chance migration. Along the lagoon beach of most islands is a narrow strip of scattered trees such as *Cordia subcordata, Hernandia ovigera, Terminalia catappa, Barringtonia asiatica, Thespesia populnea,* and, in rocky places, *Pemphis acidula.* Mangrove species, where found at all, occur in small depressions in the centers of the islands.

[8] Sources for botanical nomenclature: Kanehira (1935), Lane-Poole (1925), Merrill (1945). For full references see pp. 629-630.
[9] Fosberg (1946).
[10] Christophersen (1927).

OCEANIC HIGH ISLANDS. The oceanic high islands display endless variations, but basically they consist of volcanoes. They not only occur in chains and groups but also in such total isolation as that of Easter Island. The original formations were pahoehoe and aa lavas, with bombs, ash, cinders, dust, and other ejecta. Erosion may have advanced to such a degree as to leave knife-edge ridges and deep valleys (sometimes amphitheater-headed, because of greater precipitation upstream), footed by coastal plains. Ancient coral reefs, developed at previous higher sea levels, may appear along an island's flanks. Soil maturation has progressed variably from the different parent materials, with the development of distinctive profiles. Despite this profusion of types, a pattern emerges of interest to the forester.

This is expressed in Fig. 58 as a series of zones, arranged consecutively from sea level to summit. Each zone, except in the driest, coldest, and cloudiest sites, has a characteristic assemblage of forest, savanna, and grassland,[11] with certain apparent correlations with contributing factors, although implications of causality are still premature. Sunlight attains a maximum at sea level on the lee side of the typical island and decreases upward, with a marked diminution at the beginning of the so-called "cloud zone," a minimum in the mossy forest, and then a rapid increase to a second, high-altitude maximum. Precipitation varies inversely with sunlight, being low at sea level, maximal in the cloud zone, and again low at very high elevations. Cloudiness, although it may occur at any elevation, is of significance only within the cloud zone, where its intensity increases rapidly to a maximum at its upper level. Altitude, perhaps because of the ease of obtaining data regarding it, is mentioned *ad extremum* by botanists and foresters, but does not seem to exert any direct effects, at least upon the details of vegetation.

The distribution of floras in relation to vegetation zones has been considered only for Oahu, Hawaii.[12] Despite its significance in forest management, both in control of natural stands and in planting programs, foresters have almost totally neglected this subject. Its importance is illustrated by the fact that in any one zone the predominant trees may be either (*a*) those that are there capable of maximum individual development and would not thrive in an adjacent zone, or (*b*) those that have been crowded out of an adjacent zone by competition with others and would actually develop more luxuriantly if planted in the adjacent zone with the competition lessened.[13]

As a working hypothesis for Pacific high islands, Fig. 58 shows the areas characterized by six different floras: (1) the strand flora, already discussed; (2) a desert flora, which may exist on some islands where there is

[11] Only the Hawaiian Islands have been completely mapped (Ripperton and Hosaka, 1942) according to such a zonal classification.

[12] Egler (1939, 1947).

[13] One of the very few tropical foresters who have noted this phenomenon is Chipp (1927).

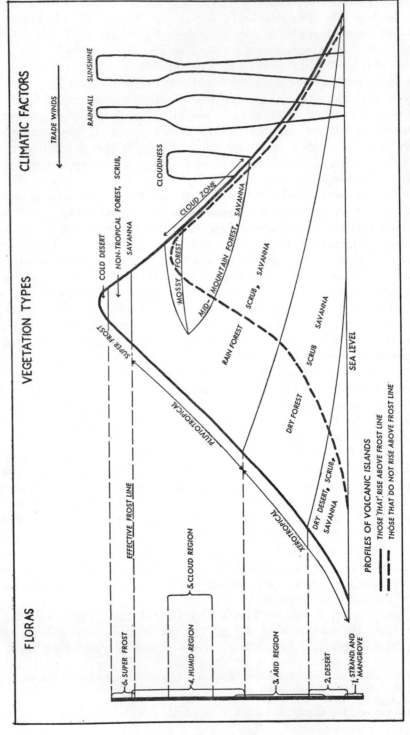

FIG. 58. Oceania: profiles of volcanic islands showing relationship of floras, vegetation types, and climatic factors.

less than 35 inches of precipitation a year (some widely naturalized *Opuntias* may occur in this area); (3) an arid-region flora on islands having roughly less than 50 inches of rain, with a maximum floristic complexity at the higher precipitation levels and attenuating out below to mingle with the desert plants (tremendous numbers of alien plants have been naturalized in this floristic area); (4) a humid-region flora occupying a region of rain forests, with high percentages of endemic species and few naturalized aliens (many of the plants pass upward into the cloud zone, where present); (5) a cool-tropical cloud-region flora; and (6) a flora or floras above the frost line. On some islands, above the cloud zone but below the frost line, the humid-region and arid-region floras are repeated, but in reverse order, as on the island of Hawaii.

The significance of an effective frost line on the islands of Oceania remains to be investigated. One might expect, judging from continental areas, that it would form a fairly distinct separation of tropical from nontropical conditions. The situation in New Caledonia and in the New Hebrides, Society, Bismarck, and Solomon islands is unknown. In oceanic Hawaii the flora at high altitudes appears to be nothing more than an extremely impoverished attenuation of plants primarily tropical, with almost no temperate American origins—mute testimony of the failure of aerial migration from that direction. Continental New Guinea, on the other hand, has an extensive super–frost-line flora, but its geographical affinities are poorly known. All the super–frost-line regions hold great potentialities for the introduction and naturalization of temperate forest species.

Each vegetation zone possesses a complex of topographic variations, ridges, valleys, and plains that make difficult the recognition of zonal differences. In those cases where a so-called rain-forest zone is predominant on coastal plains, and a "montane-forest zone" on foothills and slopes, one has reason to wonder whether a climatically significant zonal difference actually exists. The precise mapping of the boundary between two distinct zones has been attempted only on Oahu.[14] Here the line was found to pass through a wide physiognomic variety of plant communities and to vary in altitudinal range by almost 1,000 feet, bulging seaward on the ridges, where the cooler temperatures may have offset the lower rainfall to permit an equivalent moisture effectiveness.

CONTINENTAL ISLANDS. The continental islands of Oceania include Fiji, New Caledonia, the New Hebrides, the Solomons, the Bismarck Archipelago, and New Guinea. In them are found not only all the varieties of forest characteristic of coral low islands and oceanic volcanic islands, but also their own complexities, due to larger floras, more varied rock strata and topographic features, and climatic regimes ranging from slight to complete dominance by the monsoons. Nevertheless, the same basic pattern of arid, humid, cloud, and super-cloud zones occurs, if not

[14] Egler (1947).

in the orderly arrangement found on a single high volcano in the trade-wind belt.

Vegetation of the Forest Zones

MANGROVES. Mangrove vegetation is the constant associate of the shallow ocean shores, mudflats, and river embayments of almost all of the high islands throughout Oceania.[15] Only in Hawaii—most distant from sources of dispersal—were mangroves absent until relatively recent times. Yet they have been introduced here and are now developing semi-natural stands. Mangrove sites are rare on low islands.

As one progresses from open sea water landward to upland, and also to brackish water, gradual changes occur in the vegetation, which is generally segregated in definite belts. The forest fronting the ocean—usually much the largest in acreage—is dominated by *Rhizophora* spp. Frequently just back of the front *Bruguiera* spp. are common. Farther landward are large numbers of other trees: *Xylocarpus* (carapa) spp., *Sonneratia caseolaris, Heritiera littoralis, Avicennia marina, Lumnitzera littorea, Excoecaria agallocha,* and the colonial 2-meter-tall fern, *Acrostichum aureum.* The important thatch palm "nipa" (*Nipa fruticans*) is predominant in brackish waters.

Economic utilization of this vegetation is most highly developed in Fiji, where 52 square miles (33,000 acres), owned by the Crown, are commercially worked. On the basis of a mean annual increment of 130 to 150 cubic feet per acre, the lands are handled for fuel wood on a 40-year rotation, with *Bruguiera* and *Rhizophora* supplying 95 per cent of the take.

THE XEROTROPICAL ZONE. *Dry Deserts.* No survey has been made of the islands to locate those areas within the xerotropical zone where the precipitation is so light (certainly no more than 15 inches) that they have either a distinctive desert flora, or a permanently nonforest vegetation due to other causes than human interference, or both. A few small areas in New Guinea are reportedly in this category, and also a few lowlands in the Hawaiian islands, as well as some of the highest summits above the cloud zone but below the frost line. At these high elevations in Hawaii, however, where there are scattered dwarf outliers of the *Sophora chrysophylla* forest, the vegetation of pre-goat days has not been satisfactorily interpreted.

Some low coral islands, such as Jarvis,[16] may likewise belong in this class. In these cases, however, the few plants present are those of the cosmopolitan strand flora, and no distinctive desert vegetation is apparent.

It is important to distinguish between the dry descrts (as here defined), which are correlated with the "natural" or nonhuman environment, and certain large areas that now resemble such deserts because of the direct and indirect effects of man. The former are relatively unalterable, but

[15] Fosberg (1947), Merrill (1945), 49-58.
[16] Christophersen (1927).

the latter, at least in some instances, could be converted into forests and even into productive watersheds under long-range management.

Dry Forest, Scrub, and Savanna. A zone of dry forest, scrub, and savanna is generally found where there is less than 50 to 60 inches of rain per year. On typical oceanic volcanic islands it occurs at low elevations, especially on the lee sides. On very high volcanic islands it may again appear above the mossy forest, although such occurrences have not been adequately described. On continental islands it may occur at any elevation where the precipitation is low.

Very few detailed accounts [17] of this vegetation exist, for understandable reasons. In its original form it has been totally destroyed by the natives, and hordes of recent introductions have filled the vacuum. Since such areas seemingly bear only worthless herbs and shrubs, grazing rather than forestry has been their hoped-for use. Nevertheless, in all foot slopes in this zone in the Hawaiian islands the small tree *Leucaena glauca* can invade and replace various shrubs such as the ubiquitous *Acacia farnesiana,* and, in turn, is locally invaded by still other tree species. Coastal plains have, within the past half century, developed semi-natural forests of *Prosopis chilensis,* 40 feet high, that are of economic value not only for firewood but for cattle shade, cattle forage (from fruits), and apiculture. It may well be that other valuable trees could be developed in this zone.

In New Guinea areas apparently comparable bear "savanna forest." The grasses are typically *Imperata cylindrica (arundinacea)* and *Saccharum spontaneum.* The scattered trees, growing to a maximum height of 50 feet, consist, at least in Papua, of several species of eucalyptus, including *E. alba, E. papuana, E. clavigera,* and *E. tereticornis,* while elsewhere *Melaleuca* spp. and *Casuarina* spp. are common. As a source of fuel wood and post wood, these lands have value for both aborigines and European settlers. What other trees they might grow under fire management is totally unknown, for no relict unburned area has been described.

THE PLUVIOTROPICAL ZONE. This zone of pluviotropical vegetation, areally predominant on the rainy Solomons and New Hebrides, and occurring on the intermediate slopes of almost all the high islands, continental and oceanic, includes what is popularly known as "jungle" (although that Hindu term in its original sense referred to secondary thickets on uncultivated land, perhaps even in arid zones). It embraces not only the rain forests, that profuse expression of tropical luxuriance made famous by Tarzan, but also much land now covered with savanna or with thickets of worthless shrubs.

In New Guinea burned savannas mixed with secondary forest extend completely through this zone to the lower limit of the cloud zone at 5,500 feet, with *Casuarina nodiflora* common at the higher elevations. Such a

[17] Egler (1947).

mosaic of savanna and forest has much in common with the Parang vege-
tation of the Philippines, where the same species of *Imperata* and *Sac-charum* are also dominant in the grassland phase. In New Guinea
Octomeles sumatrana, an aggressive, valuable, 150-foot-tall floodplain
tree, forms one of the few pure forest types in this part of the tropics.
Nevertheless, it is all but impossible to pick any typical genera of the
mixed forest. *Castanopsis junghuhnii* has attracted attention because of
its frequency and its habit of occurring in pure patches of an acre or
more. A few dipterocarps are present, but they never predominate as
they do in the Philippines and Southeast Asia.

In New Caledonia savannas similar to those of New Guinea are widespread,[18] but complex rain forests predominate throughout the island.
Melaleuca leucadendron is a typical tree. Related species of *Araucaria*
and *Agathis* occur at higher elevations.

Fiji has its *talasinga* (sun-burnt lands), rolling plains extending up into
the mountains to altitudes of 1,500 feet. The scattered woody plants
include *Acacia richii, Casuarina equisetifolia, Dodonaea viscosa,* and
Psidium guayava. The rain forests of these islands, from sea level to 3,000
feet, are complex floristically,[19] but much less so than those of New
Guinea. Among economically important species are *Agathis vitiensis*
(Fiji "kauri"), *Calophyllum* spp., *Dacrydium elatum, Vitex vitiensis,*
Guettarda speciosa, Endospermum macrophyllum (M. Arg.) Pax &
Hoffm., *Eugenia* spp., *Metrosideros* spp., and *Podocarpus vitiensis.*

In Tahiti most of the vegetation is of the pluviotropical type [20] and
is closely related to that of other Polynesian high islands. *Stenolobium
stans,* of Atlantic tropical America, is said to be on the march here, with
"armies of young trees ascending . . . these slopes."

In Hawaii the forests of the lowest portions of this zone were destroyed
either before white men came or within their memory. Vast acreages are
now covered with lantana (*L. camara* var. *aculeata*), guava, and scrub that
is despised by beast and man, by taxonomist and ranger. And yet in
one area of this zone the tree *Psidium cattleianum* var. *lucidum* is moving
in to replace these scrub species, and in turn acquiring an understory
of native forest trees, as economically important a vegetational development as any observed by the author.[21] In many areas the scrambling
fern *Dicranopteris linearis* is especially aggressive following disturbance,
blanketing the land and even small trees, so that some have been misled
into considering it a climax. Farther up the slopes occurs *Acacia koa*
(Hawaiian mahogany), which by its growth form, height, and the quality
of its wood is the only important native timber tree, with a relation to
past fires and with silvical characteristics that are not yet well known. The
typical rain forest of Hawaii is predominantly composed of *Metrosideros*

[18] Daniker (1939), Catala (1953).
[19] Mead (1928), Smith (1951).
[20] Setchell (1926), Papy (1948).
[21] Egler (1939).

collina subsp. *polymorpha,* a tree which generally does not exceed 50 feet in height and 12 inches in diameter. Associated with it are a large number of endemic species, several of which have excellent potentialities, at least for watershed cover. On the gentle slopes of the larger islands, this same zone supports a range industry which is third only to sugar and pineapple in the islands' economy.

THE CLOUD ZONE. The vegetation of this zone is sometimes, but not always, separated into two relatively pronounced forest belts, especially in the continental islands.

New Guinea has a cloud zone with a markedly distinct flora of high-altitude continental origins. The lower belt ("mid-mountain forests") begins suddenly at the lower edge of the clouds, which may be as low as 2,000 feet, or as high as 6,000. It is the region with timber of highest commercial value, though fires set by the aborigines are destroying much of it, converting large tracts into savanna. *Araucaria cunninghamii* is one of the most striking, abundant, and valuable of the trees. In addition, there are many oaks (*Quercus pseudo-molucca, Q. lamponga,* and *Q. spicata*), with *Nothofagus* just above. *Eugenia, Cryptocarya, Sideroxylon,* and *Podocarpus* are among other trees of this belt.

The mossy forest, which in New Guinea begins between 5,500 and 8,000 feet, has one of the most distinctive appearances of all the world's vegetation. Here the trees seldom exceed 25 feet in height. Mosses and lichens cover and hang from everything, bloating the smallest twigs to ten or twenty times their diameter. The air is cloud-saturated, the moss water-saturated. In New Guinea, Lane-Poole noted *Eugenia* and *Podocarpus* as most abundant. At one time, he observed a morning drought, when all the moss was brittle and exploded to dust at the touch, a condition that may help to explain the large areas of burnt mossy forest he had seen. Thus, even here native fires have their influence.

On Fiji the mossy forest begins at about 3,000 feet. In Micronesia it is found only on Ponape and Kusaie,[22] beginning at about 1,350 and 1,450 feet respectively; here the most abundant woody plants are *Alsophila ponapeana, Gynotroches axillaris, Syzygium carolinense* (Koidz.) Hosokawa, and *Astronidium ponapense.* Samoa has a comparable type that begins at about 1,500 feet.[23] In the Hawaiian Islands this belt, sometimes suffering from pig destruction, may start as low as 1,800 feet. The predominant woody plants, rarely different from those of the forest below, include *Metrosideros, Bobea, Straussia, Fagara,* and *Labordia.* On Maui and Hawaii islands, both the cloud zone and the forest just below are squeezed out of existence on the dry, leeward side, and the dry forest that would otherwise lie below them ascends to higher elevations.

From the foregoing it can be seen that the mossy forest is highly variable in both altitude and floristic composition. Some of the variation in

22 Hosokawa (1952).
23 Setchell (1926).

floristic composition is but a part of the floristic individuality of each island. The evidence is not yet conclusive as to whether the cloud zone tends to possess its own distinctive flora, or is a reduction in tree growth and a lush growth of mosses that can be superposed on any tropical flora under conditions of excessive cloudiness.

ABOVE THE CLOUDS. Vegetation exists above the clouds in the Solomons, Hawaii, and New Guinea, and perhaps in other islands, but its organization into plant communities and zones, its prehuman past and its possible future, and the location of an effective frost line are all so imperfectly known that few generalizations can be made about them. In Hawaii (Hawaii and Maui islands) frosts are not infrequent as low as 4,000 feet and ice formation is appreciable at 7,000 feet.[24]

Much of alpine New Guinea, at least to 12,000 feet, is open and treeless, convincingly interpreted by Lane-Poole [25] as originally forest, but now fire-caused grassland. Here native agriculture is not the chief offender, but fire used as a tool in hunting the wallaby. The higher elevations in Netherlands New Guinea have other zones that are still unknown.

In the Hawaiian Islands the picture is again confused, for here feral grazing mammals have altered the vegetation to an unknown degree, and it is doubtful if there are any truly alpine forest species. This paucity of the flora veils the present position of the frost line in the native vegetation. Several thousand feet of elevation are involved, in which *Sophora chrysophylla,* an important source of fence posts, is the most abundant woody plant. These high regions have probably some of the most intriguing forestry potentialities in all of Oceania.

Forest Influences

While forest influences have long been a matter of abundant fact and fancy, their significance in tropical islands is an unexploited field of research. The fundamental thesis is that the vegetation in the normal course of its development produces certain changes in the microsite and the local environment—for example, it permits soil accumulation and increasing water infiltration and retention, which in turn, enable the vegetation itself to develop still farther. Because of water transpired, of absorption and reflection of radiant energy from the foliage canopy, and of the resultant effects on the temperature, moisture, and saturation deficits of the air above, possible alterations in the regional rainfall are also involved.

Animals introduced on small islands may destroy the vegetation, then die themselves, leaving a sandy barren. Rainstorms coming across the ocean may evaporate in the hot air over an island, but yield precipita-

[24] Ripperton and Hosaka (1942), 30.
[25] Lane-Poole (1925).

tion on each side.[26] Clouds passing across the mountains may persist over forested coves and forest plantations, but evaporate over anthropically induced savannas and grasslands. Drizzles may dry up over a roadway, as reported from Martinique in the West Indies, but fall on the forest on either side. Even a nontechnical observer will be astonished in the tropics at the contrast between a shady, dank, cool, deep- and moist-soiled forest, and the scorching rocky man-made desert adjacent. In short, the magnitude of what vegetation can do to bare land on a tropical island is on a scale for which experience confined to temperate regions does not prepare us. The remedial potentialities of revegetation in low latitudes have been only dimly perceived in research and in practice.

Forest Management and Use

VALUE OF THE FORESTS. Timber holds first place among the forest products of New Guinea and Fiji, and may do so in the future in the other continental islands, as is generally true on the continents. On the oceanic volcanic islands, however, the native forests bear very few species or individual trees of such size and quality as are suitable for commercial timber, and experiments are constantly progressing with introduced plants. The aborigines use wood for house posts, paddles, canoes, and sundry minor articles, for which individual trees are selected when needed.

In Hawaii the chief value of the Forest Reserves is in relation to watersheds, because of the demands of the sugar and pineapple plantations and of urban communities, and the same probably also holds true for the other high islands under more intensive use. Where there is mangrove vegetation, it is extensively exploited for fuel and in Fiji is under a 40-year management cycle, as we have seen. On most of the islands the main use of secondary growth is for firewood and charcoal. For fence posts, highly important in all grazing regions, the naturalized *Prosopis chilensis* is one of the chief sources of supply. There is no pulp industry of importance, although recent developments in the use of bagasse are significant. Rubber has been tried in the southwestern islands, but not successfully. Minor forest products are of no more than local importance. For the New Guinea native the principal value of the forest lands is as agricultural soil, and once the grasses take over, he moves on, or vanishes.

OWNERSHIP AND ADMINISTRATION. Organized forestry, private or governmental, exists in only a few of the island groups. During the Japanese administration of Micronesia, forestry activities were accelerated,[27] with local sawmill operations, minor exports to Japan, and a certain amount of reforestation, especially with *Casuarina equisetifolia*. The present forestry situation in American Samoa and Micronesia has recently been surveyed.[28]

26 Christophersen (1927), 3.
27 U.S. Navy (1948).
28 Marshall (1951, 1952).

New Caledonia, Fiji (where a Forest Department was established in 1938), and Hawaii have, or have had, some government administration, with Hawaii far in the lead.[29]

In Hawaii a Board of Commissioners of Agriculture and Forestry has existed since 1903.[30] Its activities have centered largely around the establishment of reserves almost entirely for watersheds, the elimination of the hordes of feral mammals, fencing, a very elaborate planting program that has involved a vast number of alien forest species, and the controversial practice of introducing game animals. In the early days, forest plantings were sometimes made in total disregard of basic silvical principles, and failures were excessive. For a long time, success was gauged on survival and rapid growth, and undoubtedly this is a chief factor in the case of a timber species that is to be harvested. For self-perpetuating forests, however, this policy may be very deceptive. An intensive report is much to be desired on all these forest plantings of the past, not only with regard to the survival of planted individuals, but also as to whether different species are capable of spreading naturally. Some species may be found to act as "nurse crops"—that is, to prepare the way for the introduction of another semi-natural plant community closer to the original self-perpetuating forest.

UTILIZATION. The original uses of the forest were generally unorganized and unplanned. The natives knew their trees and chose carefully the species and individuals best suited for house posts, canoes, paddles, fish-net floats, and other articles to meet their daily needs. The breadfruit was recognized as one of the most valuable of timber trees (propagated vegetatively and existing in endless clonal strains), but was seldom cut, because its fruits were used for food. Coconut also served numerous purposes. Other trees of the strand were selected, and many species in the coastal-plain forests of the high islands were discriminately chosen, although reports concerning the same species from different island regions vary markedly.

Before World War II organized forestry and forest exploitation can hardly be said to have existed in Oceania. There were a few sawmills on the larger islands, but they served immediate local needs only. During the war exploitation was stepped up to a high pace to serve the armed forces, especially in the larger Melanesian islands. As in so many tropical regions, the number of species here is great and bewilderingly complex, and many of the species have native names only and are unknown to scientific classification. The wartime operations helped to advance our knowledge of the dendrology and physical characteristics of these forests farther than throughout all previous history, but unfortunately most of

29 Departments of Agriculture and Agricultural Experiment Stations are beyond the scope of this paper, even though they may have published some material concerning trees.

30 They publish biennial reports. See also the *Hawaiian Forester and Agriculturist,* vols. 1-30, 1903-33.

such information exists only in unpublished reports and in the minds of the foresters who were directly involved.

RESEARCH. The forestry and agricultural organizations are carrying forward only limited programs of basic forestry research. Usually these organizations are under pressure to serve immediate needs, and hence their investigations are oriented toward the planting of exotic tree species of proven worth elsewhere, and toward the control of actively destructive factors, such as feral mammals.

On the other hand, scientific research in Oceania is beginning to advance rapidly along general lines, and this should benefit forestry in the long run. Forestry in Oceania involves the management of lands originally or potentially covered with trees, and such products of forest land as water and wildlife may locally be more important than commercial timber. For these reasons a sound forestry program must go beyond the range of conventional silvicultural activities. It must include interpretations of the vegetation of pre-European and pre-native times, and also serious studies of the remaining samples of natural and semi-natural vegetation, which in some instances have very desirable characteristics. The artificially induced forest types, such as those from plantings, should also be investigated with regard both to their continuing or self-perpetuating characteristics and to their values in other respects than for timber production. Because of the extraordinary complexity of the native and introduced floras, and because of the wide range of distinctive environmental conditions within relatively small areas, forestry in Oceania offers unsurpassed challenges to the ingenuity of the practical researcher.

SELECTED REFERENCES

CATALA, R. L. A. 1953. "Protection de la nature en Nouvelle-Caledonie," *Proc., 7th Pacific Science Congress*, 4:674-679.

CHIPP, T. F. 1927. The Gold Coast forest: a study in synecology. *Oxford Forestry Memoirs*, No. 7.

CHRISTOPHERSEN, ERLING. 1927. Vegetation of Pacific equatorial islands. *Bernice P. Bishop Mus. Bull.* 44, Honolulu.

DÄNIKER, A. U. 1939. Neu-Caledonie. (*Vegetationsbilder*, 25 Reihe, Heft 6, Tafel 31-36.) G. Fischer, Jena.

EGLER, FRANK E. 1939. "Vegetation zones of Oahu, Hawaii," *Empire For. Jour.* 18(1):44-57.

———. 1947. "Arid southeast Oahu vegetation, Hawaii," *Ecol. Monogr.* 17(4):383-435.

FOSBERG, F. RAYMOND. 1936. Vegetation of Vostok Island, Central Pacific. Reprinted from Proc. Hawaiian Acad. Sci., in *Bernice P. Bishop Mus. Spec. Publ. 30*.

———. 1947. "Micronesian mangroves," *Jour. N.Y. Botanical Garden*, 48(570):128-138.

———. 1948. Derivation of the flora of the Hawaiian islands. (*In* Elwood C. Zimmerman, *Insects of Hawaii*, vol. I, pp. 107-119; University of Hawaii Press, 1948.)

HATHEWAY, W. H. 1952. "Composition of certain native dry forests: Mokuleia, Oahu, T.H.," *Ecol. Monogr.* 22(2):153-168.

HOSOKAWA, TAKAHIDE. 1952. A plant-sociological study in the mossy forests of Micronesian islands. *Kyushu Univ. Faculty of Science Memoirs*, Series E, 1(1):65-82.

KANEHIRA, RYOZO. 1935. "An enumeration of Micronesian plants," *Jour. Dept. Agr.*, Kyushu University, 4:237-464.

KRAEMER, J. H. 1951. *Trees of the western Pacific region.* The author, West Lafayette, Ind.

LANE-POOLE, C. E. 1925. *The forest resources of the territories of Papua and New Guinea.* Government Printer for the State of Victoria, Australia.

MARSHALL, COLIN. 1951. Report on forestry in American Samoa. U.S. National Res. Council, Pacific Sci. Board, *Scientific Investigations in Micronesia, Report No. 11.* Mimeogr., unpublished.

————. 1952. *Sustained yield management of the mangrove, salt water swamp forest of Fiji.* Fiji Dept. of Forestry, Suva.

MEAD, J. P. 1928. The forests of the Colony of Fiji. *Legislative Council Paper, Fiji, 4,* Suva.

————. 1947. *A botanical bibliography of the islands of the Pacific.* (Contributions from the U.S. National Herbarium.) Smithsonian Institution, Washington, D.C.

MERRILL, E. D. 1945. *Plant life of the Pacific world.* The Macmillan Co., New York.

NEAL, MARIE C. 1948. In gardens of Hawaii. *Bernice P. Bishop Mus. Spec. Publ.* **40**:1-805.

PAPY, H. RENÉ. 1948. "Aperçu sommaire des étages de végétation à Tahiti," *Bull. Soc. Hist. Nat. Toulouse,* **83**:217-222.

RIPPERTON, J. C., and HOSAKA, E. Y. 1942. Vegetation zones of Hawaii, *Hawaii Agr. Exper. Sta. Bull. 89.*

SACHET, M.-H., and FOSBERG, F. R. 1955. Selected bibliography of vegetation of the tropical Pacific Islands. (In their *Island bibliographies,* Nat. Res. Council, Publ. 335.)

SETCHELL, W. A. 1926. Phytogeographical notes on Tahiti. I, Land vegetation; II, Marine vegetation. *Univ. Calif. Publ. in Botany,* **12**(7, 8): 241-324.

SHERMAN, G. D. 1950. "The genesis and morphology of Hawaiian ferruginous laterite crusts," *Pacific Science,* **4**(4):315-322.

SMITH, A. C. 1951. "The vegetation and flora of Fiji," *Scientific Monthly,* **73** (1):3-15.

U.S. Navy. 1948. *Handbook on the Trust Territory of the Pacific Islands.* Office, Chief of Naval Operations.

VISHER, S. S. 1925. Tropical cyclones of the Pacific. *Bernice P. Bishop Mus. Bull. 20,* Honolulu.

————. 1926. Tropical cyclones and the dispersal of life from island to island in the Pacific. *Smithsonian Report for 1925,* 313-319. Smithsonian Institution, Washington, D.C.

THE OUTLOOK

31. THE OUTLOOK FOR THE WORLD'S FORESTS AND THEIR CHIEF PRODUCTS

Erhard Rostlund

In trying to see what lies ahead for world forestry it is first necessary to take cognizance of the dimensions and the complexities of the forest problem. It is also important to keep in mind the limitations of the forecasters, for the outlook depends very much on the lookout. In varying combinations, all men have hopes and fears, tendencies to look on the bright or the dark side, inclinations to hasty or slow judgment; some are dewy-eyed about the future and for that reason cannot see clearly, while others suffer from cataracts of vested prejudice that impair the vision. Furthermore, the lookouts are not all looking in the same direction. Some can see only the truly remarkable achievements in technology, and overlook the fact that for a long time to come the main wood problem of most of mankind will not be how to obtain rayon fabrics, cellophane wrappers, or molded monocoque airplane seats, but how to secure enough firewood for cooking purposes. Others are attracted by the improved methods of silviculture, developed particularly in northwestern Europe, but fail to keep in view the hard fact that much of what can be done in Europe cannot, for economic reasons, be done in North America, and probably cannot, because of different physical conditions, be done in the tropical forests. This personal factor is no doubt the main reason for the greatly varying reports of the prospect in view, whether they deal with trends in agriculture, forestry, or any other aspect of the man-earth relationship. Some say that a wood famine is inevitable, others assure us that no world shortage of timber is in sight, and the reason for the difference in opinion obviously lies in men, not in the forest.

The Problem Defined

Forecasting in this field is not an exact science, partly because of personal factors that cannot be eliminated and partly because the information on which the forecast must be based is neither complete nor altogether accurate. Forest mensuration is excellent in a few countries, but the available data on forest area, volume of stand, annual growth, and even yearly consumption of wood in the world as a whole are at best only rough estimates. These estimates are nevertheless important. They are, in the first place, the only quantitative data we have, and they reveal the dimensions of the problem before us. The forest inventory published in 1954 by the Food and Agriculture Organization of the United Nations (FAO) shows that the annual world consumption of wood for all purposes in recent years has been over 50 billion cubic feet, and that the total area of the forests on the earth is estimated to be about 9½ billion acres. It is not easy, indeed perhaps not possible, for the human mind to comprehend such large quantities. Many have seen the forests of Washington and Oregon and been impressed by their vastness, yet in area they constitute less than half of one per cent of the world's forests. It is not easy to envisage 9½ billion acres of forest land under management on a sustained-yield basis, but that seems to be the future goal implied by the statement in *Unasylva* (September, 1954, p. 141): "The ... inventory shows that the world's forests are potentially capable of furnishing a plentiful flow of forest products for a world population much higher than that of today." It is not possible to say exactly how much forest land is managed on a sustained-yield basis at the present time, because data are lacking and because good practices have been initiated so recently in many regions that we do not yet know whether yield will actually be sustained. Management of a type is practiced on some of the forests in India, Ceylon, Burma, Australia, New Zealand, in other countries, and in some parts of Africa. In 1949, according to the American Forestry Association, about 55 million acres of public and private forest land in the United States were classed as under "intensive management," which is defined by the words: "high order of cutting and good fire protection." As of January 1955 nearly 34 million acres of private forests in the United States were in certified tree farms. However, not all of these forests are truly managed as the term is understood in northwestern Europe. It is perhaps safe to say that, after more than a century of research in silviculture and experiments with forestry practices, some 160 to 180 million acres of forest land are now under management in northwestern Europe and, with an optimistic view, possibly an equal amount outside of Europe, making a total of about 350 million acres. That is, it may be conjectured that 4 or 5 per cent of the world's forest lands are at the present time under reasonably good management, and 95 per cent are not. The sheer size of the task that remains to be done if the goal is to be achieved looms very large in the outlook.

The task is not only large but complex. The ultimate goal might be defined as *the utilization of the world's forest lands in such a manner that they will permanently yield sufficient wood for all mankind at a price people can pay, while at the same time some of the forests will provide watershed, soil, and wildlife protection, grazing opportunity, and facilities for study and recreation.* None of the terms in this definition can well be omitted. The term "forest land" must be used, for in the long run it is the land that constitutes the resource and not the generation of trees that happens to occupy the land at a given time. Forestry is only one type of land use. In many regions it competes for site with other forms of land utilization: the demands of agriculture, for example, will have a decisive effect, and the effect will be fatal to some of the forests. The term "permanently" must be included, for the problem is not merely to balance forest drain and growth in the immediate future, but to maintain the balance in perpetuity by increasing the growth to meet the rising demand of an increasing population. The phrase "all mankind" is required, for the goal cannot be regarded as having been reached so long as some forest lands produce species of trees that are considered useless because there is no market for them, while other regions are so short of wood that cow dung must be used for fuel. "Price" is perhaps the most critical term. In one way or another and regardless of type of prevailing economic theory, every forestry operation and every forest product must be paid for, whether in energy, money, or barter. Good forestry practices are simply not possible unless they are economically feasible; for all we know, some of the forests may remain inaccessible forever because access may be too costly; and technological achievement, no matter how brilliant, will be of little use if people cannot pay for the products. The terms in the last part of the definition pertain to the concept of multiple use, an idea that may or may not turn out to be practicable in the long run. In many parts of the world problems of soil and water are far more critical than those of timber supply, and large sections of the forest, probably much larger than we commonly think, will have to be reserved for the primary function of watershed protection, and will serve only secondarily, or perhaps not at all, as a source of wood. Other forest lands are withdrawn from ordinary economic utilization and reserved for recreation, study, wildlife sanctuaries, or for the purpose of saving some of the undisturbed forest for future generations. An example is found in the National Parks of the United States, which contain almost half as much timber land as there is in all of West Germany. We may not always be able to afford this luxury, but as long as the world can keep its parks and wildlife reserves they will add up to a significantly large area which, like the protection forests, cannot be included in the area of the wood-yielding forest land. There are other complicating factors. The difficulties of silviculture and management are multiplied by the many different physical characteristics of the world's forests; people have different and deeply rooted attitudes toward trees; and the problem is not made easier by the fact that the forests are under about one hundred national jurisdictions.

It is not a mere matter of balancing numbers. *Unasylva* (August, 1948) suggests that the wood needed for a moderately good standard of living would be an annual per capita consumption of about 35 cubic feet, basing the suggestion on prewar European experience; and makes the assumption, which seems plausible enough, that with reasonably good management the forests of the world can produce an annual yield of 30 cubic feet per average acre. But it would be very misleading to conclude that the balance is favorable, or that no particular problem exists because there are only 2½ billion people in the world and 9½ billion acres of forest, or almost 4 acres per person.

Expected Demands for Forest Products in 1975

The outlook for the distant future depends largely on what will happen in the near future, which may be defined conveniently as the next two decades, since 1975 is the common target year in several recently published forecasts.[1] Only the major conclusions of these reports need to be considered here.

The Paley Report (1952) expects that the cubic-foot requirement of wood for all purposes in the United States will increase by 17 per cent between 1950 and 1975, and the Stanford Report (1954) foresees an increase of 14 per cent between 1952 and 1975. These forecasts are thus not very different from earlier estimates: for example, in 1948 the Forest Service looked forward to a rise in the over-all requirement of about 50 per cent between 1945 and the year 2020, or an increase of nearly 15 per cent for each 25 years of that period. The reports are in substantial agreement in predicting a decline in the demand of wood for pilings, railroad ties, shingles, and cooperage, and a very marked decrease in the use of fuel wood, but they differ on some items. The Paley Report expects that the need of pulpwood will increase by 50 per cent; the Stanford Report, by 60 per cent. The demand for peeler logs, mostly for plywood, will rise by 40 per cent according to the Paley study; by 90 per cent in the Stanford forecast. The most notable difference is in the expected board-foot requirement of saw timber for lumber, which is by far the bulkiest item in the over-all demand: the Paley Report foresees an increase of 10 per cent; the Stanford Report, one of only 3.4 per cent. The principal reason for this difference is no doubt the fact that the Paley Report is based on the assumption of no significant change in price relationships, whereas the Stanford Report assumes that the price of lumber relative to competing materials will increase and that lumber will lose some of its markets. The Stanford assumption is well worth noting. High wood prices, causing people to prefer other materials, might have the effect of alleviating to some extent the coming pressure on the forest.

A world pulp survey of the same type as the Paley and Stanford studies is reported to be in preparation by the FAO, but, to my knowledge, projections of the future world demand for all wood are not yet available. A partial world forecast, which does not include the countries in the Soviet zone, is made in the Paley Report. The average total output and requirement of industrial wood during the years from 1947 to 1949 are

[1] For bibliographical references to these and other publications mentioned in the text of this paper, see below pp. 670-671.

compared with the average prospective output and requirement during
the decade of the 1970's. Fuel wood and charcoal are not included. The
conclusion is that the total output will probably increase by 4 per cent
and the total requirement by 40 per cent. It is very likely that the demand will rise, but the 4 per cent increase in output may be an over-
estimate. According to Egon Glesinger of the FAO, as reported in
American Forests (November 1954), the inventories have shown that the
output of the world's forests is not rising, despite increasing demands.

The type of forest products demanded and regional differences between
the United States and Latin America in the use of wood are indicated in
the table below. The products are shown as percentages of the total cut
of all timber, as measured in cubic feet.

	United States (Stanford Report)		Latin America (Paley Report)
	1952	1975	1952
Lumber	58%	59%	9%
Pulpwood	17	24	2
Fuel wood	13	3	80
Other products	12	14	9
	100	100	100

An indication of regional differences in the demand and use of wood
on a world-wide basis is presented in *Unasylva*, December 1954. Expressed in the next table as approximate percentages of world forest area,
population, and total production in cubic feet of roundwood in 1953, the
data reveal the differences between the highly industrialized countries of
the northern hemisphere and the rest of the world. By "North America"
is meant Canada and the United States, and "Europe" includes the
Soviet Union.

	Forest Area	Population	Total Wood	Fuel Wood	Industrial Wood
North America and Europe	40%	30%	70%	50%	88%
Rest of the world	60%	70%	30%	50%	12%

The heaviest production and consumption of industrial wood products,
such as lumber, plywood, pulp, and paper, are clearly concentrated in
North America and Europe, and the demand for these products is steadily
rising. Furthermore, a large part of the industrial timber cut elsewhere,
chiefly in the tropical forests, is exported to Europe and North America.
The industrial demand is preponderantly for lumber and pulp, but the
most widespread and still the largest single requirement is fuel wood.
Almost half of the total output of some 50 billion cubic feet in 1953 was
fuel wood; even in Europe this requirement accounted for slightly more
than one third of the total cut; and in many countries besides Latin
America 80 per cent or more of the entire production was for firewood.
At the present time, then, the demand on the world's forests is mainly for
fuel wood, lumber, and pulp, in that order, and this is likely to continue
at least in the near future.

Whether or not the forecasts will come true naturally depends on how valid the underlying premises turn out to be. The Stanford Report is based on the general assumptions that (1) no major war will occur, (2) no radical advance in technology will increase production at a rate faster than in the past, and (3) business cycles will become more stable, accompanied by high employment. Another assumption, based on data of the Bureau of Census, is that the population of the United States will increase by 35 per cent to reach 212 million in 1975. The premises of the Paley Report are generally similar; for example, the expectation of a 40 per cent rise in the world requirement of wood rests on the assumptions of a population increase of 47 per cent, continued high demand in the industrial countries, and rising consumption in others.

The safest of the assumptions is that population will increase, and this alone would mean a rising demand for forest products. If a major war should come, the drain on the forest would surely increase drastically, as it has in past wars, and the over-all requirement might become much larger than the forecasts indicate. If peace lasts but good economic conditions do not, the demand for industrial forest products would probably be less, but the world requirement of fuel wood might remain unaffected. The second assumption of the Stanford Report has already been questioned by some forestry people, who believe that the large sums of money currently invested in research will result in technological improvements which will have a marked effect not only on efficiency in production but will help the industry to hold and even expand its markets. An editor of *House Beautiful* magazine, speaking before the annual convention of the National Lumber Manufacturers Association in November 1954, challenged some of the Stanford predictions, declaring that the concept of abundant living demanded more lumber for dwelling units, and urged the manufacturers to gear their thinking to an expanding market and an expanding American home.

It may well be that a 15 per cent increase in the over-all requirement of wood is about what can be expected in the next quarter century. But thereafter will come other quarter centuries, and no evidence is at hand showing that this or any other country intends to stop growing in 1975. On the contrary, like the editor who spoke to the lumber manufacturers, most people hope for a steadily expanding economy, which of necessity means a steadily increasing demand on the natural resources, including the forests. If the hope is fulfilled, the outlook is that before very long the requirement will increase not by a mere 15 per cent, but by 100 or 200 per cent, and perhaps more. The question is how the forest will stand up under the rising pressure. The forecasters do not provide clear answers, only clear affirmations of their faith that the demand can be met. The conclusion of most of the reports, whether they deal with the United States or the world, is that the area of the forest is large enough to provide the wood needed in the future, even if the need should become twice or three times as large as today, but only on two conditions: much of the now inaccessible forests must be opened to utilization, and all forests must be placed under greatly improved sustained-yield management. These are not small conditions, and in them, it might be said, lies the whole forest problem.

The problem can be resolved into three major parts. The first is the question of supply: of forest area, forest soil, stand, annual growth, and natural factors affecting the trees, such as fire, insects, and diseases. The second is the problem of how best to utilize the supply: of silviculture, forest genetics, methods of cutting, logging, manufacturing—in short, technological knowledge. The third can be called cultural or institutional in nature; it is the question of our social-economic-political ability to apply the technological skill to best advantage. More particularly, then, the outlook depends on trends of development in all of these fields; and the direction of the trends cannot be determined by looking only toward the future: we must also be guided by the past. Perhaps the most important thing to grasp is that in nearly all of these fields we are dealing with processes that have the tremendous momentum of history behind them.

Human Pressure on the Forest

DIMINISHING FOREST AREA. During the last few millennia the area of the world's forests has probably been reduced by at least one third, and some people think by more than one half. The exact amount is not so important as the question of whether the cause or causes of the reduction are still operating and can be expected to continue in the future. Data obtained by archeology and pollen analysis indicate that climatic fluctuations in the past have been reflected in periodic changes in the species dominating some of the forests, but there is no clear evidence of a worldwide progressive desiccation of the climate during the last few thousand years which might account for the large reduction of the forest area. Minor parts of the forest have been lost because of volcanic activity, encroachment by swamps, drifting sand, or other natural causes, and long-continued grazing and browsing by large herds of wild animals must have had an effect on the margins of many woodlands. The principal cause of the reduction, however, has been the activity of man. The three main reasons for the human pressure on the forest have been, and continue to be, the demands for fuel wood, construction material, and space for farms and pasture, and in all of these demands there are significant regional differences.

THE DEMAND FOR FUEL WOOD. The first forest product used by man in quantity was obviously firewood. The gathering of naturally dead and fallen wood need not reduce the area of the forest, but the practice of killing and felling trees by girdling and the use of fire must have been invented or discovered at a very early time. The method has been recorded from so many peoples that it might almost be called universal. Primitive hunters and food gatherers annually set fire to the vegetation, for several reasons: to facilitate hunting by clearing away underbrush, to attract game by the salt content in the ashes, to make it easier to dig up roots and tubers or to find nuts fallen on the ground, and sometimes to drive game with fire in organized group hunts. Besides, trees and pole-wood killed by fire became more readily available for fuel. It must be assumed that regular burning, repeated for thousands of years, destroyed trees over wide areas. Henry Youle Hind,[2] while exploring the Saskatchewan River valley in 1858, observed that Indian fires had driven the forest back 180 miles from its former limit. On their expedition through the northern Rocky Mountains in 1803, Lewis and Clark found extensive prairies in valleys where trees can grow very well. Alexander Henry in 1814 and Charles Wilkes in 1841 [3] described large open grasslands in the Puget-Willamette valley of Washington and Oregon. Wilkes, as did Lewis and Clark, concluded that these prairies owed their origin to Indian fires. Evidence supporting the conclusion is seen in the fact that the forest naturally began to encroach upon the prairies again after the American settlers had occupied the land and the Indian burning had ceased. Similar evidence is known from many other parts of the world. The full effect of the ancient hunters on the vegetation can probably never be measured exactly, but it is certain that the process of reducing the forest area began long before agriculture was known.

The larger populations that became possible when farming had been introduced increased the demand for fuel wood; the inventions of the pottery kiln, fired bricks, metallurgy, and other industrial arts made further heavy demands on the forest; and today the need of fuel wood continues unabated in many lands.

In some countries deforested regions have been replanted because of the demand for fuel wood. Up to 1941, according to B. H. Hunnicutt, the Paulista Railroad in southern Brazil had harvested more than 70 million cubic feet of firewood from eucalyptus plantations started in 1904. M. D. Chaturvedi reminds us of the present emphasis on fuel-wood plantations in India, some of which have been remarkably successful (see above, p. 475). According to figures quoted by R. S. Troup, average annual increments of 500 cubic feet per acre have been obtained on plantations in southern India by the coppice or sprout method, a rate of growth that can be called phenomenal.

The consensus of all reports is that destructive fuel-wood cutting in the tropical forests is far more common than conservative use. William Vogt says that at least 75 million people in Latin America depend on the forest to provide firewood or charcoal for all their cooking and heating—if heating can be afforded—and that large areas have been so stripped that some people are practically without wood and use anything that will burn. Hunnicutt describes clear-cutting on a large scale in parts of Brazil, and the necessity of hauling wood for long distances to the railroads because

---

[2] Hind (1860) 1:405.
[3] Wilkes (1850) 4:307-358; Henry (1897) 2:810-830.

wide sections along the tracks have been deforested. In *The Amazing Amazon,* Willard Price speaks of having seen hundreds of cords of mahogany and rosewood brought aboard river steamers for firewood. H. F. Mooney informs us that charcoal burning has been the greatest single factor in forest destruction in southwestern Asia in recent years (see above, pp. 427, 429, 438). Reports in a similar vein from other countries indicate that the oldest cause of forest reduction, the demand for fuel wood, is still operating. For this reason alone the area of many of the low-latitude forests continues to shrink steadily.

To my knowledge, no practical solution of the fuel problem in most of the tropical countries is in sight, except perhaps the coppice method. It is not likely that coal, petroleum, natural gas, or electricity will become economically available to most of the people, at least not in the near future. But many tropical and subtropical trees coppice vigorously, and if this method could be widely and systematically applied it would not only tend to save the forest but would help to solve the fuel problem where it is most pressing.

An anomalous situation has come about in some countries. The thinning of growing timber and the removal of cull trees and other undesirable wood is good forestry practice, but if a market for the thinnings is lacking it may be economically impossible to perform the improvement operation. Not all of this removed material is suitable for industrial purposes, but practically all of it can be used as fuel. Much of the low-value fuel wood from the French forests is difficult to sell. Thorsten Streyffert points out that one of the serious forestry problems in Scandinavia is the finding of a greater market for firewood (see above, p. 238), and a similar problem exists in the United States, particularly in the eastern hardwood forests. The Stanford Report and the other forecasts predict a sharp decline in the use of fuel wood, not because such wood is lacking, nor for reasons of good silviculture, but because people increasingly prefer to cook their food and heat their houses with other fuels.

THE DEMAND FOR CONSTRUCTION MATERIAL. The second cause of deforestation, the demand for construction material or industrial wood in the widest meaning of the term, was hardly a factor of great significance among the ancient hunters, but in the later history of settled regions this requirement put an even greater pressure on the forest than did the cutting of fuel wood. Old London, which burned down several times, was built of wood, as were hundreds of other European cities. A large part of the forests that were clear-cut in Michigan, Wisconsin, and Minnesota during the latter part of the nineteenth century went into millions of homes built in the prairie states, and the old logged-over areas in the Pacific Northwest provided construction material for early Seattle, Tacoma, Portland, San Francisco, Los Angeles, and many other communities.

The demand for mine timber was one of the significant reasons for the early deforestation in southwestern Asia, on Cyprus, in the Sierra Nevada and Sierra Morena of Spain, in the Erzgebirge of Germany, and in many other mining regions. The need of wood in the mining industry was so critical that it led to some of the earliest forestry regulations; for example, volume allotments were instituted during the late Middle Ages in Germany and Austria in order to assure the supply of mine timber. Deforestation near the mines in Mexico had become so serious by 1550 that the native people petitioned for protection of their land and wood supply, and a forestry regulation, probably the oldest in the New World, was promulgated by the Viceroy in 1550. The effect of mining on the forest is strikingly expressed by Dan DeQuille, who says in *The Big Bonanza*—perhaps with a trace of Western overstatement—that the Comstock Lode can in truth be called the tomb of the forest of the Sierras.

The demand for ship timber put another heavy pressure on the ancient forests, particularly in western Europe, and most of all around the Mediterranean Sea. In this region, because of steep slopes, generally thin soil, and a frequently violent type of rainfall, a single clear-cutting may result in such serious soil denudation that the forest cannot come back, and a brushy vegetation takes the land instead. It may be that the primary reason for deforestation in this region was the clearing of land for agriculture and the effect of grazing livestock, particularly the browsing of free-ranging goats, but surely the second most important cause was the cutting of ship timber. The forest was one of the casualties in the naval wars fought by the Phoenicians, Etruscans, Greeks, Romans, Carthaginians, Arabs, Genoese, Venetians, and all that followed after. The mountains of Greece were nearly stripped of trees by the fifth century B.C. Thucydides informs us that one of the purposes of the Sicilian expedition of Athens in 415 B.C. was to gain control of the abundant supply of ship timber in the forests of Italy. A century later Theophrastus observed that ship timber was scarce everywhere in the eastern Mediterranean, but he praised the fine forests of Italy and other lands around the western Mediterranean. These western forests did not last long. In the first century B.C. Strabo was impressed by the superb timber in the Atlas Mountains, but in the first century after Christ Pliny observed that some of these forests were already exhausted. The demand for ship timber continued and spread northward. The Dutch fleets of the early seventeenth century were built mostly with timber from the oak forests of western Germany, which were heavily logged to raise money for indemnities after the Thirty Years War. In the opinion of Henry Cavaillés, the three main reasons for the greatly accelerated deforestation in the French Pyrenees during the seventeenth century were the consumption of wood by the Catalan forges, the clearing and burning of woodland to make pasture for sheep and goats, and the cutting of ship timber, particularly for the construction in the 1660's of a French navy consisting of 60 ships-of-the-line and 40 frigates. In Britain, as H. C. Darby says, the naval wars with the Dutch in the seventeenth century and with the French in the eighteenth, and the Napoleonic wars in the early nineteenth put such a strain on the English oak forests that they have never recovered. When "the far-flung navies melt away" they take the forests with them. Ship timber is no longer one of the major requirements, although wood in large amount is still needed in ships and shipping. It is estimated that 350,000 board feet of lumber were used in the construction of every Liberty ship built in the United States during World War II, and the wood that goes into boxes, crating, and dunnage on a modern general cargo ship runs into 100,000 board feet or more.

Today the heaviest demand for industrial wood products—lumber, pulp, plywood, and the like—is on the midlatitude forests of North America and Europe. There is a chance, however, as far as the pressure of this demand is concerned, that improved forestry methods may check any further significant reduction of the forest area in these regions. If the area is reduced in the coming years the reason is more likely to be the need of more agricultural land, or the need of space for industrial and urban expansion.

The old need for local construction material and the relatively new demand for industrial products are also felt in the tropical and subtropical forests, and one of the great uncertainties ahead is what will happen to them if and when they become fully exploited for industrial purposes. If problems of tropical silviculture, management, and economics—including aboriginal economy—should be successfully solved, these forests may become a very great source of wood products, but if the problems are not solved the exploitation may result in an enormous disaster. One of the complicating factors is that the most potent pressure on the tropical forest comes from the third of the ancient demands, namely the need of agricultural land.

THE DEMAND FOR CROPLAND AND PASTURE. Exactly how large a part of the forest reduction in the world has been caused respectively by the requirements for fuel wood, construction material, and agricultural land cannot be determined, but it seems safe to say that the forest has yielded far more ground to farms and pasture than to any other demand. Much of the world's cropland has been gained without infringing on forested areas —for example, in the interior plains and prairies of Canada and the United States, the pampas of Uruguay and Argentina, the steppes of southern Russia, and the wheat region of Australia—but even more has been made by clearing forest land. About one third of the original forest in the United States has been cleared, mostly in the eastern woodland, and much of this once timbered land is now under cultivation. Brazil has probably lost 40 per cent of her forest area, most of it to agriculture. Pollen analysis has shown that virtually all of western and central Europe was covered with forest at the beginning of Neolithic time, and it is reasonably certain that India and China were also predominantly forested when agriculture was first introduced. At the present time it is estimated that only about 9 per cent of China is forested, and 18 per cent of India, and the figure for the average of western and central Europe is also 18 per cent. The principal reason for the clearing of these vast forests was undoubtedly the need of food-producing land. In like manner the world over, farmers and herdsmen have won most of their land at the expense of the forest, and there is good reason to think that the forest will continue to lose ground.

The tradition of making farms from forest land may be 10,000 years old. Like the primitive hunters, the ancient farmers knew tree girdling and the use of fire in clearing land, a method still widely employed in the shifting agriculture that prevails in many tropical and subtropical countries from Middle America around the world to New Guinea. André Aubréville says that in the deforestation now going on in central Africa because of shifting native agriculture we are witnessing the finishing touches to a process that began long ago (see pp. 356, 357, 379). H. L. Shantz estimates that the original area of the tropical forest in Africa has already been reduced by two thirds; and P. W. Richards believes that almost the whole of the tropical virgin forest may disappear within our lifetime unless determined efforts are made to change the farming system. In the highlands of New Guinea, according to O. H. K. Spate, shifting native cultivation is eating into the main forest at an accelerating rate, and a serious crisis is likely to develop within a few decades if the system continues unchanged.

Besides giving ground to aboriginal farming, the tropical forest has yielded space to commercial plantations, and there is no indication that the pressure from this type of agriculture will be lessened in the future. On the contrary, many are looking to the tropics for more land. The amount of what is defined as unused but potentially cultivable land in the world is variously estimated from 1 billion acres by the FAO to more than 6 billion acres by C. B. Fawcett and L. Dudley Stamp. In these estimates more than half of the new land is supposed to be in tropical regions. According to the calculations of Robert M. Salter, one of the requirements for providing the people of the world with an adequate diet in 1960 is the opening of 1 billion acres of new tropical soil. It is not made clear, however, precisely where all this new soil is.

In a thought-provoking article published in the *Agronomy Journal* Robert L. Pendleton calls attention to the fallacies in estimates such as that of Salter, and cautions against overestimating the potential of tropical forestry and farming, particularly large-scale commercial grain farming. It is often overlooked, as Pendleton and many others who have studied the tropics point out, that rich alluvial soils are not abundant and that most of the tropical soils are poor in nutrients. These poorer tropical lands have been cultivated for several thousand years by farmers who have depended on forest soil, and one wonders what would happen to the remaining forest if another billion acres were to be plowed up and made into modern farms on the European or North American pattern. In all probability, the long continued aboriginal cultivation has been possible only *because* it is forest soil that has been used. The method developed by the ancient farmers makes use of the forest, which is an essential part in the cycle of shifting agriculture: the forest is the fallow and cover crop that restores fertility and maintains the soil properties, and it may well be that in the long run this method is the only sure way of producing food from the poorer tropical soils. The system is destructive of timber and has therefore frequently been condemned, particularly by foresters, but it is not destructive of soil if the rotation period is long enough. There may be more practical wisdom in the old way than in trying to change it. At any rate, whether one thinks of aboriginal or of modern commercial agriculture, it is clear that the tropical forest is under increasing pressure and will not long remain intact.

Attempts to check further agricultural encroachment upon the forest are being made. India's New Forest Policy of May 1952, as reported in *Unasylva* (March 1953), changes the previous conception that the forest has no right to a site if it can be used for agriculture and declares that land must be allotted to farms and forest according to a system of land use under which each site will yield most of the product for which it is best suited; but, the report continues, it is also recognized that the need of agricultural land is greater than ever. It may be difficult to implement this worthy policy in the future, for always and wherever agricultural need has pressed on the forest, it is the forest that has yielded.

The midlatitude forests in southern Chile, South Africa, extratropical Australia, and New Zealand, which never were very large in comparison to those in the northern midlatitudes, have in the past lost much ground to logging, fuel-wood cutting, and agriculture. At the present time it might be said that the forest area is more or less stabilized in New Zealand, Australia, and South Africa, and is even increasing somewhat because of much planting of exotic trees, especially Monterey pine. Whether the forest area of Chile can be called stabilized is more doubtful, for reports of recent heavy logging in the rough terrain of southern Chile suggest that deforestation may be the result. But in Chile, too, Monterey pine (*P. radiata*) has been introduced and is said to be growing very well.

The frontier between farm and forest in the mid-latitudes of the northern hemisphere is more or less stationary for the present; indeed, the forest has regained some ground in recent time. The clearing of land in western Europe continued until the forest was reduced to a minimum size at a time in the past that is difficult to determine for lack of comprehensive records, but was perhaps a century or two ago; and then the forest gradually began to increase because of reforestation projects. In 1750, according to authorities quoted by George P. Marsh, forests covered about 32 per cent of the area of France, and a century later only half that much. It is scarcely possible to say exactly how much the forest area has increased since 1850, for national boundaries have changed somewhat, and the definitions of what constitutes forest land are not uniform. Nevertheless, Table 31–I suggests that the forests in western Europe are appreciably larger now than a century ago. (See also above, p. 272.)

TABLE 31–I

GERMANY, FRANCE, AND GREAT BRITAIN: FOREST LAND AS PERCENTAGE
OF TOTAL AREA, 1850, 1939, 1953

	1850 [a]	1939 [b]	1953 [c]
Germany	26.7%	26.8%	
West Germany			28.1%
East Germany			25.6
France	16.8	19.1	20.7
Great Britain	5.0	5.0	6.5

[a] George P. Marsh: *Man and Nature*, New York, 1865.
[b] United Nations: *Forestry and Forest Products*, 1946.
[c] *Unasylva*, September, 1954.

The reforestation continues at the present time. After visiting Germany in 1953, Leo A. Isaac reports that he was greatly impressed by the widespread planting of trees, including North American species; he speaks of one nursery firm which alone produces and contracts with other growers for a total of 600 million seedlings a year, or about the equal of the entire annual forest planting in the United States. More than 400 forests have been established in Great Britain since 1920, and in connection with them a number of new and interesting forest villages have been built, mostly in Wales, northern England, and Scotland. The Forestry Commission of the United Kingdom hopes to afforest some 3 million acres over a 50-year period. The 2-million-acre pine forest of Les Landes in southwestern France has been built up during the last century, reforestation is under way in the French Pyrenees, and a project of planting trees on some 500,000 acres of deforested land in the southern French Alps was initiated in 1928 and is approaching completion.

Whether or not the forest area in western Europe can be permanently maintained at its present size is essentially an economic question. The highly industrialized west-European countries have long drawn upon the resources of other continents for food, fertilizers, livestock feed, and raw materials for industries, in return for manufactured goods; and the demand for imports is rising rather than falling off. A Hamburg lumber importer, interviewed by *The New York Times* on January 2, 1955, predicted that Europe will buy more and more wood products abroad. One of the reports made at the annual meeting of the American Paper and Pulp Association in February 1955 dealt with the present "immense" demand for paper in Europe, and another speaker said that the most significant development in the industry during 1954 was the emergence of the United States as a net exporter of pulp, much of which is going to Europe. These rising demands obviously imply that Europe's own forests are under heavy industrial pressure.

The agricultural land of Europe is likewise under heavy pressure. Georg Borgström expresses the opinion, which everyone shares, that Europe will be forced to develop its agriculture to the utmost, and makes the suggestion, which is not endorsed by all, that the aim should be self-sufficiency in food, or as close to it as possible. Borgström also believes, and again not everyone agrees, that a general soil depletion and deterioration in western Europe is concealed by heavy use of fertilizers, and that the high yields cannot be expected to continue to rise very much higher. He suspects that the Netherlands has almost reached the possible limit of yield at reasonable cost.

Whether Borgström is right or not, it is clear that the success of the whole economic experiment depends on Europe's ability to pay for the increasing imports, including all the fertilizers; and the fate of the forests rests on this ability. If the time should ever come when Europe can no longer draw on the resources of other continents at the same rate as now, then self-sufficiency in food would become an urgent necessity, and agriculture would surely gain priority over forestry. There will no doubt always be forests in western Europe, for some of them grow on land that is not suitable for other crops, but parts of the forests occupy soil that can be farmed if necessary. It must be remembered that nearly all of the cropland in western Europe has been made from original forest soil, improved and built up through the centuries, and the areal limit of that sort of improvement has not been reached.

Another fact to reckon with in western Europe is the increasing amount of ground needed for urban and industrial expansion, highways, airfields, and the like. Much of this ground will doubtless have to be yielded by the forest.

The large forests in the higher latitudes of North America and Eurasia —Alaska, Canada, the Scandinavian peninsula, Finland, northern Russia and Siberia—are in no great danger of agricultural encroachment at the present time and probably never will be, mainly because they grow in regions where neither soil nor climate is favorable to crop farming. To be sure, a certain amount of forest clearance for the making of farms is still going on, for example in Alaska, along the margin of the pioneer fringe in the Canadian prairie provinces, in the clay belt of northern Ontario and Quebec, and on the "cold farms" of northern Finland, and presumably clearing is still in progress here and there on the southern margin of the forests in Russia and Siberia. In view of the great extent of the northern timberlands, however, these scattered clearings can hardly be regarded as a threat to the forest; and, besides, the area of timberland thus lost to farms is more than likely balanced by reforestation of other areas.

The forest situation in the United States partly resembles that in the high latitudes and partly that in western Europe. Much of the timber, particularly in the West, occupies land that probably never can be used for agriculture; but some of it, especially on farm wood lots in the East, grows on soil that could be used for crop farming if necessary. As in western Europe, the forest area of the United States has increased somewhat in recent time. Many sections of the cutover lands in the upper

Great Lakes region have been reforested; the timbered area in the South has increased substantially because of widespread planting of pines; and a rather large amount of farm land in various regions has been abandoned, turned into pasture, or naturally reverted to forest. For example, the Alabama Black Belt, which was at least two-thirds forested 150 years ago, was largely cleared for agriculture during the nineteenth century, but more recently much of the cropland has gone back into forest. In 1936, according to the Forest Service, 45 per cent of the area of the counties in which the Black Belt lies was timbered, but the corresponding figure for 1953 was 54 per cent, showing an increase in forest acreage of about 20 per cent in 17 years.

While the forest area in the United States has increased somewhat in the recent past and the farm acreage has decreased, these trends have been characteristic only of certain regions and are not likely to affect the national balance in land use for very long. On the contrary, in a national sense a reversal of the trends seems to be coming. It is clear that timberland is already yielding ground to other forms of land use and probable that the crop acreage will soon have to be increased. All who have given thought to the future agree that the demand for farm products in the United States will rise by 35 or 40 per cent before 1975 and that this demand must be met either by higher yields per acre, or by increasing the crop acreage, or by both, and most think that both will be required. The amount of additional land needed is variously estimated. The general consensus of the participants in the section dealing with agricultural land at the Mid-Century Conference on Resources for the Future in December 1953 was that from 25 to 30 million acres of new cropland would be needed in 1975, even though most of the demand is expected to be met by greater productivity per acre. Samuel H. Ordway, Jr., makes a point that does not seem to have received sufficient attention in some of the other forecasts, namely the loss of cropland to highways, airfields, cities, and industries. If the trend of recent decades continues, this loss, in Ordway's estimate, will amount to 48 million acres by 1975, and therefore, merely to keep the crop acreage the same, 48 million acres of new land must be found; and to this must be added the new land required to meet the demand in 1975. Ordway uses the estimate of the Agricultural Research Administration, 68 million acres, and concludes that a total of 116 million acres of additional cropland will be needed. At the other extreme is the 1975 forecast of the Paley Report: a 40 per cent increase in the demand for farm products is foreseen, most of which can be met by wider application of technological improvement, which is counted on to raise the average yield per acre by 33 per cent; hence, the report considers it unlikely that any large amount of additional cropland will be required. However, some 15 million acres of new land will be needed to replace farmland lost to urban and industrial expansion, and most of this replacement is expected to come from forest land on farms.

Not everyone feels confident that the average yield per acre will in-crease by 33 per cent in the near future. In fact, some people will be happy if the present yields can be maintained. In the words of Ordway, there is no acceptable evidence, only hope, that we shall not need addi-tional productive acres in 1975. The needed farm land, whatever the exact amount may be, and the increasing space required for other types of land use add up to a total acreage that will not be small. Much of this land, perhaps most of it, will be taken from the forest, and a substantial reduction in the forest area is therefore to be expected. Richard E. McArdle, Chief of the U.S. Forest Service, summarizes his expectations for the future by saying that we shall probably have enough timber to meet our needs, but not our wants; and that we may encounter some shortage of timberland if high-quality forest land continues to go out of timber production for crop farming, highways, reservoir developments, expansion of urban areas, and other uses.

To sum up: the ancient human pressure on the forests of the world continues at the present time and in all probability will become more severe in the future. There are regional differences in the reasons for the pressure, but all have the same effect: the forests are losing ground, and it is generally the best and most accessible timberland that is being lost. Hence, the now inaccessible forests may become increasingly important, and the question is how much we can count on them in the foreseeable future.

The Inaccessible Forests

Estimates of the world's total forest area range between 6 and 10 bil-lion acres. Table 31–II shows in million acres the areas of the accessible and inaccessible forests.

TABLE 31–II

FOREST AREAS OF THE WORLD [a]

(In Million Acres)

	Accessible Forests		Inaccessible Forests
	In Use [b]	Total	
Europe	320	330	7
U.S.S.R. [b]	865	1,050	785
North America	545	770	850
Latin America	220	850	1,440
Africa	285	695	1,280
Asia	305	640	760
Pacific Area	40	50	160
Total in use	2,580		
Accessible reserve		1,805	
Total accessible		4,385	
Inaccessible			5,282
All forests			9,667

[a] *Unasylva,* September 1954.
[b] Includes unofficial estimates.

Bare numerical data can be very misleading. The large total of forest land classed as inaccessible, as in Table 31–II, has apparently led some writers to speak of "immense untapped reserves," or of "five billion acres of virgin forest awaiting exploitation." Such expressions give a wrong idea of the inaccessible forests.

The term "inaccessible" as used in the inventories has meaning only in the economy of modern industrial culture: the term implies the economic impossibility of exploiting certain forests for industrial purposes because of difficult terrain, great distance to markets, or lack of means of transportation. But these forests are not physically inaccessible to man. Aboriginal peoples—hunters, food gatherers, fisher folk, cultivators—have lived in and affected them for a very long time. Travelers crossing the Congo basin by airplane in recent years have been astonished by the numerous openings in the forest, large clearings under cultivation or abandoned after having been farmed; and similar openings, though probably not so many, are reported from the Amazon forest. Approximately 50 or 60 million acres of forest land in the Yukon drainage area of interior Alaska, most of it inaccessible except for local use, has been swept by so many devastating fires that in the opinion of Governor Frank Heintzleman,[4] formerly regional forester for Alaska, not more than 20 per cent of this forest remains intact. These fires apparently became more severe after the white settlers came, but they were not unknown before that time. On his exploration of the interior Labrador peninsula in 1862, Henry Youle Hind [5] found that fire had destroyed the vegetation and converted huge areas into what he called desert, and that stories of extensive conflagrations were traditional among the Indians; the "dark days" of Canada in October 1785 and July 1814, Hind suggested, were most likely caused by smoke from enormous forest fires in the northland. Large sections of the forests in Finland and northern interior Sweden were burned over in the early days by people practicing shifting agriculture—*svedjebruk*—a system that continued well into the nineteenth century; and from Raphael Zon's account of forestry in the U.S.S.R. we learn that forest fires, set by natives, are still common in remote parts of Russia. It would be most unrealistic to think of the world's inaccessible timberlands as a reserve consisting of 5 billion acres of unbroken virgin forest ready to be opened whenever we decide to do so.

No universally adopted definition of what constitutes forest land exists, and in all fairness it must be said that the FAO faced a well-nigh impossible task in deciding what to include in the term. Whatever the reason may have been, the category of inaccessible forest was made so broad that it came to include a large amount of land that cannot possibly be regarded as potentially productive timberland. An example is found in North America. The 770 million acres of accessible forest shown in the table is probably just about right. But the inaccessible, truly potentially

---

[4] Heintzleman (1950):363.
[5] Hind (1863), 2:111, 50.

useful timberland in the United States today scarcely amounts to 50 million acres, if that much; in the interior of Alaska, 50 million; and in Canada, about 200 million; a total of 300 million acres. Hence, in order to account for the 850 million acres of inaccessible forest shown in the FAO inventory, it would be necessary to include some 150 million acres in the United States that are covered with chaparral, piñon, juniper, mesquite, and sparse forests at high elevations, and in addition about 400 million acres of taiga land in northern Canada. None of this is regarded by American foresters as potentially productive timberland. Thus, more than half of the 850 million acres is not a true forest reserve, whether inaccessible or not. Likewise, more than half of the 785 million acres of inaccessible forest ascribed to the U.S.S.R. is probably nothing but small-stick taiga forest.

Africa provides another example. The FAO inventory shows a total of more than 1.9 billion acres of forest land on this continent, of which 695 million acres are classed as accessible. In striking contrast are the figures of André Aubréville, who says that the total area of the rain forests in the Guinea coast region, Congo basin, Abyssinia, and East Africa is about 570 million acres, and that only some 60 per cent, or 340 million acres, are covered with actual forest, the remainder being given over to shifting agriculture (see above, pp. 356-359). The other woodland in Africa, described as "dry forest" by Aubréville, consists of savanna with scattered bush and trees, yielding wood only for local needs and offering virtually no opportunity for industrial forestry. These lands are annually burned over, and the forests that remain, in Aubréville's opinion, seem to be destined for degradation and complete conversion into savanna. It is obviously this type of land that constitutes the billion and a quarter acres of inaccessible "forest" in the FAO inventory, a most dubious reserve of timberland. Even the 695 million acres classed as accessible forest become questionable if weighed against the data of Aubréville. One cannot help suspecting that a large part of the 2⅓ billion acres of inaccessible forest assigned to Latin America, Asia, and the Pacific Area may in fact be no better than the alleged reserve in Africa.

Another misconception comes from expressing the forests in areal units, a method that is particularly misleading when applied to the forests in the far north. A better expression of the forest resource is the annual growth of wood per unit area, but unfortunately this measure could not very well have been employed in the inventory, for observed annual growth rates are not available from all forest regions. But enough data are at hand for making a rough comparison between the forests in the far north and those in the midlatitudes of Europe and North America. *Unasylva* (August 1948) reports annual growth in cubic feet per acre as follows: Denmark, up to 104; average in Europe, 32; average in the U.S.S.R., 29; average in the United States, 33; average in Canada, 14. For Scandinavia, Thorsten Streyffert indicates: southern Sweden and Denmark, 86; central Sweden, 43; northern Sweden, 14; southern Norway, 26;

central Norway, 19; northern Norway, 11. The high yield in intensively managed forests, such as those of Denmark or Germany, cannot be taken as representative of the natural growth rate in the midlatitudes, but it seems safe to say that the annual natural increment in the forests of western Europe and the United States, certainly in the southern and Pacific coast states, runs from 40 to 60 cubic feet per acre. The conspicuous fact is the decrease northward: per unit area, the forests in the midlatitudes produce 4 or 5 times as much wood annually as the forests in northern Scandinavia or northern Canada, and the difference would be much greater if a comparison with the true taiga forest could be made. If there actually are, as the FAO inventory says, about 1,500 million acres of inaccessible forest land in the far north, it must be remembered that trees do not grow on all of those acres. Anyone who has made his way through the northern forests knows that the obstacle to travel is not the density of the forest but the seemingly innumerable lakes, swamps, wet bogs, and other morasses bearing no timber; and, furthermore, many scattered areas of permafrost extending well to the south of latitude 55° in the Canadian Shield and Siberia preclude the growth of real forest trees. Besides, the trees that do exist in the taiga are small and slow of growth. It may well be that midlatitude forest land annually produces 10 or 20 times as much wood per acre as the taiga forest, and perhaps the difference is even greater. The upshot is that the 1,500 million acres of inaccessible forest in the far north is not equivalent in productive capacity to more than some 200 or possibly 300 million acres of forest land in the midlatitudes.

Not many records of annual growth are available from the low-latitude regions, but there would seem to be no reason for any significant difference between the inaccessible and accessible tropical forests, for, by and large, both types occur in lands of high temperature and long growing season. Both the total stand of all timber and the rate of annual growth are high, but not markedly higher than in the midlatitudes and, in fact, perhaps not so high as in the best of the extratropical forests. Furthermore, the latter are composed of relatively few species, nearly all of which have a market, whereas the tropical forest consists of very many species, only a few of which have commercial value at the present time, and trees of such species are scattered far and wide in the forest. According to André Aubréville, the volume of the total stand of all trees (including branches) in the Guinea Forest of Africa may be as high as 300 cubic meters per hectare, of which 100 cubic meters might be considered as commercial timber, but the stands that can be utilized at the present time range only from 10 to 30 cubic meters per hectare (see above, p. 368). In comparison, the volume of standing timber in the Douglas-fir region of the Pacific Northwest is conservatively estimated to be about 38,000 board feet per acre—some estimates run as high as 50,000 board feet per acre—a value that must equal at least 400 cubic meters per hec-

Fig. 59. Forest landscape, Dalarna, Central Sweden.
(T. Streyffert.)

o. A well-timbered valley, Queen Charlotte Islands, off the west coast of Canada. (Courtesy of the National Film
Board of Canada.)

FIG. 61. In the Wasatch National Forest, Utah. (U.S. Forest Service.)

FIG. 62. A stand of virgin white oak in the Spring Mill State Park, Hoosier National Forest, Indiana. (U.S. Forest Service, photo by L. J. Prater.)

3. Great oak near Ibsley, New Forest, England. (Courtesy of the Forestry Commission, Great Britain.)

Fig. 64. Ash trees, New Forest, England. (Courtesy of the Forestry Commission, Great Britain.)

55. Veneer timber, Central Finland. (T. Streyffert.)

FIG. 66. Beech forests, serving as watershed protection and of high scenic and recreational value, South Island, Zealand. (National Publicity Department, N.Z.)

FIG. 67. A redwood forest on t.
humid marine coast of northe
California. (U.S. Forest Servic
photo by W. I. Hutchinson.)

8. A virgin stand of ponderosa pine, Deschutes National Forest, Oregon. Ponderosa pine is a characteristic species on the dry interior plateaus of the western United States. (U.S. Forest Service, photo by R. M. F. Noon.)

9. A virgin forest of mature Douglas fir on the rain-drenched western slopes of the Cascades near Mt. Baker, Washington. (U.S. Forest Service, photo by E. Lindsay.)

FIG. 70. A black-spruce swamp near Big Falls, Minnesota. Toward the southern limit of its range black spruce occurs only at high elevations, e.g. between 5,000 and 6,000 feet, in the mountains of South Carolina and Tennessee. (U.S. Forest Service, photo by F. H. Eyre.)

FIG. 71. An open stand of young longleaf pine in pine forest of the southeastern United States. (U.S. Forest Service, photo by H. H. Biswell.)

A 55-year old pine wood in the New Forest, England. (Courtesy of the Forestry Commission, Great Britain.)

Yew tree, Brockenhurst churchyard, New Forest, d. (Courtesy of the Forestry Commission, Great Britain.)

FIG. 74. Pine forest (*Pinus sylvestris*) in northern Sweden. Age 120 years, height 20 meters; has been frequently thinned. (T. Streyffert.)

FIG. 76. Grove of kauri (*Agathis australis*), Waipoua State Forest, New Zealand. (National Publicity Dept., N.Z.)

FIG. 75. Podocarp forest (*Dacrydium cupressinum*) on the wet coastal plains of the west coast, South Island, New Zealand. Forest dominant 500 to 700 years of age. (National Publicity Dept., N.Z.)

FIG. 77. A 25-year old stand of *Pinus radiata*, Kaingaroa State Forest, New Zealand. (New Zealand Forest Service.)

FIG. 78. (*Upper right.*) Stone pine (*Pinus pinea*) on red gritstone at elevation of about 1,800 feet in Lebanon. The upper slopes in the background are on limestone and carry oak. (H. F. Mooney.)

FIG. 79. (*Lower right.*) Stone pine (*Pinus pinea*) on coastal sands near Ostia, Italy. This pine produces edible seeds. (Photo by G. Giordano.)

FIG. 80. High-quality pine forest (*Pinus sylvestris*), Norway, being thinned. (T. Streyffert.)

FIG. 81. Deodar (*Cedrus deodara*), Lower Bashahr, e Punjab. (H. G. Champion.)

FIG. 82. Larch forest (*Larix decidua*), Waiotapu State Forest, New Zealand. (National Publicity Dept., N.Z.)

Fig. 83. Old chestnut trees near Turin, Italy. In spite of their age, these trees produce a good deal of fruit. (Photo by G. Giordano.)

84. A natural forest of cork oak near Iglesias, Sardinia. (Photo by G. Giordano.)

FIG. 87. *Eucalyptus regnans*, Mt. Monda, Healesville, Victoria, Australia. (Forests Commission of Victoria.)

FIG. 85. (*Upper left.*) *Argania sideroxylon*, between Marrakesh and Mogador, Morocco. (Photo by G. Giordano.)

FIG. 86. (*Lower left.*) Oak forest (*Quercus ilex*) near Segovia, Spain. (Photo by G. Giordano.)

Fig. 88. Regrowth of *Eucalyptus grandis*, New South Wales, Australia. (Forestry Commission.)

Fig. 89. Virgin karri forest (*Eucalyptus diversicolor*), Western Australia. (W. A. Forests Dept.)

FIG. 90. Eucalyptus at an elevation of 12,000 feet, Peru. (Photo by Raymond W. Miller.)

FIG. 91. Teak (*Tectona grandis*), Coimbatore, Madras, India. (M. V. Laurie.)

2. Teak plantation, Java. (R. Sewandono.)

3. A swamp forest of the southeastern coastal plain, United States. (U.S. Forest Service.)

Holdridge.)

Griffith.)

FIG. 98. Evergreen forest (*Dipterocarpus boudillon* Travancore, southern India. (M. V. Laurie.)

FIG. 99. Moist deciduous forest, Haldwani, Uttar Pradesh, India. (A. E. Osmaston.)

100. Evergreen forest (*Dipterocarpus macrocarpus*), Digboi, Assam. (J. N. Sen-Gupta.)

1. Chaparral in southern California. (U.S. Forest Service, photo by C. Miller.)

FIG. 102. Portion of virgin cypress stand on moutains above Tecpán, Guatemala. (L. R. Holdrid

FIG. 103. Evergreen rain forest in the mountains of Java. (R. Sewandono.)

04. *Acacia sundra* forest near Mangalore, Madras, India. (H. G. Champion.)

05. Himalayan dry coniferous forest (*Pinus gerardiana*), Upper Bashahr, eastern Punjab. (H. G. Champion.)

FIG. 106. Savanna forest Ceylon. (Photo by R. W. Sze

FIG. 107. Sholas on the Nilgiri Hills, Ootacamund, Madras. (H. G. Champion.)

108. Mangroves (*Rhizophora*), Andaman Islands. (M. D. Chaturvedi.)

109. A woodland of juniper and piñon pine typical of the southwestern United States. Tonto National Forest, Arizona. (U.S. Forest Service, photo by F. L. Kirby.)

FIG. 110. A mixed northern hardwood forest, Nicolet National Forest, Wisconsin. The large trees shown are (left to right): American elm, sugar maple, American elm, black ash, and American elm. (U.S. Forest Service, photo by L. J. Prater.)

FIG. 111. A high-altitude forest of alpine fir and Engelmann spruce near Cameron Pass in Colorado. The barren ridge in the background is above timber line. (U.S. Forest Service, photo by R. F. Taylor.)

FIG. 112. A mixed oak-pine forest near the Blackwater River, Waverly, Virginia. This forest forms a transition zone between the hardwood forests of the North and the pineries of the South. (U.S. Forest Service, photo by B. W. Muir.)

FIG. 113. Even-aged forest of *Picea abies* Fiemme valley near Trent, Italy. Reger through cutting in successive strips. (Ph G. Giordano.)

FIG. 114. Even-aged forest of *Larix decidua* in the western Alps, province of Torino, Italy. Here regeneration is secured through strip-cutting. This view shows a breach in an old high forest, with 20-year pole stands. (Photo by G. Giordano.)

115. Cork-oak forest near Setúbal, Portugal, with a herd of pigs. (Photo by G. Giordano.)

Fig. 116. Avenue of poplars, province of Cuneo, Italy. Many rows of poplars have been planted along roads and canals in the Po valley. (Photo by G. Giordano.)

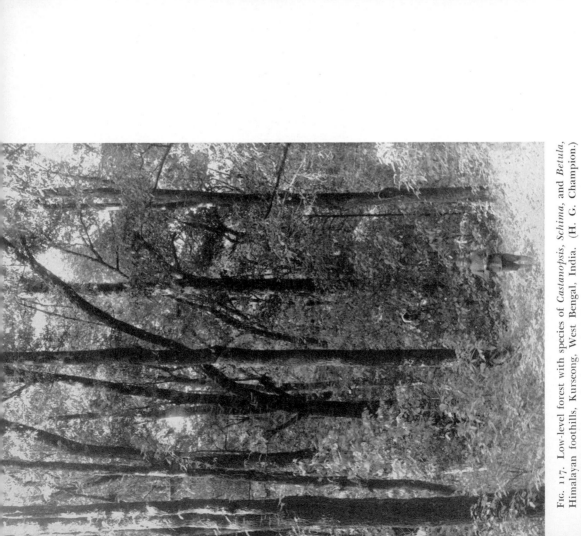

Fig. 118. High-level silver fir (*Abies pindrow*) with blue pine (*Pinus excelsa*), Upper Bashahr, eastern Punjab, India. (H. G. Champion.)

Fig. 117. Low-level forest with species of *Castanopsis*, *Schima*, and *Betula*, Himalayan foothills, Kurseong, West Bengal, India. (H. G. Champion.)

FIG. 119. Government forest nursery near Chichicastenango, Guatemala. (L. R. Holdridge.)

FIG. 120. (Right.) Twenty-two year old plantation of *Cupressus lusitanica* near Guatemala City.
(L. R. Holdridge.)

FIG. 121. Open slash-pine plantation, Kisatchie National Forest, Louisiana. This plantation has been damaged by fire and sleet storms. (U.S. Forest Service, photo by J. P. Cassady.)

FIG. 123. Reforestation in Scotland. (Photo by Raymond W. Miller.)

FIG. 122. Conifers planted on a coal tip, Michaelston Forest, South Wales. (Courtesy of the Forestry Commission, Great Britain.)

FIG. 124. Babul (*Acacia arabica*) in fields, Uttar Pradesh, India. (M. D. Chaturvedi.)

FIG. 125. *Cupressus lusitanica* serving as windbreaks on the slopes of Barba Volcano, Costa Rica. (L. R. Holdridge.

126. Terraces ("banquettes") for soil conservation, Algeria. (Photo by G. Giordano.)

127. A ground fire in a coniferous forest, Angeles National Forest, California. (U.S. Forest Service, photo by E. A. Grant.)

FIG. 128. Natural regeneration in conifers. (Photo by Raymond W. Miller.)

FIG. 129. Stands of beech (*Fagus sylvatica*) on the central Apennines, near Cappadocia. Note, in the foreground degradation of the stand and the soil erosion due to excessive pasturing. (Photo by G. Giordano.)

30. Reforestation with *Cupressus sempervirens* on extremely poor clayey soil in the Apennines near Florence. (Photo by G. Giordano.)

31. Oak coppice degraded by pasturing and partially cleared, on the Ulu Dag, Bursa province, Turkey. (Photo by G. Giordano.)

Fig. 133. Primary clearing for agriculture in white-oak forest, lower montane belt, Costa Rica. (L. R. Holdridge.)

Fig. 132. A mixed forest once composed of American chestnut, chestnut oak, and yellow poplar, Powell County, Kentucky. The dead trees are American chestnut killed by the chestnut blight. (U.S. Forest Service, photo by W. H. Mohin.)

Fig. 135. Mother seed-conifers, Finland. (Photo by Raymond W. Miller.)

Fig. 134. Natural regeneration in conifers, central Sweden. (T. Streyffert.)

FIG. 136. Forest association at altitude of 3,000 feet, Lebanon. *Pinus pinea*, with *Quercus infectoria*. (H. F. Mooney.)

FIG. 137. Sundri (*Heritiera fomes*) with pneumatophores, Sundarbans, West Bengal, India. (M. V. Laurie.)

Fig. 138. Natural regeneration of *Pinus merkusii*, Achin, Sumatra. (R. Sewandono.)

Fig. 139. Land cleared for shifting cultivation (chena), Ceylon. (C. Felsinger.)

Fig. 140. The traditional method of charcoal burning in stacks in the forest, on the Apennines, province of Salerno, Italy. Beech forest. (Photo by G. Giordano.)

Fig. 141. (*Right*). Resin tapping from chir pines in the Himalayas, Hazara District, Pakistan. (Photo by M. H. Ahl, Forest Research Institute, Abbottabad.)

Fig. 143. Transporting teak logs by rail, Java. (R. Sewandono.)

Fig. 142. Topping a spar tree in British Columbia, Canada. A spar tree is used as an anchor point for hauling in logs from the surrounding area. (Courtesy of the National Film Board of Canada.)

FIG. 144. (Upper left.) Moving logs with oxen, province of Avellino, southern Apennines, Italy. (Photo by G. Giordano.)

FIG. 145. (Lower left.) Truck logging as commonly practiced in the Philippine mahogany-cutting operations. Agusan province, Mindanao. (F. Tamesis.)

FIG. 146. (Right.) Unloading logs into a Canadian waterway. This picture shows a powered "A" frame used for this purpose. The trailer will be loaded

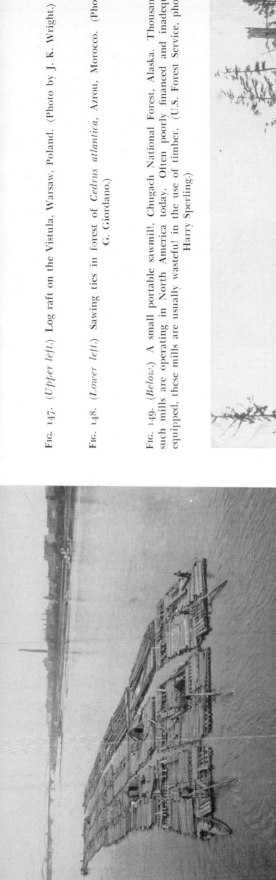

FIG. 147. (*Upper left.*) Log raft on the Vistula, Warsaw, Poland. (Photo by J. K. Wright.)

FIG. 148. (*Lower left.*) Sawing ties in forest of *Cedrus atlantica*, Azrou, Morocco. (Photo by G. Giordano.)

FIG. 149. (*Below.*) A small portable sawmill, Chugach National Forest, Alaska. Thousands of such mills are operating in North America today. Often poorly financed and inadequately equipped, these mills are usually wasteful in the use of timber. (U.S. Forest Service, photo by Harry Sperling.)

FIG. 150. Erosion on white marl in the Baruk valley, near 'Ain Zehalta, Lebanon. (H. F. Mooney.)

FIG. 151. Gypsies burning charcoal, New Forest, England. (Courtesy of the Forestry Commission, Great Britain.)

152. Experimental veneer lathe at the Forest Products Laboratories, Ottawa, Canada. (Courtesy of the National Film Board of Canada.)

153. Pulpwood booms floating down a Canadian river. (Courtesy of the National Film Board of Canada.)

Fig. 154. (*Left.*) Scandinavian log frame-saw in use in New Zealand. (New Zealand Forest Service.)

Fig. 155. Wood yard and plant of the kraft pulp mill of the Champion Paper and Fibre Co., Canton, N.C., U.S.A. (U.S. Forest Service.)

Fig. 156. A stock of boards of cork in a bottle-cork factory near Lisbon, Portugal. (Photo by G. Giordano.)

Fig. 157. (Right.) A cork-oak tree with bark recently removed. (Photo by G. Giordano.)

FIG. 158. A Canadian paper mill, with rolls of newsprint being transferred to the dock for shipment. (Courtesy of the National Film Board of Canada.)

FIG. 159. The Weyerhaeuser Timber Company mills at Longview, Washington, U.S.A., one of the world's largest integrated timber-using operations in which a sawmill, veneer and plywood mill, bark mill, mill-work plant, briquetting plant, and research laboratory combine to eliminate waste and get the maximum values from the timber felled in a sustained-yield operation. (Courtesy of the Weyerhaeuser Timber Co.)

FIG. 160. Logs being raised from the water to the floor of a Canadian sawmill by a toothed steel conveyor chain. (Courtesy of the National Film Board of Canada.)

FIG. 161. Experimental sawmill, Forest Products Laboratories, Ottawa, Canada. The instrument panel in the foreground records speeds, stresses, and strains. (Courtesy of the National Film Board of Canada.)

FIG. 162. Floating logs on a river in Norway. (Henriksen & Steen A/S.)

FIG. 163. Bamboo poles floating along the Karnaphuli River, Chittagong Hill Tracts, East Pakistan. (S. A. Vahid.)

FIG. 164. Raw material for the pulp mill held in storage on a Canadian river. (Courtesy of the National Film Board of Canada.)

. 165. Pulpwood storage yard of the Minnesota and Ontario Paper Co., International Falls, Minnesota. Northern pulp mills usually keep at least a year's supply of pulpwood in storage. (Courtesy of the M. & O. Paper Co.)

Fig. 166. Canadian lumber being stamped before shipment. (Courtesy of the National Film Board of Canada.)

FIG. 167. Houses under construction, New Zealand. These houses are almost entirely of radiata pine, including the subflooring, which is of treated timber. More than 90 per cent of the houses in New Zealand are of wood-frame construction. (New Zealand Forest Service.)

Fig. 168. The Forest Research Institute, Dehra Dun, Uttar Pradesh, India. (M. Bakshi.)

tare, practically all of which is merchantable timber. The tropical forest potential is high, but it is well not to exaggerate it.

It is not possible at the present time to gauge exactly the reserve in the inaccessible forests, whether expressed in acres or in annual growth per acre, for most of these forests have not been surveyed. *Unasylva* (September 1954) warns that the "bald summary" of the inventory exaggerates the world's potential forest resources, for some of the forests have primarily a protective function and for that reason should not be counted on as a future source of timber. After leaving the protection forests out of the reckoning, *Unasylva* concludes that the world still has a reserve of some 3.4 billion acres (1,400 million hectares) of potentially productive forest, or considerably more than the total forest area exploited today. I suspect that the reserve is greatly overestimated.

As part of the task in evaluating the outlook, it has seemed necessary to review the reports on the inaccessible forests, the alleged large reserves of which appear to have given some of the lookouts a comfortable, but I think false, sense of security. It does not really matter how large the reserves are if they are not accessible. It is reasonable to expect that a certain amount of new timberland will become available in the near future, but nothing in the evidence we now have suggests that we shall be able to open up a really large amount, say, a billion acres or more, in the next generation or two. The important point is that for all practical purposes *the forestry problem of the world is the problem of making the best use of the forest land within reach*. We are deluding ourselves if we expect the solution to come from the inaccessible forests. The chance of achieving the best use of the forest land depends on trends in silviculture, wood technology, management, and other technical knowledge, and on our ability to make effective use of such knowledge.

The Half-Promise of Technology

Like a log, the wood industry has two ends, one in the forest where the trees grow, the other at the mill where the timber is cut up and made into different products. It has often been said that roughly one quarter of the wood is wasted in the forests and another quarter at the mill, so that only one half reaches the market. The saying is misleading, for the slash, "left to rot in the forest," as one report puts it with misplaced indignation, is not really wasted but decays and helps to maintain the fertility of the soil; and much of the mill waste is utilized as fuel, providing energy that drives the mill. However, much wood is still wasted by some operators, and one of the main problems of silviculture in the forest, technology at the mill, and management at both ends is the elimination of needless waste.

Recent developments—resulting from forest-products research that has been dealt with in a preceding chapter—have eliminated practically all waste at some of the mills. At the modern integrated plants, some of which can be seen, for example, in the Pacific Northwest, the visitor is impressed by the smooth efficiency of new machinery and methods of operation that convert the log into lumber, plywood, pulp, paper, and a long list of by-products made from material that formerly was wasted. Everything in the log is utilized, and almost everything can be made from it. Technology is no doubt one of the brightest promises for the future, but we need to be clear about the distinction between promise and fulfillment.

Not all the plants are integrated. Again the Pacific coast can serve as example. The *Forest Products Directory of Western North America* lists about 3,400 sawmills, most of which are situated in the Pacific coast states. In 1952, according to *The Lumberman* (Portland, March 25, 1953), approximately one third of the lumber produced came from 100 large plants, and the rest from small or medium-sized sawmills. Complete use of the log is made only at the large mills, which are integrated with pulp, paper, and other wood-products factories. At more than 3,000 sawmills in the West the most conspicuous structure in the landscape is the big, black waste burner, in which a never-dying fire consumes bark, sawdust, slabs, trimmings—in short everything that is not merchantable lumber. It might be thought that this appalling waste is needless and could easily be eliminated, but the meaning of the term "needless" depends on the definition of need, and it certainly would not be easy to change the system. The small mills, which account for two thirds of the lumber production, are needed in order to meet the market demand, and as long as they are needed and continue to operate they must dispose of the mill waste in some manner, and the easiest way is to burn it. An integrated plant capable of using everything in the log requires more capital than the small operators have, and the waste can be sold only if there is a market for it. Pulp mills, utilizing chips, and the new hardboard industry in the West have begun to provide such a market, but we have no assurance that it will ever be able to absorb all the residual from some 3,000 sawmills. There is hope that a substantial part of the waste can be eliminated, but not much hope that all of it will be. The reason for the big incinerators lies at least partly in ingrained custom: mill waste has always been burned, so one continues to burn it; but the main reason is economic and not lack of technical knowledge, or wasteful habits in the operators—nobody throws away material if it can be turned into money. This waste might be completely eliminated if the entire wood industry were organized into large combines financially able to build a few hundred integrated plants, but such a reorganization would require profound economic and cultural changes. Deeply rooted in American tradition is the belief that there is and ought to be a place for the little man engaged in small, independent enterprise: farmer on the land, lumberman in the forest, and mill operator in the wood industry. Technology runs into the dilemma of small ownership, a dilemma that cannot be resolved by technicians, for it is not a technical problem. Perhaps the nation will have to choose some day between preserving the old tradition or going all out for technology. Meanwhile technology is a half-promise, because it can effectively reach only half or less than half of the industry.

The situation in western North America is not representative of the world; there is less waste in some regions, but more in others. In a report to the British Wood Preserving Association in 1952, T. J. Price says that estimates of forest officers in the Gold Coast indicate that only about one fortieth of the timber felled in the colony is shipped as exportable logs or lumber. This is perhaps an extreme case, but it is probably true that on the average much less than half of the timber cut for industrial purposes in the tropical forests ever reaches the market.

One of the reasons for the great loss of tropical wood is the attack by fungi and insects on felled timber, a problem that can be solved only by the wood-preserving industry. The significance of wood preservatives deserves wider general recognition, for the future success of the wood industry, particularly in tropical regions, will in large measure rest on the development and widespread use of chemical solutions that will not only save the timber but prolong the useful life of forestry products. Railroad ties, pilings, poles, fence posts, and mine timber treated with creosote last more than twice as long as formerly when they were untreated, and in some instances have lasted more than five times as long. Mechanical wear, not decay, is now the main reason for the replacement of railroad ties. Virtually colorless and odorless chemical preservatives that act as fungicides, insect repellants, and fire retardants, and help to prevent warping and splitting have appeared on the market of late and are coming into wider use as applications on finished wood, such as window sash, doors, partitions, flooring, and the like. In recent years some 300 million cubic feet of wood have been treated with preservatives annually in the United States, or about 5 per cent of the total amount of wood used, not counting pulpwood and firewood. There is no reason to think that all wood will ever be so treated, but the use of preservatives will doubtless increase, and therefore, because wood products will last longer, a commensurate easing of the demand on the forest might be expected.

Preservatives are even more important in the tropical regions, where they might well be called indispensable. T. J. Price reports that tropical woods rarely arrive in Britain free from fungus stains or wormholes, and for that reason several desirable species have already lost their market; preservation in the tropics, he suggests, must begin in the forest the moment the tree is felled, for it is the log that must be preserved. J. Benoit, Chief of the Wood Preservation Service at the Centre Technique Forestier Tropical in France, makes the same suggestion. Reporting on African field experiments before the British Wood Preserving Convention in 1953, he describes how insects (including ambrosia or pinhole borer beetle, the most troublesome of all) swarm over a tree as soon as it is felled, and he states that in most cases the only effective way of preserving the log is to spray it directly after felling. It has been found that ordinary preservatives and insecticides, including DDT, are ineffective against ambrosia; in fact, under certain conditions this beetle is attracted by creosote derivatives. However, mixtures have been achieved that promise good results (benzene hexachloride, known in Britain as BHC, in France as HCH); and on the whole, Benoit concludes, the development of preservatives for use in the tropics is showing a substantial advance. Judging from other reports, Benoit's conclusion seems to be a fair statement of the present trend, although many technical problems besides that of ambrosia remain to be solved. The outlook for preservatives in the tropics can be evaluated only by experts in this field, but even a layman can see that utilization of tropical woods is bound to be highly wasteful unless logging and wood preserving go hand in hand in the forest. Whether they will successfully join hands is another question, and one that cannot be answered by technology. Discussions at the British Wood Preserving Convention revealed that tropical woods allegedly treated with preservatives before they are exported arrive in England full of fungus and wormholes. The question is not only what they may have been treated with, but whether the treatment may not have been more fictitious than real. Technologists may provide preservatives, but someone else must apply them.

A moot question, which needs more attention than seems to have been given to it, is whether technological improvements in the long run will have the effect of decreasing or increasing the demand on the forest. According to the Paley Report, technical developments in the United States have had two opposite effects on materials: they have increased our efficiency of use, but have also greatly increased the drain upon the resources. The Stanford Report, which is primarily an analysis of the demand, does not go into the question of whether the forest can provide the supply; but the Weyerhaeuser Timber Company, at whose request the study was made, introduces the summary of the report with some conclusions of its own, one of which is that technical developments will make it possible to manufacture a larger volume of products from the same amount of wood, so that timber supplies will stretch farther than in the past. It is true that many new wood products have appeared on the market, and that the consumption of them does not increase the demand on the forest, provided they are made from parts of the log that were formerly wasted. Some of them are, but others are not. Hardboard, for example, which is made from millwaste, can replace lumber for certain purposes, and if it were only a question of hardboard and lumber the timber supply would indeed stretch farther. But plywood and veneer, which cannot be made from waste, compete with lumber for saw logs and increase the demand for timber. Some of the plywood companies have found it necessary to purchase timberland in order to assure their supply of peeler logs. And the demand for plywood and veneer in 1975, according to the Stanford Report, will be at least ten times as great as the demand for hardboard. It is perfectly clear that technological improvement has resulted in a much more efficient use of the raw material and the production of many new articles, but it is also true that we are consuming more different wood products than ever, and in larger amounts. It may be that technology has, so to say, whetted the appetite of the consumer for new products and stimulated the desire for rapidly replacing them as soon as new models appear on the market. The Stanford Report expects the lumber requirements in the near future to increase more slowly than does the population; but the anticipated demand for veneer, plywood, and pulp and all its derivatives, typical products of the "new technology," will increase much faster than does the population, in some instances more than twice as fast.

A vast undertaking of research in forest products and wood use is being carried on at the present time: at Dehra Dun in India, Nogent-sur-Marne in France, Madison in Wisconsin, Princes Risborough in England, and at hundreds of other institutions throughout the world. In recent years, according to the American Forestry Association (1950), 1,600 organizations in the United States alone have been engaged in more than 12,000 projects of wood research. It would seem that more of this energy, money, and intellect might well be concentrated on the question of how technology will affect the supply in the forest. It can scarcely be said today that we really know what the answer is.

Trends in Silviculture, Management, and Forest Genetics

Forestry is in one sense a very ancient practice. It is related in Genesis that Abraham planted a grove at Beersheba; according to Plato, the Greeks of the fifth century B.C. raised forest trees; Cato says that Roman farmers began at an early time to cultivate plantations of trees to provide timber for local needs; and Pliny describes at length the system of coppicing woods in regular rotation to obtain firewood, vineyard stakes, and the like. But forestry and silviculture in the modern sense are not very old, dating from the work of Heinrich Cotta and G. L. Hartig in Germany in the 1780's and from that of Bernard Lorentz and Adolphe Parade in France shortly thereafter. The age of modern silviculture, it might be said, is about the same as three or four generations of forest trees, and in terms of certain species as only two or three generations. A plant breeder working with annuals would hardly feel confident about the outcome of his experiment after only two or three generations of the plant he is studying. He can observe many successive generations and is able to correct a mistake after only a few years have elapsed, but the forester, as R. S. Troup puts it, rarely lives long enough to see the result of his mistake.

It would be captious not to recognize the great contribution of silviculture and the remarkable improvements in forestry that have been achieved in recent years, but we must keep in view the fact that modern silviculture is still in its early stages; the outcome of the great experiment is not yet certain. New systems are still being tried out: Mark L. Anderson of England has recently described the result of "spaced-group planting"; the method of "area selection" or "patch-cutting," now prevalent in the Douglas-fir forest of the Pacific Northwest, is scarcely twenty-five years old in that region; and in the mixed coniferous forest of the Sierra Nevada in California, after analysis of forty years of research and experience, a new system known as "unit-area control" is to be initiated.

There are two major types of silvicultural systems: coppice methods, probably the oldest, depending on vegetative or sprout reproduction; and what are known in Europe as high-forest systems, which depend on seed reproduction. The use of coppice is declining, except perhaps for firewood production in some regions, and industrial forestry in the future will no doubt depend increasingly on seed reproduction. About a dozen high-forest systems are in use, most of them developed in western Europe during the nineteenth century, and they can also be divided into two major groups: clear-cutting types and selection-cutting types. A number of variant forms have come into existence, such as "irregular shelterwood," "strip system," "coulisse method," "wedge-cutting," "two-storied high forest," "high forest with standard," and several others. Some of them are essentially clear-cutting in different patterns, others are fundamentally selection-cutting. On the whole, regeneration after clear-cutting produces even-aged stands, often dominated by a single species, while a forest under selection-cutting remains mixed both as to age classes and species. It is not necessary to discuss these systems in detail; it will suffice to say that each has advantages and disadvantages, and that none can be called the best system for all regions. Clear-cutting has sometimes been uncritically condemned, but under certain circumstances it is undoubtedly the most suitable method and, in fact, the only system that can be used in some regions. It is not so much the method as the manner of employing it that may be dubious.

Another grouping can be made according to two different trends in recent silviculture, or two different attitudes toward the forest, and these attitudes will surely be of more critical importance in the future than any particular system of forestry. The attitudes are not always well expressed, but in their clearest form, one of them can be described as faith in artificial forest, the other as faith in natural forest. (The terms employed by Eilhard Wiedemann in indicating the two trends are *vorgeschriebenen Generalregeln* and *naturgemässe Waldbau*.) On the one hand, there are those who believe that the forest should be treated as a plantation producing a maximum amount of the type of wood that is most profitable to man, the pace of production being forced by human action; on the other hand, those who think that the best result in the long run will be obtained if natural conditions in the forest are disturbed as little as possible, and the forest, while encouraged by the co-operating hand of the silviculturist, sets the pace of timber production. The difference somewhat resembles the contrast in agriculture between those who believe in "organic farming" and those who have what Sir Albert Howard calls the "N K P mentality" and place their faith in forced feeding with commercially produced chemical fertilizers. These attitudes toward the forest are found in every country, but the history of German forestry provides the clearest examples and the longest record.

Coppice, clear-cutting, and selection-cutting have been practiced ever since the Middle Ages in the forests of Germany and western Europe generally, locally more or less regulated at certain times but more commonly not. Unregulated selective cutting in high forest was widespread, but it was the wrong kind of selection: the best trees were cut out, leaving the poorer specimens to regenerate the forest. Some of the forests were excessively grazed by livestock; the custom of gathering fallen material for fuel and the raking up of leaves for bedding the livestock in winter denuded many forests of their litter; and yet other forests, because of the passion for hunting among the nobility, became overstocked with game, causing great damage to the forest seedlings. The result was a general deterioration of the forest, which by the end of the eighteenth century had become so serious that strong remedial measures were initiated. Heinrich Cotta,[6] Director of the Forest Academy at Tharandt, suggested that the only way of rehabilitating the forest was by clear-cutting and making a fresh start, helping the regeneration by the planting of trees, if necessary. This method became common in the forests of Saxony and was adopted in many other regions as well. It should be noted that the proposal was remedial in purpose, not intended as a permanent system, and Cotta himself warned against the danger of monoculture. But that is what the method turned out to be. It became standard practice in the nineteenth century and early part of the twentieth to clear-cut, plant, and harvest on short rotations, and the upshot was that many forests became dominated by even-aged, nearly pure stands of spruce or pine, while fir, and beech, oak, and other deciduous trees well-nigh disappeared. The dominant motive was profit: spruce or pine, worked on short rotations for lumber, pulp, mine timber, and the like, gave—for a while—the highest and quickest economic returns. This was the earliest and one of the clearest expressions of the first of the two attitudes, faith in artificial forest. As Franz Heske says, wood changed from a carefully rationed essential material to an ordinary commodity, the production of which was governed primarily by financial considerations.

But signs that all was not well began to appear: stunted growth of trees, yellowish needles, increasing growth of lichens and peat, decrease in grass, formation of hardpan in some soils; and it also became apparent that the

---

6 Heinrich von Cotta's own writings (*Anweisung zum Waldbau*, Dresden, 1817) were not available to the author. Sources for Cotta's work and ideas are Roth (1879):640-644; Troup (1952):18, 45; Heske (1938):28. Other references to Cotta's ideas are found in Felix von Hornstein (1951), *Wald und Mensch*, Otto Maier Verlag, Ravensburg. This study is particularly interesting to geographers concerned with the forest.

trees suffered increasing damage from wind, frost, fungus, and insects. A series of thorough investigations of forest conditions in Saxony, undertaken by E. Wiedemann in the 1920's, revealed marked soil deterioration and a loss in the average annual growth rate, which according to estimates quoted by R. S. Troup amounted to more than 9 cubic feet per acre over a 100-year period, or a total loss of 3½ billion cubic feet over the whole of the state forests in Saxony. Unsatisfactory results in managed forests have also been observed in other regions. Reports from the large planted pine forest of the Landes in southwestern France indicate that the heavy losses of recent years have resulted not only from catastrophic fires, windfalls, and attack by beetles, but also from the more fundamental cause of soil deterioration. After about 100 years of intensive management, described by G. Roux as "absolute monoculture," the trees are less healthy, the annual increment has dropped, the yield of turpentine has decreased, and natural regeneration is almost impossible to obtain; seed cones have long been imported. J. L. Arend estimates that the area underlain with hardpan in the region has increased by approximately one half. One of the proposed remedies is the introduction of broadleaf species to mix with the pines. Anders Holmgren, after fifty years of work in the forests of Swedish Norrland, during which time he has given much of his attention to the problems of regeneration and methods of cutting, recommends greater reliance on natural forest and natural reproduction, advises against clear-cutting with the coulisse method in the mountains and the far north, and suggests that, if the method must be used, the areas cut should not be larger than 25 to 35 acres.

The experience of Saxony does not prove, as many foresters have pointed out, that clear-cutting alone was responsible for the deterioration, nor that pure stands are necessarily bad: some forests naturally consist of nearly pure stands, and adverse results have also been observed in mixed forests managed with different systems. The reasons for the unsatisfactory outcome were many and complex, but certainly the fundamental cause was the forced pace dictated by financial considerations. It is not likely that any forest soil, whether supporting pure or mixed stands, can long stand up under intensive short-rotation cropping.

Not all foresters approved of the system. Strong protests were made, particularly by Karl Gayer (*Der Waldbau,* 1878), who advocated the reestablishment of forestry operations based upon, and not contrary to, natural laws. Many followed Gayer's lead, and a reaction set in against clear-cutting and monoculture, reaching an opposite extreme in the idea of *Dauerwald,* or forest with continuous cover and selective-cutting in such a manner that "the forest hardly notices it." Clear-cutting and artificial regeneration are still practiced in many regions, but the present trend in European silviculture is in another direction. E. W. Jones summarizes his survey of present-day ideas among European foresters by saying that opinions preponderantly favor mixture of species, natural regeneration, constant preservation of the forest canopy, and flexible cutting methods, and stress particularly the importance of giving careful attention to soil and site conditions in reaching decisions on silvicultural policy for a given region. That forestry is essentially an economic operation is not overlooked; on the contrary, the belief is that these methods of co-operating with the bent of nature will in the long run give the highest returns and at the same time preserve the health and beauty of the forest. It is interesting to note, as an indication of the trend, that Joseph Köstler concludes a recent major work by reminding us that "forestry is also landscape care," and leaves the reader with a quotation from Goethe: "We must eavesdrop on Nature to learn her ways, lest we coerce her into obstinacy by procedures against her will." Here is the clearest expression of the second attitude, faith in natural forest.

The trend of European silviculture may be toward natural forest, but whether the industry as a whole will follow suit is another question. There is no doubt about the persistence of strong faith in artificial forest and forced pace in countries outside of Europe. The new fast-growing pine forests in Chile, New Zealand, Australia, Kenya, and South Africa are essentially monoculture plantations, with some of the rotations as short as thirty years. The technique developed in South Africa, as described by W. E. Hiley, consists of early and heavy thinning according to mathematical rules, and "has the object of producing the greatest value of timber in as short a time as possible, and the prescriptions are based on strictly economic principles." No better definition of nineteenth-century forestry in Saxony could be found, but whether the result will be the same only future generations will know. Hiley concludes that it is too early to pronounce judgment on the principles of this "daring experiment."

The large industrial forests in the southeastern part of the United States, where pines have always been abundant, are becoming dominated by softwoods at the expense of hardwoods because of the emphasis on planting pine for industrial purposes. Southern forestry, in fact, seems to be destined for monoculture. The prevailing attitude is indicated in speeches made at the meeting of the Southern Pulpwood Conservation Association in February 1954. As reported in *American Forests* (March 1954), one of the speakers said: "Put every acre to work—that's good management, make every acre work harder—that's applied research, make every acre grow better trees faster—that's basic research." The speakers also questioned the wisdom of growing high-grade saw timber on 80-year rotations in the national forests of the South, where there are so many pulpmills. The planting of trees is certainly a commendable practice, and no one can object to improvements in management and yield, but it is obvious that here we are again on the old Saxon road. The intention is to *make* the acres do what we bid. It will also be observed that the statement of the speaker reflects the widespread confusion over what constitutes basic research. Not only is the task of basic research assigned, but the expected result is laid down. One can imagine the feeling of a research scientist: produce better trees, or else! In the rugged terrain of the dense Douglas-fir forest in the Pacific Northwest the method now almost universally employed, and approved by virtually every forester familiar with the region, is clear-cutting of staggered blocks, sometimes called "area selection." There is no standard size of the blocks to be logged, for conditions vary from place to place, but in conversation with foresters having lifetime experience with Douglas fir one hears the opinion that, by and large, the blocks ought not to exceed 30 or 40 acres. It may be recalled that Holmgren made the same suggestion for northern Sweden. But the economic advantage of cutting larger blocks is great, and clear-cut areas of 300 acres are common. It can hardly be said that the long-run effect on the forest of such large blocks is known, but many foresters suspect that it will not be good. The size of the blocks is indicative of an attitude that is determined more by financial interest than by silviculture.

We are clearly moving in a direction opposite to that suggested by Goethe. We intend to coerce nature, hoping that she will not respond with obstinacy, but there is plenty of evidence that she will and none that she will not. The claim that good management can cause—or force—the American forest soil to yield twice as much wood as now on a sustained basis has almost become sacrosanct doctrine. Some speak of increasing the yield even more. We know that forestry has improved remarkably in recent years, we know that good management can raise the annual growth, but we do not know, we only hope, that the total annual production can be doubled and permanently maintained at that level.

The science of genetics has come to the fore during the last half century and may conceivably have a tremendous effect on the forests of the future. The renewed interest in natural forest during Karl Gayer's time was accompanied by a reawakening curiosity about the nature of the forest, the ironic result of which may be the end of both the concept and the existence of natural forest. Like silviculture, modern forest genetics has its precursors. In *American Forests* (November 1953) J. W. Duffield points out that as early as the 1780's a German forester by the name of Wangenheim was aware of hereditary strains in forest trees and recommended the planting of seeds from superior individuals, and that Patrick Matthew, a British forester, in 1831 proposed a theory of natural selection derived from his experience with raising trees. In more recent years it has been discovered that there are local races within the species of trees, and that a number of traits are hereditary, such as form of trunk, type of branching, rate of growth, vigor of seeding. Applied forest genetics is based on these discoveries. It is no longer a question merely of planting seeds but of planting seeds from the best trees. Several thousand "elite" trees have been registered in the forests of Scandinavia and Finland, seeds are regularly collected from these protected individuals—with the aid of specially constructed steel ladders erected from movable platforms, making it possible to harvest the seeds without harming the tree—and careful records are kept of the progeny. C. Syrach-Larsen began to establish seed-tree orchards in Denmark during the 1930's for the purpose of raising scions of superior trees and to carry out cross-pollination experiments. In Sweden pines from the north, characterized by slow growth but high-quality wood, have been crossed with faster growing southern stock in the hope of combining the best qualities of both parents. Experiments with X-ray treatment to achieve polyploid varieties have produced a "giant aspen" having twice the ordinary number of chromosomes and maturing in 30 years. J. W. Duffield and F. I. Righter report about two dozen new pine varieties produced at the experiment station near Placerville in California, many of which show decided hybrid vigor, grow faster, and are more resistant to cold, insects, and diseases than either of the parent species. A cross between eastern white pine and Himalayan white pine (*P. strobus* X *griffithi*) is watched with particular interest, for this hybrid not only outgrows eastern white pine but has shown itself resistant to blister rust in a rigorous exposure test that now has been in progress for nearly a decade.

Perhaps we are on the threshold of a period that future historians will refer to as the time when forest trees were domesticated and natural forests passed away. It is to be expected, if the domestication succeeds, that the character of the future forests will depend on present trends in applied forest genetics. While all geneticists work in the same general direction with controlled breeding experiments, there seem to be different opinions about the advantage of exotics over native species, some placing most of the faith in elite indigenous trees, others expecting more from introduced species, or from a combination of exotics and superior native stock. The principal trend is no doubt in the direction of combination. On the whole, European experience with introduced species has not been particularly happy; and J. S. Boyce, in a thought-provoking article, describes the risks of spreading diseases and insect pests by introducing foreign trees, warns against placing too much faith in them, and concludes by saying that "exotics are not all foredoomed to failure, but for every exotic the chance of failure appears to be much greater than the chance for success." The "combination" idea is expressed by Syrach-Larsen in the following statement, although, if anything, he seems to favor exotics: "Broadly speaking, for improvement of the forest stock intensive silviculture places most reliance on the introduction of exotics, and on selection of the best indigenous trees." He also says: "To succeed to any appreciable extent we must soon approach the stage when it becomes obvious how much more profitable it will be to create rapid-growing pure plantations on favorably situated areas."

This is artificial forest with a vengeance. The image conjured up resembles a field of hybrid corn: super-trees, single cropping, and fast rotations. Perhaps the forest operator of the future, like the farmer now, will have to spend a large part of the income for fertilizers. In line with this trend a representative of the fertilizer industry attended the Fourth

American Forest Congress in 1953 and suggested a program of spreading fertilizers from airplanes on forest soils, thereby "permitting the cutting of trees perhaps ten years sooner."

The problems in nature facing the forester are many and complex: fire, windfalls, frost damage, insects, and fungi, but surely the most critical long-run problem in any silvicultural system, whether of the traditional type or the new, is the maintenance of a fertile and healthy forest soil; for if the soil fails, everything fails. Fortunately the foresters, at least in some regions, are well aware of the problem. C. W. Scott stresses the importance of watching the soil in the new Chilean plantations of Monterey pine, and André Aubréville has given the same advice to the managers of eucalyptus groves in Brazil. Most of the larger companies in the forest industries of the Pacific Northwest have had soils experts on their staffs for several years. Watching the soil is one thing, but providing a remedy if it should turn out to be deteriorating is another. It would hardly be economically feasible, even if it were physically possible, to raise forest trees with the aid of fertilizers, as we raise many of our crops. My own belief is that the best promise for the future lies in another direction, namely natural forest, but we do not seem to be going that way.

In a purely technical sense, silviculture in the forest is perhaps as bright a promise as technology at the mill, but both run into the dilemma of the small-ownership and economic problems not of their making. Excellent results have been obtained by application of the Dauerwald idea in some of the European forests, but Dauerwald, which requires, so to say, *Dauerpflege* or continuous and careful attention to details and much hand labor, is, for economic reasons, impossible in most of the world and certainly impossible on both small and large forest holdings in North America. Every forest operator knows that he cannot always follow even the best advice of the silviculturist, for he would go broke if he tried. Clear-cut patches in the Pacific Northwest on which Douglas-fir seedlings should be coming up are in many regions taken over by alder or choked with brushy vegetation; some of the young stands need thinning; and many trees should be pruned for best results. Only the larger companies are able to perform improvement operations of this type, for money spent on pruning, thinning, or fighting brush might not be returned until 75 or 100 years have elapsed, and under present circumstances most of the operators are unable to finance such long-term investments. The result is that much of the forest is growing up unattended, and the land is not producing so much good timber as it might. According to the Annual Report of the Forest Experiment Station at Portland in 1952, the use of pulp chips obtained from mill waste in Oregon and Washington has meant an annual salvaging of material in recent years equivalent to several hundred million board feet of logs, a very good saving, but at the same time the practice has had a detrimental effect on the market for pulpwood obtained by thinning, making good forest management more difficult. Thus, what is good economy at the mill is not always good silviculture in the forest.

Cultural Promises and Blocks

The outlook can be summarized as follows: Although shrinking, the area of the accessible forest is large enough, and our technical skill, even though problems remain, is now good enough to supply all mankind with a reasonably adequate amount of wood in the near future, provided the skill be freely applied over the area and the yield of the forest be equitably distributed. But deeply entrenched cultural factors interfere with both the application of the skill and the distribution of the yield. This is the root of the forestry problem and the most difficult part of it.

We know how to change the number of chromosomes in aspen and how to produce pines that are resistant to blister rust, but we are less successful in dealing with ingrained human habits and the blister rust on our cultural institutions. Some people want to save the world by changing the old ways of life, others want to save it by resisting change, but it is not clear that the first group really understands what is involved in its proposal, nor the second what it is resisting. Culture history can be called a history of change, but it is also a history of the persistence of customary ways, and we still have much to learn about both. We hear much today about the need of basic research, and if anything is in need of close scrutiny it is the man-earth relationship, not only for what are called academic reasons but also for practical purposes. The future of the forest depends on such research, for between man and the timber is always a third factor, human culture. Some of the cultural factors affecting forestry are promises, others are blocks, and both are so numerous and complex that only a few examples can be considered here.

It is a promising sign that more people than ever seem to be aware of the fact that there *is* a forest problem. Throughout the world, movements are afoot to save the forest, to plant trees, to introduce more efficient uses of wood, and to foster a better and more widespread understanding of the importance of the forest in the protection of soil and water. There is, however, an element of risk involved. Silviculture can never be in a hurry, but popular movements sometimes are, and the danger is that mistakes may be made because of the hurry. An error in the forest may take a century or two to correct, if it can be corrected at all. We have blister rust in the United States today because of the mistake of introducing infected white-pine seedlings.

Mention has already been made of economic difficulties that encumber technology and silviculture, and of the fact that both are caught in the dilemma of small ownership. This dilemma has been resolved—or removed, rather—in the countries where the state holds all the forest land. But this is not to say that the forest problem has been solved, and systems of land tenure are changing so fast at the present time in many regions that not much can be said about what may come out of the flux. In most of the Western world, however, the problem of small ownership remains. It is regarded as a problem by foresters because it is generally on the small lots that forest management is poorest and most difficult to improve. Even in the Scandinavian countries and Finland, where the populations are relatively small, culturally homogeneous, and strongly forest-minded, management on many small properties leaves something to be desired. Franz Heske refers to the small private woodland—*Bauernbusch*—as the "child of sorrows" of German forestry; and the consensus among foresters in the United States is that one of the most critical problems is how to improve management on the small holdings. It is not a little problem. One half of the land classified as commercial forest in the United States—the half that is generally most accessible and potentially productive—is owned by some four million persons, holding on the average about sixty acres each. Most of this land is in the form of wood lots owned by three million farmers, and the rest is held by a million nonfarmers, many of whom are absentee owners. Numerous difficulties stand in the way of better forest management on the wood lots: their uneconomically small size for the purpose of timber production; the commonly frequent change of ownership; the lack of capital and experience in forestry; sometimes the lack of interest, for the farmer is primarily occupied with raising food crops, not trees; and problems of marketing. A promising development is the formation of associations of wood-lot owners for dealing with these problems, for example the "Otsego Forest Products Cooperative Association" in New York, "Connwood, Inc." in Connecticut, "The Shelton Cooperative Sustained-Yield Unit" in western Washington, and others. The technical assistance of some two or three hundred government foresters is available to wood-lot owners, and a number of industry-sponsored organizations are also encouraging better forestry on the small holding, such as "Trees for Tomorrow" and "Cash Crops from Your Woods." There must be several thousand wood-lot owners now belonging to associations and actively engaged in improving forest management on their lots, but that is still a long way from four million members.

Improvement is a good thing, but we have fallen into a rut in talking about the imperative necessity of raising the timber production on the farm lots, and we need to give some thought to another side of the question, the farmer's side. There is wisdom in what Franz Heske says: "The small woodlot must not be judged by its yield of timber, for its importance lies in other values: fuelwood, protection of soil and water, and shelter from the wind. The woodlot will probably never be an important source of supply for the timber market." This comment also applies to North America. I suspect that many an owner likes his wood lot as it is and does not think of it as commercial forest land, but rather as a place for getting some firewood and fence posts, doing a little hunting and fishing, or just walking in the woods. "There are some who can live without wild things," says Aldo Leopold, "and some who cannot." Wood-lot owners wishing to improve timber management on their lands should certainly be encouraged, but we have no right to force the farmer into forestry, and the number of people who like their woods just as they are may be larger than we think. It is unrealistic and gives a false impression of the timber resource in the United States to classify some 200 million acres of wood lots as commercial forest land, when in fact many of them are not and perhaps never will be. It might be wiser to count them under some other heading in the census, and face the timber problem on the basis of what we *know* is commercial forest land. Likewise, it would be sounder to think of the areas given over to shifting cultivation in the tropical regions as farm land, which they are, instead of calling them potential timberland. We have as yet no adequate practical way of changing either the system of shifting agriculture in the tropics or the wood lots in the midlatitudes. Both are firmly rooted cultural institutions.

Some of the problems are perhaps no more than vexatious, but nevertheless tend to hinder good management. In the United States, for example, most of the land is mapped according to the well-known township and range system, which is a good system in level country, but its suitability in the rough terrain of the western forest lands can be questioned. The sections lie over the country like squares on a checkerboard, and property lines run straight across mountains, ridges, valleys, and rivers without regard to the lay of the land. Ownerships are chaotically mixed up, and the chaos is worst precisely where the best timber grows—that is, in the redwood belt of California and the Douglas-fir region of Oregon and Washington. The system naturally creates difficulties with access roads and causes other trouble. It is a basic principle in forestry that good management is facilitated by contiguous holdings and rendered difficult by scattered property. The intricate pattern of ownership may in time be unscrambled even though the process of unscrambling does not seem to move very fast, but there is little hope of ever changing the checkerboard system, for it is an institution so thoroughly fixed in American tradition that no one even talks about changing it.

Another problem is forest taxation, which in one form or another has probably troubled forestry in every country. In the United States, at least, the manner of taxing timber has in the past worked against rather than helped good forest management, and in many states of the union it still does. Property taxes on growing timber, paid annually and increasing as the trees approach maturity, have forced many owners to clear-cut prematurely in order to salvage some of the value of the timber before it is all eaten up by taxes. New Hampshire has introduced a "yield tax" calculated on the anticipated value of the timber at the time when it will be cut, and furthermore allows a rebate to owners who manage their forest lands according to certain standards. Several other states have also begun to change their tax systems, but most have not. Other factors having an adverse effect on forest management in the United States are the banking and insurance regulations, which make it difficult and in some instances virtually impossible to insure forest land or to obtain a loan with standing timber as security.

The tradition of the virgin forest, or the lure of new timberland to be opened for utilization, is as old as forestry itself and is still very strong. The timber in the lands of the western Mediterranean probably looked as inexhaustible to the ancient Greeks and Phoenicians as did the forests of Germany to Caesar and Tacitus, or the American forests to the European colonists, or the tropical forests to some people today. This tradition is not helping us to settle down to good management, for we seem unable to face the problem as long as there are virgin forests over the hill waiting to be opened up and made "fully productive." There is truth in the saying that good forestry is the child of necessity. According to Theophrastus, the ancient rulers of Cyprus began to conserve their more accessible cedar groves only when it became too expensive to transport timber from the interior. The forest regulations that came into existence in western Europe during the late Middle Ages were in large measure stimulated by the fear of wood famine. In the Pacific Northwest, as a veteran forester once told me with a trace of bitterness in his voice, the timber buccaneers began to practice conservation after they had slashed their way across the continent to the coast and could go farther. However, we should not visit the sins of the fathers on the present generation of lumbermen, for many of them are helping to create a better tradition. It is significant that the leading timber companies now regard the forest land they hold—the soil—as their most valuable possession, not the timber standing on it at the present moment. The distinction is important. But the emergence of the new tradition does not mean that the old yearning for virgin forests has ceased. On the contrary, the pressure for opening more timberland continues as strong as ever. One can scarcely read anything dealing with forestry, whether it is a government report, industry-sponsored publication, or proceedings of a forest convention, without encountering the claim that one of the greatest needs is more access roads into the mature and overmature virgin forests.

It is true that more timberland will gradually be needed in order to replace forest areas lost to other forms of land use in the future, but it would also seem to be true wisdom not to open the virgin forests any faster than we must. There are several good reasons for a cautious approach. An understanding of how trees reproduce is fundamental to silviculture, but very little is known about the fruiting habit or, in fact, about the whole regeneration process of most of the species of trees in the tropical forests. P. W. Richards suggests that we need more basic research into the nature of the tropical forest before we try to manage it. Even in the midlatitudes, as J. W. Duffield points out, the phenomenon of seed years is not yet fully understood. Forest trees have always suffered from diseases and insects, but in recent years the attacks of these enemies have developed into dangerous epidemics that threaten the very existence of some species of trees. W. B. Greeley reminded the Mid-Century Conference on Resources for the Future that in trying to control insects and diseases we are seriously handicapped by a lack of fundamental knowledge. Furthermore, we do not know to what extent these epidemics are the result of our opening of the forests. It is not inconceivable that opening the virgin forests might be tantamount to inviting a more intensive attack upon them by insects and diseases. The truth of the matter is that modern silviculture and forest management are still in the experimental stage, and it seems unwise to experiment with our last reserves of virgin timber, particularly since we have an experimental field closer at hand. If it is true, as has often been claimed, that good management can double the yield of the forest, and if we think we are skilled in managing timberland, it would seem only common sense not to go into the virgin forests until we have proved our skill by first putting in order some 75 or 100 million acres of already accessible but unproductive and poorly stocked forest lands that lie strewn over the United States in a cut-over, burned-over, and generally wretched condition as reminders of the fact that a short while ago we did not manage well. In the "Letters" column of *American Forests* (November 1954) Dean H. L. Shirley of the College of Forestry at Syracuse makes this suggestion: "We should recognize the importance of placing heavy investments on denuded lands or poor quality stands that occupy the best quality lands. This is more important for long-run future production than rushing into our few remaining virgin stands." One would expect that this sensible and important suggestion should have stimulated a lively discussion among the letter writers, or for that matter on the editorial page, but to my knowledge the response has been a dead silence. The prevalent mode of thinking seems to be that we must open all the timberlands as soon as possible, and *then,* presumably, we shall put the whole house of forestry in order.

The real drive behind the demand for opening the reserves, I suspect, is the old yearning for virgin timber, but the tradition has been rationalized in recent times by saying that it is not good conservation to leave the virgin forests alone. The argument is that wood is "wasted" in the mature forests because old trees are dying. It is a specious argument, based on the old mistaken idea that the standing timber constitutes the resource, whereas the real resource is the land that produces the timber. It is true that trees are dying in the mature forests, but trees are also growing up, as they have been doing for millions of years. There will be timber, and what is more important, there will be timberland in the virgin forests even if we do not get into them for a long time to come. We are not wasting any of the true resource—timberland—by staying out of the virgin forests until we actually need them, but we will be wasting a part of the resource unless we soon concentrate a major effort on restoring the lands that are denuded or poorly stocked because of former mismanagement.

It is not possible to place the cultural promises and blocks in a balance free from personal bias in order to see which outweighs the other. The chances are that the inclination of the person doing the weighing would decide the outcome, so that one might see a bright future ahead and another would not. Cultural institutions are not fixed forever; they change, and it may be that the culture blocks will be removed in time, but the evidence at hand does not suggest to me that we have been very successful in this removal. The best I can say for the outlook is that there are bright patches on the horizon but also dark clouds and much thick weather.

SELECTED REFERENCES

American Forestry Association. 1950. *The progress of forestry 1945-1950.* Washington.

———. 1953. *Proceedings of the Fourth American Forest Congress.* Washington.

American Wood Preservers' Association. 1945. *Proceedings.*

ANDERSON, M. L. 1953. "Spaced-group planting," *Unasylva,* 7:55-63.

AREND, J. L. 1948. "Hardpan development in the Landes region of France," *Ecology,* **29**: 375-376.

AUBRÉVILLE, A. M. A. 1947. "The disappearance of the tropical forests of Africa," *Unasylva,* 1:5-11.

———. 1948. "Notes on Parana pine and eucalyptus in Brazil," (in "News of the world") *Unasylva,* 2:278-279.

BENOIT, J. (See, British Wood Preserving Association, 1952).

BORGSTRÖM, GEORG. 1953. *Jorden—vart öde: kan en permanent världshunger avvärjas?* (The earth—our fate: can permanent world hunger be avoided?) Forum, Stockholm.

BOYCE, J. S. 1954. "Introduction of exotic trees; dangers from diseases and insect pests," *Unasylva,* 8:8-14.

British Wood Preserving Association. 1952. *Record of the second annual convention, Cambridge, June 23rd-25th, 1952.*

CAVAILLÈS, HENRI. 1903. "Le déboisement dans les Pyréneés françaises," *Revue de Paris,* **10**: 287-314.

Conservation Foundation. 1952. "Forests for the future," *Amer. Forests,* **58** (12, pt. 2).

DARBY, H. C. 1951. "The clearing of the English woodlands," *Geography,* 36 (2):71-83.

DUFFIELD, J. W., and RICHTER, F. I. 1953. Annotated list of pine hybrids made at the Institute of Forest Genetics. U.S. Forest Service, Forest & Range Expt. Sta., *Forest Res. Notes, 86.* Berkeley, Calif.

FAWCETT, C. B. 1930. "The extent of the cultivable land," *Geog. Jour.* 74:504-509.

HEINTZLEMAN, B. FRANK. 1950. Forests of Alaska. (In *Trees: Yearbook of Agriculture, 1949,* pp. 361-372). Washington.

HENRY, ALEXANDER. 1897. *The manuscript journals of Alexander Henry and of David Thompson, 1799-1814.* Ed. by ELLIOTT COUES. 3 vols. New York.

HESKE, FRANZ. 1938. *German forestry.* Yale University Press, New Haven.

HILEY, W. E. 1949. "Craib's thinning prescriptions for conifers in South Africa," *Quart. Jour. Forestry,* **42.**

HIND, HENRY Y. 1860. *Narrative of the Canadian Red River Exploring Expedition of 1857 and of the Assiniboine and Saskatchewan Exploring Expedition of 1858.* 2 vols. London.

———. 1863. *Explorations in the interior of the Labrador Peninsula, the country of the Montagnais and Nasquapee Indians.* 2 vols. London.

HOLMGREN, ANDERS. 1954. "Trakthuggning och föryngring i norrlandsskogarna," *Norrdlands Skogsvårdsforbund Tidskrift,* 1.

HOWARD, ALBERT. 1940. *An agricultural testament.* Oxford University Press, London.

HUNNICUTT, B. H. 1949. *Brazil, world frontier.* D. Van Nostrand Co., Inc., New York.

ISAAC, L. A. 1952. Biological aspects of forest conservation in Washington and Oregon. *Biology Colloquium,* 13:12-15.

ISAAC, L. A., and HOPKINS, H. G. 1937. "The forest soil of the Douglas fir region and changes wrought upon it by logging and slash burning," *Ecology,* 18:264-279.

JONES, E. W. (See Troup, R. S., 1952.)

KÖSTLER, JOSEPH. 1950. *Waldbau: Grundriss und Einführung als Leitfaden zu Vorlesungen über Bestandesdiagnoso und Waldtherapie.* Parey, Berlin.

LEOPOLD, ALDO. 1949. *A Sand County almanac.* Oxford University Press, New York.

McArdle, R. E. 1955. "The Forest Service looks ahead," *Amer. Forests*, 61(3):20-23, 90-91.

Marsh, G. P. 1865. *Man and nature*. Sampson Low, London, 1864.

Ordway, S. H., Jr. 1953. *Resources and the American dream*. The Ronald Press Co., New York.

"Paley Report" (see U.S. President's Materials Policy Commission, below).

Pendleton, R. L. 1950. "Agricultural and forestry potentialities of the tropics," *Agronomy Jour. 42*.

Price, T. J. (See British Wood Preserving Association, 1952.)

Price, Willard. 1952. *The amazing Amazon*. John Day Co., Inc., New York.

Resources for the Future, Inc. 1954. *The nation looks at its resources: report of the Mid-Century Conference on Resources for the Future*. Washington, D. C.

Richards, P. W. 1952. *The tropical rain forest*. Cambridge University Press, London.

Roth, Karl. 1879. *Geschichte des Forst- und Jagdwesens in Deutschland*. Berlin.

Roux, G. 1946. "Le reboisement de la région landaise," *Rev. des Eaux et Forêts*, 44:473-491.

Salter, R. M. 1947. "World soil and fertilizer resources in relation to food needs," *Science*, 105:533-538.

Scott, C. W. 1954. "Radiata pine in Chile," *Unasylva*, 8:159-164.

Shantz, H. L. 1948. "An estimate of the shrinkage of Africa's tropical forests," *Unasylva*, 2: 66-67.

Spate, O. H. K. 1953. "Changing native agriculture in New Guinea," *Geog. Jour*, 43:151-172.

Stamp, L. Dudley. 1952. *Land for tomorrow: the underdeveloped world*. Indiana University Press, Bloomington.

Stanford Research Institute. 1954. "America's demand for wood—1929-1975." *Forest Prod. Res. Soc. Jour.*, 4:181-195. (Summary of the Report to the Weyerhaeuser Timber Company, Tacoma, 1954. Commonly known as the "Stanford Report.")

Syrach-Larsen, C. 1951. "Advances in forest genetics," *Unasylva*, 5:15-19.

Troup, R. S. 1952. *Silvicultural systems*. 2d ed. Ed. by E. W. Jones. Oxford University Press, London.

United Nations. Food and Agriculture Organization. 1955. *Yearbook of forest products statistics, 1954*. Rome.

U.S. Department of Agriculture. Forest Service. 1948. Forests and national prosperity; a reappraisal of the forest situation in the United States. *Misc. Publ. no. 668*. Washington, D.C.

U.S. Department of Agriculture. Forest Service. Pacific Northwest Forest Expt. Sta. 1953. *Annual report, 1952*. Portland, Oregon.

U.S. President's Materials Policy Commission. 1952. *Resources for freedom*. (Commonly known as the "Paley Report.") 5 vols. (U.S. Congress, 82d, 2d. session. House Document 527) Government Printer, Washington, D.C.

Vaux, H. J. 1952. "Economic measures of forest conservation," *Biology Colloquim*, 13:19-24

Vogt, William. 1948. "Latin-American Timber, Ltd." *Unasylva*, 2(1):19-25.

Wiedemann, Eilhard. 1951. *Erträgskundliche und Waldbauliche Grundlagen der Forstwirtschaft*. 3 vols. Sauerländer, Frankfurt-am-Main.

Wilkes, Charles. 1850. *Narrative of the United States Exploring Expedition, 1838 to 1842*. 5 vols. Philadelphia.

BIBLIOGRAPHICAL NOTE

Eileen Teclaff

Those who wish to investigate further the various topics discussed in the present volume will find useful material in the chapter references supplied by certain of the authors. Owing, however, to the scattered nature of the references, it is impossible from them alone to gain a rapid introduction to the literature of the field. The editors have felt that, for the benefit of the many users of this book, and, in particular, for those not already familiar with the subject, there should be a general introduction to the outstanding reference works on forests, forestry, and forest products. These are listed under six main headings.

INITIAL ORIENTATION. Of the manuals of general orientation perhaps the three most outstanding are H. G. Champion's *Forestry* (Oxford University Press, London, 1954), Raphael Zon and W. N. Sparhawk's *Forest Resources of the World* (McGraw-Hill Book Company, Inc., New York, 1923, 2 vols.), and the *Forestry Handbook* (The Ronald Press Co., New York, 1955), edited for the Society of American Foresters by R. D. Forbes and A. B. Meyer. The first is a compact little volume in the Home University Library series. It covers all aspects of the subject and has a useful bibliography. The second, though written half a century ago and now out of print, is still the classic work of its kind. The third is a reference book of practical forestry, clearly written and containing a wealth of diagrams and tables.

LIBRARIES. The outstanding special library pertaining to forestry in the United States is that of the Forest Service (U.S. Dept. of Agriculture), with headquarters in Washington and more than thirty branches at forest research stations and forest regional offices in different parts of the country. Other important collections are those of the Yale School of Forestry at New Haven, Connecticut; the Moon Memorial Library of the New York State College of Forestry at Syracuse; the library of the University of California Department of Forestry, at Berkeley; and the Forestry Library of the University of Michigan at Ann Arbor. Among libraries devoted more especially to the subject of forest products and industries, mention should be made of those of the Madison (Wisconsin) Branch of the Forest Products Laboratory; U.S. Department of Agriculture; the

673

National Lumber Manufacturers' Association, Washington, D.C.; the Weyerhaeuser Sales Co., St. Paul, Minn.; the Mead Corporation, Chillicothe, Ohio (pulp and paper industry); and, in Canada, the Forest Products Laboratory (Dept. of Resources and Development), Ottawa. For further details concerning these and other similar collections in the United States and Canada consult *Special Libraries Resources*, New York, Special Libraries Association, 4 vols., 1941-47; and *American Library Directory*, 20th ed., New York, R. R. Bowker Co., 1954.

The collections of the American Geographical Society, New York City, contain many maps, periodicals, and government documents, as well as books of interest to the student of forest geography and ecology. These are conveniently catalogued by subjects. A particularly useful feature is the catalogue of forest maps, which includes maps in books and periodicals.

Outside the United States the most important forestry collections are held by the Food and Agriculture Organization of the United Nations, in Rome; the Skogsbiblioteket, Stockholm; the École Nationale des Eaux et Forêts, Nancy; and the Forest Research Institute, Dehra Dun. Mention should also be made of the libraries of the Imperial Forestry Institute, Oxford; the Forestry Commission of Great Britain, Farnham; the Royal Scottish Forestry Society, Edinburgh; the Forest Research Institute, Kepong, Malaya; the Forest Research Institute, Gunung Batu, Indonesia; the Forest Department, Entebbe, Uganda; and the State Forestry School at Hranice and State High School of Forestry at Pisek, both in Czechoslovakia. Other important collections containing works on forestry are those of the Royal Botanic Garden, Kew, England; the Ministry of Agriculture and Forestry, Rome; the Landbouwhoogeschool, Wageningen, Netherlands; the Hochschule für Bodenkultur, Vienna; the Central School of Rural Economics, Warsaw: the Kongelige Veterinaer-og Landbohøjskoles, Copenhagen; the East African Agriculture and Forestry Research Organization, Kikuyu, Kenya; and the Bolus Herbarium, Capetown.

BIBLIOGRAPHICAL SOURCES. As a general guide to the present status and future progress of national bibliographies, union catalogues, and indexes to periodicals, L. N. Malclès' *Bibliographical Services Throughout the World* (UNESCO, Paris, 1955) is invaluable.

General bibliographical sources on forestry or including sections on forestry are *Forestry Abstracts*, published by the Imperial Forestry Institute, Oxford; the *Bibliography of Agriculture*, of the U.S. Dept. of Agriculture, Washington; the *Agricultural Index*, published by the H. W. Wilson Co., New York; the German *Agrarbibliographie* and *Internationale Bibliographie für Forstwirtschaft;* and the Norwegian *International Bibliography of Forestry*. In 1948 the Food and Agriculture Organization of the United Nations began publication of a monthly, trilingual *Bibliography of Forestry and Forest Products*. Unfortunately this ceased publication in 1952, but will be found useful for those years.

BIBLIOGRAPHICAL NOTE

Forestry periodicals are far too numerous to list here. However, mention should be made of *Unasylva,* published by the Food and Agriculture Organization of the United Nations. This quarterly review of forestry and forest products contains articles on world conditions and developments, reports on conferences, commodity reports, news items, and reviews of current technical literature. For other periodical sources, Franz Grünwoldt's *Repertoire international des périodiques forestiers* (Centre Internationale de Sylviculture, Berlin-Wannsee, 1940) may be consulted; in it are listed 1,254 forestry serials.

EUROPE

BELGIUM

Bibliographia universalis belgica sylvicultura. (Current bibliography.)

BRITISH ISLES

SMART, J., ed. 1954. *Bibliography of key works for the identification of the British fauna and flora.* 2nd ed. Systematics Assn., c.o. Brit. Mus. Nat. Hist., London.

GERMANY

Forstarchiv. (Current bibliography, reappeared in 1950.)
Bibliographie des ausländischen forst- und holzwirtschaftlichen Schrifttums.

NORWAY

Litteraturutdrag. (Abstracting journal published by Papirindustriens Forskningsinstitutt.)

POLAND

PISARSKA, MARIA. 1951. Bibliografia polskiego piśmiennictwa leśnego za pięciolecie 1945-49 (Bibliography of Polish forest literature for 1945-49). Państwowe wydawnictwo rolnice i leśne, Warsaw.

U.S.S.R.

"New books on forestry." 1955. *Lesnoe khoziaistvo,* 8(7):88.

YUGOSLAVIA

BUJUKALIĆ, H. 1954. Jedan prilog šumarskoj bibliografiji, 1945-53. (Contribution to the bibliography of silviculture.) Veselin Masleša, Sarajevo.
Yugoslavia. Federal Centre of Technical & Scientific Documentation. [1952.] Bulletins. Series III, A. *Agriculture and sylviculture.*

ASIA

PAKISTAN

GHANI, A. R., and SIAL, N. M. 1953. "Need for a comprehensive multilingual dictionary of Pakistani plant-names; together with a list of existing glossaries and indexes," *Pakistan Journal of Forestry,* 3(1).

JAPAN

Bibliography of technical history of forestry (in Japanese). 1952. Forestry Agency, Tokyo.

AUSTRALIA AND OCEANIA

AUSTRALIA

Australian science abstracts. 1922- (Includes articles on botany). National Research Council, Sydney.

OCEANIA

SACHET, M.-H., and FOSBERG, F. R. 1955. *Island bibliographies: Micronesian botany, land environment and ecology of coral atolls, vegetation of tropical Pacific islands.* National Academy of Sciences Publication 335.

LEESON, I. 1955. *Bibliography of bibliographies of the South Pacific.* Oxford University Press, London.

LATIN AMERICA

BARNES, H. V., and ALLEN, J. M. 1951. A bibliography of plant pathology in the tropics and Latin America. U.S. Dept. Agr., *Bibliogr. Bull. 14.* Government Printing Office, Washington, D.C.

FLICK, F. J. 1952. Forests of continental Latin America, including European possessions; a bibliography of selected literature, 1920-1950. U.S. Dept. Agr., *Bibliogr. Bull. 18.* Government Printing Office, Washington, D.C.

NORTH AMERICA

CANADA

ADAMS, J., and NORWELL, M. H., comps. 1936. "A bibliography of Canadian plant geography, 1931-35," *Trans. Roy. Can. Inst.,* 21(1):95-119.

———. 1950. "Some further additions to the bibliography of Canadian plant geography," *Trans. Roy. Can. Inst.,* 28(2):161-163.

ROBERTSON, W. M. 1949. Selected bibliography of Canadian forest literature, 1917-46. *Misc. Silvicultural Res. Note No. 6.* Canada. Forest Service.

UNITED STATES

DAYTON, W. A. 1952. United States tree books; a bibliography of tree identification. U.S. Dept. Agr., *Bibliogr. Bull. 20.* Government Printing Office, Washington, D.C.

FLICK, F. J., comp. 1953. Forest research programs, selected bibliography of United States literature. (In cooperation with Forest Res. Division, Forest Service.) U.S. Dept. Agr., *Library List 58.* Government Printing Office, Washington, D.C.

———. 1955. Economics of forestry; a bibliography of the United States and Canada, 1948-1952. U.S. Dept. Agr., *Library List 52.* Government Printing Office, Washington, D.C.

SELECTED SUBJECT BIBLIOGRAPHIES

PLANT DISEASES

GRAVATT, G. F. and MANGANARO, S. G. 1949. List of translations pertaining to forest pathology. U.S. Department of Agriculture. Bureau of plant industry, soils, and agricultural engineering. Beltsville, Maryland.

CORK OAK

WATROUS, R. C., and BARNES, H. V., comps. 1946. Bibliography on cork oak. U.S. Dept. Agr., *Bibliogr. Bull. 7.* Washington, D.C.

AERIAL SURVEY AND FORESTRY

GARRARD, C. W. 1951. *Annotated bibliography of aerial photographic applications to forestry,* College of Forestry, Syracuse University.

U.S. Department of Agriculture. Forest Service. 1946. *Selected bibliography on forest surveys with aerial photos.* Comp. by Pacific Northwest Forest and Range Experiment Station. Washington, D.C.

FOREST PRODUCTS AND WOOD TECHNOLOGY

Forest products and utilization abstracts. (Sections 3, 7, and 8 from *Forestry Abstracts,* Imperial Forestry Bureau, Oxford). Available from vol. 8, no. 1.

KRAEMER, J. H. 1952. Wood conservation bibliography: a selection of references in the field of production and utilization of lumber and other wood products. U.S. Dept. Commerce, *Domestic Commerce Series, No. 30.* Washington, D.C.
ROSS, J. D. 1955. *Bibliography of wood distillation, 1907-1953.* Oregon Forest Products Laboratory, Corvallis.

STATISTICAL SOURCES, DIRECTORIES, AND YEARBOOKS. Since 1936 the world forestry situation has, except for a short gap between 1943 and 1946, been admirably covered by the publications of the International Institute of Agriculture and the Food and Agriculture Organization of the United Nations listed below:

International Yearbook of Forestry Statistics. Year 1932 (published 1933); Vol. I: Europe and U.S.S.R. (1936); Vol. II: America (1938); Vol. III: Africa (1942); Supplement to Vol. III: Africa (1943). International Institute of Agriculture.
Timber Statistics for the Years 1946-47. Geneva (1948).
Timber Statistics. Quarterly Bulletin. (1948–). Geneva.
Yearbook of Forest Products Statistics, 1947–. Rome.
World Forest Resources. 1955. Washington, D.C.

For Europe the publications of the European Forestry Commission, Rome, *European Timber Trends and Prospects* and *European Timber Statistics, 1913-50,* are excellent; the former not only gives statistical data but also a useful analysis of the current situation and outlook for the future.

Directories are regrettably few. There is nothing of the nature of a "Who's Who in Forestry," but for those seeking information about research institutions the FAO's *Research in Forestry and Forest Products* (Rome, 1953) will be helpful. For the United States and Canada a comprehensive reference book on forestry activities, particularly on those of the Forest Service, is *The Forestry Directory,* published annually (except 1934-42) by the American Tree Association, Washington, D.C.

DICTIONARIES AND GLOSSARIES. Forestry terminology is highly technical and those unacquainted with the practical side of the subject will find the Society of American Foresters' *Forestry Terminology* (Washington, D.C., 1950) a useful aid. Many terms are not to be found in the general foreign language dictionaries and for these the following technical dictionaries may be consulted:

ARGY, M., and SUPPER, H. L. 1948. *Vocabulaire papetier: français-anglais et anglais-français.* La Papeterie, Paris.
ARO, P., *et al.* 1944. *Finnish, Swedish, German, English forest dictionary.* Otava, Helsinki.
BACKER, C. A. 1949. *Dutch-English taxonomic botanical vocabulary.* Flora Malesiana & Rijksherbarium, Leiden.
BEDEVIAN, A. K. 1936. *Illustrated polyglottic dictionary of plant names in Latin, Arabic, Armenian, English, French, German, Italian, and Turkish languages.* Argus & Papazian Presses, Cairo.
BRUTTINI, A. 1930. *Dictionnaire de sylviculture en cinq langues. français (texte), allemand, anglais, espagnol, italien.* Lechevalier, Paris.
LABARRE, E. J. 1952. *Dictionary and encyclopedia of paper and paper making.* (Technical terms in French, German, Dutch, Italian, Spanish, and Swedish) 2nd ed. Oxford University Press, London.

LITSCHAUER, R. VON. 1930. *Vocabularium polyglottum vitae-silvarum—Latein, Deutsch, Englisch, Französisch, Spanisch, Russisch.* Parey, Hamburg.

MRUGOWSKI, H. 1948. *English and German dictionary for the wood and timber trade.* Schaper, Hanover.

Organization for European Economic Cooperation. 1951. *Bois tropicaux africains: nomenclature-description.* OEEC, Paris.

STEINMETZ, E. F. 1947. *Vocabularium botanicum: plant terminology: nomenclature in six languages (Latin, Greek, Dutch, German, English, and French) of the principal scientific words used in botany.* Steinmetz, Amsterdam.

Skogslexicon: Svenska, Engelska, Tyska, Franska. 1954. (Forestry dictionary: Swedish, English, German, French.) Svenska, Skogsvårdsföreningen, Stockholm.

U.S. Department of Agriculture, Forest Service. 1939. *German-English dictionary for foresters.* Washington, D.C.

For languages or subjects not covered here, consult the UNESCO *Bibliography of Interlingual Scientific and Technical Dictionaries* (3rd ed., Paris, 1953).

MAPS AND ATLASES. Mention has been made above of the American Geographical Society's collection of maps pertaining to the subject of forests. The following is a brief selection of sheet maps and atlases.

ATLASES

Weltforstatlas. 1951. Kartographische Ausführung: W. HOFFMAN, CH. OPFERMANN. Gebr. Sulter, Hamburg. (Contents are listed separately below. This is the only modern world atlas of forests. When complete it will be an indispensable reference tool.)

Steirischer Waldatlas. 1950. 46 maps. (Scale 1:500,000.) Landeskammer für Land- und Forstwirtschaft, Steiermark, Graz.

Österreichischer Sägewerk Atlas. 1954. Ed. by ALOIS SCHENK and MAXIMILIAN MÜLLER. Internationaler Holzmarkt, Wien. 32 folding maps.

MAPS

World. 1956. "The forest area of the world and its potential productivity," by STEN STURE PATERSON. (1:30,000,000.) With separate volume of text. Department of Geography, Royal University of Göteborg, Sweden.

Africa. 1918. The forests of Africa. (1:20,000,000.) U.S. Forest Service, Washington.

Alaska. 1946. Tongass National Forest. (1:750,000.) U.S. Forest Service, Washington.

Algeria. 1932. Carte vinicole et forestière. (1:1,500,000.) Fasc. XI in *Atlas d'Algérie et de Tunisie.* Gouvernement Général de l'Algérie, Algiers.

Asia. 1918. The forests of Asia. (1:20,000,000.) U.S. Forest Service, Washington.

Asia. 1951. General view on the forest distribution in northern Eurasia. (1:10,000,000.) In *Weltforstatlas.*

Belgian Congo. Kivu. 1931. Carte forestière des territoires Unya-Bongo-Buhavu-Buhunde. (1:200,000.) Comité National du Kivu, Brussels.

Borneo. 1945. Cultivated areas, natural vegetation, major crops, and forest products. (1:5,000,000.) Office of Strategic Services, Washington.

British Columbia. 1951. Forest Reserves. (1:3,400,000.) B.C. Department of Lands and Forests, Victoria.

Bulgaria. 1953. 6 maps: distribution of species—oak, beech, pine; distribution of high forest and coppice; accessibility of forests; distance of forests from railways; distance of forests from first and second class roads. In *Weltforstatlas.*

Canada. 1945. Map showing pulp and paper industries in Canada and Newfoundland. (1 inch: 100 miles.) Department of Mines and Resources, Ottawa.

Canada. 1950. Forest classification of Canada. Spec. ed. (1:6,336,000.) Department of Resources and Development, Forestry Branch, Ottawa.

Canada. 1946–. (Sheets) Forestry series. (1:63,360.) Dominion Forest Service, Ottawa.

Costa Rica. 1953. "Formacion forestal" by Dr. L. R. Holdridge. (1:1,750,000.) Plate 33 in *Atlas Estadistico de Costa Rica.* Min. de Economica y Hacienda, C.R.

Denmark. 1953. General view on the forest distribution in Denmark. (1:600,000.) In *Welt-forstatlas.*

Ecuador. 1942. Map of essential agricultural and forest products. (1:500,000.) Pan American Society for Tropical Research, Quito.

Europe. 1918. The forests of Europe. (1:10,000,000.) U.S. Forest Service, Washington.

Europe. 1951. General view on the forest distribution in Europe. (1:8,000,000.) In *Welt-forstatlas.*

Europe. 1951. General view on the percentage of forests in Europe. (1:8,000,000.) In *Welt-forstatlas.*

Finland. 1951. General view on the forest distribution in Finland, Sweden, and Norway. (1:3,000,000.) In *Weltforstatlas.*

France. 1951. General view on the forest distribution in France. (1:2,000,000.) In *Welt-forstatlas.*

French West Africa. 1923. Carte economique de l'Afrique Occidentale Française. No. 4: Forests. (1:1,600,000.) Gouvernement Général de l'Algérie, Algiers.

Germany. 1951. General view on the forest distribution in Germany. (1:2,000,000.) In *Welt-forstatlas.*

Great Britain. 1951. General view on the forest distribution in Great Britain. (1:2,000,000.) In *Weltforstatlas.*

Greece. 1940. Forest map of Greece. (1:1,000,000.) Ministry of Agriculture, General Direction of Forests, Athens.

Greece and Turkey. 1951. General view on the forest distribution in Turkey and Greece. 2 maps. (1:3,000,000.) In *Weltforstatlas.*

Hungary. 1944. Forests and primary wood industries. U.S. State Dept., Washington, D.C.

Indochina. 1931–. (Sheets) Carte forestière de chaque province. (1:1,000,000.) Inspection générale de l'Agriculture, de l'Elévage, et des Forêts de l'Indochine, Hanoi.

Indonesia. 1953. General view on the forest distribution in Indonesia. (1:5,000,000.) In *Weltforstatlas.*

Italy. 1936. Carta forestale d'Italia. (1:100,000.) Milizia Nazionale Forestale, Florence.

Italy. 1952. 5 maps: percentage of forest area; percentage coniferous, broadleaf forest and mixed forest; percentage high forest, coppice with standards, and coppice; percentage timber, firewood, and charcoal; annual cut in cubic meters per hectare of forest area. In *Weltforstatlas.*

Italy. 1952. General view on the forest distribution in Italy. (1:2,000,000.) In *Weltforstatlas.*

Italy. 1952. Distribution of species in Italy. 5 maps on one sheet. In *Weltforstatlas.*

Japan. 1954. General view of the forest distribution in Japan. (1:3,000,000.) With 20 insets. In *Weltforstatlas.*

Japan. 1954. Percentage of forest area. 5 maps. In *Weltforstatlas.*

Java. 1953. Distribution of species in Java. (1:1,500,000.) In *Weltforstatlas.*

New Zealand. 1949. South Island and North Island. 2 sheets. (1:2,000,000.) New Zealand Forest Service, Wellington.

Nigeria. 1949. Forest and game reserves. (1:3,000,000.) Survey Dept., Lagos.

North America. 1918. The forests of North America. (1:15,000,000.) U.S. Forest Service, Washington.

Palestine. 1945. Forest lands. (1:250,000.) Survey of Palestine, Jaffa.

Rumania. 1953. General view on the forest distribution in Rumania. (1:1,250,000.) In *Weltforstatlas.*

Sierra Leone. 1948. Vegetation and forests. (1:1,000,000.) Survey and Lands Dept., Freetown.

Sierra Leone. 1951. Forest reserves, protected forest and soil conservation areas. (1:1,000,000.) Survey Dept., Lagos.

South Africa. 1953. State forestry map of South Africa. (1:2,000,000.) Trigonometrical Survey Office, Pretoria.

South America. 1918. The forests of South America. (1:12,500,000.) U.S. Forest Service, Washington.

Spanish Guinea. 1951. Mapa topografico y forestal de Guinea. (1:100,000.) Servicio Geografico del Ejercito, Madrid.

Thailand. 1952. Types of forests. (1:2,500,000.) Cadastral Survey Office, Bangkok.

Ukraine. 1953. Distribution of species. (1:1,500,000.) In *Weltforstatlas.*

United States. 1951. National forests, state forests, national parks, national monuments and Indian reservations. (1:7,000,000.) U.S. Dept. Agriculture, Forest Service, Washington, D.C.

United States. 1949. Areas characterized by major forest types in the United States. (1: 5,000,000.) U.S. Dept. Agriculture, Forest Service, Washington, D.C.

U.S.S.R. (Asiatic). 1951. General view on the forest distribution in northern Eurasia. (1: 10,000,000.) In *Weltforstatlas*.

U.S.S.R. 1953. General view on the forest distribution in Soviet Russia. (N. & S. sheets). In *Weltforstatlas*.

Venezuela. 1951. Mapa forestal. (1:2,500,000.) Direccion Forestal, Oficina Technica, Caracas.

Yugoslavia. 1952. General view on the forest distribution in Yugoslavia. (1:1,300,000.) In *Weltforstatlas*.

CONVERSION FACTORS

General Measures

Units of Length

1 inch	2.540 cm.
1 centimeter	0.3937 in.
1 foot	0.3048 cm.
1 meter	3.281 ft.
1 yard	0.9144 m.
1 meter	1.091 yd.
1 mile	1.609 km.
1 kilometer	0.621 mile
1 yard	{ 3 ft. / 36 in. }

Units of Area

1 square inch	6.452 cm.2
1 square centimeter	0.155 sq. in.
1 square foot	0.0929 m.2
1 square meter	10.76 sq. ft.
1 square mile	259 ha.
1 hectare	0.003861 sq. mile
1 acre	0.4047 ha.
1 hectare	2.471 acres
1 square mile	640 acres

Units of Volume

1 cubic inch	16.39 cm.3
1 cubic centimeter	0.061 cu. in.
1 cubic foot	0.02832 m.3
1 cubic meter	35.31 cu. ft.

Units of Mass

1 pound	0.454 kg.
1 kilogram	2.205 lb.
1 short ton	0.9072 metric tons
1 metric ton	1.102 short tons
1 long ton	1.016 metric tons
1 metric ton	0.9842 long tons

1 cubic foot/acre	0.07 m.3/ha.
1 cubic meter/hectare	14.29 cu. ft./acre

Wood Measures

ROUNDWOOD

		Solid Volume Without Bark	
Product	Unit	Cubic Meters	Cubic Feet
Saw logs	1,000 board feet	4.53	160
Pulp wood	Cord (128 cu. ft.)	2.55	90
Fuel wood	Cord (128 cu. ft.)	2.12	75

PROCESSED WOOD

Solid Volume of Lumber		1,000 Board Feet Measure	Equivalent Solid Volume of Saw Logs	
Cubic Meters	Cubic Feet		Cubic Meters	Cubic Feet
1	35.3	0.424	1.67	59.0
0.0283	1	0.012	0.0476	1.68
2.36	83.3	1	3.96	140

BOTANICAL INDEX

Abelia triflora, 470
Abies, 150, 154, 321, 338, 396, 443, 535
   alba, 262, 274, 305, 320, 321, 327, 332
   amabilis, 118, 127
   balsamea, 122, 127, 153
   borissii-regis, 304
   cephalonica, 332
   cilicica, 334, 338
   concolor, 155
   densa, 472
   firma, 553
   grandis, 127, 154, 259
   guatemalensis, 188
   holophylla, 565, 566
   lasiocarpa, 118, 131, 154
   nephrolepis, 566
   nordmanniana, 334, 405
   numidica, 345
   pindrow, 448, 470, 471, 493, 502, fig. *118*
   pinsapo, 320, 321, 345
   religiosa, 188
Aboudikro, 371
Abura, 363, 370, 372
Acacia, 324, 337, 340, 341, 342, 344, 347, 348,
     381, 426, 444, 461, 462, 465, 467, 588
   aneura, 573
   arabica, 434, 444, 447, 463, 465, 466, fig. *124*
   caesia, 464
   catechu, 462, 464, 465
   decurrens, 509, 516
   edgeworthii, 434
   ehrenbergiana, 434
   farnesiana, 185, 623
   flava, 434
   koa, 624
   latronum, 462
   leucophloea, 463, 465
   melanoxylon, 489
   modesta, 443
   mollissima, 390
   orfota, 434
   pennata, 474
   planifrons, 462
   richii, 624
   senegal, 382, 435
   seyal, 434, 435
   sundra, 462, fig. *104*
   tortilis, 342, 344
Acajou, 371
Acanthaceae, 381, 388, 461
Acantholimon, 426, 430

Acanthus ——
   ilicifolius, 472, 473
   racemosus, 435
Acapro, 208, 223
Acapú, 215, 220
Acer, 148, 331, 339, 396, 443, 470, 535
   caesium, 471
   campbellii, 472
   campestre, 261, 304
   canescens, 425
   cinerascens, 430
   circinatum, 131
   insigne, 424
   laetum, 424
   laevigatum, 472
   macrophyllum, 131
   mandschuricum, 406
   mono, 406
   monspessulanum, 331
   obtusatum, 304
   palmatum var. *coreanum*, 565
   pectinatum, 472
   pictum, 406
   platanoides, 232
   pseudoplatanus, 259, 298
   rubrum, 128, 152
   saccharum, 128
   sizuense, 567
   suberosum, 349
   tegmentosum, 565
Achras zapota, 186, 194
Acrocarpus fraxinifolius, 460
Acronychia pedunculata, 483
Acrostichum aureum, 622
Actinodaphne, 468
   hookeri, 461
Adenanthera pavonina, 474
Adenium, 434
   sokotranum, 435
Adenostoma, 156
Adhatoda vasica, 464
Adina, 514
   cordifolia, 461, 462, 463, 467
Aegialitis rotundifolia, 473
Aegle marmelos, 464
Aesculus, 443, 470
Afara, 361, 368, 369, 372
Afzelia, 371
   africana, 383
   pachyloba, 372
   quanzensis, 382

683

684 *BOTANICAL INDEX*

Agathis, 493, 508, 509, 510, 511, 514, 592, 624
  alba, 523, 527
  australis, 595, *fig. 76*
  borneensis, 508
  labillardieri, 513
  loranthifolia, 516
  robusta, 580
  vitiensis, 624
Agba, 367, 370, 372
Aglaia ——
  gigantea, 502
  roxburghiana, 486
Agoho, 523
Ailanthus, 469
  grandis, 468
  triphysa, 488
Akle, 522, 524, 526
Albarco, 208, 209, 220
Albizzia, 424, 535
  acle, 522, 524
  amara, 462
  julibrissin, 424
  lebbek, 474
  procera, 444, 445, 513
Alder, 70, 118, 128, 131, 150, 155, 156, 259, 262, 286, 296, 297, 298, 304, 305, 327, 336, 339, 405, 424, 427, 553
  Japanese, 567, 569
  Korean, 569
Alerce, 213, 217, 224
Aleurites ——
  cordata, 543
  fordii, 543
  moluccana, 527
  montana, 543
Alfa, 344, 349
Alfa grass, 322, 348
Algarroba, 212, 216, 217, 225, 229
Algarrobillo, 213
Allium, 426
Almaciga, 523, 527
Almácigo, 208, 224
Almon, 520, 522, 524
Almond, 339
Alnus, 118, 150, 188, 424
  acuminata, 199
  glutinosa, 259, 262, 327
  japonica, 565, 567
  nepalensis, 472
  orientalis, 337, 339
  rubra, 128
  subcordata, 424
Aloe sabaea, 434
Alseodaphne semecarpifolia, 485
Alsodeia bengalensis, 474
Alsophila ponapeana, 625
Alstonia ——
  macrophylla, 488
  scholaris, 489
Altingia, 468, 508
  excelsa, 469

Alupag, 522
Amarillo, 211, 220
Amlaki, 445
Amoora, 468, 498
  wallichii, 469
Amygdalus, 339, 426
  communis, 437
  orientalis, 425, 429
  spartioides, 425, 429
Anabiong, 527
Anacardiaceae, 219, 222, 227, 469, 492, 526
Anacardium, 222
  excelsum, 186
Anagyris foetida, 429
Anahaw, 526
Anaxagorea luzoniensis, 474
Andira, 225
  inermis, 186
Andiroba, 215, 226
Andoung, 370, 372
Andropogon, 462
Aneurophyton, 20, 21, 25
Angelim, 215, 225
Angelin, 225
Angelino, 209, 219
Angélique, 225
Angico, 215, 225, 227
Angiosperm, 24
Angsana, 513
Aniba rosaeodora, 228
Anime, 208, 209, 228
Anisoptera, 501
  cochinchinensis, 498
  polyandra, 513
  thurifera, 520, 524
Ankenda, 483
Anogeissus, 462
  latifolia, 462, 463, 464, 467, 468, 485
  pendula, 463, 465, 466
Anthistiria ciliata, 463
Antiaris toxicaria, 489
Apamate, 208, 209, 223
Apartium junceum, 437
Ape, 372
Api-api, 523
Apitong, 520, 522, 523, 524
Apocynaceae, 222, 363, 492
Apodytes dimidiata, 386
Apple, 408
Apricot, 339
Apuleia leiocarpa, 225
Aquifoliaceae, 229
Araça, 215, 224
Araliaceae, 194, 472
Aralu, 485
Araraúba, 215, 220
Araucaria, 202, 203, 204, 213, 214, 489, 493, 624
  angustifolia, 223, 582
  araucana, 223, 228
  bidwillii, 578, 580

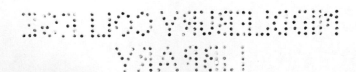

GENERAL INDEX

707

S. Africa, 389
Southeast Asia, 498, 500, 501, 503, 516
Spain, 321
Sweden, 244
tropical Africa, 375
Turkey, 336
U.S.S.R., 399, 409
United States, 671 *r*
Forest soils; *see* Soil
Forest statistics, 677 *r*
Northern Europe, 234-35
Forest surveys, 676 *r; see also* Forest inventories
Austria, 314
Canada, 145-46
Eire, 267
New Guinea, 513-14
New Zealand, 599
Northern Europe, 234-35
Norway, 248
Pakistan, 453
Philippines, 528
Sweden, 244
United States, 182
Forest taxation, 181, 667
Forest types; *see also* Forest regions; Forest zones; Forests, distribution of; Vegetation types; *and cross references for* Forests
Canada, 147
Ceylon, 483-86
Greece, 331-32
India, 456-74
Italy, 325-27
New Zealand, 592-96
N. Africa, 344-45
Pakistan, 443-45
Philippines, 522-23
Southeast Asia, 491-95
Turkey, 334
United States, 149-56
Forest zones; *see also* Forest types
China, 533-35
Italy, 325-27
Japan, 553-54
Korea, 562 *m*, 565-66
Middle America, 184-88
N. Africa, 344-45
Oceania, 622-26
Spain, 320-21
Foresters
British Isles, 257, 260-61
France, 281
India, 480
Norway, 248
Southeast Asia, 500, 501, 503
U.S.S.R., 418-19
United States, 180, 181
Forestry, 59-60, 635, 643; *see also* Forest; Forests; Silviculture
Australia, 588
bases of, 68-73

Belgium, 301 *r*, 302 *r*
branches of, 73-81
British Isles, 260-61, 263-65
definition of, 68
Denmark, 234
dictionaries, 677-78
economics of, 82 *r*
Finland, 249-51
future prospects, 633
Germany, 291, 301 *r*, 302 *r*, 670 *r*
history of, 66-67, 316 *r*, 670 *r*
Europe, 301 *r*
Germany, 287-88, 671 *r*
Japan, 675
Iran, 426-27
Iraq, 432
Ireland, 264-67
Jordan, 439
Middle America, 199-200 *r*
Northern Europe, 237-38
Oceania, 628, 629 *r*
Pakistan, 451-53
S. Africa, 390-91 *r*
S. America, 207-8, 210, 214, 217
Sweden, 242-43
terminology, 677-78 *r*
tropical, 645, 671 *r*
U.S.S.R., 417-19 *r*
United States, 82 *r*, 178-82
Western Europe, 301 *r*, 302 *r*
Yugoslavia, 316 *r*
Forestry associations
American Forestry Association, 634 *r*, 657, 670 *r*
Empire Forestry Association, 82 *r*
Heidemaatschappij, Arnhem, 298
Metsäkeskus Osakeyhtiö, 251
Skogskultur, 250
Societé Suisse des Forestiers, 301 *r*
Society of the Men of the Trees, 266
Tapio, 250
Forestry conferences
First International Congress of Silviculture (1926), 351-52 *r*
First Pakistan Forestry Conference (1949), 450
Fourth American Forest Congress (1953), 664, 670
Fourth World Forestry Conference (1954), 499 *r*
Sixth British Commonwealth Forestry Conference (1952), 147 *r*
Forestry education
Australia, 585-86
Belgium, 295
Burma, 498
Ceylon, 490
Finland, 250-51
France, 281
Germany, 291
India, 480-82

and culture (social), 10-11, 665-70
and man, 3-12
and religion, 11
  British Isles, 253
  India, 455
  Mediterranean region, 319
and water, 49-57, 63 *r*
artificial, 658, 661, 663-64; *see also* Forests,
  exotic; Forests, natural; Plantations
as renewable resources, 65
bibliographies, 673-76
depletion of; *see also* Forests, destruction
  of; Overcutting; Timber, drain
  Canada, 140-41 *t*
  France, 275
  Korea, 563
  Luxembourg, 296
  Middle America, 187, 189-90, 196
  New Zealand, 601
destruction of, 11, 66, 639; *see also* Defor-
  estation; Forests, depletion of; Forests,
  destructive agencies in
  Ceylon, 486-87
  China, 530
  East-Central Europe, 305
  England, 257
  Finland, 249
  Greece, 332
  Hawaii, 624
  India, 456, 466, 475, 477
  Iraq, 429
  Korea, 566
  Madagascar, 383
  Mediterranean region, 317
  New Zealand, 595
  Oceania, 622-23
  S. Africa, 385, 388
  Southeast Asia, 516
  Southwest Asia, 421
  Spain, 321
  tropical Africa, 379, 671 *r*
  Turkey, 335
  U.S.S.R., 399, 404
  United States, 157-59
destructive agencies in, 72-75, 660, 669; *see
  also* Animals; Charcoal burning; Fire;
  Fungus damage; Grazing; Insect damage
  East-Central Europe, 310
  Oceania, 615
  United States, 163
distribution of, 35-44, 678-80 *r; see also*
  Forest types; Forest zones
  Alaska, 115-19
  Arabia, 434-35
  Australia, 576-80
  Belgium, 294
  Canada, 128-33
  Ceylon, 483
  China, 532-37
  Europe, 300
  France, 272-73

Germany, 285, 286
India, 456-74
Iran, 421-22
Iraq, 428
Italy, 325
Japan, 552-53 *t*
Jordan, 437-38
Korea, 561-64 *t*
Luxembourg, 296
Middle America, 184-89
New Zealand, 592-96
N. Africa, 344
Northern Europe, 231-34
Oceania, 622-26
Pakistan, 441-45
Philippines, 519-21
S. Africa, 385-88
S. America, 201-17
Southeast Asia, 491-95
Spain, 320
Syria and Lebanon, 338
Switzerland, 292
tropical Africa, 353-56
Turkey, 334
U.S.S.R., 394-95, 402
United States, 149-56
Western Europe, 271, 300
disturbed, 33, 39
  Iraq, 431
edaphic types; *see* Soil
exotic, 663, 670 *r; see also* Forests, artificial
  New Zealand, 596-97, 601
future prospects, 633-71
  Canada, 147
  Ceylon, 490
  East-Central Europe, 315-16
  France, 281, 284
  Japan, 558-59
  Luxembourg, 297
  Middle America, 199
  New Zealand, 596, 609
  Northern Europe, 242
  Pakistan, 451-53
  S. America, 217-18
  Southeast Asia, 514-17
  tropical Africa, 375
  U.S.S.R., 416
  United States, 181-82
  Western Europe, 299
geologic, 13-35
history of, 3-5, 66-67, 640, 641, 644, 657-64;
  see also Forestry, history of; Forests,
  geologic
  Belgium, 294
  British Isles, 253
  Ceylon, 487
  China, 529-30
  East-Central Europe, 305-11
  Europe, 301 *r*
  Finland, 249-50
  France, 272, 275-76